DIFFERENTIAL GEOMETRY AND
THE CALCULUS OF VARIATIONS

This is Volume 49 in
MATHEMATICS IN SCIENCE AND ENGINEERING
A series of monographs and textbooks
Edited by RICHARD BELLMAN, *University of Southern California*

A complete list of the books in this series appears at the end of this volume.

DIFFERENTIAL GEOMETRY AND
THE CALCULUS OF VARIATIONS

Robert Hermann

UNIVERSITY OF CALIFORNIA
SANTA CRUZ, CALIFORNIA

ACADEMIC PRESS   New York and London   1968

ACADEMIC PRESS INC.
111 Fifth Avenue, New York, New York 10003

United Kingdom Edition published by
ACADEMIC PRESS INC. (LONDON) LTD.
Berkeley Square House, London W.1

LIBRARY OF CONGRESS CATALOG CARD NUMBER: 68-14664

PRINTED IN THE UNITED STATES OF AMERICA

Preface

Differential geometry has radically changed in the last twenty years: A "global" approach based on the theory of manifolds and inspired, at least in part, by progress in the sister field of topology has replaced the traditional methods. However, unlike topology (and like, say, analysis) the problems have not really changed, and the student who ignores the history of the subject cuts himself off from the richest sources of intuition. In fact, one might say that the new methods are just a systematization of viewpoints that have always been inherent in the subject, at least in the work of such masters as Lie, Darboux, Cartan, Levi-Civita, and Carathéodory. (These are the men from the classical period of differential geometry whose work will appear often in this book.)

This volume is meant to serve a variety of functions. It was originally planned to show to mathematically inclined engineers and physicists how differential forms and vector fields could be used in the calculus of variations and Hamilton–Jacobi theory, i.e., in the mathematics of classical mechanics. However, over the years the book has been written its scope has widened, and now differential geometry itself is emphasized. Hopefully, enough of the applied flavor remains to interest the audience for whom it was originally intended.

Half of the book is an exposition of the geometric side of the classical one-independent variable calculus of variations and Hamilton–Jacobi theory, corresponding to the classical treatise "Leçons sur les Invariants Integraux" by E. Cartan, and "Variationsrechnung" by C. Carathéodory. Now, this material has been in a complete form for at least 50 years. The reasons for giving it such prominence are (a) I like it, feel it has great beauty, and deplore that it has virtually disappeared from mathematical education, and (b) I think that its combination of qualitative geometric reasoning and detailed computation is very useful as a model for training in differential geometry and mathematical physics. Especially important, the student can really learn how vector fields and differential forms, the building blocks of the subject, are used. However, this is not a systematic general treatment of the calculus of variations. (The excellent treatise by Gelfand and Fomin is highly recommended here.) In differential geometry today the most important variational structures are Riemannian metrics. Accordingly, I have gone as far as seemed profitable in a study of general variational structures, then switched to Riemannian geometry, which has a different flavor because of the intervention of the theory of affine connections. This switch causes a discontinuity in the nature of the material presented in the book. In the first two parts the reader will find the material presented along more classical lines, while in the third and fourth parts we change gears in order to present to the reader the different outlook of contemporary differential geometry. Although in principle the only prerequisites would be a good course in advanced calculus and possibly some vector and/or tensor analysis, it probably would be best for the reader to be familiar with the introduction to differential forms given in the book by H. Flanders [1] and in the introduction to Lie groups and the vector field concept given in the book by Auslander and Mackenzie [1]. Spivak's book [1] is recommended as preparation in calculus, and we have referred to it occasionally for proofs. Abraham's book [1] can be consulted for an alternate treatment of many topics, as well as an introduction to the advanced parts of classical mechanics.

The beginner in differential geometry will find that the matter of notations is the most annoying obstacle to grasping the fundamental ideas. In fact, there is an amusing definition of modern differential geometry as "the study of invariance under change of notation." I believe that the situation is not really this bad, and that there is a reasonably optimal notation available, namely what can be called the differentiable manifold–vector field–differential form notation. However, one must be prudent in using the big guns of modern mathematics, and the reader will notice that various currently fashionable bits of jargon have been exorcised from the treatment. The aim is not to construct a quasi-algebraic apparatus to tackle a few central problems, but rather to achieve a synthesis of algebraic, analytical, and topological techniques to cover a variety of topics. While it would be desirable in the abstract to say that the "global" problems are the central ones, it is usually not possible to make a decisive distinction between "local" and "global."

This is the first in what might be a two volume work. Several items in this volume may seem isolated from the rest of the book. Some were put in for their own sake as interesting side points, but others are planned as introductions to topics that will be covered more systematically in the second volume.

This book was begun at the Lincoln Laboratory of Massachusetts Institute of Technology; I am greatly indebted to my colleagues there. A grant of support for one year from the Mathematics Division of the Air Force Office of Scientific Research enabled me to extend the scope of the book; it was completed at Argonne National Laboratory. I am, of course, indebted to many colleagues for conversations and ideas and I would like to thank them. I shall attempt a partial listing: W. Ambrose, L. Auslander, M. Berger, S. S. Chern, J. M. Cook, R. Crittenden, B. Friedman, P. Griffiths, S. Helgason, R. Kalman, W. Klingenberg, N. Kuiper, C. C. Moore, J. Moser, R. Palais, R. Prosser, S. Smale, I. M. Singer, D. C. Spencer, S. Sternberg, and H. C. Wang. J. Moyal and Harley Flanders have read part of the manuscript and made many suggestions.

April, 1968 R. HERMANN

Contents

Part 4. Differential Geometry and the Calculus of Variations: Additional Topics in Differential Geometry

DIFFERENTIAL GEOMETRY AND
THE CALCULUS OF VARIATIONS

Part **1** DIFFERENTIAL AND
INTEGRAL CALCULUS ON MANIFOLDS

1 Introduction

We begin by recalling the main principles of ordinary three-dimensional vector analysis. The underlying space is the space of three real variables $x = (x_1, x_2, x_3)$. A *scalar field* is a real-valued function $f(x_1, x_2, x_3)$. A *vector field*, denoted by X, say, is an ordered triplet $(A_1(x), A_2(x), A_3(x))$ of scalar functions. (In the usual geometric representation of a vector as a directed line segment in *Euclidean* space, they are just the components along the three coordinate axes. However, we shall try to avoid using the Euclidean properties of three-dimensional number space.) Gibbsian *vector analysis*, as commonly used in the physical sciences, is concerned with the rules of calculation and the physicogeometric interpretation of the six basic operations on vector and scalar fields.

The three basic algebraic operations are:

(a)   Multiplication of a scalar f by a vector X:

$$fX = (fA_1, fA_2, fA_3).$$

(b)   *Dot* or *inner* product of vector fields. If

$$X = (A_1, A_2, A_3), \qquad Y = (B_1, B_2, B_3),$$

then $X \cdot Y$ is the scalar of $A_1 B_1 + A_2 B_2 + A_3 B_3$.

(c)   *Vector* or *cross product* of vector fields X and Y:

$$X \times Y = (A_2 B_3 - B_2 A_3, B_1 A_3 - A_1 B_3, A_1 B_2 - B_1 A_2).$$

These operations really involve only the algebraic properties of the range spaces of the scalar and vector fields. However, when we turn to the following three basic operations, which involve differentiation as well, it is clear that the domain spaces play a vital role also:

(a)   *Gradient.* If f is a scalar field, grad f is the vector field:

$$\left(\frac{\partial f}{\partial x_1}, \frac{\partial f}{\partial x_2}, \frac{\partial f}{\partial x_3} \right).$$

(b)   *Divergence.* If $X = (A_1, A_2, A_3)$ is a vector field, div X is the scalar field:

$$\frac{\partial A_1}{\partial x_1} + \frac{\partial A_2}{\partial x_2} + \frac{\partial A_3}{\partial x_3}.$$

3

(c) *Curl.* If X is a vector field, curl X is the vector field:

$$\left(\frac{\partial A_3}{\partial x_2} - \frac{\partial A_2}{\partial x_3}, \frac{\partial A_1}{\partial x_3} - \frac{\partial A_3}{\partial x_1}, \frac{\partial A_2}{\partial x_1} - \frac{\partial A_1}{\partial x_2}\right).$$

These operations involve, in the last analysis, writing out everything in terms of three components, which is cumbersome. However, there are a few simple rules of combination that, when proved once and for all, enable one to calculate problems of physics, differential geometry, and others without referring back to the components at each stage. For example:

$$\text{curl}(\text{grad } f) = 0,$$
$$X \times (Y \times Z) = (X \times Y) \times Z + Y \times (X \times Z),$$
$$X \times Y = -Y \times X, \qquad X \cdot Y = Y \cdot X.$$

Of course these operations also have a simple physical or geometric interpretation, but we shall not consider either in detail at this time. As examples:

(1) grad f is the direction of steepest ascent of the function f; or, which says the same thing in different words, grad f is perpendicular to the level surfaces of f.

(2) $\Delta f = \text{div}(\text{grad } f) = 0$ expresses the absence of sources and sinks of a flow with a potential f.

However, the simplicity and beauty of this scheme when applied to everyday problems of the physical sciences almost inevitably forces difficulties and awkwardness when problems involving change of coordinates are encountered. This awkwardness can often be circumvented by a clever combination of physical and mathematical reasoning, but there are limits to what can be done because these operations depend on the flat or Euclidean structure of the underlying space. One might suppose that tensor analysis offers a way out of this dilemma by bringing the requirements of invariance under change of coordinates to the foreground, but the geometric properties, at least, of the fundamental objects and operations are often hidden in a maze of indices and conventions. The great advantages of tensor analysis are that some of the formal simplicity of ordinary vector analysis is retained and that it is the supreme tool in subjects where extensive computations must be made.

However, in this book we shall develop and use what we call the formalism of vector-fields-differential forms in n-dimensional spaces and manifolds. Despite the fact that this formalism may, as justly as tensor analysis, be regarded as the direct generalization of the ordinary vector analysis outlined above, it has up to now occupied almost no place in the mathematical arsenal of the theoretical physicist or engineer. We shall attempt to provide the reader with a link between his presumed knowledge of ordinary vector analysis and/or tensor analysis by defining as explicitly as possible the notion of vector field and differential form on the Euclidean n-space; further, we shall motivate this notion by applications to the theory of ordinary differential equations and the calculus of variations.

2 Tangent Vector-Vector Field Formalism

It will be assumed that the reader knows the rudiments of finite dimensional vector-space theory and point-set topology. For the latter, this should include familiarity with such notions as "compactness," "continuity," "Hausdorff," and "topological space," and with the elementary general theorems interrelating these notions. However, in order to correlate these principles with material that the reader may have encountered in physics or engineering (for example, tensor analysis), we shall show in the next chapter how the notions introduced in this chapter assure a more familiar form for Euclidean spaces. Most of our work in Parts 1 and 2 will be concerned with them.

The aim of our formalism is to be able to carry over differential calculus from Euclidean spaces to more general (finite or infinite dimensional) spaces. Now, the primitive notion in calculus is the idea of a derivative of a real-valued function $t \to f(t)$ of a real variable t:

$$\frac{df}{dt}(t) = f'(t) = \lim_{\Delta t \to 0} \frac{f(t + \Delta t) - f(t)}{\Delta t}. \tag{2.1}$$

This is extended to real-valued functions $f(x_1, \ldots, x_n)$ of n-real variables by defining the partial derivatives:

$$\frac{\partial f}{\partial x_1}, \ldots, \frac{\partial f}{\partial x_n}.$$

However, this is just a special case of (2.1):

$$\frac{\partial f}{\partial x_1}(x_1, \ldots, x_n) \tag{2.2}$$

is the derivative of the function

$$t \to f(x_1 + t, x_2, \ldots, x_n) \qquad \text{at } t = 0.$$

The coordinates $(x_1, \ldots, x_n)$ play a special role in this definition, since if $x_1'(x), \ldots, x_n'(x)$ are new coordinates, the

$$\frac{\partial f}{\partial x_1'}, \ldots, \frac{\partial f}{\partial x_n'} \quad \text{are quite different from the} \quad \frac{\partial f}{\partial x_1}, \ldots, \frac{\partial f}{\partial x_n}.$$

However, let us analyze what is done in (2.2). We take the curve $t \to (x_1 + t, \ldots, x_n)$ in R^n, restrict the function to the curve, and differentiate

6

it by the rule (2.1).† However, notice that we have used only curves of a special type here; namely, those that are coordinate lines.

When we change coordinates, naturally we change this system of curves. Thus we can encompass all possible changes of coordinates by considering this "directional derivative" process applied to all‡ curves in R^n. We shall now describe the mathematical structure (the "tangent bundle") to which this leads.

Suppose $t \to x(t)$ is such a curve, with t running over the interval $0 \le t \le 1$. Let us pick any point in the curve. For illustrative purposes, suppose this is the point $t = 0$. Consider the mapping

$$f \to \frac{d}{dt} f(x(t)) \bigg|_{t=0} \tag{2.3}$$

from the vector space of real-valued functions of x to real numbers. There are two algebraic rules satisfied by this process:

(a) It is linear.
(b) If $f(x)$ and $g(x)$ are functions

$$\frac{d}{dt}(fg)(x(t)) \bigg|_{t=0} = \left(\frac{d}{dt} f(x(t)) \right) \bigg|_{t=0} g(x(0)) + \left(\frac{d}{dt} g(x(t)) \right) \bigg|_{t=0} f(x(0)). \tag{2.4}$$

Explicitly, of course, if $x(t) = (x_1(t)), \ldots, (x_n(t))$, and if

$$v_1 = \frac{dx_1}{dt}(0), \ldots, v_n = \frac{dx_n}{dt}(0),$$

then

$$\frac{d}{dt} f(x(t)) \bigg|_{t=0} = \sum_i \frac{\partial f}{\partial x_i}(x(0)) v_i. \tag{2.5}$$

We are accustomed to interpreting $(v_1, \ldots, v_n)$ as the "tangent vector" to the curve $t \to x(t)$ at $t = 0$. But (2.5) tells us that by making use of the *Euclidean* structure of R^n and by using its ordinary coordinate system, the linear mapping (2.3) can be essentially identified with the "tangent vector" to the curve.

This suggests in general that we can say that two curves $t \to x(t)$ and $t \to y(t)$ have the same tangent vector or "have contact to first order" at $t = 0$

---

† R^n denotes the set of n-tuples of real numbers considered, say, as a vector space over the real numbers. We shall also use a vector notation $x = (x_1, \ldots, x_n)$ when it is convenient; no confusion is likely.

‡ Of course we are not making precise questions of differentiability of curves and functions that are necessary to enable the derivatives to make sense. This will be made more precise in the next chapter; in general, we assume everything is differentiable infinitely many times.

if the functional defined by (2.3) is the same. Also (2.5) tells us that two such curves must meet at $t = 0$. Thus we can say that the set of "tangent vectors" to a point $x(0)$ of R^n is the set of mappings of the form (2.3). This is an idea that is obviously independent of coordinates. Let us use it to define analogous notions for more general spaces.

Let M be a space. The set of real-valued functions on M forms a *ring*. Such functions can be added and multiplied in the usual way. Let $F(M)$ be a sub-ring of the ring of all functions that we shall regard as the "basic" functions on M. For example, if M is R^n, we shall want $F(M)$ to be the ring of all functions that depend on the underlying variables $x_1, \ldots, x_n$ in an infinitely differentiable (C^∞) way.

In this chapter we shall not be so precise about this ring, but shall regard it as given. We shall denote points of M by such letters as p, q, and elements of $F(M)$ by such letters as f, g, $\ldots$, occasionally confusing the function f with its values $f(p)$, and abbreviating $F(M)$ to F if M is fixed in the discussion.

Definition

Let p be a point of M. A *tangent vector* to p is a linear mapping, typically denoted by v, of $F(M)$ to R, such that

$$v(fg) = v(f)g(p) + v(g)f(p) \qquad \text{for } f, g \in F. \tag{2.6}$$

(Note that (2.6) corresponds to (2.4b).)

The set of all such linear mapping is called the *tangent space* to M at p, denoted by M_p. Since two such mappings *defined* at the *same* point p can be added and multiplied by real scalars, the tangent vectors at p form a real vector space. The union $\bigcup_{p \in M} M_p$ of tangent spaces to all points of M forms a new space called the *tangent bundle* to M, denoted by $T(M)$.

We can consider a *curve* in M as a mapping (typically denoted by such letters as σ or γ) of an interval of real numbers into points of M. Throughout this book t will denote such a real parameter. For simplicity, we normalize the interval to $0 \le t \le 1$. (Occasionally, s will also serve to denote a real parameter.) For each point of the interval we define the *tangent vector* to σ at t, denoted by $\sigma'(t)$, as follows:

$$\sigma'(t)(f) = \frac{d}{dt} f(\sigma(t)) \qquad \text{for } f \in F(M). \tag{2.7}$$

(Of course σ cannot be an arbitrary continuous curve, since the derivative in (2.7) must exist, but we assume that the reader has enough experience from advanced calculus to formulate the correct differentiability hypotheses.) Thus

$$\sigma'(t) \in M_{\sigma(t)} \qquad \text{for } 0 \le t \le 1.$$

At this general level, it is not possible to assert that, for each point $p \in M$ and each $v \in M_p$, there is a curve passing through p whose tangent vector is v. Thus a "tangent vector" is not necessarily, as was found for Euclidean space, an equivalence class of curves passing through p, with two curves "identified" if they meet at p to "first order of contact." The definition we have adopted is the appropriate one if we want tangent vectors to form a vector space.

Regard a curve as a mapping $\sigma: [0, 1] \to M$. Its tangent vector $t \to \sigma'(t)$ then defines a mapping $\sigma': [0, 1] \to T(M)$. It is a *cross section* in the sense that applying the "projection mapping" $T(M) \to M$ (which assigns to each vector $v \in T(M)$ the point to which it is "attached") gives back σ. Here we touch on the theory of fiber bundles. It will repay our investment to pause and explain the geometric idea of a "vector bundle," which is a special case of a fiber bundle.

Definition

Consider a mapping π of a space E onto a space M. It is called a *vector bundle* if, for each $p \in M$, the inverse image $\pi^{-1}(p)$ (the *fiber* above p) is a real vector space. (In the case $E = T(M)$, the fiber above p is just M_p, the tangent space to M at p.)

The vector-bundle concept permeates all modern mathematics, and is relevant to many ideas in physics, particularly in quantum field theory. Intuitively, the space M (the base space of the bundle) is "nonlinear," while the fibers are linear: E is "nonlinear" horizontally and is "linear" vertically. (See Fig. 1.)

FIGURE 1

In this book we shall not consider vector bundles very extensively, although some of the language and naive geometric intuition built up for their study will be helpful. (For example, the book by Auslander and MacKenzie [1] is recommended for its more extensive treatment of many ideas mentioned here.)

Associated with a vector bundle $\pi: E \to M$ is the concept of *cross section*, denoted when general vector bundles are being discussed by ψ. It is a map $M \to E$ such that

$$\pi\psi(p) = p \qquad \text{for all } p \in M. \tag{2.8}$$

The set of cross sections is denoted by $\Gamma(E)$.

Although the points of E that are in different fibers cannot be added, cross sections can be:

$$(\psi_1 + \psi_2)(p) = \psi_1(p) + \psi_2(p) \qquad \text{for } p \in M, \quad \psi_1, \psi_2 \in \Gamma(E). \qquad (2.9)$$

Notice that (2.8) guarantees that $\psi_1(p)$ and $\psi_2(p)$ lie in the same fiber $\pi^{-1}(p)$, and the basic postulate of a vector bundle allows us to add $\psi_1(p)$ and $\psi_2(p)$.

Further, $\psi \in \Gamma$ can be multiplied by a function $f \in F(M)$:

$$(f\psi)(p) = f(p)\psi(p) \qquad \text{for } p \in M. \qquad (2.10)$$

In algebraic jargon, $\Gamma(E)$ forms a *module* over the ring $F(M)$. As we shall see, many concepts in differential geometry take on optimally elegant *analytical* form when expressed in this module language.

For example, let us look at the case $E = T(M)$. A cross section, which we denote in this case by such letters as $X, Y, \ldots$, can be geometrically described, then, as a *vector field*, since to each $p \in M$ it assigns a tangent vector $X(p)$ lying in M_p. In this case we denote $\Gamma(E)$ by $V(M)$. The "module" description of $V(M)$ will be very convenient for us.

Let $X \in V(M)$, that is, X assigns a tangent vector $X(p) \in M_p$ to each $p \in M$. Thus, for $f \in F(M)$, $p \to X(p)(f)$ defines another function on M. Assume that it too belongs to $F(M)$, and denote it by $X(f)$. X then defines a linear mapping: $F(M) \to F(M)$, called the *Lie derivative* operation. $X(f)$ is called the *Lie derivative* of f by X. By definition,

$$X(f)(p) = X(p)(f). \qquad (2.11)$$

The basic property (2.6) of tangent vectors then allows us to note a property of X as a mapping: $F(M) \to F(M)$.

$$X(fg) = X(f)g + fX(g) \qquad \text{for } f, g \in F(M), \qquad (2.12)$$

that is, X is a *derivation* of the ring $F(M)$.

This property enables us in favorable cases (for example, if M is a differentiable manifold and $F(M)$ is the ring of C^∞ functions) to define a vector field as a derivation of $F(M)$. In local coordinates, we shall see that such a derivation is nothing but a *first-order, linear differential operator*.

Conversely, suppose $X: F(M) \to F(M)$ satisfies (2.12). Then X defines a cross section $p \to X(p) \in M_p$ of the tangent bundle to M:

$$X(p)(f) = X(f)(p).$$

For the purposes of this chapter, we have not made any distinction between the objects X defined in either of two ways, either "geometrically" as cross sections of $T(M)$ or "algebraically" as derivations of $F(M)$.

3 Differential Forms

Whenever we are given a vector bundle $\pi: E \to M$, we can construct "new" vector bundles by the operations of tensor algebra on the fibers. As an example, we mention the dual space and the skew-symmetric multilinear forms.

Let V be a real vector space whose elements we denote by v and call "vectors." A "covector" is a linear mapping, typically denoted by ω, of V into R, the real numbers. The space V^* of covectors forms a new vector space called the *dual space* to V.

If V is finite dimensional, V^* has the same dimension as V. In fact, suppose $v_1, \ldots, v_n$ is a basis for V; that is, every element $v \in V$ can be written in the unique form

$$v = a_1 v_1 + \cdots + a_n v_n.$$

The coefficients $a_1, \ldots, a_n$ in this expansion depend linearly on v, and hence define linear forms on V, that is, elements of V^*, which we denote by $\omega_1, \ldots, \omega_n$. One can prove (as an exercise) that $\omega_1, \ldots, \omega_n$ forms a basis for V^*, called the *dual basis* to the given basis $(v_1, \ldots, v_n)$ of V. It can also be characterized by the condition†

$$\omega_i(v_j) = \delta_{ij}, \qquad 1 \le i, \ j \le n.$$

An *r-covector* on V is a mapping

$$(v_1, \ldots, v_r) \to \omega(v_1, \ldots, v_r)$$

with domain the n-tuples of elements of V with values in the real numbers. We can indicate this by the notation $\omega: V x \cdots x V \to R$.

We require that ω be *multilinear* in the sense that it is linear in each of the variables $v_1, \ldots, v_r$ when all others are held fixed. In addition, we require that it be *skew-symmetric* in the sense that $\omega(v_1, \ldots, v_r)$ changes sign when neighboring arguments are permuted; that is,

$$\omega(v_1, \ldots, v_r) = -\omega(v_2, v_1, v_3, \ldots, v_r)$$

$$\omega(v_1, v_2, v_3, \ldots, v_r) = -\omega(v_1, v_3, v_2, v_4, \ldots, v_r)$$

and so forth.

Again, the set of these r-covectors forms a vector space, which we shall denote by V^{*r}. If $\omega \in V^{*r}$, $v \in V$, we shall define $v \lrcorner \omega$, the *contraction* of ω

† δ_{ij} is the "Kronecker delta" symbol; it is zero except when $i = j$, when it is 1.

11

by v, or the *inner product* of ω with v, in the following way:

$$(v \lrcorner\, \omega)(v_1, \ldots, v_{r-1}) = \omega(v, v_1, \ldots, v_{r-1}).$$

Thus $v \lrcorner\, \omega$ is the element of V^{*r-1} resulting from holding fixed one of the r-arguments of ω. We shall find the mapping from V^{*r} to V^{*r-1} convenient for proving facts about r-covectors by induction on r.

If $r = 1$, of course $v \lrcorner\, \omega$ coincides with $\omega(v)$, the value of the linear form ω on v. We shall use both notations interchangeably.

If ω_1 is an r-covector and ω_2 an s-covector, a "product" form denoted by $\omega_1 \wedge \omega_2$ can be defined as an $(r + s)$-covector. It is called the *exterior product* of ω_1 and ω_2. Roughly, it is obtained in the following way: Consider $(r + s)$-vectors $v_1, \ldots, v_{r+s}$. One can assign to them the number

$$\omega_1(v_1, \ldots, v_r)\omega_2(v_{r+1}, \ldots, v_{r+s}).$$

However, this assignment does not depend skew-symmetrically on all variables. It can be made so by permuting the variables and adding up the results, with appropriate signs. For example, if $r = s = 1$,

$$(\omega_1 \wedge \omega_2)(v_1, v_2) = \omega_1(v_1)\omega_2(v_2) - \omega_1(v_2)\omega_2(v_1).$$

Notice that from this formula follows

$$v \lrcorner\, (\omega_1 \wedge \omega_2) = +\omega_1(v)\omega_2 - \omega_2(v)\omega_1$$
$$= (v \lrcorner\, \omega_1) \wedge \omega_2 - \omega_1 \wedge (v \lrcorner\, \omega_2).$$

(If c is a constant, $c \wedge \omega$ is taken to be just $c\omega$.)

The general formula can be guessed as

$$v \lrcorner\, (\omega_1 \wedge \omega_2) = (v \lrcorner\, \omega_1) \wedge \omega_2 + (-1)^r \omega_1 \wedge (v \lrcorner\, \omega_2). \tag{3.1}$$

Now we turn things around and use (3.1) to *define* the exterior product $\omega_1 \wedge \omega_2$ by induction on $r + s$. Suppose it is defined for covectors whose degree adds up to a number less than $r + s$, with (3.1) true. Define $\omega_1 \wedge \omega_2$ by the formula:

$$(\omega_1 \wedge \omega_2)(v_1, \ldots, v_{r+s}) = v_1 \lrcorner\, (\omega_1 \wedge \omega_2)(v_2, \ldots, v_{r+s}), \tag{3.2}$$

where $v_1 \lrcorner\, (\omega_1 \wedge \omega_2)$ is given by the right-hand side of (3.1).

We must show that $\omega_1 \wedge \omega_2$ as defined really depends skew-symmetrically on the variables $(v_1, \ldots, v_{r+s})$. That it depends skew-symmetrically on the variables $v_2, \ldots, v_{r+s}$ follows from our inductive hypotheses that the right-hand side of (3.1) is a genuine $(r + s - 1)$-covector. We must check that it changes sign when v_1 and v_2 are permuted:

$$(\omega_1 \wedge \omega_2)(v_1, \ldots, v_{r+s}) = v_2 \lrcorner\, (v_1 \lrcorner\, (\omega_1 \wedge \omega_2))(v_3, \ldots, v_{r+s}).$$

But

$$v_2 \lrcorner (v_1 \lrcorner (\omega_1 \wedge \omega_2)) = v_2 \lrcorner (v_1 \lrcorner \omega_1) \wedge \omega_2$$
$$+ (-1)^r \omega_1 \wedge (v_1 \lrcorner \omega_2)$$
$$= (v_2 \lrcorner (v_1 \lrcorner \omega_1)) \wedge \omega_2$$
$$+ (-1)^{r-1} (v_1 \lrcorner \omega_1) \wedge (v_2 \lrcorner \omega_2)$$
$$+ (-1)^r (v_2 \lrcorner \omega_1) \wedge (v_1 \wedge \omega_2)$$
$$+ (-1)^{2r} \omega_1 \wedge (v_2 \lrcorner (v_1 \lrcorner \omega_2)).$$

It is now clear that this changes sign when v_1 and v_2 are permuted.

We have shown that $\omega_1 \wedge \omega_2$ is defined as an $(r + s)$-covector, satisfying (3.1). The "bilinear" rules

$$(\omega_1 + \omega_1') \wedge \omega_2 = \omega_1 \wedge \omega_2 + \omega_1' \wedge \omega_2, \tag{3.3a}$$

$$\omega_1 \wedge (\omega_2 + \omega_2') = \omega_1 \wedge \omega_2 + \omega_1 \wedge \omega_2', \tag{3.3b}$$

are easy to prove by induction also, and are left to the reader. The "anticommutativity" of the exterior product, namely,

$$\omega_1 \wedge \omega_2 = (-1)^{rs} \omega_2 \wedge \omega_1 \tag{3.4}$$

will also be proved by induction on $r + s$.

Notice that an identity such as (3.4) between $(r + s)$-forms holds if and only if the identity resulting from applying $v \lrcorner$ to both sides holds for all $v \in V$. But

$$v \lrcorner (\omega_1 \wedge \omega_2) = (v \lrcorner \omega_1) \wedge \omega_2 + (-1)^r \omega_1 \wedge (v \lrcorner \omega_2)$$
$$= (-1)^{(r-1)s} \omega_2 \wedge (v \lrcorner \omega_1) + (-1)^{r+(s-1)r} (v \lrcorner \omega_2) \wedge \omega_1$$

(assuming (3.4) is true for forms whose sum of degrees is $< r + s$)

$$= (-1)^{rs} [(-1)^s \omega_2 \wedge (v \lrcorner \omega_1) + (v \lrcorner \omega_2) \wedge \omega_1]$$
$$= v \lrcorner ((-1)^{rs} \omega_2 \wedge \omega_1).$$

Then (3.4) is proved.

THEOREM 3.1

Suppose $\omega_1, \ldots, \omega_n$ is a basis of V^*. Then, for each r, the r-covectors

$$\omega_{i_1} \wedge \cdots \wedge \omega_{i_r}, \qquad 1 \leq i_1 < i_2 < \cdots < i_r \leq n \tag{3.5}$$

form a basis for V^{*r}.

In particular, each $\omega \in V^{*r}$ admits a unique expansion of the form

$$\omega = \sum a_{i_1 \ldots i_r} \omega_{i_1} \wedge \cdots \wedge \omega_{i_r},$$

with coefficients $(a_{i_1 \ldots i_r})$ depending skew-symmetrically on the indices. Then, in the language of tensor analysis, V^{*r} is the space of skew-symmetric (covariant) tensors on V.

Proof. Again we proceed by induction on r, using (3.1) to reduce the case r to case $r - 1$. First let us prove that the elements (3.5) are linearly independent. Suppose that there is a linear dependence of the form

$$\sum_{1 \le i_1 < i_2 < \cdots < i_r \le n} a_{i_1 \cdots i_r} \omega_{i_1} \wedge \cdots \wedge \omega_{i_r} = 0. \tag{3.6}$$

Let $v_1, \ldots, v_n$ be a basis of V dual to $\omega_1, \ldots, \omega_n$; that is, $\omega_i(v_j) = \delta_{ij}$. Apply $v_1 \lrcorner$ to (3.6). The result is a relation of the form

$$\sum_{2 \le i_2 < i < \cdots < i_r} a_{1 i_2 \cdots i_m} \omega_{i_2} \wedge \cdots \wedge \omega_{i_r} = 0$$

(since over the indicated range of indices, only i_1 can have the value 1). By induction hypotheses, $a_{1 i_2 \cdots i_m} = 0$. Then (3.6) takes the form

$$\sum_{2 \le i_1 < i_2 \cdots i_r} a_{i_1 \cdots i_r} \omega_{i_1} \wedge \cdots \wedge \omega_{i_r}.$$

Apply $v_2 \lrcorner$ to this relation. Similarly, one obtains $a_{2 i_2 \cdots i_r} = 0$. Continuing in this way, we see that eventually all coefficients are zero, which proves linear independence of the elements (3.5).

We must show that every element ω of V^{*r} can be written as the sum of elements of the form (3.5). By induction hypotheses, $v_1 \lrcorner \omega$ has an expansion of the form

$$\sum b_{i_2 \cdots i_r} \omega_{i_2} \wedge \cdots \wedge \omega_{i_r} \qquad \text{for } i = 1, \ldots, n.$$

Since $v_1 \lrcorner (v_1 \lrcorner \omega) = 0$, this expansion takes the form

$$v_1 \lrcorner \omega = \sum_{2 \le i_2 < \cdots < i_r \le n} b_{i_2 \cdots i_r} \omega_{i_2} \wedge \cdots \wedge \omega_{i_r}.$$

Thus

$$\omega - \sum_{2 \le i_2 < \cdots < i_r} b_{i_2 \cdots i_r} \omega_1 \wedge \omega_{i_2} \wedge \cdots \wedge \omega_{i_r} = \omega'$$

has the property that applying $v_1 \lrcorner$ to it gives zero. Continue in a similar way with $v_2 \lrcorner$ applied to ω', etc. Eventually one obtains an element of V^{*r} that is a difference between ω and a sum of elements of the form (3.5), which has zero contraction with every element of the basis of V. This element must be identically zero; that is, ω itself has an expansion in terms of elements of the form (3.5). Q.E.D.

Notice that Theorem 3.1 has as consequence that there is but one linearly independent element in V^{*n} (namely, $\omega_1 \wedge \cdots \wedge \omega_n$) and that V^{*r} is zero if $r > n$. This plays an important role in linear algebra (leading to the properties of the determinant) and in differential geometry (leading to the concept of differential forms as "volume elements").

Now we must examine the properties of the r-covectors when V is subjected to a linear transformation. Suppose that $\alpha\colon V \to V'$ is a linear transformation from V to a vector space V'. The associated transformation on linear forms goes *backward* from V' to V. Precisely, if $\omega' \in V'^*$, $\alpha^*(\omega^*)$ is the linear form on V, given by

$$\alpha^*(\omega')(v) = \omega'(\alpha(v)) \qquad \text{for } v \in V.$$

α^* is a linear mapping $V'^* \to V^*$, called the *dual mapping* to α. α^* can be extended to a mapping $V'^{*r} \to V^{*r}$ by the rule

$$\alpha^*(\omega')(v_1, \ldots, v_r) = \omega(\alpha(v_1), \ldots, \alpha(v_r)).$$

It is easily seen that $\alpha^*(\omega_1' \wedge \omega_2') = \alpha^*(\omega_1') \wedge \alpha^*(\omega_2')$.

Suppose $(v_1, \ldots, v_n)$ and $(v_1', \ldots, v_m')$ are respectively the bases of V and V'. Then

$$\alpha(v_i) = \sum_{i \le j \le m} \alpha_{ji} v_j', \qquad i = 1, \ldots, n.$$

The $m \times n$ matrix (α_{ij}) is called the *matrix* associated with the linear transformation and the bases. Let us compute the matrix associated with the dual α^*:

$$\alpha^*(\omega_j') = \sum_i \alpha_{ji}^* \omega_j.$$

Then

$$\alpha^*(\omega_j')(v_i) = \alpha_{ji}^*.$$

But it also equals

$$\omega_j'(\alpha(v_i)) = \omega_j'\!\left(\sum_j \alpha_{ji} v_j'\right) = \alpha_{ji}^*; \qquad \text{that is, } \alpha_{ij}^* = \alpha_{ji},$$

where the matrix of α^* relative to the dual bases is the *transpose* of the matrix of α relative to the two given bases of V and V'.

In general, this passing back and forth between linear transformations and the matrices defining them is rather confusing. It is more in the spirit of modern geometry to work in basis-free terms, but occasionally it throws fresh light on a problem to regard it in both "pictures."

The following facts are readily proved, and are left to the reader.

If $\alpha\colon V \to V'$ and $\beta\colon V' \to V''$ are linear transformations, with $\beta\alpha\colon V \to V''$ the composite transformation, then

$$(\beta\alpha)^* = \alpha^*\beta^*. \qquad (3.7)$$

Choose bases for V, V', and V''. The matrix associated with $\beta\alpha$ is then the product (in the usual sense of matrix multiplication) of that associated with β and α. (It is to get this correspondence that we chose $\alpha(v_i) = \sum_j \alpha_{ji} v_j$ rather than $\sum_j \alpha_{ij} v_j$.) We see that α is 1-1, that is, has zero kernel,† if and only if α^* is onto, that is,

$$\alpha^*(V'^*) = V^*, \tag{3.8}$$

and

$$\alpha \text{ is onto } V' \text{ if and only if } \alpha^* \text{ is 1-1.} \tag{3.9}$$

(In matrix language, (3.8) and (3.9) translate into statements about the rank and nullity of a matrix and its transpose.)

Now suppose that α is a linear transformation of a vector space V *into itself*, that is, $V' = V$. Let $\omega_1, \ldots, \omega_n$ be a basis for V^*. Then, since V^{*n} is one-dimensional, $\alpha^*(\omega_1 \wedge \cdots \wedge \omega_n)$ is a scalar multiple of $\omega_1 \wedge \cdots \wedge \omega_n$. Call this scalar multiple the *determinant* of α denoted by $\det \alpha$. Thus

$$\alpha^*(\omega_1 \wedge \cdots \wedge \omega_n) = (\det \alpha)\omega_1 \wedge \cdots \wedge \omega_n.$$

Suppose that β is another linear transformation: $V \to V$. Then

$$\beta^*(\alpha^*(\omega_1 \wedge \cdots \wedge \omega_n)) = (\alpha\beta)^*(\omega_1 \wedge \cdots \wedge \omega_n)$$
$$= \det(\alpha\beta)\omega_1 \wedge \cdots \wedge \omega_n.$$

It also equals

$$\beta^*(\det(\alpha)\omega_1 \wedge \cdots \wedge \omega_n) = \det(\alpha) \det(\beta)\omega_1 \wedge \cdots \wedge \omega_n,$$

that is,

$$\det(\alpha\beta) = \det(\alpha) \det(\beta),$$

so that the determinant of the product of two linear transformations is the product of the determinant.

We can use this remark to show that $\det \alpha$ is independent of the basis chosen. Suppose that $\omega_1', \ldots, \omega_n'$ is another basis for V^*. There is then a linear transformation $\beta: V \to V$ such that

$$\beta^*(\omega_i) = \omega_i', \qquad i = 1, \ldots, n.$$

Also, then,

$$\beta^{-1*}(\omega_i') = \omega_i, \qquad i = 1, \ldots, n.$$

Then

$$\alpha^*(\omega_1' \wedge \cdots \wedge \omega_n') = \alpha^*(\beta(\omega_1) \wedge \cdots \wedge \beta^*(\omega_n))$$
$$= \alpha^*\beta^*(\omega_1 \wedge \cdots \wedge \omega_n) = \det(\alpha\beta)\omega_1 \wedge \cdots \wedge \omega_n.$$

---

† The *kernel* of a linear transformation α is the set of $v \in V$ such that $\alpha(v) = 0$, that is, $\alpha^{-1}(0)$.

Also,

$$\det \alpha(\omega_1' \wedge \cdots \wedge \omega_n') = \det \alpha \cdot \beta^*(\omega_1 \wedge \cdots \wedge \omega_n)$$
$$= (\det \alpha)(\det \beta)\omega_1 \wedge \cdots \wedge \omega_n.$$

Since $\det(\alpha\beta) = (\det \alpha)(\det \beta)$, we see that

$$\alpha^*(\omega_1' \wedge \cdots \wedge \omega_n') = (\det \alpha)(\omega_1' \wedge \cdots \wedge \omega_n'),$$

that is, the determinant does not depend on the basis chosen to compute it.

We shall not carry out all details necessary to show the traditional definition of determinant in terms of matrices. Suppose (α_{ij}) is the matrix of α. Then

$$\alpha^*(\omega_i) = \sum_j \alpha_{ij}\omega_j.$$

$$\alpha^*(\omega_1 \wedge \cdots \wedge \omega_n) = \left(\sum_j \alpha_{1j}\omega_j\right) \wedge \cdots \wedge \left(\sum_j \alpha_{nj}\omega_j\right).$$

Using the rules for exterior multiplication would give the correspondence: $\det \alpha = \det(\alpha_{ij})$. Suppose we verify this only for $n = 2$:

$$\alpha^*(\omega_1 \wedge \omega_2) = (\alpha_{11}\omega_1 + \alpha_{12}\omega_2) \wedge (\alpha_{21}\omega_1 + \alpha_{22}\omega_2)$$
$$= \alpha_{11}\alpha_{22}\omega_1 \wedge \omega_2 + \alpha_{12}\alpha_{21}\omega_2 \wedge \omega_1$$
$$= (\alpha_{11}\alpha_{22} - \alpha_{12}\alpha_{21})\omega_1 \wedge \omega_2.$$

That is,

$$\det \alpha = (\alpha_{11}\alpha_{22} - \alpha_{12}\alpha_{21}),$$

as required.

Let us now apply this brief excursion into multilinear algebra to the tangent bundle $T(M)$ to a space M. For each $p \in M$, M_p^* is the dual space to M_p (that is, to space of covectors at p), while M_p^{*r} is the space of r-covectors to p.

$$T^*(M) = \bigcup_{p \in M} M_p^*; \qquad T^{*r}(M) = \bigcup_{p \in M} M_p^{*r}$$

on the corresponding vector bundles. A *differential form* (of degree r) on M is now a cross section of the vector bundle $T^{*r}(M)$. That is, it is a mapping (which we again denote by ω) that assigns to each point $p \in M$ a multilinear, skew-symmetric form on the tangent vectors to M and p: $(v_1, \ldots, v_r) \to \omega(v_1, \ldots, v_r)$. But ω also defines a multilinear map on vector fields. For $X_1, \ldots, X_r \in V(M)$, assign the function $p \to \omega(X_1(p), \ldots, X_r(p))$, which we denote by $\omega(X_1, \ldots, X_r)$. Notice that this assignment is $F(M)$-multilinear; that is,

$$\omega(fX_1, X_2, \ldots, X_r) = f\omega(X_1, \ldots, X_r) \qquad \text{for } f \in F(M).$$

Now it will turn out that the spaces we study (for example, differentiable manifolds) will have the property that any $F(M)$-multilinear, skew-symmetric map

$V(M)x \cdots xV(M) \to F(M)$ comes from a cross section of the bundle $T^{*r}(M)$. We can then interchangeably regard a differential form "geometrically" as a cross section or "algebraically," using in this way the module structure of $V(M)$ over the ring $F(M)$. We denote by $F^r(M)$ the set of rth degree differential forms, with $F^0(M)$ identical to $F(M)$, which of course is also an $F(M)$-module.

The differential forms and the vector fields are the main objects of our "differential calculus" on manifolds. So far, of course, we have not talked about differentiation except to motivate the original definition of the tangent bundle, but it appears with the introduction of the three principal, coordinate-free, "natural," differential operators: exterior differentiation, Jacobi bracket, and Lie derivative. The full development will be given in the next chapter. Here, we introduce exterior differentiation d on functions.

The operator d of exterior differentiation will ultimately be defined as a linear (but not an $F(M)$-linear) map: $F^r(M) \to F^{r+1}(M)$ for all r. For the moment, we define it only for $r = 0$, that is, on functions.

Let $f \in F(M)$; df is a first-degree differential form defined as

$$df(X) = X(f) \qquad \text{for } X \in V(M),$$

or alternatively,

$$df(v) = v(f) \qquad \text{for } v \in T(M).$$

Note that $d(fg) = g\, df + f\, dg$ for $f, g \in F(M)$.

Proof.

$$d(fg)(X) = X(fg) = X(f)g + X(g)f$$
$$= g\, df + f\, dg(X) \qquad \text{for } X \in V(M).$$

We have said that d is a "natural" differential operator. What is meant by this is that d has particularly simple properties when the space M is subject to a mapping.

Let ϕ be a mapping of M into a space M'. Suppose M' also has a ring of functions $F(M')$ on it, used to define tangent vectors, differential forms, etc. Now, if f' is a real-valued function on M', we can define function $\phi^*(f')$ in the following way:

$$\phi^*(f')(p) = f'(\phi(p)) \qquad \text{for } p \in M.$$

We shall assume that ϕ satisfies the following condition: $\phi^*(F(M')) \subset F(M)$. (In case M and M' are differentiable manifolds, and $F(M)$, $F(M')$ are the ring of C^∞ functions, this condition means that ϕ is a C^∞ mapping.) Notice that the mapping ϕ induced on functions goes *backward* from the mapping of ϕ itself on points. This is a typical "dual" situation; in tensor analysis one says

that this indicates that scalar functions transform like covariant tensors. We say that ϕ induces a map on tangent vectors which goes in the same "direction" as ϕ itself, namely, from $T(M)$ to $T(M')$. For $p \in M$, $v \in M_p$, let $\phi_*(v)$ be the following tangent vector to $\phi(p) \in M'$:

$$\phi_*(v)(f) = v(\phi^*(f)) \qquad \text{for } f \in F(M').$$

ϕ_* is a *linear* mapping from M_p to $M_{\phi(p)}$.

Proof. $\phi_*(v_1 + v_2)(f) = (v_1 + v_2)(\phi^*(f)) = v_1(\phi^*(f)) + v_2(\phi^*(f))$, which is occasionally called the *differential* of ϕ.

The geometric interpretation of ϕ_* is very natural: Suppose $t \to \sigma(t)$ is a curve in M. Let $t \to \phi\sigma(t) = \sigma_1(t)$ be the image curve in M'. Then

$$\phi_*(\sigma'(t)) = \sigma_1'(t);$$

that is, the tangent vector of the image curve is the image of the tangent vector to the original curve in M under ϕ.

Proof

$$\phi_*(\sigma'(t))(f) = \sigma'(t)(\phi^*(f))$$

$$= \frac{d}{dt} \phi^*(f)(\sigma(t)) = \frac{d}{dt} f(\phi\sigma(t))$$

$$= \frac{d}{dt} f(\sigma_1(t)) = \sigma_1'(t)(f).$$

Notice that ϕ does not have to be either 1-1 or onto in order that ϕ_* can be defined on *tangent vectors*. However, the situation with regard to *vector fields* is not so simple. Suppose that $X \in V(M)$. Then $p \to \phi_*(X(p))$ is a mapping $M \to T(M')$. One cannot associate a vector field on M' with this mapping in an unambiguous way unless ϕ^{-1} exists. (Then one can define an "image" vector field $\phi_*(X)$ as $p' \to \phi_*(X(\phi^{-1}(p'))) = \phi_*(X)(p'))$.) However, differential forms *do* admit a simple law of transformation under ϕ: This is one main reason for their usefulness in differential geometry. (The other is that they serve as "volume elements" for integration.)

Recall that ϕ^* maps $F(M')$ onto $F(M)$, that is, maps $F^0(M')$ onto $F^0(M)$. We shall now extend this to a map of $F^r(M')$ to $F^r(M)$ for all r, that is, to a map sending a differential form ω' on M' *back* to a differential form $\phi^*(\omega')$ on M. Recall that the linear map $\phi_*: M_p \to M_{\phi(p)}'$ induces a "dual" map ϕ^* from covectors on $M_{\phi(p)}'$ back to covectors on M_p, that is, $\phi^*: M_{\phi(p)}'^* \to M_p^*$. Regard ω' as a cross section $p' \to \omega'(p') \in M_{p'}'^{*r}$ of $T^{*r}(M')$. Then $\phi^*(\omega')$ is by definition the cross section $p \to \phi^*(\omega'(\phi(p)))$; that is,

$$\phi^*(\omega')(v_1, \ldots, v_r) = \omega'(\phi_*(v_1), \ldots, \phi_*(v_r)) \qquad \text{for } v_1, \ldots, v_r \in T(M). \quad (3.10)$$

Now we have the following very nice property of the exterior derivative operation:

$$\phi^*(df) = d\phi^*(f) \qquad \text{for } f \in F(M'). \tag{3.11}$$

(When we extend d to higher-degree differential forms, this property will also extend.)

Proof.   For $v \in T(M)$,

$$\phi^*(df)(v) = df(\phi_*(v)) = \phi_*(v)(f) = v(\phi^*(f)) = d\phi^*(f)(v).$$

Notice also that the definition of ϕ^* would be *impossible* if differential forms were defined solely in terms of the $F(M)$-module structure of $V(M)$ and were not the same as those defined as cross sections of the covector bundles.

Exercises

1.   Suppose $v_1, \ldots, v_n$ is a basis of a vector space V. Define $\omega_1, \ldots, \omega_n \in V^*$ such that $v = \omega_1(v)v_1 + \cdots + \omega_n(v)v_n$ for all $v \in V$. Prove that $\omega_1, \ldots, \omega_n$ are a basis of V.

2.   Prove (3.7).

3.   Prove the traditional explicit formula for the determinant of a matrix, using the definition of the determinant of a linear transformation given in the text.

4.   Prove (3.11) in an explicit way for mappings between Euclidean spaces.

4 Specialization to Euclidean Spaces: Differential Manifolds

Let R^n be the space of n real variables $(x_1, \ldots, x_n)$. Thus, a point of R^n is an ordered n-tuple of real numbers; such an n-tuple will be denoted by (x_j), $1 \leq j \leq n$, or by a vector notation x when no confusion is likely. Also, x_j, without parentheses, will denote the real-valued function on R^n that assigns the jth coordinate to each point of R^n.†

Consider a domain D in R^n; say, for simplicity, that it is *convex*‡: Let $F(D)$ be the ring of real-valued functions that depend on a C^∞ way on the points of D, that is, such that the partial derivatives of all orders exist. If $f \in F(D)$, $\partial f/\partial x_i$, $\partial^2 f/(\partial x_i\, \partial x_j)$, etc., denote the partial derivatives with respect to the indicated variables. We shall now show how the objects such as "tangent vector," "vector field," and "differential form," which were introduced rather abstractly in Chapter 3, take a very familiar form here.

THEOREM 4.1

Let $X \in V(D)$. Then, there are uniquely determined functions $A_1, \ldots, A_n \in F(D)$ such that§

$$X(f) = A_i \frac{\partial f}{\partial x_i} \qquad \text{for } f \in F(D). \tag{4.1}$$

Proof. Let $x^0 = (x_i{}^0)$ be a fixed (for the moment) point of D. Then, given

---

† The reader should note that much of the notational confusion in undergraduate differential calculus is caused by not making this distinction.

‡ A domain in R^n is an open, connected set of point. It is *convex* if it contains, for any two points x^0 and x^1 in it, the whole line segment $tx^0 + (1-t)x^1$, for $0 \leq t \leq 1$.

§ We shall use the summation convention from now on. The general rules (as far as they can be formalized) are that when two indices occur in expressions multiplied together, they are to be summed over their "natural range of values" (which, presumably, has already been specified). We do not use lower and upper indices as in tensor analysis; where upper indices are used, usually they will be ordinary counting indices. The same indices should not occur three or more times; this always indicates that a mistake has been made. Occasionally it will be required that indices occurring together not be summed, but this will be stated explicitly. Part of the convention requires that one index standing "alone" take on all values from its natural range; for example, $\gamma_{ijk}\beta_j$ means $\Sigma_j \gamma_{ijk}\beta_j$ for i and $k = 1, 2, \ldots, n$.

any C^∞ function $f(x)$ in D, Taylor's formula implies that f has a representation of the form

$$f(x) = f(x^0) + \frac{\partial f}{\partial x_i}(x^0)(x_i - x_i^0) + g_{ij}(x)(x_i - x_i^0)(x_j - x_j^0). \qquad (4.2)$$

(The functions $g_{ij}(x)$ are those obtained from any of the classical formulas for the remainder; they are C^∞ if f is also.)

Calculate $X(f)$, using the linearity and (2.12), and evaluate it at x^0 to obtain $X(f)(x^0)$. Notice, for example, that $X(f(x^0)) = 0$, since X applied to any constant function is, from (2.12), zero. The result is

$$X(f)(x^0) = \frac{\partial f}{\partial x_i}(x^0)X(x_i)(x^0).$$

(The third terms drop out when x^0 is substituted.) Now x_i is merely another function on D: Call $X(x_i) = A_i$. Thus, letting x^0 vary also, we have

$$X(f) = A_i \frac{\partial f}{\partial x_i} = A_i \frac{\partial}{\partial x_i}(f),$$

whence the theorem.   Q.E.D.

Theorem 4.1 can be interpreted in the following way: Consider the differential operators $\partial/\partial x_i$, $i = 1, \ldots, n$, which map f into $\partial f/\partial x_i$. They satisfy (2.12) and hence define elements of $V(D)$ (if we define $V(D)$ as derivations of $F(D)$). Theorem 4.1 then asserts that they form a basis for the module of $V(D)$ over the ring $F(D)$.

Now we can state precisely how vector fields are defined as cross sections of the tangent bundle.

THEOREM 4.2

Let x^0 be a point of D, and let $v \in D_{x^0}$. Then

$$v(f) = v(x_i)\frac{\partial f}{\partial x_i} \qquad \text{for all } f \in F(D),$$

that is, $$v = v(x_i)\frac{\partial}{\partial x_i}(x^0). \qquad (4.3)$$

In particular, we see that the values of the vector fields $\partial/\partial x_i$ at each point of D form a basis of the tangent space.

Proof.   Applying v to (4.2) gives the result, using (2.6).   Q.E.D.

Theorem 4.2 tells us that $T(D)$ itself is parametrized by a domain $D' \subset R^{2n}$, for, any $v \in D_x$ admits a unique representation of the form

$$a_j \frac{\partial}{\partial x_j}(x'):$$

The assignment $v \to (x, a_j)$ defines the correspondence. We can use this to require that a cross section map $X: D \to T(D)$ be C^∞-differentiable. The condition for this is clearly that the functions $x^0 \to X(x_j)(x^0) = A_j(x^0)$ be elements of $F(D)$. We see from Theorem 4.2 that X considered as a cross section arises from the derivation $A_j(\partial/\partial x_j)$ of $F(D)$: There is equivalence of the two possible definitions of vector field.

Let us now examine differential forms. The coordinate function x_j are elements of $F(D)$. Their differentials dx_j are both $F(D)$-linear functions on $V(D)$ and cross sections of the bundle $T^*(D)$:

$$dx_j(X) = X(x_j) \qquad \text{for } X \in V(D),$$
$$dx_j(v) = v(x_j) \qquad \text{for } v \in T(D).$$

Suppose ω is any 1-differential form on D in the sense that it is an $F(M)$-linear map of $V(D) \to F(M)$. Then

$$\left[\omega - \omega\left(\frac{\partial}{\partial x_i}\right) dx_i\right]\left(\frac{\partial}{\partial x_j}\right) = 0 \qquad \text{for all } j,$$

that is, $\omega = \omega(\partial/\partial x_i)\, dx_i$. In particular, every such form arises from a cross section of the bundle $T^*(D)$, and the particular "coordinate" differential forms dx_j form a *basis* for the module $A^1(D)$.

A similar remark holds for r-degree forms. Once we know that the dx_j forms a basis, arguments identical to those used in Theorem 3.1 imply that the $dx_{j_1} \wedge \cdots \wedge dx_{j_r}$, $1 \le j_1 < j_2 < \cdots \le n$ form a basis for all forms of degree r, whether they are defined as $F(D)$-multilinear skew-symmetric maps $V(D) \times \cdots \times V(D) \to F(D)$ or as a cross section of the bundle of r-covectors. In particular, every r-form admits a unique expansion of the form

$$\omega = a_{j_1 \ldots j_r}\, dx_{j_1} \wedge \cdots \wedge dx_{j_r},$$

with skew-symmetric coefficients $a_{j_1 \ldots j_r}$.

We shall now switch from domains in Euclidean space, denoted by D, D', etc., to general differentiable manifolds (of differentiability class C^∞), denoted by M, N, etc. A differentiable manifold carries several sorts of structures, since intuitively it should be considered as a space that locally looks like a convex domain in Euclidean space, with all the local Euclidean structures tied together globally by the topology of the space. (Think of a closed surface in 3-space, say a sphere or a torus.)

Definition

A space M is said to be a *differentiable manifold (of class C^∞)* of dimension n if it carries the following structures:

(a) M is a Hausdorff topological space and is the union of a countable number of compact subsets.

(b) M has a covering by a family of open subsets, the typical ones denoted by U, U', ..., and each open subset U of the family has associated with it a convex domain D in R^n and a homeomorphism ϕ of U with D such that, whenever two open sets U, U' of the covering intersect, the associated transition mapping of $\phi(U \cap U')$ with $\phi'(U \cap U')$ is a map of differentiability class C^∞ in the usual sense for Euclidean space. (Explicitly, this map assigns to an $x \in D$ such that $\phi(p) = x$, for $p \in U \cap U'$, the point $\phi'(p) \in D'$.)

In addition, for differential-geometric purposes, it is convenient to suppose that the underlying topological space is connected (hence arcwise connected). We shall suppose that this is so implicitly, noting any exceptions explicitly. Each of these admissible homeomorphisms of an open set U with a subset D of R^n will be called a *chart*. U itself will be called a *coordinate neighborhood*. The collection of all these charts will be called the *atlas* that defines the manifold structure. Notice that any open subset of R^n has a manifold structure: The covering can be taken as that defined by its open, convex subsets.

A mapping $\phi: M \to M'$ between two manifolds will be said to be of differentiability class C^∞ if, whenever referred back via charts for $M \to M'$, it defines a C^∞ map in the usual sense for R^n. As in the earlier part of this work, we shall deal mainly with C^∞ maps; hence we shall not so specify every time one is introduced. Non-C^∞ maps (usually piecewise C^∞, though) will appear later, but we shall identify them explicitly. In particular, a real-valued C^∞ function on a manifold M is a well-defined concept, that is, just a map $M \to R$. The set of these functions will be denoted by $F(M)$. We base the definitions of the fundamental concepts of tangent vector-vector field, differential form, and similar terms on the properties of $F(M)$, as described before.

A few details must be settled before proceeding further, to assure that everything works as smoothly as for domains in R^n. First, the manifold structure on the tangent and cotangent bundles should be made precise. This can be done in the following way: Let U be a coordinate neighborhood with a chart giving a correspondence with a domain $D \subset R^n$. Then, under this correspondence, the tangent vectors above points of U correspond in a 1-1 way to the tangent bundle $T(D)$, which we have seen to be homeomorphic to a domain in R^{2n}. These " charts " for $T(M)$ can be used to give it a manifold structure, and the vector fields are defined as the C^∞ cross-section maps $M \to T(M)$. It can be verified (exercise) that this is equivalent to the condition that a cross-section map $X: M \to T(M)$ is C^∞ if and only if the function $p \to X(p)(f)$ is C^∞ for each $f \in F(M)$. Then one shows the identity between vector fields as cross sections of $T(M)$ or as derivations of $F(M)$ by relating the proof back to the special case where M is a domain in R^n. We leave the details of this as exercises.

Let M be a manifold. A set of functions $x_1, \ldots, x_n$ defined on an open subset U of M is a *coordinate system* for U if the map $p \to (x_1(p), \ldots, x_n(p))$ of $U \to R^n$ is a diffeomorphism.† Then the differentials $dx_1, \ldots, dx_n$ form a basis for differential forms in U. We *define* $\partial/\partial x_j$ as the dual basis of vector fields in U; that is, $(\partial/\partial x_j)(f)$ are the coefficients in the expansion:

$$df = \frac{\partial}{\partial x_j}(f)\, dx_j \qquad \text{for } f \in F(U). \tag{4.4}$$

Conversely, suppose (x_j) are functions such that the dx_j form a basis for the differential forms in U. Do they form a coordinate system for U, at least if U is a sufficiently small open set of M? The answer is "yes," by the use of the implicit function theorem. Suppose that ϕ is a chart diffeomorphism from U to a domain D of R^n, with coordinates on *this* R^n denoted by $y_1, \ldots, y_n$. Transferring back to D, the $x_1, \ldots, x_n$ become functions of the y. By (4.4),

$$dx_j = \frac{\partial x_i}{\partial y_j}\, dy_j. \tag{4.5}$$

Thus the $(dx_1, \ldots, dx_n)$ form a basis for differential forms if and only if the Jacobian matrix $(\partial x_i/\partial y_j)$ is nonsingular, that is, has nonzero determinant. If this is so, the implicit function theorem (see Chapter 5) asserts that the mapping $y \to x$ is a local diffeomorphism, that is, if U is sufficiently small.

Classical tensor analysis works by describing geometric objects completely in terms of such local coordinate systems. Suppose we regard (x_i) and (y_i) as two different local coordinate systems for the same neighborhood U of M. Then (4.5) enables us to express the transformation law of components of covariant tensors (like differential forms) from one coordinate system to the other. For example, if $\omega = a_i\, dx_i = b_i\, dy_i$, then

$$a_i \frac{\partial x_i}{\partial y_j} = b_j,$$

which is the characteristic transformation law. The transformation law for controvariant tensors (like vector fields) is most readily derived from (4.5).

---

† A map ϕ from manifold M to manifold M^1 is a *diffeomorphism* if the inverse map $\phi^{-1}: M^1 \to M$ exists and is C^∞. (A map may be 1-1 and onto, with inverse mapping not C^∞; for example, the map $x \to x^3$ from $R \to R$.)

Recall that $\partial/\partial x_i$ and $\partial/\partial y_i$ are defined as the vector fields dual to the dx_i and dy_i. Suppose

$$\frac{\partial}{\partial y_i} = A_{ij} \frac{\partial}{\partial x_j}.$$

Then

$$dx_k\left(\frac{\partial}{\partial y_i}\right) = A_{ij}\, dx_k\left(\frac{\partial}{\partial x_j}\right) = A_{ik}$$

$$= \left(\frac{\partial x_k}{\partial y_j}\, dy_j\right)\left(\frac{\partial}{\partial y_j}\right) = \frac{\partial x_k}{\partial y_j}.$$

That is,

$$\frac{\partial}{\partial y_i} = \frac{\partial x_j}{\partial y_i} \frac{\partial}{\partial x_j}. \tag{4.6}$$

Then (4.6) is a differential-geometric version of the chain rule for differentiation.

However, this restriction to the use of " flat " bases of differential forms and vector fields is the major defect of classical tensor analysis. Many geometric structures (for example, Riemannian metrics) take a very awkward form when their description is forced into this mold. E. Cartan, in his work on differential geometry and Lie groups (which is the foundation of all " modern " differential geometry), worked with a formalism that is halfway between tensor analysis and the formalism used today. Roughly, he worked with bases $(\omega_1, \ldots, \omega_n)$ of the 1-differential forms in neighborhoods of M that are not necessarily just the differentials of coordinate functions. He used the greater freedom to choose the "moving frames" to reduce many geometric problems to much simpler form than was possible in classical language.

Exercises

1.   If M is a manifold, $T(M) = \bigcup_{p \in M} M_p$ is its tangent bundle, prove that the procedure sketched in the text defines a manifold structure for $T(M)$. Prove that a cross-section map: $M \to T(M)$ is C^∞ if and only if $X(f)$ is C^∞ for each $f \in F(M)$.

2.   Let M be a manifold, with $p_0 \in M$. Show that there exists two open neighborhoods U_1, U_2 of p_0 and a function $f \in F(M)$ such that:

(a)   The closure of U_1 is contained in U_2.
(b) $f(p) = 1$ for $p \in U_1$.
(c) $f(p) = 0$ for $p \in M - U_2$.

3.   Show that a vector field on a manifold M can be defined either as a derivation of $F(M)$ or as a C^∞ cross section of the tangent bundle $T(M) \rightarrow M$.

4.   Similarly, show that a differential form can be defined either as a C^∞ cross section of the covector bundle, or as a $F(M)$-multilinear form on $V(M)$.

5.   Prove (4.2).

6.   Suppose $\phi: M \rightarrow M'$ is a C^∞ map between manifolds. Suppose X, X' are vector fields on M and M'. Let us say that they are ϕ-related if

$$\phi^*(X'(f')) = X(\phi^*(f')) \qquad \text{for each } f' \in F(M').$$

Prove: If X, $Y \in V(M)$ are ϕ-related to X', $Y' \in V(M')$, then $[X, Y]$ is ϕ-related to $[X', Y']$. Prove this abstractly, and then by using coordinate systems.

7.   Suppose Δ is the Laplace operator in the plane:

$$\Delta = \frac{\partial^2}{\partial x^2} + \frac{\partial^2}{\partial y^2}.$$

Work out its expression in polar coordinates:

$$X = r \cos \theta; \qquad y = r \sin \theta$$

using (4.6).

5 Mappings, Submanifolds, and the Implicit Function Theorem

We now develop the implicit function theorem and its consequences for the theory of mappings between manifolds, based on the "inverse function theorem" in the version given by Spivak [1, p. 35]. In fact, this result takes the following form for manifolds.

THEOREM 5.1

Suppose M and M' are manifolds of the same dimension, and $\phi: M \to M'$ is a map between them. (Let p be a point of M, $p' = \phi(p)$. Suppose that $\phi_*(M_p) = M'_{p'}$. Then there is an open subset U containing p such that:

(a) $\phi(U)$ is an open subset of M'.

(b) ϕ is a diffeomorphism between U and $\phi(U)$, that is, there is a map $\pi: \phi(U) \to U$ such that

$$\phi\pi(p') = p' \quad \text{for } p' \in \phi(U), \qquad \pi\phi(p) = p \quad \text{for } p \in U.$$

For example, suppose M and M' are identified with convex subsets D and D' of R^n. One often wants to regard ϕ as defining a "new coordinate system" for D. For example, suppose $x \in D$ is of the form $(x_1, \ldots, x_n)$, with $\phi(x) = (\phi_1(x), \ldots, \phi_n(x)) = (x_1', \ldots, x_n')$. Then, regarding $x_1', \ldots, x_n'$ as real-valued functions on M', we have $\phi^*(x_i') = \phi_i(x)$. Now

$$d\phi_i = \frac{\partial \phi_i}{\partial x_j} dx_j.$$

Since $(\partial \phi_i / \partial x_j)$ is the matrix of ϕ_* with respect to the natural bases for the tangent spaces of M and M' defined by their being in R^n, the condition: $\phi_*(M_p) = M_{p'}$ is equivalent to any one of the following conditions:

(a) $\det(\partial \phi_i / \partial x_j) \neq 0$.
(b) $d\phi_1, \ldots, d\phi_n$ are linearly independent at every point.
(c) $d\phi_1 \wedge \cdots \wedge d\phi_n \neq 0$.

We can now turn to the case of mapping between manifolds of different dimensions.

THEOREM 5.2

Let $\phi: D \to D'$ be a map of domains, $D \subset R^n$, $D \subset R^m$, $m \leq n$. Suppose that ϕ satisfies the following condition:

$$\phi_*(D_x) = D'_{\phi(x)} \qquad \text{for all } x \in D.$$

(ϕ is then said to be a maximal rank mapping). Then, if D is sufficiently small, it can be changed by a diffeomorphism so that ϕ is just the standard projection of R^n onto R^m. Schematically, there is a diagram of maps as follows:

$$D \to R^n$$
$$\phi \searrow \quad \downarrow \text{projection}$$
$$R^m$$

(The map $R^n \to R^m$ is that which assigns, say, the point $(x_1, \ldots, x_m) \in R^m$ to the point $(x_1, \ldots, x_n) \in R^n$. (Recall that $m \leq n$.))

Proof. Suppose coordinates for D are $x_1, \ldots, x_n$; coordinates for D' are $y_1, \ldots, y_m$. Then the map is defined by $\phi(x_1, \ldots, x_n) = (\phi_1(x), \ldots, \phi_n(x)) = (y_1, \ldots, y_m)$. The $n \times m$ matrix

$$\left(\frac{\partial \phi_a}{\partial x_i}(x) \right) \qquad 1 \leq i \leq n, \quad 1 \leq a \leq m,$$

is the matrix of the linear transformation $\phi_*: D_x \to D'_{\phi(x)}$ with respect to the natural bases of these vector spaces. To say that ϕ_* is onto is to say that the rank of this matrix is maximal, that is, m. After possibly relabeling coordinates and shrinking D, we may then suppose that

$$\det \left(\frac{\partial \phi_a}{\partial x_b}(x) \right) \neq 0. \tag{5.1}$$

Consider the functions $\phi_1, \ldots, \phi_m, x_{m-1}, \ldots, x_n$ on D. We want to show that they form a new coordinate system for D. (This is precisely what is required to prove the theorem, since the diffeomorphism $D \to R^n$ is defined by $(x_1, \ldots, x_n) \to (\phi_1(x), \ldots, \phi_m(x), x_{m+1}, \ldots, x_n)$. We must then show that the 1-forms $d\phi_1, \ldots, d\phi_m, dx_{m+1}, \ldots, dx_n$ are linearly independent. Suppose that there is a linear relation of the form

$$\sum_{a=1}^{m} \lambda_a \, d\phi_a + \sum_{i=m+1}^{n} \lambda_i \, dx_i = 0, \tag{5.2a}$$

or

$$\sum_{a,b=1}^{m} \lambda_a \frac{\partial \phi_a}{\partial x_b} dx_b + \cdots = 0 \tag{5.2b}$$

(the terms $\cdots$ involve $dx_{m+1}, \ldots, dx_n$), forcing

$$\sum_{a=1}^{m} \lambda_a \frac{\partial \phi_a}{\partial x_b} = 0;$$

hence $\lambda_a = 0$ by (5.1); hence $\lambda_{m+1} = 0 = \cdots = \lambda_n$ by (5.2), which completes the proof.

This result can be rephrased in another way that is often useful in practice. Suppose M is a manifold, and $f_1, \ldots, f_n$ is a set of real-valued functions on M. Suppose also that $df_1, \ldots, df_n$ are linearly independent at every point of M. Then if $(x_1, \ldots, x_m)$ is a coordinate system for M, the map $(x_1, \ldots, x_m) \rightarrow (f_1(x), \ldots, f_n(x))$ of a domain in R^m into R^n is of maximal rank. We conclude that in a neighborhood of each point of M, a coordinate system of functions can be introduced for which $f_1, \ldots, f_n$ are the first n-elements.

Now we study submanifold maps.

Definition

Let N and M be manifolds, $\phi: N \rightarrow M$ a map. ϕ is said to define an *immersion* of N in M if the following condition is satisfied:

For each $p \in N$, the tangent map $\phi_*: N_p \rightarrow M_{\phi(p)}$ is 1-1.   (5.3)

If, in addition, ϕ is 1-1, it is said to be a submanifold map of N in M, or defines N as a submanifold of M.

Remarks. Strictly speaking, a submanifold consists of the ordered triple (N, M, ϕ) satisfying these two conditions. It is often convenient and customary to relax this precise statement and regard the submanifold as $\phi(N)$, when no confusion is likely.

THEOREM 5.3

Let $\phi: N \rightarrow M$ be an immersion map. Then, each point $p \in N$ has a neighborhood U such that:

(a) ϕ restricted to U is a submanifold map.
(b) $\phi(p)$ has a neighborhood V with a coordinate system $z_1, \ldots, z_m$ for V such that $\phi(U) \subset V$, and $\phi(U)$ is the set of all points of V on which the functions $z_{n+1}, \ldots, z_m$ are zero.

Proof. Since $\phi_*: M_p \rightarrow M_{\phi(p)}$ is onto, the dual map $\phi^*: M^*_{\phi(p)} \rightarrow N_p^*$ on covectors is 1-1. Then we can find a coordinate system $y_1, \ldots, y_m$ valid in a neighborhood of $\phi(p)$ such that:

The values of the 1-forms $\phi^*(dy_1), \ldots, \phi^*(dy_n)$ in a neighborhood of p form a basis for the 1-covectors.

Then, by Theorem 5.1, in a neighborhood of p the functions $\phi^*(y_1), \ldots, \phi^*(y_n)$ form a coordinate system of N.

Now, the functions $\phi^*(y_{n+1}), \ldots, \phi^*(y_m)$ are functionally dependent on the $\phi^*(y_1), \ldots, \phi^*(y_n)$, say,

$$\phi^*(y_{n+1}) = F_{n+1}(\phi^*(y_1), \ldots, \phi^*(y_n)),$$
$$\vdots \qquad \vdots$$
$$\phi^*(y_m) = F_m(\phi^*(y_1), \ldots, \phi^*(y_m)).$$

We may suppose without loss of generality that the F are defined over all R^n. Consider the following functions on the neighborhood of $\phi(p)$:

$$y_1, \ldots, y_n, y_{n+1} - F_{n+1}(y_1, \ldots, y_m), \ldots, y_m - F_m(y_1, \ldots, y_n).$$

Their differentials are linearly independent in this neighborhood and hence there is a new coordinate system, say, $z_1, \ldots, z_m$, for a possibly smaller, neighborhood of $\phi(p)$ such that $\phi^*(z_1), \ldots, \phi^*(z_n)$ is a coordinate system for D; $\phi^*(z_{n+1}) = 0 = \cdots = \phi^*(z_m)$. These properties imply (a) and (b) required for the theorem.

Next, we inquire about the intersection of two immersed submanifolds. Here we must make the distinction between the case where the two submanifolds intersect "in general position" and where they do not. Intuitively, two such submanifolds are *not* in "general position" when they can be deformed slightly to change the dimension of the intersection, although this will not be the precise definition.

First we shall deal with a problem in linear algebra. Let V be a vector space over the real numbers, and let V', V'' be linear subspaces. Construct the direct sum vector space $V' \oplus V''$. We can map this into V, sending $v' \oplus v''$ into $v' + v''$. The kernel of this linear map is $V' \cap V''$, the range is $V' + V'' \subset V$. Thus we have the relation

$$\dim V' + \dim V'' - \dim(V' \cap V'') = \dim(V' + V'') = \dim V,$$

or

$$\dim(V' \cap V'') \geq \dim V' + \dim V'' - \dim V.$$

This inequality suggests that we make the following definition:

Definition

The linear subspaces V' and V'' of V are in *general position* if:

(a) $\dim(V' \cap V'') = \dim V' = \dim V'' - \dim V$ for the case $\dim V' + \dim V'' \geq \dim V$.

(b) $\dim(V' \cap V'') = 0$ for the case $\dim V' + \dim V'' \leq \dim V$.

Roughly, we may say that V' and V'' are in general position if $\dim(V' \cap V'')$ has minimal dimension compatible with the above inequality. Notice that, in case (a), $\dim(V' + V'') = V$; that is, $V' + V'' = V$. The crucial geometric property of this definition can now be stated.

THEOREM 5.4

If (V_t', V_t'') are two families of linear subspaces of V, depending continuously on a parameter t (say, $0 \le t \le 1$) and if (V_0', V_0'') are in general position, then (V_t', V_t'') are in general position for t sufficiently small.

Proof. The general position condition is equivalent to the condition that the linear map $V' \oplus V'' \to V$, constructed above, when made into a matrix by means of bases, have maximal rank; that is, a subdeterminant of maximal order must be nonzero. Since the determinant must vary continuously, this subdeterminant remains nonzero for sufficiently small t.

THEOREM 5.5

Let N, N', M be manifolds, and let $\phi: N \to M$, $\phi': N \to M'$ be immersion maps. Suppose $p \in N$, $p' \in N'$ are points such that $\phi(p) = \phi'(p')$; $\phi_*(N_p)$ and $\phi_*(N_{p'}')$ are in general position within $M_{\phi(p)}$. Then there are neighborhoods U of p, U' of p', in N and N' such that $\phi(U) \cap \phi'(U')$ is a submanifold of M whose dimension is equal to $\dim N + \dim N' - \dim M$.

Proof. Let $n = \dim M - \dim N$. By Theorem 5.3, there is a neighborhood V of $\phi(p)$, a neighborhood U of p, and a maximal rank map $\psi: V \to R^n$ such that

$$\psi(\phi(p)) = 0, \qquad \phi(U) = \psi^{-1}(0), \qquad \phi_*(N_p) = \psi_*^{-1}(0).$$

Let $U' = \phi'^{-1}(U)$. Consider the map $\psi\phi': U' \to R^n$. In case $\dim N + \dim N' = \dim M$, $(\psi\phi')_* = \psi_*\phi_*': N_{p'}' \to R_0^n$ must be 1-1; hence $\psi\phi'$ is an immersion map if U is sufficiently small. But

$$(\psi\phi)(\phi(U) \cap \phi'(U')) = 0,$$

which shows that $\phi(U) \cap \phi'(U') = \phi'(p)$ only, as required.

Consider the case that $\dim N + \dim N' > \dim M$. Then $(\psi\phi')_*$ must map $N_{p'}'$ onto R_0^n; that is, $\psi\phi'$ is a maximal rank mapping if everything is sufficiently small. Then, again,

$$\phi^{-1}(\phi(U) \cap \phi'(U')) = (\psi\phi')^{-1}(0).$$

But $(\psi\phi)^{-1}(0)$ can be represented by an immersion map of the required dimension by Theorem 5.3, which finishes the proof.

Finally we remark that all these different versions of the implicit function theorem may be intuitively summarized by saying that arbitrary C^∞ mappings satisfying maximal rank conditions behave locally just as linear mappings of vector spaces. Thus there is a good technical reason why a thorough knowledge of linear algebra is one of the most important prerequisites for the study of differential geometry!

Exercises

1.   Suppose $\phi: M \to N$ is a maximal rank mapping of manifolds (that is, $\phi_*(M_p) = N_{\phi(p)}$ for all $p \in M$). Prove that for $p \in \phi(M)$, the "fiber" $\phi^{-1}(p)$ is an embedded submanifold of M.

2.   Prove that the intersection of two embedded submanifolds which always meet in general position is a submanifold. (Determine whether they are embedded or immersed.) What is the global structure of the general-position intersection of two immersed submanifolds?

6 The Jacobi Bracket
and the Lie Theory of Ordinary Differential Equations

Jacobi Bracket

So far, the basic objects—vector fields and differential forms—have been considered in order to set up a formalism equivalent to ordinary differential calculus which, in addition, is independent of the choice of local coordinates. However, these ideas were first developed by S. Lie, not only for formal reasons but also for expressing in geometric form the many subtle and interesting relations between the theory of ordinary differential equations and the theory of Lie groups. Although the modern theory of Lie groups emerged from this work, it is an area that seems to be neglected in modern research. Here, we shall indicate only a few of the simpler ideas, partly for their own sake and partly to motivate the introduction of the Jacobi bracket operation on vector fields, which will play a major role in our work. We shall work with domains D in R^n with coordinates x_i. The extension to general manifolds will usually be evident.

Recall that a vector field on D is defined as a derivation, say X, of $F(D)$. It was proved in Chapter 4 that X took the form of a first-order partial differential operator:

$$X = A_i \frac{\partial}{\partial x_i}.$$

If X and Y are vector fields, XY is not, since as an operator it is a second-order differential operator. Explicitly, for $f, g \in F(D)$,

$$(XY)(fg) = X(Y(f)g + fY(g))$$
$$= XY(f)g + Y(f)X(g) + X(f)Y(g) + fXY(g).$$

However, note that the "bad" middle terms cancel out if $(YX)(fg)$ is subtracted from $XY(fg)$; that is, if $f \to XY(f) - YX(f)$ is a derivation of $F(D)$, and hence defines another vector field that we call the *Jacobi bracket* of X and Y, and denote by $[X, Y]$.

The following formal laws follow from direct (although occasionally tedious) computations, which we leave to the reader:

34

$$[c_1 X_1 + c_2 X_2, c_3 X_3 + c_4 X_4] = c_1 c_3 [X_1, X_3] + c_2 c_3 [X_2, X_3]$$
$$+ c_1 c_4 [X_1, X_4] + c_2 c_4 [X_2, X_4]. \qquad (6.1a)$$

$$[X, Y] = -[Y, X]. \qquad (6.1b)$$

$$[X, [Y, Z]] = [[X, Y], Z] + [Y, [X, Z]] \qquad \text{(Jacobi identity).} \quad (6.1c)$$

$$[X, fY] = X(f)Y + f[X, Y]. \qquad (6.1d)$$

If $X = A_i(\partial/\partial x_i)$, $Y = B_i(\partial/\partial x_i)$, then

$$[X, Y] = \left(\frac{\partial B_i}{\partial x_j} A_j - \frac{\partial A_i}{\partial x_j} B_j\right) \frac{\partial}{\partial x_i}. \qquad (6.1e)$$

$(X, X_1, \ldots, Y, Z, \ldots$ denote vector fields, $c_1, c_2, \ldots$ denote real constants, $f \in F(D)$.)

Properties (6.1a), (6.1b), and (6.1c) express the fact that $V(D)$ is, as a real vector space, also a *Lie algebra*. (A *Lie algebra* is a vector space with a " multiplication" $(X, Y) \rightarrow [X, Y]$ defined for any two elements X and Y satisfying (6.1a), (6.1b), and (6.1c).)

A curve $\sigma(t)$, $a \leq t \leq b$, is said to be an *integral curve* of a vector field X if $\sigma'(t) = X(\sigma(t))$ for $a \leq t \leq b$. Suppose the expression in coordinates for X is

$$X = A_i \frac{\partial}{\partial x_i}.$$

Now

$$\frac{d}{dt} x_i(\sigma(t)) = \sigma'(t)(x_i) = X(\sigma(t))(x_i)$$

$$= A_j(\sigma(t)) \frac{\partial}{\partial x_j}(x_i) = A_i(\sigma(t)).$$

Thus we see that σ is an integral curve of X if and only if its coordinate functions $x_i(t) = x_i(\sigma(t))$ satisfy the system of first-order differential equations:

$$\frac{d}{dt} x_i(t) = A_i(x(t)). \qquad (6.2)$$

Invoking the existence theorem for systems of ordinary differential equations, we have:

THEOREM 6.1

Suppose X is a vector field (of class C^∞) in the domain D.† Then

---

† All these statements will hold for manifolds also.

(a) Two integral curves $\sigma: [a, b] \rightarrow D$ and $\sigma_1: [a_1, b_1] \rightarrow D$ of X that coincide at just one common point t_0 of their domains of existence must coincide in their entire common domain.

(b) Given $x^0 \in D$, there is a number $a > 0$ and an integral curve $t \rightarrow \sigma(t, x^0)$, $0 \leq t \leq a$, of X with $\sigma(0, x^0) = x^0$. This function depends in a C^∞ way on x^0. In addition, a depends on x^0, but can be chosen independent of x^0 over any compact subset of D.

(c) If $\sigma(t), a \leq t \leq b$, is an integral curve of X, so is the curve $\sigma_1(t) = \sigma(t+c)$, $a - c \leq t \leq b - c$, obtained by translating the "time" parametrization of σ.

All these statements are the geometric analogs of fundamental analytical properties of systems of differential equations of the type (6.2). For example, condition (a) of the theorem is just the uniqueness of solutions of (6.2); (b) follows from the usual Picard iteration method of solving (6.2); (c) follows from the uniqueness and the fact that (6.2) does not contain t explicitly on the right-hand side (that is, it is a so-called *autonomous system*).

These properties of integral curves enable us to try to "continue" solutions of (6.2) so that we can obtain integral curves defined over maximal domains of t. For example, start off with an integral curve $\sigma(t), 0 \leq t \leq a_1$, with $\sigma(0) = x^0$. Find an integral curve $\sigma_1(t), a_1 \leq t \leq a_2$, with $\sigma_1(a_1) = \sigma(a_1)$. By uniqueness, the two curves can be fitted together (without corners) to obtain an integral curve over $0 \leq t \leq a_2$. Repeat the process beyond a_2 and also in the negative direction. Although we do not want to go into the details here, we can say that the process will succeed in proving the existence of an integral curve defined over $(-\infty, \infty)$ unless "barriers" are met in the form of two numbers α, β, $\alpha < 0, \beta < 0$, such that:

> There is an integral curve $\sigma(t)$, $\alpha < t < \beta$, with $\sigma(0) = x^0$, but there is no such integral curve in a domain containing (α, β).

One reason for the existence of these "barriers" may be that the integral curve wants to escape from D into the remainder of R^n. However, barriers may occur even if $D = R^n$; for example, suppose that $n = 1$, $D = R^1$, $X = x^2(\partial/\partial x)$, and (6.2) becomes

$$\frac{d}{dt} x(t) = x^2(t) \quad \text{or} \quad x(t) = \frac{x^0}{1 - x^0 t}.$$

Intuitively, the curve wants to escape to ∞ at $t = 1/x^0$. One might think that one way of remedying this would be to "add" a point at ∞ to R^1. This can be done successfully, but it leads to a differentiable manifold. (In this case, the manifold is the circle.)

With these warnings in mind, let us, for the sake of understanding the geometric meaning of the Jacobi bracket, suppose that X and Y are vector fields defined in D, all of whose integral curves can be extended over $(-\infty, \infty)$. Suppose $\sigma(t)$, $0 \le t \le a$, is an integral curve of X. For each t construct the curves $s \to \sigma(t, s)$, $0 \le s \le b$, such that:

(a) $\sigma(t, 0) = \sigma(t)$ for $0 \le t \le a$.
(b)   For each t, the curve $s \to \sigma(t, s)$ in an integral curve of Y.

We ask: If we hold s fixed, and consider the curve $t \to \sigma(t, s)$, when will this curve become an integral curve of X for each such s? In terms of the coordinates (x_i) for R^n, suppose that

$$X = A_i \frac{\partial}{\partial x_i}, \qquad Y_i = B_i \frac{\partial}{\partial x_i}, \qquad x_i(t, s) = x_i(\sigma(t, s)), \qquad x_i(t) = x_i(\sigma(t)).$$

Then our constructions translate into the conditions

$$x_i(t, 0) = x_i(t), \qquad \frac{dx_i(t)}{dt} = A_i(x(t)), \qquad \frac{\partial x_i(t, s)}{\partial s} = B_i(x(t, s)).$$

Put

$$C_i(t, s) = \frac{\partial}{\partial t} x_i(t, s) - A_i(x(t, s)).$$

Now

$$\frac{\partial^2 x_i(t, s)}{\partial t\, \partial s} = \frac{\partial B_i}{\partial x_j}(x(t, s)) \frac{\partial x_j}{\partial t}$$

$$= \frac{\partial B_i}{\partial x_j}(x(t, s))(C_j(t, s) + A_j(x(t, s)),$$

$$\frac{\partial C_i}{\partial s}(t, s) = \frac{\partial B_i}{\partial x_j}(x(t, s))(C_j(t, s) + A_j(x(t, s)) - \frac{\partial A_i}{\partial x_j}(x(t, s))B_j(x(t, s)).$$

THEOREM 6.2

If $[X, Y] = 0$, then for each s the curve $t \to \sigma(t, s)$ is an integral curve of X. Intuitively, knowing one integral curve of X and all integral curves of Y starting on this curve, a whole family of integral curves of X can be obtained.

Proof. $[X, Y] = 0$ if and only if

$$\frac{\partial B_i}{\partial x_j} A_i - \frac{\partial A_i}{\partial x_j} B_j$$

is *identically* zero. Then $C_i(t, s)$ satisfies the equations

$$\frac{\partial C_i}{\partial s}(t, s) = \frac{\partial B_i}{\partial x_j}(x(t, s))C_j(t, s),$$

which comprise a system of linear homogeneous first-order ordinary differential equations for C_i in s (with t held fixed). $C_i(t, 0) = 0$, since $\sigma(t)$ is an integral curve of X. Then we take it as known from the theory of ordinary differential equations (uniqueness!) that $C_i(t, s)$ is identically zero, which implies that for each s, $t \to \sigma(t, s)$ in an integral curve of X.   Q.E.D.

We now turn to the interpretation of Theorem 6.2 and the integral curves of a vector field in terms of the theory of groups (assuming always that those integral curves of vector fields that we shall be considering can be extended indefinitely within D). Suppose $t \to \sigma(t; x^0)$ is the integral curve for X, $-\infty < t < \infty$, such that $\sigma(0) = x^0$. Since $t \to \sigma(t + a; x^0)$ is also an integral curve, which takes on the value $\sigma(a; x^0)$ at $t = 0$, we must (by the uniqueness of integral curves, that is, by part (a) of Theorem 2.1) have

$$\sigma(t + a; x^0) = \sigma(t; \sigma(a; x^0)).$$

For each $t \in (-\infty, \infty)$ define a transformation T_t of D into itself as follows:

$$T_t(x^0) = \sigma(t; x^0) \qquad \text{for each } x^0 \in D.$$

Now $x^0 \to T_t(x^0)$ is a transformation of D into itself (of differentiability class C^∞, by the fundamental existence theorem for ordinary differential equations). Also,

$$T_{t+a}(x^0) = \sigma(t + a; x^0) = \sigma(t; \sigma(a; x^0)) = T_t(T_a(x^0)).$$

Since this holds for each $x^0 \in D$, we have $T_{t+a} = T_t T_a$. In particular, T_0 is the identity transformation $T_t T_{-t} = T_{-t} T_t$; that is, T_{-t} is the inverse of T_t and T_t is an invertible transformation of D into itself (a "diffeomorphism"). The property $T_{t+a} = T_t T_a$ tells us that the family $\{T_t: -\infty < t < \infty\}$ of transformations forms a *one-parameter group of transformations* of D into itself. This is the *one-parameter group generated by* X. X can be reconstructed from T, since the curves $t \to T_t(x^0)$ are integral curves of X for each $x^0 \in D$.

Suppose that Y is another such vector field, with $[X, Y] = 0$, and that Y generates the one-parameter group S_s, $-\infty < s < \infty$. Transcribing Theorem 6.2 into group language, we have several equivalent statements:

(a)   For each integral curve $\sigma(t)$ of X, the transform by each S_s, $t \to S_s(\sigma(t))$ (which, in the notation of Theorem 2.2, $= \sigma(t, s)$) is also an integral curve of X. Thus the one-parameter group S_s permutes the integral curves of X, or *leaves invariant* the differential equations, giving the integral curves of X. This interpretation is basic to the Lie theory of ordinary differential equations.

(b)   For each $x^0 \in D$, each $s, t \in (-\infty, \infty)$, $S_s(T_t(x^0))$ must equal $T_t(S_s(x^0))$, since the curve $t \to S_s(T_t(x^0))$ is an integral curve of X starting at

$S_s(x^0)$ when $t = 0$. Since this is true for each $x^0 \in D$, we have $S_s T_t = T_t S_s$; that is, *the one-parameter groups generated by X and Y commute.*

Suppose now that ϕ is a diffeomorphism of a domain D in the domain D'. Thus ϕ^* sets up an isomorphism of $F(D')$ and $F(D)$. Hence vector fields on D and D' correspond. Given $X \in V(D)$, define $\phi_*(X) \in V(D')$ as follows:

$$\phi_*(X)(f') = \phi^{-1*}(X(\phi^*(f))) \qquad \text{for } f' \in F(D'). \tag{6.3}$$

This is equivalent to the property

$$\phi_*(X)(x') = \phi_*(X(\phi^{-1}(x'))) \qquad \text{for } x' \in D'. \tag{6.4}$$

Proof. Using (6.3),

$$\phi_*(X)(x')(f) = \phi_*(X)(f')(x') = \phi^{-1*}(X(\phi^*(f')))(x')$$
$$= X(\phi^*(f'))(\phi^{-1}(x')).$$

However, this is just the right-hand side of (6.4).

This mapping $X \to \phi_*(X)$ has two main properties:

$$\phi_*([X, Y]) = [\phi_*(X), \phi_*(Y)] \qquad \text{for } X, Y \in V(D), \tag{6.5}$$

that is, ϕ_* is a Lie algebra isomorphism.

(c)   If $t \to \sigma(t)$ is an integral curve of X, then the image curve $t \to \phi(\sigma(t))$ is an integral curve of $\phi_*(X)$. Conversely, if the image curves of all integral curves of X under ϕ are integral curves of $Y \in V(D')$, then

$$Y = \phi_*(X). \tag{6.6}$$

The proofs of these statements are straightforward, and are therefore left to the reader.

To provide some practice with this formalism, we discuss the local canonical form theorem for nonsingular vector fields and give some indications of its importance in the Lie theory of ordinary differential equations.

THEOREM 6.3

Suppose that X is a vector field in a domain D of R^n, of coordinates $x = (x_i)$, and x^0 is a point of D with $X(x^0) \neq 0$ (that is, if $X = A_i(\partial/\partial x_i)$, then not all $A_i(x^0)$ are zero). Then, if D is small enough, there is an invertible transformation $\phi: D \to D'$, where D' is a domain in the space of variables y_i such that

$$\phi_*(X) = \frac{\partial}{\partial y_1}.$$

Proof. We shall give a geometric proof, but shall leave verification of certain analytical details to the reader.

At most reordering the coordinates, we can suppose that $A_1(x^0) \neq 0$. Suppose that $x^0 = 0$. Construct a mapping of $(y_1, \ldots, y_n)$-space into D by mapping $(y_1, \ldots, y_n)$ into $x_1(y_1), \ldots, x_n(y_1)$, where $t \to (x_i(t))$ is the integral curve of X, which is equal at $t = 0$ to $(0, y_2, \ldots, y_n)$. This mapping is invertible (and is left to the reader to verify); hence the $y_1, \ldots, y_n$ can be introduced in a neighborhood of x^0. When one follows an integral curve of X in these new coordinates, y_1 increases linearly while the $y_2, \ldots, y_n$ remain the same. This, however, is just the condition that X in these new coordinates is $\partial/\partial y_1$.

Q.E.D.

Theorem 6.3 is the simplest of the "canonical form" theorems that play a central role in the modern theory of ordinary differential equations. Notice that actually putting X into this canonical form is more or less equivalent to "solving" the differential equations defined by the integral curve.

Applications to the Lie Theory of Ordinary Differential Equations

The "Lie theory" is merely an interplay between the geometric interpretation of a system,

$$\frac{dx_i}{dt} = A_i(x(t)), \tag{6.7}$$

of ordinary differential equations as the integral curves of the vector field $X = A_i(\partial/\partial x_i)$ and the interpretation of X as a generator of a one-parameter group of transformations. Actually, we have been using "Lie theory" all along. However, one may consider the Lie theory in the more restricted sense as the discussion of those parts of the general theory that have relevance to the sort of problem one faces in "explicitly" solving differential equations.

As a first remark: Suppose X is a vector field, f is a function with $X(f) = 0$. Suppose $\sigma(t)$ is an integral curve of X. Then

$$\frac{d}{dt} f(\sigma(t)) = \sigma'(t)(f) = X(\sigma(t))(f) = X(f)(\sigma(t)) = 0,$$

that is, f is constant along all the integral curves of X. Classically, the function f is called an *integral* of X, or of the system (6.7), defining the integral curves. Conversely, functions having this property satisfy $X(f) = 0$; that is, f satisfies the first-order partial differential equation

$$A_i \frac{\partial f}{\partial x_i} = 0.$$

One may interpret the problem of "explicitly" solving the system (6.7) as that of finding $(n - 1)$ functionally independent integral functions, say, $f_2, \ldots, f_n$, for then the submanifolds $f_2 = $ constant, $\ldots, f_n = $ constant, in x-space, are one-dimensional and in fact are the sets of points described by each integral curve of (6.7). Thus, "explicitly solving" involves some formal process that converts a set of integral functions into a possibly larger set of interest. To see an example of such a formal process, suppose we are given another vector field Y on D such that $[Y, X] = gX$ for some $g \in F(D)$. If f is an integral of X, so is $Y(f)$.

   Proof. $X(Y(f)) = Y(X(f)) + [X, Y](f) = 0 - gX(f) = 0$. Thus, Lie derivation by Y is the formal process generating (possibly) "new" integrals.
   Let us now see what the condition $[Y, X] = gX$ means geometrically. First we ask whether there is a function h in D such that the vector field $X' = hX$ satisfies $[Y, X'] = 0$.
   Obviously, h must satisfy:

$$Y(h) + hg = 0 \qquad \text{or} \qquad Y(\log h) = -g.$$

Thus $\log h$ (and hence h) can be found *locally* if, for example, $Y(x) \neq 0$ for $x \in D$, for then we can suppose, in view of Theorem 6.3, that $Y = (\partial/\partial x_1)$; hence $\log h$ can be found by a simple quadrature:

$$\frac{\partial(\log h)}{\partial x_1} = -g(x_1, x_2, \ldots, x_n) \qquad \text{or} \qquad \log h = \int g(x_1, \ldots, x_n) \, dx_1.$$

Now notice that the integral curves of $X' = hX$ and X differ only by a change in parametrization, provided $h(x) \neq 0$ for $x \in D$. (We may say that two curves $\sigma(t)$, $a \leq t \leq b$, and $\sigma_1(t)$, $a_1 \leq t \leq b_1$, differ only by change in parametrization if there is a map $\alpha: [a, b] \rightarrow [a_1, b_1]$, that is, between the intervals of parametrization, such that $d\alpha/dt$ is always $\neq 0$ and such that $\sigma(t) = \sigma_1(\alpha(t))$ for $a \leq t \leq b$. If $d\alpha/dt$ is always >0 (resp. <0), we say that σ and σ_1 have the same (opposite) orientation.) For suppose $\sigma(t)$ is an integral curve of X and $\sigma_1(t) = \sigma(\alpha(t))$ is a curve resulting from a change in parametrization. To calculate $\sigma_1'(t)$, notice that for $f \in F(D)$:

$$\sigma_1'(t)(f) = \frac{d}{dt} f(\sigma_1(t)) = \frac{d}{dt} f(\sigma(\alpha(t)))$$

$$= \frac{d}{ds} f(\sigma(s)) \bigg|_{s = \alpha(t)} \frac{d\alpha}{dt}$$

(using the ordinary chain rule for differentiating composite functions of one variable)

$$= \sigma'(\alpha(t))(f)\frac{d\alpha}{dt} \, ;$$

hence

$$\sigma_1'(t) = \sigma'(\alpha(t))\frac{d\alpha(t)}{dt} \, .$$

Thus, $\sigma_1(t)$ will be an integral curve of $hX = X'$, provided

$$\sigma'(\alpha(t))\frac{d\alpha}{dt} = \sigma_1'(t) = X'(\sigma_1(t)) = h(\sigma(t))X(\sigma_1(t)).$$

But $\sigma'(\alpha(t)) = X(\sigma(\alpha(t)))$. Thus $\alpha(t)$ must satisfy

$$\frac{d\alpha(t)}{dt} = h(\sigma(\alpha(t))). \tag{6.8}$$

This is simply an ordinary differential equation for $\alpha(t)$ (of the type solvable by separation of variables); hence there is no trouble showing that for each $x \in D$, there are integral curves of X and X' passing through x, differing by construction only by a change in parametrization; one may paraphrase this by saying that "*integral curves* of X and X' are *the same up to a change of parametrization*."

Suppose we return to the case $[Y, X] = gX$. At least locally, $X' = hX$, with $h(x) \neq 0$ and $[Y, X'] = 0$. As we have seen, the one-parameter group generated by Y maps integral curves of X' into integral curves. Combining this with the remark about the integral curves of X and X', we see that:

> The one-parameter group generated by Y permutes the integral of X with a change of parametrization if $[Y, X] = gX$ for some function $g \in F(D)$.

Suppose now that $[Y, X] = 0$. The coordinate system may be chosen so that $Y = \partial/\partial x_1$. Further, looking through the details of Theorem 6.3, we see that this coordinate system may be easily "found" when the explicit equations of the one-parameter group determined by Y are known. If we write $X = \partial/\partial x_1$, we must have

$$0 = [X, Y] = \frac{\partial B_i}{\partial x_1}\frac{\partial}{\partial x_i};$$

hence the B_i are functions $B_i(x_2, \ldots, x_n)$ not depending on x_1. The equations of the integral curves of X are then

(i)
$$\frac{dx_i}{dt} = B_i(x_2(t), \ldots, x_n(t)), \qquad i \geq 2.$$

(ii)
$$\frac{dx_1}{dt} = B_1(x_2(t), \ldots, x_n(t)),$$

that is,

$$x_1(t) = \int B_1(x_2(t), \ldots, x_n(t)) \, dt.$$

Thus the system of order $(n - 1)$ can be solved first, and then $x_1(t)$ can be found by "quadrature," that is, by an integration. The order of the differential equations defining the integral curves of Y has been essentially reduced by 1. If $n = 2$, this is ideal, since the system (i) can also be solved by "quadrature." These observations constitute Lie's main contribution to the classical problem of solving differential equations in the plane. If

$$\frac{dy}{dx} = \frac{P(x, y)}{Q(x, y)}$$

is such a differential equation, the solution curves, when written in parametric form, are the integral curves of

$$P(x, y) \frac{\partial}{\partial y} + Q(x, y) \frac{\partial}{\partial x}.$$

Lie observed that all the classical tricks for "solving" this equation by quadrature were associated, in the way we described above, with a one-parameter group of transformations in the plane.

Exercises

1. Suppose $X = B_i(\partial/\partial x_i)$, where all the $B_i(x)$ are homogeneous of degree 1; that is, $B_i(\lambda x) = \lambda B_i(x)$ for each $\lambda > 0$. Show that for each, the transformation $x \to e^s x$ permutes the integral curves of X. Deduce that $[X, Y] = 0$, where $Y = x_i(\partial/\partial x_i)$. Now verify this directly.

2. In the (x, y) plane, consider the vector field

$$Y = y \frac{\partial}{\partial x} - x \frac{\partial}{\partial y}.$$

Show that the one-parameter group it generates is the group of rotations: $(x, y) \rightarrow (x \cos t + y \sin t, x \sin t - y \cos t)$. Let X be another vector field

$$A \frac{\partial}{\partial x} + B \frac{\partial}{\partial y}$$

in the plane. Find the condition: The one-parameter group generated by Y permutes the integral curves of X up to a change in parameter.

3. Find the coordinate system in which the infinitesimal generator of the one-parameter group of rotations in the plane has its canonical form. If

$$X = A \frac{\partial}{\partial x} + B \frac{\partial}{\partial y}$$

is such that $[Y, X] = fX$ (that is, if the problem is rotationally symmetric), find the "explicit" formulas for the integral curves of X.

4. Consider the space of one variable x, and on this space the three vector fields

$$X_1 = \frac{d}{dx}, \qquad X_2 = x \frac{d}{dx}, \qquad X_3 = x^2 \frac{d}{dx}.$$

Compute the Jacobi brackets. Show that the one-parameter group generated by any linear combination of these three vector fields with constant coefficients is contained in the group $x \rightarrow (ax + b)/(cx + d)$ of linear fractional transformations.

5. Suppose $X = A_i(\partial/\partial x_i)$ and $Y = B_i(\partial/\partial x_i)$ are vector fields such that $[X, Y] = Y$ and such that the n-vectors, $(A_i(x^0))$ and $(B_i(x^0))$, are linearly independent. Show that the coordinate system can be chosen so that $x^0 = 0$, and about this point,

$$Y = \frac{\partial}{\partial x_1}, \qquad X_1 = \frac{\partial}{\partial x_1} + \frac{\partial}{\partial x_2} + \alpha(x_2, \dots, x_n) \frac{\partial}{\partial x_1},$$

where α is some function of the indicated variables. Suppose that $Z = B_i(\partial/\partial x_i)$ is such that $0 = [X, Y] = [Y, Z]$. Show that the integral curves of Z in this coordinate system can be found by solving a system of order $n - 2$, followed by quadratures.

6. Suppose

$$X = A_i \frac{\partial}{\partial x_i}, \qquad Y = B_i \frac{\partial}{\partial x_i}, \qquad Z = C_i \frac{\partial}{\partial x_i}$$

are vector fields such that $[X, Y] = Y$, $[X, Z] = Z$, $[Y, Z] = 2X$ and such that the vectors $(A_i(x^0)), (B_i(x^0)), (C_i(x^0))$ are linearly independent. Show that the coordinate system can be chosen so that $x^0 = 0$, and about this point,

$$Y = \frac{\partial}{\partial x_1}, \qquad X = x_1 \frac{\partial}{\partial x_1} + \frac{\partial}{\partial x_2} + \alpha(x_2, \ldots, x_n) \frac{\partial}{\partial x_1},$$

$$Z = (x_1^2 + 2\alpha x_1 + \beta(x_2, \ldots, x_n)) \frac{\partial}{\partial x_1} + (2x_1 + \gamma(x_2, \ldots, x_n)) \frac{\partial}{\partial x_2} + e^{x_2} \frac{\partial}{\partial x_3},$$

where α, β, γ are functions of the indicated variables. Show that the problem of finding the integral curves of any vector field W that satisfies $0 = [X, W] = [Y, W] = [Z, W]$ in these coordinates can be reduced to solving a system of differential equations of order $n - 3$, quadratures, and a Riccati equation. (A Riccati equation is one of the form $dx/dt = a(t) + b(t)x + c(t)x^2$.)

7. Prove (6.5) and (6.6).

7 Lie Derivation and Exterior Derivative; Integration on Manifolds

Let us return to the study of differential forms on a manifold M. We have described the Jacobi bracket operation $(X, Y) \to [X, Y]$ on vector fields, the Lie derivative $f \to X(f)$ of a function by a vector field, and exterior derivative $f \to df$ of a function. We shall now extend the latter two operations from functions f (that is, differential forms of degree zero) to differential forms of any degree. Note first that the definition of $[X, Y]$ can be rewritten as

$$X(Y(f)) = Y(X(f)) + [X, Y](f).$$

The key idea is that X acting on $Y(f)$ acts first on Y, leading to $[X, Y]$, and then on f, leading to $X(f)$. Suppose now that ω is an rth degree differential form. For $X_1, \ldots, X_r \in V(M)$, $\omega(X_1, \ldots, X_r)$ is then a function. Let X be another vector field. Let us apply X to this function and write

$$X(\omega(X_1, \ldots, X_r)) = X(\omega)(X_1, \ldots, X_r) + \omega([X, X_1], X_2, \ldots, X_r)$$
$$+ \cdots + \omega(X, \ldots, [X, X_r]). \qquad (7.1)$$

Now, we use (7.1) as the *definition* of the r-form $X(\omega)$, and call it the *Lie derivative* of ω by X.

We must verify that $X(\omega)$ is well defined by (7.1). That it depends skew-symmetrically on $X_1, \ldots, X_r$ should be obvious. The only nontrivial point is that it is $F(M)$ multilinear, that is,

$$X(\omega)(fX_1, X_2, \ldots, X_r) = fX(\omega)(X_1, \ldots, X_r) \qquad \text{for } f \in F(M). \quad (7.2)$$

(Here we use the algebraic "module" definition of differential forms. It is much more convenient for the purpose of doing things in a coordinate-free way than is the vector bundle definition.) Now

$$X(\omega)(fX_1, \ldots, X_r) = X(\omega(fX_1, \ldots, X_r))$$
$$- \omega([X, fX_1], X_2, \ldots, X_r) - \omega(fX_1, X, X_2, \ldots, X_r)$$
$$= X(f)\omega(X_1, \ldots, X_r) + fX(X_1, \ldots, X_r)$$
$$- \omega(X(f)X_1, \ldots, X_r) - \omega(f[X, X_1], X_2, \ldots, X_r) \cdots.$$

Notice that the first and third terms now cancel, as required in order to prove (7.2).

For $\omega \in F^r(M)$, $X \in V(M)$, define the contraction of ω by X, $X \lrcorner \omega$,† as the $(r-1)$-form given by

$$(X \lrcorner \omega)(X_1, \ldots, X_{r-1}) = \omega(X, X_1, \ldots, X_{r-1}). \qquad (7.3)$$

It is readily verified that (7.1) gives the rule

$$X(Y \lrcorner \omega) = [X, Y] \lrcorner + Y \lrcorner X(\omega) \qquad \text{for } X, Y \in V(M). \qquad (7.4)$$

Using this, we can prove that

$$X(\omega_1 \wedge \omega_2) = X(\omega_1) \wedge \omega_2 + \omega_1 \wedge X(\omega_2) \qquad \text{for } X \in V(M). \qquad (7.5)$$

Proof. Suppose degree $\omega_1 = r$, degree $\omega_2 = s$. Then (7.5) is true for $r = s = 0$. Proceed to prove (7.5) by induction on $r + s$.

Let Y be another vector field:

$$
\begin{aligned}
Y \lrcorner X(\omega_1 \wedge \omega_2) &= \text{(using (7.4))} \ X(Y \lrcorner (\omega_1 \wedge \omega_2)) - [X, Y] \lrcorner (\omega_1 \wedge \omega_2) \\
&= X((Y \lrcorner \omega_1) \wedge \omega_2 + (-1)^r \omega_1 \wedge (Y \lrcorner \omega_2)) \\
&\quad - ([X, Y] \lrcorner \omega_1 \wedge \omega_2 + (-1)^r \omega_1 \wedge ([X, Y] \lrcorner \omega_2)) \\
&= \text{(using (7.4) again and the induction hypothesis)} \\
&\quad ([X, Y] \lrcorner \omega_1) \wedge \omega_2 + (Y \lrcorner X(\omega)) \wedge \omega_2 \\
&\quad + (Y \lrcorner \omega_1) \wedge X(\omega_2) + (-1)^r (X(\omega_1) \wedge (Y \lrcorner \omega_2) \\
&\quad + \omega_1 \wedge ([X, Y] \lrcorner \omega_2) + \omega_1 \wedge (Y \lrcorner X(\omega_2)) \\
&\quad - ([X, Y] \lrcorner \omega_1) \wedge \omega_2 + (-1)^r \omega_1 \wedge ([X, Y] \lrcorner \omega_2)).
\end{aligned}
$$

When the cancellations are made, we get Y applied to the right-hand side of (7.5). Since Y is an arbitrary vector field, (7.5) holds for forms of this degree also.

$$\text{If } f \in V(M), \qquad \text{then } X(df) = dX(f). \qquad (7.6)$$

Proof. For $Y \in V(M)$,

$$
\begin{aligned}
Y \lrcorner X(df) &= X(Y \lrcorner df) - [X, Y] \lrcorner df \\
&= X(Y(f)) - [X, Y](f) \\
&= Y(X(f)).
\end{aligned}
$$

But,

$$Y \lrcorner d(X(f)) = YX(f). \qquad \text{Q.E.D.}$$

The geometric meaning of the Lie derivative by X is not so evident in this formal treatment: It will become clearer when we deal with Lie groups.

---

† In some differential geometry books, $X \lrcorner \omega$ is denoted by $i(X)(\omega)$ and $X(\omega)$ is denoted by $\theta(X)(\omega)$ or $L_X(\omega)$.

Roughly, $X(\omega)$ is a measure of the extent to which ω is invariant under the one-parameter group generated by X. Suppose, for example, that we examine the geometric consequences of the condition $X(\omega) = 0$. If X is identically zero, it means nothing, since $X(\omega)$ is always zero. Pick a point p at which $X(p) \neq 0$, and introduce a coordinate system x_i about p in which $X = \partial/\partial x_1$. Now ω admits an expansion in this neighborhood of the form

$$\sum a_{j_1 \ldots j_r} \, dx_{j_1} \wedge \cdots \wedge dx_{j_r}.$$

Using the rules developed above,

$$0 = X(\omega) = \sum X(a_{j_1 \ldots j_r}) \, dx_{j_1} \wedge \cdots \wedge dx_{j_r}$$
$$+ \, a_{j_1 \ldots j_r} \, d(X(x_{j_1})) \wedge \cdots \wedge dx_{j_r} + \cdots$$
$$= \sum \frac{\partial a_{j_1 \ldots j_r}}{\partial x_1} \, dx_{j_1} \wedge \cdots \wedge dx_{j_r} + 0,$$

since $d(X(x_j))$ is always zero. Hence

$$\frac{\partial a_{j_1 \ldots j_r}}{\partial x_1} = 0, \tag{7.7}$$

that is, $a_{j_1 \ldots j_r}$ is a function of $x_2, \ldots, x_n$ above. The one-parameter group $t \to \phi_t$ generated by X then leaves $x_2, \ldots, x_n$ alone and increases x_1 linearly; $x_1 \to x_1 + t$. We see that (7.7) is the condition that ω be invariant under each of these transformations; that is,

$$\phi_t^*(\omega) = 0 \qquad \text{for all } t.$$

This holds in a neighborhood of p; however, the set of points where it holds is open and closed in M, and since we are assuming M to be connected, it holds everywhere on M.

Now we turn to extending d to forms of all degree, sending an r-form ω onto an $(r + 1)$-form $d\omega$. We shall want the following basic formula relating d to Lie derivative to hold:

$$X(\omega) = X \lrcorner \, d\omega + d(X \lrcorner \, \omega) \qquad \text{for } X \in V(M). \tag{7.8}$$

Let us take advantage of the fact that we have already defined $X(\omega)$, and can assume that $d(X \lrcorner \, \omega)$ is defined by induction, to define $d\omega$ for forms of degree r, assuming it is defined (and satisfies (7.8)) for forms of degree less than r. Explicitly,

$$d\omega(X_1, \ldots, X_{r+1}) = X_1(\omega)(X_2, \ldots, X_{r+1})$$
$$- \, d(X_1 \lrcorner \, \omega)(X_2, \ldots, X_{r+1}). \tag{7.9}$$

Now, as in the earlier definition of $X(\omega)$, we must verify that (7.9) really defines $d\omega$ as a skew-symmetric, $F(M)$-multilinear function of $X_1, \ldots, X_{r+1}$. This is similar to the earlier computation and is left as an exercise. The three remaining important properties of d are

$$X(d\omega) = dX(\omega), \tag{7.10}$$

$$d(\omega_1 \wedge \omega_2) = d\omega_1 \wedge \omega_2 + (-1)^r \omega_1 \wedge d\omega_2, \tag{7.11}$$

(if ω_1 is an r-form), and

$$d(d\omega) = 0 \qquad \text{for all forms } \omega. \tag{7.12}$$

All three can be proved by the technique we have used already; namely, we assume that they are true for forms of lower degree and apply the inner product $Y \lrcorner$ to both sides, for an arbitrary vector field Y. As an example, we prove (7.12) with this technique:

$$
\begin{aligned}
Y \lrcorner d(d\omega) &= Y(d\omega) - d(Y \lrcorner d\omega) \\
&= Y(d\omega) - d(Y(\omega) - d(Y \lrcorner \omega)) \\
&= Y(d\omega) - dY(\omega)
\end{aligned}
$$

(the third term vanishes by induction hypotheses)

$$= 0 \qquad \text{(by (7.10))}.$$

In principle, (7.9) can be worked out to give a noninductive, explicit definition of $d\omega$. However, this is never used in practice. Either (7.8) is used or d can be calculated very simply in local coordinates. Suppose x_j are coordinate functions on a neighborhood of M. Then

$$\omega = \sum a_{j_1 \ldots j_r} \, dx_{j_1} \wedge \cdots \wedge dx_{j_r}.$$

Using (7.11) and (7.12), we see that

$$d\omega = \sum da_{j_1 \ldots j_r} \wedge dx_{j_1} \wedge \cdots \wedge dx_{j_r}. \tag{7.13}$$

(Notice that (7.13) requires (7.12) only for zero forms, where it is easily proved directly, and (7.11). But (7.10) for forms of degree greater than zero is an easy consequence of (7.5) and (7.10) for forms of degree zero. Thus (7.10) could be proved quite simply by using (7.13) instead of the formal method indicated above as an exercise.)

We find that (7.13) has as consequence the basic rule for the behavior of d under mappings between manifolds. Suppose ϕ is a map: $M' \to M$ of manifolds. Then we have

$$\phi^*(d\omega) = d\phi^*(\omega) \qquad \text{for each differential form } \omega \text{ on } M. \tag{7.14}$$

Proof. We have already verified (7.14) for zero forms. But it suffices to verify (7.14) in each coordinate patch, and (7.13) obviously enables us to do this, since

$$\phi^*(\omega) = \sum \phi^*(a_{j_1 \dots j_r})\phi^*(dx_{j_1} \wedge \cdots \wedge dx_{j_r}).$$
$$d\phi^*(\omega) = \sum \phi^*(da_{j_1 \dots j_r}) \wedge d\phi^*(x_{j_1}) \wedge \cdots \wedge d\phi^*(x_{j_r})$$
$$= \phi^*(d\omega).$$

Integration on Manifolds

Our main concern in this book is with differential calculus on manifolds. Since we shall also occasionally need some of the basic facts of integral geometry, we now present a short survey of what we need. The reader can refer to Spivak [1] for a fuller treatment of the integration theory.

Let M be a manifold (always assumed to be C^∞ and representable as a countable union of compact sets). Suppose dim $M = n$.

Definitions

M is *orientable* if it admits at least one n-differential form ω of degree n whose value is nonzero at each point of M. Two such forms ω and ω' are *equivalent* (for the purposes of orientation) if $\omega = f\omega'$, with $f \in F(M), f(p) > 0$, for all $p \in M$.

An *orientation* of M is just an equivalence class of such forms. It readily verified that if M is connected, it admits either no orientation or two. (For if an n-form ω defines an orientation, $-\omega$ defines an orientation in a different class. If ω' also defines an orientation, ω' must equal $f\omega$ for some everywhere nonzero $f \in F(M)$. Since M is connected, either $f > 0$ or $f < 0$ everywhere on M. In the former case, ω' is equivalent to ω; in the latter, to $-\omega$.) If M is disconnected, fixing an orientation on each connected component of M defines an orientation for M in an obvious way.

A coordinate system $(x_1, \dots, x_n)$ valid in a connected open set U of M is *positively* (respectively, *negatively*) *oriented* with respect to an orientation defined by an n-form ω if

$$dx_1 \wedge \cdots \wedge dx_n = f\omega,$$

with $f > 0$ in U (respectively, $f < 0$ in U).

A *partition of unity* for M is a sequence $f_1, f_2, \dots$ of functions from $F(M)$ such that

(a) $\sum_{j=1}^{\infty} f_j(p) = 1$ and $f_j(p) \geq 0$ for all $p \in M, j = 1, 2, \dots$.

(b) Each function f_j has assigned to it an open subset U_j of M such that f_j vanishes outside U_j, and each U_j meets only a finite number of the other sets of the sequence.

(c) Each set U_j is a coordinate neighborhood of the manifold, with a coordinate system of functions $x_1, \ldots, x_n$ valid in U_j.

It follows from (a) and (b) that M is the union of the U_j. Conversely, it can be proved that any open covering $U_1, U_2, \ldots$ of M such that each set meets only a finite number of the other sets has a set of functions $f_1, f_2, \ldots$ associated with it satisfying (a) and (b). The proof can be found quite easily in Helgason [1, p. 8] or Spivak [1, p. 63].

Now, let M be orientable, with a fixed orientation. Let θ be an n-form on M and let f be a *continuous* real valued† function on M. We define the *integral* of f over M with respect to θ, denoted by $\int_M f\theta$, as follows:

Case 1

f vanishes outside a coordinate neighborhood U.

Let $\phi: D \to U$ be a diffeomorphism of U with a convex domain D in R^n, chosen so that the coordinate system defined by ϕ on U is positively oriented. Let $(x_1, \ldots, x_n)$ be coordinates on D, $\phi^*(\theta) = g\, dx_1 \wedge \cdots \wedge dx_n$. Then put

$$\int_M f\theta = \int_D \phi^*(f)g\, dx_1 \cdots dx_n,$$

where the integral on the right-hand side is the ordinary‡ Riemann integral for the function $\phi^*(f)g$ on the domain D.

We pause to show that this is independent of the choice made of ϕ and D. Suppose then that $\phi': D' \to U$ is another diffeomorphism of U with a convex domain D' in R^n, with $\phi'^*(\theta) = g'\, dx_1 \wedge \cdots \wedge dx_n$. Let ψ be the mapping $D' \to D$ defined as: $\psi = \phi^{-1}\phi'$. Then

$$\psi^*(dx_1 \wedge \cdots \wedge dx_n) = \phi'^*\phi^{-1*}(dx_1 \wedge \cdots \wedge dx_n)$$

$$= \phi'^*\left(\frac{\theta}{\phi^{-1*}(g)}\right) = \frac{g'}{\psi^*(g)}.$$

But, $\psi^*(dx_1 \wedge \cdots \wedge dx_n)$ also equals $J\, dx_1 \wedge \cdots \wedge dx_n$, where J is the Jacobian of the mapping ψ from D' to D. Now we take, as known from advanced calculus, the behavior of the Riemann integral under a diffeomorphism $\psi: D' \to D$, namely,

$$\int_D h\, dx_1 \cdots dx_n = \int_{D'} \psi^*(h)\,|J|\, dx_1 \cdots dx_n \qquad \text{for all } h \in C(D').$$

But $J = g'/\psi^*(g)$, which is positive, since both ϕ and ϕ' define coordinate

---

† Of course the theory can be trivially extended to complex functions by separating them into real and imaginary parts.

‡ When we write $dx_1 \cdots dx_n$ with no wedge products, we just mean the ordinary, unoriented Riemann integral. Thus, to be pedantic, it should as a symbol be distinguished from $\int_D \phi^*(f)g\, dx_1 \wedge \cdots \wedge dx_n$, although, of course, it is equal to it as a number.

systems that are oriented positively. Now

$$\int_M f\theta = \int_D \phi^*(f)g\, dx_1 \cdots dx_n$$

$$= \int_{D'} \psi^*\phi^*(f)\psi^*(g)\,|J|\, dx_1 \cdots dx_n$$

$$= \int_{D'} (\phi\psi)^*(f)g'\, dx_1 \cdots dx_n$$

$$= \int_{D'} \phi'^*(f)g'\, dx_1 \cdots dx_n,$$

which shows explicitly the invariance in the definition of $\int_M f\theta$.

Case 2

f vanishes outside a compact subset of M.

Let $\{f_1, f_2, \ldots\}$ be functions on M defining a partition of unity for M. Then f can be written as

$$f = \sum_{j=1}^{\infty} ff_j.$$

The sum on the right-hand side is really finite, for by property (b) of a partition of unity, the compact subset outside of which f vanishes meets only a finite number of the elements of the covering of M associated with the partition of unity. Since each ff_j vanishes outside a coordinate neighborhood, by case 1,

$$\int_M ff_j\,\theta \text{ is defined.}$$

Now let us *define*

$$\int_M f\theta \qquad \text{as} \quad \sum_{j=1}^{\infty} \int_M ff_j\,\theta.$$

(Again, this is really only a finite sum.) We must prove that this is independent of the partition of unity chosen. Suppose, then, that $\{f_1', f_2', \ldots\}$ is another partition of unity. Now $\{f_jf_k': 1 \leq j, k < \infty\}$ is also a partition of unity, since†

$$\sum_{j,k=1}^{\infty} f_jf_k'(p) = \sum_{j=1}^{\infty}\sum_{k=1}^{\infty} f_jf_k'(p)$$

$$= \sum_{j=1}^{\infty} f_j(p)\sum_{k=1}^{\infty} f_k'(p) = 1.$$

† Some analysis is needed to prove that the double summation can be broken up, but the justification (left to the reader) readily follows from theorems on convergence of infinite series, since all terms are nonnegative.

Now consider $\sum_{j,k=1}^{\infty} \int_M f f_j f_k' \theta$. Since this is really a finite sum, it can be split up into

$$\sum_{j=1}^{\infty} \sum_{k=1}^{\infty} \int_M f f_j f_k' \theta.$$

For fixed j, $f f_j f_k'$ vanishes outside a coordinate neighborhood; hence the additivity of the Riemann integral implies that

$$\sum_{k=1}^{\infty} \int_M f f_j f_k' \theta = \int_M f f_j \left(\sum_{k=1}^{\infty} f_k' \right) \theta = \int_M f f_j \theta.$$

Performing the double summation in the reverse order, we see that

$$\sum_{k=1}^{\infty} \int_M f f_k' \theta = \sum_{j,k=1}^{\infty} \int_M f f_j f_k' \theta = \sum_{j=1}^{\infty} \int_M f f_j \theta,$$

which proves invariance.

Case 3

The General Case. Let $C_c(M)$ be the vector space of continuous, real-valued functions on M that vanish outside a compact subset of M. We can sum up what we have proved above in the following way: An n-differential form θ on M defines a linear functional $f \to \int_M f\theta$ on $C_c(M)$ with the following property:

> Given a compact set K of M, there exists a number $\alpha > 0$ such that, whenever $f \in C_c(M)$ vanishes outside K and is everywhere bounded in absolute value by 1, $\int_M f\theta \le \alpha$.

(Tracing through case 2 and referring back to the properties of the Riemann integral in bounded domains in R^n, we see that α is fixed, once a particular finite set of coordinate neighborhoods covering K is chosen.) Now, this is just the property needed to extend $\int_M f\theta$ to functions f on M that are merely Borel measurable. (Following the pattern established in extending the Riemann integral from continuous functions on closed intervals to a Lebesgue integral over the whole real line, roughly, one approximates f by sequences from $C_c(M)$, while defining the integral by a limiting operation.) As usual in measure theory, we say that such an f is *integrable* if $\int_M |f| \theta$ is finite. We have all the general tools of integration theory that are available on, say, the real line for the Lebesgue integral. However, all immediate work in this chapter is concerned with continuous functions, so that we are really dealing only with the analog of the Riemann integral.

It must be emphasized, however, that one should not go too far in trying to regard this from the point of view of functional analysis. The main aims in integral geometry are *computation* of such integrals, or at least statements of

theorems showing how such computations can be reduced to computation
of geometric invariants, and of theorems about the behavior of the integrals
under mappings. In addition, in the future the problem of singularities of
such integrals will be increasingly important. In such problems it is important
to be able to utilize the intuitive tricks of integrating that are learned in
integral calculus. In these computations, our standard notation is sometimes
awkward,† and more intuitive notations are desirable. For example, for
$\int_M f\theta$ we sometimes write

$$\int_M f(p)\theta_p; \qquad \int_M f(p)\theta(p); \qquad \int_M f(p)\,dp; \qquad \int f\theta,$$

and so forth. The third notation is useful when one form of θ is fixed throughout the discussion; it can be called dp. Physicists have devised a useful
notation for integrating over domains in Euclidean space of variables $x_1, \ldots,$
x_n, which goes something like this: $\int f(x)\,d^n x$.

We now turn to the question of behavior under mappings, which is really
the main problem of integral geometry. The most immediate concern is
behavior under diffeomorphisms, which follows more or less from the
definitions.

THEOREM 7.1

Let $\phi: M \to M'$ be a diffeomorphism between manifolds, and let θ' be a
volume element‡ form on M', $f' \in F(M)$. Then

$$\int_{M'} f'\theta' = \int_M \phi^*(f')\phi^*(\theta').$$

Proof. When f vanishes outside a coordinate neighborhood of M, this is
inherent in the proof given above that the defining Riemann integral depends
on the coordinate neighborhood. The general case can be obtained from this
one by using a partition of unity.

Next, suppose that M is a manifold, that ω is a p-form on M, that N is a
p-dimensional manifold, and that the map $\phi: N \to M$ defines N as a submanifold of M. Then $\phi^*(\omega)$ is a volume element form with respect to N; hence we

† Although, conversely, sometimes problems in integral calculus become much more
amenable when written in a more abstract than usual notation. This is particularly true of
"change of variable" arguments; writing down explicitly the mappings involved and using
the general formalism often clears up much confusion.

‡ By this we mean a form of the same degree as the dimension of the space. We shall state
things for C^∞ functions f, but of course everything that does not involve differentiation of f
usually extends to at least continuous f. In addition, we shall not state explicitly unless there
is a possibility of confusion about whether we are working with a particular orientation on
each manifold.

can define $\int_N \phi^*(\omega)$ as above. As usual, it is often convenient to suppress mention of ϕ and write this simply as $\int_N \omega$.

Defining the integral of a p-form over a p-dimensional manifold is very natural and easy, since differential forms can be "pulled back" under mappings. Now let us suppose that $\phi: M \to B$ is a map of manifolds and that ω is a volume element differential form on M. Of course it makes no geometric sense to think of defining an object like $\phi_*(\omega)$, since differential forms are covariant objects; that is, they behave under mappings as functions rather as points. However, ω does define a linear form on functions, namely, $f \to \int_M f\omega$, which, as the dual of a covariant object, is contravariant. Thus it may be expected that the linear functional defined by ω on forms does get "pushed" by ϕ to define a linear functional on functions of B. We shall denote this functional by $\phi^{-1*}(\omega)$. Thus, as definition, $\phi^{-1*}(\omega)$ is a linear map $C_c(B) \to R$, defined by

$$\phi^{-1*}(\omega)(f') = \int_M \phi^*(f)\omega \qquad \text{for } f' \in C_c(B).$$

Now there is one immediate difficulty with this definition, namely, $\phi^*(f)$ may not be integrable with respect to the measure defined by ω. However, there are two main cases where this difficulty does not arise:

(a)   All continuous functions on M are integrable with respect to ω.

(b) ϕ is a *proper* map; that is, the inverse image of every compact subset of M' under ϕ is a compact subset of M.

For the moment, the reader can assume that we are working with one of these assumptions—there are various devices available for weakening them.

To justify this unorthodox notation, namely, $\phi^{-1*}(\omega)$, note that by Theorem 7.1 (in case ϕ^{-1} exists; that is, ϕ is a diffeomorphism) $\phi^{-1*}(\omega)$ as a functional agrees with the functional defined by the *form* $\phi^{-1*}(\omega)$. In addition, if $\psi: B \to C$ is another map, the reader can easily check that $(\psi\phi)^{-1*}$ is just $\psi^{-1*}\phi^{-1*}$, so that the notation will not lead to inconsistency on iteration of mappings. We also believe that the notation has some intuitive geometric content. If ϕ^{-1} exists as a map, $\phi^{-1*}(\omega)$ is of the same degree as ω. If not (for example, if B is of lower dimension than M), then $\phi^{-1*}(\omega)$ is something like a volume element form on B so that ϕ^{-1*} "collapses" the degree of ω. In fact, we shall see below that ϕ^{-1*} acts by "collapsing" the component of ω along the fibers of ϕ by a process of "integration over the fibers."

There is *another* mapping associated with ϕ that carries measures on B back into measures on M. Let θ be any fixed volume element form on B. Then any $f \in F(B)$ defines a measure on B, namely, that associated with the volume element form $f\theta$. But we can pull back f to $\phi^*(f)$, then multiply $\phi^*(f)\omega$ to get a volume element, and hence get a measure on M. We can thus regard this as a mapping of $F(B)$ into the space of measures on M, or more generally, as the space of linear functionals on $C(M)$. Thus we have the possibility of extending this map, defined by ϕ and ω of $C(B)$ into† $C_c(M)^*$ from certain generalized functions‡ on B, into certain generalized functions on M; we shall continue to use the notation ϕ^* for this mapping.

The most important such generalized function is the Dirac delta function. Suppose, then, that b is a point of B, that $d_1, d_2, \ldots$ are a sequence of elements of $C_c(B)$ that converge to the Dirac delta function $\delta_{b'}$; that is,

$$\lim_{j \to \infty} \int_{M'} d_j \, f\theta = f(b) \qquad \text{for all } f \in C_c(B).$$

Then, according to our definition, $\phi^*(\delta_b)$ is the linear functional on $C_c(M)$ such that

$$\phi^*(\delta_b)(f) = \lim_{j \to \infty} \int_M \phi^*(d_j) f\omega \qquad \text{for all } f \in C_c(M).$$

Physicists use the notation

$$\phi^*(\delta_b) = \delta_{\phi^{-1}(b)},$$

regarding $\delta_{\phi^{-1}(p)}$ as the "delta function" corresponding to the set $\phi^{-1}(p)$ just as the usual Dirac functions associated with a set consisting of one point.

Using this bit of formalism, we can write the relation between $\phi^{-1}*$ and ϕ^* in an interesting, but purely formal, way. Suppose the measure $\phi^{-1}*(\omega)$ on M' is defined by a volume element differential form on M'; for example, by one of the forms $g\theta$. Thus

$$\int_M \phi^*(f)\omega = \int_B fg\theta = \int_B f(b)g(b) \, db \qquad \text{for all } f \in F(B),$$

where db is a suggestive shorthand for θ. Now, formally, g can be written as

$$g(b) = \int_B \delta_b(b')g(b') \, db';$$

thus, formally again,

$$\int_B f(b)g(b) \, db = \int_B \int_B f(b) \, \delta_b(b')g(b') \, db \, db'.$$

Using the relation $\phi^{-1}*(\omega) = g\theta$ again, we have (purely formally, of course)

$$\int_M \phi^*(\delta_b)\omega = \int_B \delta_b(b')g(b') \, db'.$$

---

† This just denotes the set of real-valued linear forms on $C_c(M)$.
‡ We refer to Gelfand-Šilov [1] for the notion of "generalized function."

Finally,

$$\int_M f\omega = \int_B \left(\int_M f\phi^{-1*}(\delta_b)\omega \right) db \qquad \text{for all } f \in F(M). \qquad (7.15)$$

This is one of the two main formulas of integral geometry (the other is the Stokes' formula); it describes how an integration over M can be decomposed into an integration over the fibers of ϕ, and then into an integration over B. (It is a generalization of the formula

$$\int_a^b \int_c^d f(x, y) \, dx \, dy = \int_a^b \left\{ \int_c^d f(x, y) \, dy \right\} dx,$$

which is well known in integral calculus. However, (7.15) contains a good deal more information, since it holds in cases where the map ϕ is much more complicated than the simple projection map associated with a Cartesian product.) At any rate, one of the most urgent tasks of integral geometry is to find broadest conditions under which (7.15) holds, that is, in which the formal tricks we used can be justified. We shall now mention one general theorem that is relevant.

Let M be a manifold, $\phi: M \to B$ a map of M onto B, with $\dim B \le \dim M$ and with both M and B orientable. We say that a point $p \in M$ is a nonsingular point of the mapping if $\phi_*(M_p) = B_{\phi(p)}$, and we then say that a point $b \in B$ is a nonsingular image point of the mapping if $\phi^{-1}(b)$ consists only of non-singular points. Let ψ be an everywhere nonzero volume element form on B. A theorem of Sard tells us that the singular image points of ϕ form a subset of measure zero on B. (By "measure zero" we mean relative to that measure defined by ψ on B. We must refer to the exposition given by Sternberg [1, p. 47].) Now, if $b \in B$ is a nonsingular image point of ϕ, it follows from the implicit function theorem that $\phi^{-1}(b)$ is a submanifold of M whose dimension is equal to $(\dim M - \dim B)$.

Now, let $f \in C_c(B)$ and let ω be a differential form that vanishes outside a compact subset of M and whose degree is equal to $(\dim M - \dim B)$. Thus

$$\theta = \omega \wedge \phi^*(f\psi)$$

is a volume element form on M; hence $\int_M \theta$ is well defined. We want to express this integral in terms of an integration over the fibers of ϕ and over the base manifold B.

THEOREM 7.2

With the above notations,

$$\int_M \phi^*(f\psi) \wedge \omega = \int_B \left\{ \int_{\phi^{-1}(b)} \omega \right\} f(b)\psi. \qquad (7.16)$$

A word of explanation of the notations inherent in this formula is necessary. If b is a singular image point, we must regard $\int_{\phi^{-1}(b)} \psi$ as undefined. If b is a nonsingular image point, we define $\int_{\phi^{-1}(b)} \psi$ as follows: ψ restricted to $\phi^{-1}(b)$ is a volume element form for the submanifold. The points where this submanifold is nonzero form an open subset of the submanifold (hence also a submanifold of M), and $\int_{\phi^{-1}(b)} \psi$ is defined as the integral of ψ over this submanifold. Thus $b \to f(b) \int_{\phi^{-1}(b)} \psi$ is a real-valued function defined except for a set of measure zero on B; hence the right-hand side of (7.16) is defined as the integral of this function over B.

The proof of formula (7.16) can be found in all generality in a paper by Federer [1], although it is expressed there in a different language. We shall not give the proof of (7.16) in full here, but only in the case where ϕ has no singular points, that is, where ϕ is a maximal rank, onto-mapping. Actually, the fact that (7.16) can allow singularities is its most interesting and delicate point, but the "nonsingular" version we prove here is adequate for most of the applications we have in mind.

Since (7.16) is linear in ψ, notice first that it suffices to prove it in case ψ vanishes outside a coordinate neighborhood of M. By the implicit function theorem, M can be covered by coordinate neighborhoods U having coordinate systems $x_1, \ldots, x_n$ with the following properties:

(a) $0 < x_1, \ldots, x_n < 1$.
(b) $\phi(U)$ is a coordinate neighborhood for B, with coordinate system $y_1, \ldots, y_m$ such that $\phi^*(y_1) = x_1, \ldots, \phi^*(y_m) = x_m$.

Suppose that in $\phi(U)$, $f\psi$ is given by a form $h(y) \, dy_1 \wedge \cdots \wedge dy_m$. We can suppose without loss of generality that ω is of the form $k(x) \, dx_{m+1} \wedge \cdots \wedge dx_n$ (since any of the factors involving $dx_1, \ldots, dx_m$ will not affect either side of (7.16)).

Thus the left-hand side of (7.16) is

$$\int_0^1 \cdots \int_0^1 h(x)k(x) \, dx_1 \cdots dx_n.$$

The right-hand side is

$$\int_0^1 \cdots \int_0^1 h(x) \, dx_1 \cdots dx_m \left(\int_0^1 \cdots \int_0^1 k(x) \, dx_{m+1} \cdots dx_n \right),$$

and the two are then equal by the property of the Riemann integral that asserts that multiple integrals can be evaluated by iterated partial integrals.

Q.E.D.

COROLLARY TO THEOREM 7.2

Suppose that $\phi^*(\psi) \wedge \omega$ is a volume element form for M that is nonzero on $\phi^{-1}(b)$, with b a nonsingular image point for ϕ. Then $\phi^*(\delta_b) = \delta_{\phi^{-1}(b)}$, the

"Dirac delta function" of the fiber $\phi^{-1}(b)$, is just ω in the sense that

$$\delta_{\phi^{-1}(b)}(f) = \int_{\phi^{-1}(b)} f\omega \qquad \text{for } f \in C_c(M).$$

To make this more explicit we give an example: Suppose that M is R^n itself and that ϕ is a map of $R^n \to R$; that is, ϕ is just a real-valued function on R^n, say, of the form

$$x \to \phi(x).$$

Suppose, say, that $b = 0$. The condition that b be a regular image point is then just $d\phi(x) \neq 0$ for each x such that $\phi(x) = 0$.

Let grad ϕ be the vector field

$$\sum_{i=1}^{n} \frac{\partial \phi}{\partial x_i} \frac{\partial}{\partial x_i}.$$

Then grad $\phi(x) \neq 0$ for each x such that $\phi(x) = 0$. Suppose the form ψ on R is just the Riemann integral form. Then $\phi^*(\psi) \equiv d\phi$.

Let us then try to find an $(n-1)$-form ω such that

$$\theta = dx_1 \wedge \cdots \wedge dx_n = d\phi \wedge \omega.$$

Apply the inner product of grad ϕ to both sides:

$$\text{grad } \phi \lrcorner \theta = \text{grad } \phi(\phi)\omega - d\phi \wedge (\text{grad } \phi \lrcorner \omega).$$

Now $d\phi$ is zero when restricted to the fibers of ϕ:

$$\text{grad } \phi(\phi) = \sum_{i=1}^{n} \frac{\partial \phi}{\partial x_i} \frac{\partial \phi}{\partial x_i},$$

which, anticipating the notation to be introduced in Part 3, we write as

$$\|\text{grad } \phi\|^2.$$

Thus, we see that

$\delta_{\phi^{-1}(0)}$ can be represented by the $(n-1)$-form $(\text{grad } \phi \lrcorner \theta)/\|\text{grad } \phi\|^2$, in the sense that $\delta_{\phi^{-1}(0)}$ applied to a function $f \in C_c(M)$ is just the integral of f over the hypersurface $\phi^{-1}(0)$ with respect to this form.

At this point we make contact with the material in the first volume of a treatise by Gelfand and Šilov [1] on "generalized functions," and we refer the reader to that discussion for more detail and for the fascinating applications to partial differential equations.

We have now completed our admittedly fragmentary remarks about the general facts concerning the behavior of measures defined by differential forms under mappings. We now turn to the second basic general fact about integration on manifolds, namely "Stokes' formula." Now, just as the behavior of measures under mappings can ultimately be reduced (if things are not too pathological) to the very simple theorem that a multiple Riemann integral can be reduced to iterated one-dimensional Riemann integrals, so can "Stokes' formula" be reduced to the fact that the integral of a derivative of a function is the function itself. Here, again, it is rather difficult to state and prove precisely a version of Stokes' formula that is comprehensive for all geometric applications (at least without detouring into considerable technicalities). We shall compromise again by stating it in reasonable generality and by proving it under simple hypotheses.

Let M be a (an oriented) manifold that will be fixed throughout the discussion. Let ω be a form of degree equal to $(\dim M - 1)$, and let D be an open subset of M. Let D' be the boundary of D in M (that is, $D' = \bar{D} - D$, where $\bar{D}$ is the closure of D in M). Now, of course, D' can be quite pathological. However, "nice" domains will have boundaries that can be exhibited as the union of a "large piece" that is a submanifold of M of codimension 1 (that is, a hypersurface) and various smaller pieces of lower dimension. Suppose this hypersurface is orientable: One of the two possible orientations can be chosen as follows:

Let $p \in D'$ be a point on the hypersurface boundary N of D, and let $u \in M_p$ be the vector such that sufficiently small curves with tangent vector u point inside D. Then, a basis $v_1, \ldots, v_{n-1}$ ($n = \dim M$) for N_p is *positively oriented* if $(v_1, \ldots, v_{n-1}, u)$ is a positively oriented basis of M_p (in terms of the given orientation on M, that is, if θ is the everywhere nonzero volume element form on M, then $\theta(v_1, \ldots, v_{n-1}, u) > 0$.) This orientation of N will be called the *positive orientation* of N *relative* to D. We denote by ∂D this hypersurface on the boundary of D (possibly nonconnected, of course) with the *orientation described above. Stokes' formula* then states that

$$\int_{\partial D} \omega = \int_D d\omega. \tag{7.17}$$

(Of course, under suitable conditions, one can allow ∂D to be the whole boundary of D if the proper precautions are taken to orient the hypersurface part of the boundary and the convention adopted is that the integral of ω over a subspace of lower dimension is zero; but our procedure is more in line with ∂D as it is defined in topology.)

Now we can prove one simple, but adequate version of Stokes' formula:

THEOREM 7.3

Let D be an open subset of an oriented manifold M, and let ∂D be an oriented hypersurface of M that lies on the boundary of D and is positively oriented relative to D. Suppose that $U_1, U_2, \ldots$ is a sequence of open subsets of M which covers $D \cup \partial D$ and such that, in each $U_j, j = 1, 2, \ldots$, there is a function f_j such that

$$\partial D \cap U_j = \{p \in U_j: f_j(p) = 0\}, \tag{7.18a}$$

$$df_j \neq 0 \quad \text{in } U_j, \tag{7.18b}$$

$$D \cap U_j = \{p \in U_j: f_j(p) > 0\}, \tag{7.18c}$$

and such that

each U_j meets only a finite number of the others. (7.19)

Then Stokes' formula holds in D for each form ω that is defined and smooth in a neighborhood of $D \cup \partial D$.

Proof. Using a partition of unity, it suffices to deal with the case where ω vanishes outside one of the sets of the covering having the properties described in (7.18). If necessary, making the covering smaller, we can suppose that each of the sets carries a coordinate system $x_1, \ldots, x_n$ such that x_1 is just the function f_j. Thus we can reduce to the case where:

(a) D is the subset $\{(x_1, \ldots, x_n) \in R^n: x_1 > 0\}$.
(b) ∂D is the subset $\{(x_1, \ldots, x_n) \in R^n: x_1 = 0\}$.
(c) ω vanishes outside a compact subset of D.

Suppose, for example, that

$$\omega = g_1(x) \, dx_2 \wedge \cdots \wedge dx_n - g_2 \, dx_1 \wedge dx_3 \wedge \cdots \wedge dx_n$$
$$+ \cdots \pm g_n \, dx_1 \wedge \cdots \wedge dx_{n-1}.$$

Since (7.17) is linear in ω and $d\omega$, it suffices to deal with essentially just two cases, namely,

$$\omega = g_1(x) \, dx_2 \wedge \cdots \wedge dx_n \quad \text{or} \quad \omega = g_2(x) \, dx_1 \wedge dx_3 \wedge \cdots \wedge dx_n.$$

In both cases, g_1 and g_2 vanish outside a compact set. Then

$$d\omega = \frac{\partial g_1}{\partial x_1} \, dx_1 \wedge \cdots \wedge dx_n \quad \text{or} \quad d\omega = -\frac{\partial g_2}{\partial x_2} \, dx_1 \wedge \cdots \wedge dx_n.$$

In the first case,

$$\int_D d\omega = \int_{\substack{x_1 > 0 \\ (x_2, \ldots, x_n) \in R^{n-1}}} \frac{\partial g_1}{\partial x_1} \, dx_1 \cdots dx_n;$$

integrating first with respect to x_1, we find that

$$\int_D d\omega = \int_{R^{n-1}} g_1(0, x_2, \ldots, x_n) \, dx_2 \cdots dx_n = \int_{\partial D} \omega.$$

In the second case,

$$\int_D d\omega = - \int_{\substack{x_1 > 0 \\ (x_2, \ldots, x_n) \in R^{n-1}}} \frac{\partial g_2}{\partial x_2} \, dx_1 \cdots dx_n$$

$$= 0,$$

after integrating with respect to x_2 and remembering that g_2 vanishes at infinity. But $\int_{\partial D} d\omega$ also vanishes, since $dx_1 = 0$ on ∂D.   Q.E.D.

Remark. In both Theorems 7.2 and 7.3 we have used the same trick, namely, find a formula that is expressed in completely geometric, coordinate-free language. To prove the formula, we first verify it in the simplest possible cases, where it reduces to a well-known property of the Riemann integral, and then extend it, using "partition of unity" tricks, to more complicated situations that are built up from the simple ones. In fact the whole procedure is the prototype for many of the ideas of algebraic topology.

Exercises

1. Prove that $d\omega$ as defined by (7.9) depends skew-symmetrically on its arguments.

2. Work out $d\omega(X, Y)$ and $d\theta(X, Y, Z)$ explicitly if ω and θ are 1- and 2-forms. Guess and prove the general formula $d\omega(X, \ldots, X_{r+1})$ for an r-form.

3. Prove (7.10) and (7.11), two ways: first, using local coordinates; then completely intrinsically.

4. In the proof of (7.14) given, show why "it suffices to verify (7.14) in each coordinate patch."

5. Suppose M is an orientable manifold, and N is an embedded submanifold of M of one less dimension. Suppose that a function $f \in F(M)$ is identically zero on N, and $df \neq 0$ at each point of N. Show that N is orientable.

6. Show that the classical Gauss, Green, and Stokes' theorems (proved in vector analysis) are specializations of the general Stokes' theorem.

8 The Frobenius Complete Integrability Theorem

Let M be a manifold, and let $V(M)$ be the set of its vector fields. Originally, we defined an $X \in V(M)$ as a cross section of the tangent bundle to M. However, we have established that X can be alternatively defined as a linear mapping: $F(M) \to F(M)$ such that

$$X(fg) = X(f)g + fX(g) \qquad \text{for } f, g \in F(M).$$

This property can be described algebraically by saying that a vector field is a *derivation* of the ring $F(M)$.

Now, given $X, Y \in V(M)$, we established (in Chapter 6) that the vector field $[X, Y]$, the *Jacobi bracket* of X and Y, can be defined by the rule

$$f \to [X, Y](f) = X(Y(f)) - Y(X(f)).$$

Formula (6.1) gave some of the algebraic properties of this bracket operation. In particular, they showed that $V(M)$ is a Lie algebra (over the real numbers) and established a connection with the theory of Lie groups, which will be explained in more detail in Chapter 10. In this section, we establish a connection between this algebraic structure and certain geometric facts.

A set H of vector fields on M is said to define a *vector-field system* on M if it is an $F(M)$-submodule of $V(M)$; that is, if

$$fX + gY \in H \qquad \text{for } X, Y \in H, \quad f, g \in F(M).$$

We shall suppose that such a vector-field system is given on M. For $p \in M$, define H_p, the "value" of H at p, as the set of all vectors of M_p of the form $X(p)$, for $X \in H$. H_p is a linear subspace of M_p: Its dimension is called the *rank* of H at p and is denoted by $r(p)$; the point p is said to be a *maximal point* for H if $r(p) \geq r(q)$ for all $q \in M$.

LEMMA 8.1

$r(p) \leq r(q)$ for all points q sufficiently close to p. In particular, the set of maximal points of H is an open set of points in M.

Proof. Let X_a, $1 \leq a \leq r(p)$ be elements of H such that the $(X_a(p))$ are a basis of H_p. To prove the lemma it suffices to show that the $(X_a(q))$ are linearly independent elements of H_q whenever q is sufficiently close to p.

This is indeed a general fact. Suppose that

$$X_a = A_{ai}\frac{\partial}{\partial x_i}.$$

Since the values of the vector fields $(\partial/\partial x_i)$ form a basis of the vector space of tangent vectors at each point, the dimension of the subspace of M_q spanned by the $X_a(q)$ is equal to the rank of the $r \times n$ matrix $(A_{ai}(q))$; that is, it is equal to the number of rows of the largest square submatrix whose determinant is nonzero. Since the determinant of a matrix of continuous functions is a continuous function, the $r \times r$ subdeterminant, which is $\neq 0$ at $q = p$ (since the rank is r at p, by construction) will remain $\neq 0$ when q varies in some neighborhood of p. This proves the lemma.

LEMMA 8.2

Let p be a maximal point for H. Then there is a neighborhood U of p and a set of elements (X_a), $1 \leq a \leq r$, in H such that

(a) $(X_a(q))$ is a basis for H_q for all $q \in U$.
(b) Each $X \in H$ can be written in the form $X = f_a X_a$, with $f_a \in F(U)$. (Such a set of vector fields is called a *basis* for H in U.)

The proof is a corollary to the argument of Lemma 8.1. The vector fields (X_a) chosen for that proof are linearly independent at every point q sufficiently close to p; hence they form a basis for H_q, since dim $H_q = $ dim H_p. This proves (a).

To prove (b), choose an $X \in H$. $X(q)$ can be written as $f_a(q)X_a(q)$ for q sufficiently close to p. The assignment $q \rightarrow (f_a(q))$ defines the functions f_a. It remains only to show that they are C^∞. This can be done, as in the proof of Lemma 8.1, by writing the X_a in terms of local coordinates.

Definition

A mapping $\phi: N \rightarrow M$ of a manifold N into M is called an *integral map* of H if $\phi_*(N_p) \subset H_p$ for all $p \in N$.
A function $f \in F(M)$ is called an *integral function* of H if $X(f) = 0$ for all $f \in M$.

Notice that this notion generalizes ideas we have already discussed for the case where H has a basis consisting of a single vector field. In that case, the integral maps that are submanifolds are one-dimensional, that is, are determined locally by ordinary differential equations. As we shall see, integral maps of more general vector-field systems are determined locally by partial differential equations.

Suppose for the rest of this chapter that all points of M are maximal points for H. Notice that an integral function $f \in F(M)$ is constant along an integral submanifold map $\phi: N \to M$. For suppose $t \to \sigma(t)$ is a curve in N. Notice that

$$df(H_p) = 0 \qquad \text{for all } p \in M. \qquad (8.1)$$

Since $\phi_*(\sigma'(t)) \in H_{\sigma(t)}$, we see that

$$\frac{d}{dt}(f(\phi(\sigma(t)))) = 0,$$

which shows that f is constant along N (if it is connected, of course).

Now, we may ask: When are the integral submanifolds determined by the integral functions? Precisely, we mean the following: For $p \in M$, let H_p' be the set of all vectors $v \in M_p$ such that:

$$df(v) = 0 \qquad \text{for all integral functions } f \text{ defined in a neighborhood of } p.$$

By (8.1), we have $H_p \subset H_p'$. If

$$H_p = H_p' \qquad \text{for all } p \in M, \qquad (8.2)$$

we say that the integral functions determine the integral submanifolds. In fact, suppose $f_1, \ldots, f_s$ are a maximal set of functionally independent integral functions of H defined in a neighborhood of p. Consider the submanifolds defined locally about p by setting these functions all equal to constants. One obtains submanifolds locally defined about p that will also be integral submanifolds of H if (8.2) is satisfied; that is, if $r = \dim N - s$.

However, H cannot be an arbitrary vector-field system if this condition is satisfied. For then H can locally be defined as the set of all $X \in V(M)$ such that

$$df_1(X) = 0 = \cdots = df_s(X).$$

Thus, if $X, Y \in H$,

$$df_1([X, Y]) = 0 = \cdots = df_s([X, Y]),$$

that is,

$$[H, H] \subset H. \qquad (8.3)$$

Algebraically, this means that H is a Lie subalgebra of the Lie algebra $V(M)$. Geometrically, (8.3) is an "integrability condition," as we shall now prove.

THEOREM 8.3   (FROBENIUS COMPLETE INTEGRABILITY THEOREM, LOCAL VERSION)

Suppose H is a vector-field system on H which satisfies the integrability condition (8.3). Suppose that p is a maximal point for M, with $r = \dim H_p$.

Then p has a neighborhood U and a coordinate system (y_i), $1 \leq i \leq n$, defined in U such that

(a) The $\partial/\partial y_a$, $1 \leq a \leq r$, form a basis for H in U.
(b) The y_u, $r + 1 \leq u \leq n$, form a basis for integral functions of H in U (in the sense that any integral function f can, in this coordinate system, be written as a function of the y_u alone).
(c) The submanifolds $y_u =$ constant are integral submanifolds for H.

(A coordinate system with these properties is called a *flat* coordinate system for H.)

The proof will proceed by induction on n; this induction will involve repeated application of Theorem 6.3, and the following trick.

LEMMA 8.4

If M is sufficiently small, there exists a basis (X_a) for H in M so that $[X_a, X_b] = 0$.

Proof. We can first suppose that M is sufficiently small so that there are elements $X_a' \in H$ forming a basis of H in M. Suppose that

$$X_a' = A_{ai} \frac{\partial}{\partial x_i},$$

in terms of any local coordinate system (x_i). Thus, rank $(A_{ai}(q)) = r$ for all $q \in M$. By at most relabeling the coordinate system and possibly choosing M smaller, we can suppose that

$$\det(A_{ab}(q)) \neq 0 \qquad \text{for } q \in M.$$

Let (B_{ab}) be the inverse matrix to (A_{ab}); that is, $B_{ab} A_{bc} = \delta_{ac}$. If $X_a = B_{ab} X_b'$, then

$$X_a = B_{ab} A_{bi} \frac{\partial}{\partial x_i} = B_{ab} A_{bc} \frac{\partial}{\partial x_c} + B_{ab} A_{bu} \frac{\partial}{\partial x_u}$$

$$= \frac{\partial}{\partial x_a} + B_{ab} A_{bu} \frac{\partial}{\partial x_u}.$$

The (X_a) also form a basis for H in M, since (B_{ab}) is everywhere a nonsingular matrix. Thus: $[X_a, X_b]$ must be a linear combination of the X_c; that is, $[X_a, X_b] = f_{abc} X_c$ for some functions $f_{abc} \in F(M)$. Note, however, from the form of X_a given above, that $[X_a, X_b]$ does not have any terms involving $\partial/\partial x_c$. This forces $f_{abc} = 0$.   Q.E.D.

Suppose now that (X_a) is a basis for H in M satisfying $[X_a, X_b] = 0$. Using Theorem 6.3, choose a new coordinate system (y_i) for M (if necessary, making M even smaller) so that

$$X_1 = \frac{\partial}{\partial y_1}.$$

Suppose $X_a = C_{ai}(\partial/\partial y_i)$. Then

$$0 = [X_1, X_a] = \frac{\partial C_{ai}}{\partial y_1} \frac{\partial}{\partial y_i};$$

that is, $\partial C_{ai}/\partial y_1 = 0$ and hence

$$X_a = C_{a1}(y_2, \ldots, y_n)\frac{\partial}{\partial y_1} + \sum_{i=2}^m C_{ai}(y_2, \ldots, y_n)\frac{\partial}{\partial y_i}, \qquad \text{for } 2 \le a \le r.$$

Suppose

$$X_a' = \sum_{i=2}^m C_{ai}\frac{\partial}{\partial y_i}, \qquad 2 \le a \le r.$$

Then, for $2 \le a, b \le r$,

$$0 = [X_a, X_b] = [C_{a1}X_1 + X_a', C_{b1}X_1 + X_b']$$

$$= [X_a', X_b'] + \text{terms containing } \frac{\partial}{\partial y_1} \text{ alone.}$$

Thus, also $[X_a', X_b'] = 0$, $2 \le a, b \le r$.

The $\partial/\partial y_1 = X_1$ and the X_a', $2 \le a \le r$, form a new basis for H in M. But (X_a'), $2 \le a \le r$, is a basis for a completely integrable vector-field system in a domain of the space of variables $(y_2, \ldots, y_n)$. Part (a) of Theorem 8.3 thus follows by induction on n. Parts (b) and (c) are then obvious consequences of (a).

For example, let us prove (a). Let $f(y)$ be an integral function expressed in terms of these coordinates (y_i). Since $(\partial/\partial y_a) \in H$, we have $\partial f/\partial y_a = 0$; that is f is a function of $y_{r+1}, \ldots, y_n$ above.   Q.E.D.

Remarks. Theorem 8.3 provides us with r-dimensional integral submanifolds locally defined about each point. The global form of the Frobenius theorem provides (if every point is a maximal point) a unique, maximal, connected integral manifold passing through each point. The intuitive idea in its proof is to take the piece of an integral submanifold provided by the local version (that is, Theorem 8.3) and "analytically continue" it. For example, the process we described earlier for finding integral curves of a vector field defined over maximal intervals of real numbers is a special case. We shall give more details below.

There is a dual description of vector-field systems that is also useful. Suppose $\omega_{r+1}, \ldots, \omega_n$ are 1-differential forms on M. Define H as the set of vector fields X such that

$$0 = \omega_{r+1}(X) = \cdots = \omega_n(X).$$

Suppose (x_i) is a coordinate system for M, and $\omega_u = a_{ui} \, dx_i$. If the rank of the $(n-r) \times n$ matrix $(a_{ui}(p))$ is $(n-r)$ at every point of M, then every point of M is a maximal point, and $r = \text{rank } H$. Suppose, for example, that:

$$\omega_u = dx_u + a_{ua} \, dx_a . \tag{8.4}$$

Now an integral submanifold $\phi: N \to M$, of H, satisfies

$$\phi^*(\omega_u) = 0, \tag{8.5}$$

since

$$\phi^*(\omega_u)(N_p) = \omega_u(\phi^*(N_p)) = \omega_u(H_{\phi(p)}) = 0 \qquad \text{for } p \in N.$$

If the ω_u are given by (8.4), we can attempt to define integral manifolds of H by giving $f_u(x_a)$ to x_u as a function. Then (8.5) requires that the following system of differential equations be satisfied:

$$\frac{\partial f_u}{\partial x_a} + a_{ua}(x_b, f_u(x_c)) = 0.$$

The integrability conditions (8.3) can also be expressed in terms of differential forms. In fact, we have the following result, which we leave to the reader.

LEMMA 8.5

H is completely integrable, that is, satisfies (8.3), if and only if $d\omega_u$ can be written in the form $\theta_{uv} \wedge \omega_v$, for some choice of 1-forms θ_{uv}; that is, $d\omega_u$ belong to the "ideal" (in the Grassman algebra of forms) generated by the ω_u.

Now we turn to the global form of the Frobenius theorem. Let H be a vector-field system on M; suppose that every point of M is a maximal point of H (we then say that H is *nonsingular*), and the integrability condition (8.3) is satisfied. Recall that an *integral curve* of H is a C^∞ map $t \to \sigma(t)$ of an interval $[a, b] \to M$ such that

$$\sigma'(t) \in H_{\sigma(t)}. \qquad \text{for } a \le t \le b.$$

Let us extend this notion to define an *integral path* of H as a continuous image of an interval of real numbers that is composed of a finite number of pieces of integral curves. For $p \in M$, let L^p denote the set of points of M that can be joined to p by an integral curve. L^p is called the *leaf* of H which passes through the point p.

THEOREM 8.6   (GLOBAL VERSION OF THE FROBENIUS COMPLETE INTEGRABILITY THEOREM)

Each L^p can be made into a submanifold of M so that it is a maximal connected integral submanifold of H, and so that

$$L_q^{\ p} = H_q \qquad \text{for all } q \in L^p. \tag{8.6}$$

We can sketch the proof of this theorem from the local version proved in Chapter 8. First of all, recall that a function f defined on an open set of M is an integral of H if

$$X(f) = 0 \qquad \text{for all } X \in H.$$

This condition is satisfied by f if and only if it is *constant* along all integral paths of H. Let $q \in L^p$. By the local version, there is a neighborhood U of q on M and a coordinate system $x_1, \ldots, x_n$ for U such that

$$x_{r+1}, \ldots, x_n \text{ are integrals of } H(r = \dim H_q).$$

Such a coordinate system will be said to be a *flat* one with respect to H. Any other $f \in F(U)$ that is an integral of H can be written as a function of the $x_{m+1}, \ldots, x_n$.

A basis for the open sets of L^p will be obtained as follows: For $q \in L^p$, let U be an open set containing q and carrying a flat (with respect to H) coordinate system $x_1, \ldots, x_n$. Since $x_{r+1}, \ldots, x_n$ are constant on L^p, the map

$$q' \to (x_1(q'), \ldots, x_r(q'))$$

defines a 1-1 correspondence of the subset

$$\{q': x_{r+1}(q') = x_{r+1}(q), \ldots, x_n(q') = x_n(q)\}$$

of $L^p \cap U$ with an open subset of R^r. We call this set of L^p a *slice* of L^p with respect to the flat coordinate system. All such slices will be taken as the basis for open sets on the topology of L^p.

The slices determine a system of coordinate systems, with open subsets of R^r, for a possible manifold structure on L^p. The transition map between two such coordinate systems is C^∞, since it is given by functions inherited from the transition maps for coordinate systems of the manifold structure of M. What is not obvious a priori is that, with the topology so defined, L^p can be covered with a countable number of open sets. In fact, this is a rather deep fact, whose proof we shall not give here, but for which we shall refer the reader to Chevalley [1]. Let $\phi: L^p \to M$ be the inclusion map. It is clearly C^∞, and 1-1; that is, it is a submanifold map.

It should be obvious from its construction that (8.6) is satisfied. However, what is meant by "maximal" integral manifold? Suppose that $\phi': N \to M$ defines a connected integral manifold of H, and that the inclusion map $\phi: L^p \to M$ can be written as $\phi = \phi'\psi$, where ψ is a map: $L^p \to N$, and ϕ' is an integral submanifold map: $N \to M\psi$, with N connected. Since $\phi'\psi$ is a submanifold map, so is ψ. Now $\phi(N)$ is contained in L^p, since every point in $\phi(N)$ can be joined to p by an integral path of H; hence $\psi(L^p) = N$. Then, ψ is a 1-1 onto submanifold map and hence must be a diffeomorphism. It is in this sense that L^p is a "maximal" integral submanifold.

This finishes the proof of Theorem 8.6. However, as a by-product of the proof we obtain the following theorem, which plays a very important role in the theory of Lie groups.

THEOREM 8.7

Let $p \in M$, and let L^p be the leaf through p of the nonsingular completely integrable vector-field system H. Suppose that $\phi: N \to M$ is a map of manifolds such that $\phi(N) \subset L^p$. Then ϕ can be factored through a differentiable map $\psi: N \to L^p$; that is, ψ followed by the inclusion map: $L^p \to M$ is ϕ.

Proof. Evidently, there is a point-set map $\psi: N \to L^p$ with this property, but it is not obvious that it is a C^∞ map. Suppose, then, that $f \in F(L^p)$. We must show that $\psi^*(f) \in F(N)$.

Since L^p is a manifold, f can be written as the sum of functions that vanish to the outside of slices of L^p. To see this, note that we have taken over the proof given by Chevalley [1] that L^p can be covered by a countable number of slices by flat coordinate systems of H. The existence of a "partition of unity" (see Chapter 7) for this covering of L^p then guarantees this property, since f can be written

$$f = \sum_{j=1}^{\infty} ff_j,$$

where $f_1, f_2, \ldots$ is the "partition of unity," with each of its elements contained in a slice-coordinate neighborhood of L^p. Now any such function can be written as $F(x_1, \ldots, x_r)$. This function can evidently be extended to a C^∞ function in a neighborhood of N surrounding the slice. Thus $\psi^*(f)$ is obtained by pulling back via ϕ a C^∞ function on M, and hence is C^∞ on N.

Q.E.D.

Theorem 8.7 guarantees that the submanifolds defined as leaves do not have one kind of possible pathology. However, there is another sort of pathology that they might have, namely, they may not be regularly embedded in the sense of the following definition:

Definition

Let $\phi: N \to M$ be a submanifold of the manifold M. It is said to be *regularly embedded* if ϕ is a homeomorphism of N with $\phi(N)$, that is, if the map $\phi^{-1}: \phi(N) \to N$ (which exists in the point-set sense, since ϕ is assumed 1-1) is continuous.

In fact, N is regularly embedded if and only if the following property is satisfied:

> Every point $p \in \phi(N)$ has a neighborhood U such that $\phi^{-1}(U \cap \phi(N))$ consists of one connected coordinate neighborhood of N.

Then, if we think of a curve on a space winding around it an infinite number of times, coming nearer and nearer to a given point each time, it is not regularly embedded.

We leave the discussion of the global properties of completely integrable systems at this point, with an apology to the reader for lack of details and examples concerning this rich subject, which deserves a book of its own. Our immediate aim here is to do only enough to use the results as a tool in Lie group theory.

Exercises

1. Suppose M is a manifold and $X_1, \ldots, X_r$ are vector fields such that $[X_i, X_j] = 0$ for $1 \le i, j \le r$, and such that the $(X_i(p))$ are linearly independent at a point $p \in M$. Show that there is a coordinate system $(x_i, \ldots, x_m)$ valid in a neighborhood of p such that

$$X_i = \frac{\partial}{\partial x_i} \qquad \text{for } 1 \le i \le r.$$

2. The torus is defined as the space obtained by identifying two points $x = (x_1, x_2)$, $x^1 = (x_1', x_2')$ whose coordinates differ by an integer. Consider the system of parallel lines in R^2 whose slope is a given vector $a = (a_i, a_2)$. Show that this, projected down to the torus, is a one-dimensional foliation† whose leaves are those lines. Find the conditions on a that the leaves be nonregularly embedded, or dense, or both. Also examine the question of the existence of global integrals of the foliation. (Approached directly, one probably has to use facts from number theory, which can be found if necessary

---

† The system of leaf-submanifolds defined by a nonsingular, completely integrable vector field system is called a *foliation*.

in appropriate texts. There are other indirect proofs using Lie or topological group theory or both. It would be instructive to compare the two approaches.)

3.   There is another proof (given by Cartan [1]) of the local existence of leaves that starts from (8.4). Construct the functions $x_u = f_u(x_a)$ by finding ordinary differentials for the functions $t \to f_u(tx_a)$, with (x_a) regarded as a "parameter." Work this out as a problem, and show directly that the resulting functions actually do define an integral submanifold.

4.   Suppose H is a vector-field system on M, with dim $H(p) = n$ for all $p \in M$. Suppose that each point of M has an n-dimensional integral sub-manifold of H passing through it. Must H be completely integrable?

9 Reduction of Dimension when a Lie Algebra of Vector Fields Leaves a Vector-Field Invariant

As we have said, the Lie theory of ordinary differential equations is concerned with discussing the interrelation between a set of differential equations and a group of its "symmetries," with particular emphasis on the question of how various properties of the group help in the practical problems connected with the differential equations. We shall now examine one typical situation.

Let M be a manifold, $X \in V(M)$ a vector field on M, and L a linear set of vector fields on M such that

$$[L, L] \subset L, \tag{9.1a}$$

$$[L, X] = 0. \tag{9.1b}$$

(Condition (9.1a) means that L forms a Lie algebra of vector fields.) Let p be a point of M. We shall suppose that in a neighborhood U of p, there are elements $Y_1, \ldots, Y_r \in L$ such that each $Y \in L$ can be written uniquely in the form

$$Y = f_a(Y)Y_a + f(Y)X, \tag{9.2}$$

with functions $f_a(Y)$, $f(Y) \in F(U)$. (Choose indices $1 \le a \le r$ and the summation convention.) Using condition (9.1b), we have

$$0 = [X, Y] = X(f_a(Y))Y_a + X(f(Y))X.$$

Hence

$$X(f_a(Y)) = 0 \qquad \text{for } 1 \le a \le r, \quad Y \in L. \tag{9.3}$$

This means that *all* the $f_a(Y)$ are integrals of X. Since we are trying to "solve" X, that is, find as many integrals as possible, note that any function f that can be expressed as a polynomial in the $f_a(Y)$ is an integral. Designate Ω the set of integrals obtained in this way. (In other words, Ω is the smallest algebra (over the real numbers) of functions defined in U containing all the $f_a(Y)$, $1 \le a \le$, $Y \in L$.)

LEMMA 9.1

If $Z \in L, f \in \Omega$, then $Z(f) \in \Omega$.

73

Proof.   It suffices to prove this when f occurs among one of the generators of Ω, that is, as one of the $f_a(Y)$, for $Y \in L$.

$$Y = f_a(Y)Y_a + f(Y)X.$$

$$[Z, Y] = f_a([Z, Y])Y_a + F([Z, Y])X,$$

since $[Z, Y] \in L$, while

$$[Z, Y] = Z(f_a(Y))Y_a + f_a(Y)[Z, Y_a] + Z(f(Y))X$$

$$= (Z(f_b(Y)) + f_a(Y)f_b([Z, Y_a]))Y_b$$

$$+ [f_a(Y)f([Z, Y_a]) + Z(f(Y))]X.$$

Comparing these two expressions, we see that $Z(f_a(Y)) \in \Omega$, as required.

Let N be the subset of U consisting of the points q such that

$$f(q) = f(p) \qquad \text{for all } f \in \Omega.$$

We shall suppose that N is a submanifold of M. Note that the vector field X is tangent to N; hence we can reduce the problem of finding its integral curves to finding the integral curves of X restricted to the submanifold N. (This process can be repeated about every point of M of course.)

Let L_N consist of those vector fields X in L that are tangent to N, that is, $X(q) \in N_q$ for $q \in N$. Then L_N is a Lie subalgebra of L, that is, $[L_N, L_N] \subset L_N$.

Let X_N be the vector field X restricted to N so that, also

$$[L_N, X_N] = 0.$$

Then the process can be iterated. Let us examine this. Suppose the $Y_1, \ldots,$ $Y_r \in L$ were chosen so that $Y_1, \ldots, Y_s \in L_N$, $Y_{s+1}, \ldots, Y_r$ are linearly independent mod L_N; that is, no linear combination of them lies in L_N. If $Y \in L_N$, then

$$Y = f_a(Y)X_a + f(Y)X.$$

$$Z = \sum_{a=s+1}^{r} f_a(Y)X_a \tag{9.4}$$

is tangent to N.

Let us suppose that Ω has a certain number of functions that, in the neighborhood of p, are functionally independent, and such that every other function in Ω can be written as a function of them. We can suppose these functions, $x_1, \ldots, x_n$, are part of a coordinate system, $x_1, \ldots, x_m$ for M. Choose indices $1 \leq i \leq n$. Then we can suppose without loss of generality that N is determined by the equations: $x_i = 0$, and that p is the point 0 of R^m.

LEMMA 9.2

If $Y \in L$ satisfies $Y(p) \in N_p$ for one point $p \in N$, then $Y \in L_N$.

Proof. We know that $Y(x_i)$ for $1 \leq i \leq n$ are functions and $F_i(x_1, \ldots, x_n) Y$ is tangent to N if $F_i(0) = 0$ for $1 \leq i \leq n$. But, this is so if and only if $Y(p) \in N_p$.

Q.E.D.

We see from this lemma that Z defined by (9.4) is identically zero on N. For otherwise there is a point $q \in N$ such that $\sum_{a=s+1}^{r} f_a(Y)(q) \cdot Y_a \in L_N$, which is a contradiction. Thus, we have for $Y \in L_N$,

$$Y = \sum_{a=1}^{r} f_a(Y) Y_a + f(Y) X,$$

restricted to N. Now the $f_a(Y)$ are constant on N, since they belong to Ω. There are then essentially two cases:

Case 1 $f(Y) = 0$ on N for all $Y \in L_N$

In this case, notice that $Y \in L_N$ is everywhere nonzero on N if it is nonzero as an element of the vector space L. A Lie algebra of vector fields with this property is said to act *simply*. Thus we may say that the reduction process reduces the general case to the case where the given Lie algebra of vector field acts simply.

Case 2 $fY \neq 0$ for some $Y \in L_N$

Then $Y - \sum_{a=1}^{s} f_a(Y) Y_a$ and X are vector fields whose integral curves differ only by a change in parametrization. However, the former vector field is an element of L; hence its integral curves may be considered as "known." Thus the integral curves of X are "known" also by a simple quadrature, once $f(Y)$ is known.

Now we consider another method for reducing dimension when a known Lie algebra L of vector fields commutes with a given vector field X, that is,

$$[X, L] = 0.$$

Recall that a function $f \in F(M)$ is called an integral of L if

$$Y(f) = 0 \qquad \text{for all } Y \in L.$$

Note that:

If f is an integral of L, so is $X(f)$.

Suppose that (x_a), $1 \leq a \leq m$, is a functionally independent basis for the integrals of L; that is, any integral function f on M is a function of the $x_1, \ldots, x_m$ above. Let (y_i), $1 \leq i \leq n$, be a set of functions on M such that (x_a, y_i) forms a coordinate system from M.

Now X can be written in the form

$$X = A_a(x) \frac{\partial}{\partial x_a} + A_i(x, y) \frac{\partial}{\partial y_i}.$$

Let X' be the vector field in x-space defined by

$$X' = A_a(x)\frac{\partial}{\partial x_a}.$$

Then the integral curves $(x(t), y(t))$ for X can be obtained by solving two lower dimensional systems:

$$\frac{dx_a}{dt} = A_a(x(t)); \tag{9.5a}$$

$$\frac{dy_i}{dt} = A_i(x(t), y(t)). \tag{9.5b}$$

Thus (9.5a) can be solved first for $x(t)$, which is then substituted in the right-hand side of (9.5b) to be solved for $y(t)$. For example, we may be able to change coordinates for x_a-space so that $X' = \partial/\partial x_1$. (In fact, this is what is meant by "solving" (9.5a).) Then (9.5b) takes the form

$$\frac{dy_i}{dt} = A_i(c_1 + t, c_2, \ldots, c_m; y(t)), \tag{9.6}$$

for a choice of constants $c_1, \ldots, c_m$.

Continuing on a general level, suppose that L and L' are Lie algebras of vector fields, that $L \subset L'$, and $[L', X] = 0$. Suppose, as above, that the coordinate system (x_u, y_i) is chosen so that $\partial/\partial x_u$ is a basis for the vector-field system defined by L. Then

$$X = A_a(x_1, \ldots, x_m)\frac{\partial}{\partial x_a} + A_i\frac{\partial}{\partial y_i}, \qquad X' = A_a\frac{\partial}{\partial x_a}.$$

We do *not* assume that $[L', L] \subset L$, so that the elements of L' not contained in L do *not* "pass to the quotient" to define vector fields on x_a-space leaving X' invariant. Thus they are no help in the problem of integrating X'. However, once X' is "solved," they can be of use in solving (9.6). As an explanation, suppose that the coordinate system (x_a) is chosen so that $X' = \partial/\partial x_1$. Then

$$X = \frac{\partial}{\partial x_1} + A_i\frac{\partial}{\partial x_i}$$

and $x_2, \ldots, x_m$ are integrals of X. Hence the $Y(x_2), \ldots, Y(x_m), Y_1 Y_2(x_2)$, $\ldots, Y_1 Y_2(x_m), \ldots$ are integrals of X for all $Y_1, Y_2, \ldots \in L'$. We need $(n - m)$ integrals of X that are independent of $Y_2, \ldots, Y_m$ in order to say that X has been completely "solved." The point is: "Purely algebraic" conditions can be given for L and L' which guarantee that this is so.

We now turn to the following more explicit example.

Matrix-Riccati Systems

Change notations slightly. Let $i, j, \ldots$, range between 1 and n. The underlying space is that of the variables (t, x_{ij}), a space of dimension $n^2 + 1$. Consider a vector field

$$X = \frac{\partial}{\partial t} + a_{ij}(t)x_{jk}\frac{\partial}{\partial x_{ik}}.$$

Thus the parametrization of the integral curves of X is precisely the given t, and the integral curves are determined by the following system of linear homogeneous ordinary differential equations:

$$\frac{dx_{ik}}{dt} = a_{ij}(t)x_{jk}(t).$$

If $\mathbf{b} = (b_{ij})$ is a constant matrix, let

$$X_{\mathbf{b}} = x_{ik}b_{kj}\frac{\partial}{\partial x_{ij}}.$$

$$[X_{\mathbf{b}}, X_0] = \left[x_{ik}b_{kj}\frac{\partial}{\partial x_{ij}}, \frac{\partial}{\partial t} + a_{hl}x_{lm}\frac{\partial}{\partial x_{hm}} \right]$$

$$= a_{hl}x_{ik}b_{kj}\,\delta_{ij,lm}\frac{\partial}{\partial x_{hm}} - a_{hl}x_{lm}\,\delta_{ik;hm}b_{kj}\frac{\partial}{\partial x_{ij}}$$

$$= a_{hl}x_{lk}b_{km}\frac{\partial}{\partial x_{hm}} - a_{hl}x_{lm}b_{mj}\frac{\partial}{\partial x_{hj}}$$

$$= a_{hl}x_{lk}b_{km}\frac{\partial}{\partial x_{hm}} - a_{hl}x_{lk}b_{km}\frac{\partial}{\partial x_{hm}} = 0.$$

If $\mathbf{b}' = (b_{ij})$, then

$$[X_{\mathbf{b}}, X_{\mathbf{b}'}] = \left[x_{ik}b_{kj}\frac{\partial}{\partial x_{ij}}, x_{hl}b'_{lm}\frac{\partial}{\partial x_{hm}} \right]$$

$$= x_{ik}b_{kj}\,\delta_{ij;hl}\,b'_{lm}\frac{\partial}{\partial x_{hm}} - x_{hl}b'_{lm}\,\delta_{ik;hm}b_{kj}\frac{\partial}{\partial x_{ij}}$$

$$= x_{ik}b_{kj}b'_{jh}\frac{\partial}{\partial x_{ih}} - x_{ik}b'_{kj}b_{jh}\frac{\partial}{\partial x_{ih}}$$

$$= x_{ik}(b_{kj}b'_{jh} - b'_{kj}b_{jh})\frac{\partial}{\partial x_{ih}}.$$

Thus,

$$[X_{\mathbf{b}}, X_{\mathbf{b}'}] = X_{\mathbf{bb}'-\mathbf{b}'\mathbf{b}},$$

and the collection of the $X_{\mathbf{b}}$ forms a Lie algebra of vector fields that leaves X invariant. Hence the above theory can be applied. However, the set of all $X_{\mathbf{b}}$ is too big, since the vector-field system it determines is the set of all vectors on x_{ij}-space. Thus we look for a *subalgebra* of such vector fields to which to apply the theory. There is an obvious advantage in choosing the subalgebra as large as possible, since then the system (9.5a) will be as small as possible. Rather than go any further here into the general algebraic details, we shall deal only with a special choice.† Divide the indices $1 \leq i, j, \ldots, \leq n$ into two groups: $1 \leq a, b, \ldots, \leq m$; $m + 1 \leq u, v, \ldots, \leq n$. Consider the set of all matrices $\mathbf{b} = (b_{ij})$ such that

$$b_{au} = 0. \qquad (9.7)$$

If $\mathbf{b}$ and $\mathbf{b}'$ satisfy (9.7), so do $\mathbf{bb}'$ and $\mathbf{b}'\mathbf{b}$; hence so does $\mathbf{bb}' - \mathbf{b}'\mathbf{b}$. To see this,

$$(\mathbf{bb}')_{au} = b_{ai} b'_{iu} = b_{av} b'_{vu} = 0.$$

Let L be the set of vector fields $X_b = x_{ij} b_{jk}(\partial/\partial x_k)$ such that $\mathbf{b}$ satisfies (9.7). Let L' be the set of all vector fields of the form $X_{\mathbf{b}}$, with $\mathbf{b}$ an arbitrary matrix. According to the general theory described above, the next step is to solve the completely integrable vector-field system defined by L'. This can be done explicitly in a certain neighborhood U of the identity matrix $I = (\delta_{ij})$‡; let U be the subset of matrices (x_{ij}) such that $\det(x_{uv}) \neq 0$. For each $n \times n$ matrix $\mathbf{x} \in U$, let $y(x)_{uv}$ be the functions of x such that $(y(x)_{uv})$ is the inverse matrix of (x_{uv}); that is,

$$x_{uv} y(x)_{vw} = \delta_{uw}. \qquad (9.8)$$

Let $f(\mathbf{x})_{av} = x_{au} y(\mathbf{x})_{uv}$ be the indicated *nm* functions defined for each $n \times n$ matrix $\mathbf{x} \in U$. We shall show that the f_{av} are integrals of the vector fields of the form $X_{\mathbf{b}}$, where $\mathbf{b}$ satisfies (9.7).

First suppose that X is any vector field. Apply X to both sides of

$$X(x_{uv}) y_{vw} + x_{uv} X(y_{vw}) = 0 \qquad (9.9a)$$

or

$$y_{xu} X(x_{uv}) y_{vw} + X(y_{xw}) = 0. \qquad (9.9b)$$

Hence

$$X(f_{av}) = X(x_{au}) y_{uv} + x_{au} X(y_{uv})$$
$$= X(x_{au}) Y_{uv} - x_{au} y_{ux} X(x_{xw}) y_{wv}.$$

† Algebraically, the set of all X_b is isomorphic as a Lie algebra to the linear Lie algebras of all $n \times n$ matrices. The subalgebras we now describe are maximal subalgebras.
‡ Note that the vector fields $X_{\mathbf{b}}$ are independent of t.

But if $X = X_b = x_{ik}b_{kj}(\partial/\partial x_{ij})$, with $b_{au} = 0$, we have

$$X(x_{au})y_{uv} = x_{ak}b_{ku}y_{uv} = x_{av}b_{vu}y_{uv}.$$

$$x_{au}y_{ux}X(x_{xw})y_{wv} = x_{au}y_{ux}x_{xk}b_{kw}y_{wv}$$

$$= x_{au}y_{ux}x_{xy}b_{yw}y_{wv}$$

$$= x_{au}\delta_{uy}b_{yw}y_{wv}$$

$$= x_{ay}b_{yw}y_{wv}.$$

Hence we see that $X_b(f_{au}) = 0$ for all b satisfying (9.7), that is, for all $X \in L$. It is also easily seen that the functions f_{au} in U are functionally independent; that is, the df_{au} are everywhere independent. In fact the functions $(f_{av}, x_{uv}, x_{ab}, x_{va})$ form a new coordinate system for U.

According to the general theory, the next step is to calculate $X(f_{av})$, for then

$$X' = Y_0(f_{av})\frac{\partial}{\partial f_{av}} + \frac{\partial}{\partial t}.$$

$$X(f_{av}) = Y_0(x_{au})y_{uv} + x_{au}Y_0(y_{uv})$$

$$= Y_0(x_{au})y_{uv} - x_{au}y_{ux}Y_0(x_{xw})y_{wv}$$

$$= a_{aj}(t)x_{ju}y_{uv} - x_{au}y_{ux}a_{xj}(t)x_{jw}y_{wv}$$

$$= a_{ab}f_{bv} + a_{av} - f_{ax}a_{xb}f_{bv} - f_{ax}a_{xv}.$$

In summary, we have proved:

THEOREM 9.3

Consider a system of linear homogeneous differential equations:

$$\frac{dx_{ik}(t)}{dt} = a_{ij}(t)x_{jk}(t), \qquad 1 \le i,j, \ldots, \le n; \quad 1 \le a,b,c, \ldots, \le m;$$

$$m + 1 \le u,v,w,x,y, \ldots, \le n. \tag{9.10}$$

Consider U, the open set in the space of all $n \times n$ matrices $(x_{ij}) = x$ determined by the conditions:

(a) $\det(x_{uv}) \ne 0$.

(b)   Let $y(x)_{uv}$ be the inverse matrix of (x_{uv}). Introduce a space of variables z_{au} and on this space a system of ordinary, time-dependent differential equations (a matrix-Riccatti system):

$$\frac{dz_{au}(t)}{dt} = a_{ab}(t)z_{bu}(t) + a_{au}(t) - z_{av}(t)a_{vb}(t)z_{bu}(t) - z_{av}(t)a_{vu}(t).$$

Consider the map ϕ from U to this z-space which assigns to each $x \in U$ the point $\phi(\mathbf{x}) = \mathbf{z} = (z_{au})$, with $z_{au} = x_{av} y(\mathbf{x})_{vu}$.

(a)　If $\mathbf{x}(t)$ is a solution of (9.10) that lies completely in U, $\phi(\mathbf{x}(t)) = \mathbf{z}(t)$ is a solution of (9.11).

(b)　Suppose $\mathbf{z}(t) = (z_{au}(t))$ is a solution of (9.11). Suppose that $(x_{ij}^a = x^a \in U$ is such that $\phi(\mathbf{x}^a) = \mathbf{z}(a)$. Let $\mathbf{x}(t)$ be the solution of (9.10) such that $\mathbf{x}(a) = \mathbf{x}^a$. If $x(t)$ lies in U, then $\phi(x(t)) = \mathbf{z}(t)$.

10 Lie Groups

It will be assumed that the reader is acquainted with the elementary algebraic properties of groups. Recall that a group denoted typically by G, with elements g, g_1, g', etc., has associated with it a multiplication operation $(g, g_1) \rightarrow gg_1$, satisfying the rules:

$$g(g_1 g_2) = (gg_1)g_2 \qquad \text{(associative law)}.$$

There is an identity element $e \in G$ such that

$$eg = ge = g \qquad \text{for all } g \in G. \tag{10.1}$$

For each $g \in G$, there is an inverse element $g^{-1} \in G$ such that

$$g^{-1}g = e = gg^{-1}.$$

Definition

Let G be a group and let $\alpha: G \times G \rightarrow G$ be the map that assigns $g_1 g_2^{-1}$ to the pair $g_1, g_2 \in G$. If G in addition has a topological structure so that α is a continuous map, we call it a *topological group*. If, further, G has a manifold structure so that α is a differentiable (that is, C^∞) map, we speak of a *Lie group*.

It can be proved that two such manifold structures that give rise to the same topological structure must coincide, so for most practical purposes we think of the manifold structure as determined by the group structure.

Historically, groups arose as transformation groups on spaces. Some typical examples would be: The group of permutations of a finite set; the group of linear or affine transformations of a vector space; the group of canonical transformations in classical mechanics; the group of unitary transformations in quantum mechanics; the group of Lorentz transformations in the theory of special relativity.

Definition

Let G be a group and let M be a space. An action of G by transformations on M is defined by a map: $G \times M \rightarrow M$, $(g, p) \rightarrow gp$, such that

$$g_1(g_2\,p) = (g_1 g_2)p \qquad \text{for } g_1, \quad g_2 \in G, \quad p \in M.$$

$$ep = p \qquad \text{for } p \in M,$$

where gp is thought of as the transform of p by the transformation g.

If M is a manifold and G is a Lie group, we speak of G as a *Lie transformation group* if this map $G \times M \to M$ is differentiable.

Let us study the simplest type of transformation group, where the group G acts as a group of linear transformations on a real vector space V. We assume that to each element $g \in G$ is assigned a linear transformation $\rho(g): v \to u$, and the map $G \times V \to V$, $(g, v) \to \rho(g)(v)$, satisfies the transformation-group conditions described above. We call ρ a *linear representation* of G. For certain applications, to be described later, V must be infinite dimensional. We shall suppose that it is a topological vector space, that is, the concept of the limit $\lim_{n \to \infty} v_n = v$ of a sequence of elements of V is well defined, and the sum of limits equals limit of sums, that is,

$$\lim_{n \to \infty}(v_n + u_n) = v + u, \qquad \text{if} \quad \lim_n v_n = v, \qquad \lim_n u_n = u.$$

This enables us to define the derivative $dv(t)/dt$ of curves $t \to v(t)$ in V:

$$\frac{dv(t)}{dt} = \lim_{\Delta t \to 0}(v(t + \Delta t) - v(t))/\Delta t,$$

with the usual rules of differential calculus satisfied.

Suppose that $t \to g(t)$ defines a one-parameter subgroup of G; that is, a map $R \to G$ is given such that

$$g(t_1 + t_2) = g(t_1)g(t_2) \qquad \text{for } t_1, t_2 \in R.$$

As we have already seen, such objects play a very important role in the application of group-theoretic ideas to differential equations. Lie group theory (as opposed to abstract group theory) is concerned with studying a group by means of its one-parameter subgroups.

Definition

Let ρ be a linear representation of a Lie group G by linear transformations on a vector space V, with $t \to g(t)$ a one-parameter subgroup of G. A linear transformation $A: V \to V$ is called the *infinitesimal generator* of the one-parameter group $t \to \rho(g(t))$ of linear transformations if

$$A(v) = \frac{d}{dt}\rho(g(t))v\bigg|_{t=0} = \text{(by definition)} \quad \lim_{t \to 0}\frac{\rho(g(t))v - v}{t}.$$

We shall suppose that each one-parameter subgroup of G has in this sense an infinitesimal generator. (If V is finite dimensional and if G acts as a Lie transformation group on V, then this condition is obviously satisfied. Certain infinite dimensional V, to be described below, also satisfy it.) Let us also suppose that the mapping $G \times V \to V$, $(g, v) \to \rho(g)(v)$, is continuous in the sense of mapping convergent sequences into convergent sequences, with limits mapped into limits.

Conversely, $\rho(g(t))$ is determined by a linear differential equation involving A: This is the reason for the terminology of "infinitesimal generator."

$$\frac{d}{dt}\rho(g(t))(v) = \lim_{\Delta t \to 0} \frac{\rho(g(t + \Delta t))(v) - \rho(g(t))(v)}{\Delta t}$$

$$= \lim_{\Delta t \to 0} \frac{\rho(g(\Delta t))\rho(g(t))(v) - \rho(g(t))(v)}{\Delta t}$$

$$= A(\rho(g(t))(v));$$

that is, the "orbit" $t \to \rho(g(t))(v) = v(t)$ of the one-parameter group satisfies the linear differential equation

$$\frac{d}{dt}v(t) = A(v(t)); \qquad v(0) = v. \tag{10.2}$$

Conversely, these steps are reversible: If A is a given linear transformation: $V \to V$ and if (10.2) has a unique solution, then a one-parameter group of linear transformations, denoted by $\exp(tA)$, is defined by the rules

$$\exp(tA)(v) = v(t).$$

The motivation for this notation is that $\exp(tA)(v)$ is defined by the power series

$$\sum_{n=0}^{\infty} \frac{(tA)^n(v)}{n!} \tag{10.3}$$

within its domain of convergence. For example, if v is finite dimensional, (10.3) always converges. (See Chevalley [1, Chap. 1].)

Such operator-power series can indeed be handled much as real or complex power series, provided one handles the possible noncommutativity of operators with care. (See Exercise 2.)

Having associated linear transformations with one-parameter subgroups, we may ask for the relation between the algebraic operations possible on linear transformations and the properties of the one-parameter subgroups. For example, operators may be added:

$$(A + B)(v) = A(v) + B(b) \qquad \text{for } v \in V,$$

multiplied by (real) scalars

$$(cA)(v) = cA(v),$$

and the commutator $[A, B] = AB - BA$ of two operators may be defined. The addition and scalar multiplication imply that the operators form a vector space (over the real numbers). The commutator operation defines it then as a *Lie algebra* in the sense of the following definition.

Definition

A real Lie algebra, typically denoted by **G**, with elements denoted by X, Y, ..., is defined by requiring that:

(a) **G** is a vector space (over the real numbers).
(b) A bilinear multiplication operation $(X, Y) \to [X, Y]$, $\mathbf{G} \times \mathbf{G} \to \mathbf{G}$, is defined for elements of **G**, satisfying the following law, called the *Jacobi identity*:

$$[X, [Y, Z]] = [[X, Y], Z] + [Y, [X, Z]] \qquad \text{for } X, Y, Z \in \mathbf{G}.$$

(c) $[X, Y] = -[Y, X]$ for $X, Y \in \mathbf{G}$.

Of course, on this purely algebraic level, the real numbers are not sacred: The definition makes sense for an arbitrary field of scalars, for example, for the complex numbers, the rational numbers, and the integers mod a prime number. However, Lie algebras over a field of nonzero characteristic have certain unpleasant features. The most interesting cases are the real, complex, and rational numbers, and accordingly one speaks of a real, complex, or rational Lie algebra. For the purposes of Lie group theory, the real case is by far the most important, and when we talk about a Lie algebra without mentioning the scalars, we shall always mean a real one.

It is readily verified that the commutator definition $(A, B) \to [A, B] = AB - BA$ makes the linear operators on V into a Lie algebra. How does this translate back into terms of one-parameter groups? Explicitly, we ask the following question: Suppose $t \to g_i(t)$, $i = 1, 2, 3, 4$, are one-parameter subgroups of G, with

$$\rho(g_1(t)) = \exp(tA), \qquad \rho(g_2(t)) = \exp(tB),$$

$$\rho(g_3(t)) = \exp(t(A + B)), \qquad \rho(g_4(t)) = \exp(t[A, B]);$$

how are $g_3(t)$ and $g_4(t)$ related to $g_1(t)$ and $g_2(t)$? To answer this question, let us work formally for the moment.

LEMMA 10.1

If A is a linear operator, $V \to V$, then *formally*:

$$\exp(tA) = \lim_{n \to \infty} \left(I + \frac{At}{n}\right)^n. \tag{10.4}$$

Proof. There are two approaches. First, purely as an operator equation, we have, using the binomial expansion,

$$\left(I + \frac{At}{n}\right)^n = I + At + \frac{n(n-1)}{2}\left(\frac{At}{n}\right)^2 + \cdots$$

$$= I + At + \frac{(At)^2}{2} \cdot \frac{n-1}{n} + \frac{(At)^3}{3!}\frac{(n-1)(n-2)}{n^2} + \cdots.$$

Formally, as $n \to \infty$, this goes over to the power series for $\exp(tA)$.

Another approach would be to work with the differential equation (10.2). Set

$$v_n(t) = \left(1 + \frac{At}{n}\right)^n (v) \qquad \text{for } v \in V.$$

$$\frac{dv_n}{dt} = n\left(1 + \frac{At}{n}\right)^n \frac{A}{n}(v)$$

$$= A\left(1 + \frac{At}{n-1}\left(\frac{n-1}{n}\right)\right)^n (v).$$

Hence

$$v_n(t) - v = \int_0^t A\left(1 + \frac{As}{n-1}\left(\frac{n-1}{n}\right)\right)^n (v)\, ds. \tag{10.5}$$

Then, if $\lim_{n \to \infty} v_n(t)$ exists and equals, say, $v(t)$, and if the formal limiting operations in (10.5) are justified, we have

$$v(t) - v = \int_0^t A(v(s))\, ds,$$

which is the integral equation form of (10.2).

We shall not get involved with the material in functional analysis necessary to justify these formal limits, since it would take us too far afield. (See Yosida [1]). However, these results will be very useful to us as intuitive motivation.

LEMMA 10.2

If A, B are linear operators, $V \to V$, we have formally:

$$\exp(t(A + B)) = \lim_{n \to \infty} \left[\exp\left(\frac{tA}{n}\right) \exp\left(\frac{tB}{n}\right) \right]^n, \tag{10.6}$$

$$\exp(t[A, B]) = \lim \left[\exp\left(\frac{tA}{n}\right) \exp\left(\frac{tB}{n}\right) \exp\left(\frac{-tA}{n}\right) \exp\left(\frac{-tB}{n}\right) \right]^{n^2}. \tag{10.7}$$

Proof. We prove only (10.6). Equation (10.7) is similar, and is left as an exercise.

Set

$$C(t) = \exp(tA) \exp(tB).$$

Then

$$\frac{dC}{dt}(0) = A + B.$$

(Since $(d/dt) \exp(tA)$ is, formally, $A \exp(tA)$, $\exp(0A) = I$, the identity operator, and the product law for differentiation holds as long as the order of the operation is respected.)

Suppose Taylor's expansion holds. Then

$$C(t) = I + (A + B)t + t^2 A_2(t),$$

where $A_2(t)$ is a well-behaved function in the neighborhood of $t = 0$. Then

$$\left[\exp\left(\frac{t}{n} A\right) \exp\left(\frac{t}{n} B\right) \right]^n = \left[I + \frac{(A + B)t}{n} + \left(\frac{t}{n}\right)^2 A_2\left(\frac{t}{n}\right) \right]^n.$$

Note that the right-hand side will not be affected by the third term as $n \to \infty$, since it has an n^2 in the denominator and the product involves n terms. Then the limit as $n \to \infty$ is

$$\lim_{n \to \infty} \left(I + \frac{(A + B)t}{n} \right)^n = \exp(t(A + B)),$$

which proves (10.6) formally. Equations (10.6) and (10.7) are the key formulas connecting Lie algebras and Lie groups. They suggest the following ideas.

The "Lie algebra" of a Lie group denoted by **G** should be defined as the set of one-parameter subgroups of G. The algebraic operations necessary to define a Lie algebra can be, intuitively, presented as follows:

If $t \to g(t)$ is a one-parameter subgroup, if $c \in R$, then the "scalar product" of c with the subgroup is the subgroup $t \to g(ct)$. (10.8)

If $t \to g_1(t)$ and $t \to g_2(t)$ are one-parameter subgroups, the "sum" of the two is the one-parameter
subgroup $t \to g_3(t)$ such that

$$g_3(t) = \lim_{n \to \infty} \left[g_1\left(\frac{t}{n}\right) g_2\left(\frac{t}{n}\right) \right]^n. \tag{10.9}$$

The "bracket" one-parameter subgroup $t \to g_4(t)$ is "defined" by the
formula

$$g_4(t) = \lim_{n \to \infty} \left[g_1\left(\frac{t}{n}\right) g_2\left(\frac{t}{n}\right) g_2\left(\frac{t}{n}\right) g_1\left(\frac{-t}{n}\right) g_2\left(\frac{-t}{n}\right) \right]^{n^2}. \tag{10.10}$$

Now, so far there is no guarantee that these limits exist or that they satisfy
the identities needed to express a "Lie algebra." However, this suggests such
a direct and intuitive approach toward defining the Lie algebra of a Lie group
that we shall do it anyway. Use the symbol X to denote the one-parameter
subgroup $t \to g(t)$, and write $g(t) = \exp(tX)$. If $\exp(tX) = g_1(t)$, $\exp(tY) = g_2(t)$, define $X + Y$ and $[X, Y]$ so that

$$\exp(t(X + Y)) = g_3(t), \qquad \exp(t[X, Y]) = g_4(t).$$

Since Helgason does in fact prove [1, Chap. 2] that necessary limits exist, we
shall adopt this definition of the Lie algebra. We may say then that we have
shown, if the formal steps can be made rigorous, that this "notation" for **G**
suggests an algebraic interpretation of our work on linear transformations and
infinitesimal generators. Suppose ρ is a linear representation of G by operators
on V. To each one-parameter group denoted by the "symbol" X, that is, the
group is $t \to \exp(tX) = g(t)$, associate the infinitesimal generator $A: V \to V$:

$$\rho(\exp(tX)) = \exp(tA).$$

Let $A = \rho(X)$. Regard ρ as a mapping of **G** $\to$ (Lie algebra of linear operators
on V). Then Lemma 10.2 asserts that ρ is a Lie algebra homomorphism; that
is,

$$\rho(X + Y) = \rho(X) + \rho(Y), \qquad \rho([X, Y]) = [\rho(X), \rho(Y)].$$

Since the foundations of Lie group theory are not our main concern, we shall
leave the development of this general approach at this point and turn to more
geometric material.

Suppose G acts as a transformation group on a manifold M. For topology,
adopt that of pointwise convergence; that is, a sequence (f_n) of functions
converges if

$$\lim_{n \to \infty} f_n(p) = f(p) \qquad \text{for all } p \in M.$$

The linear representation ρ of G by transformations on v is defined as follows:

$$\rho(g)(f)(p) = f(g^{-1}p) \qquad \text{for } f \in F(M), \quad p \in M. \tag{10.11}$$

Let **G** be the collection of *differentiable* (say, C^∞), one-parameter subgroups $t \to g(t) = \exp(tX)$ of G. Then, if ρ denotes the infinitesimal generator of the one-parameter group $t \to (\rho(t))$ of linear transformations on $F(M)$, we have

$$\rho(X)(f)(p) = \frac{d}{dt} f(\exp(-tX)p)\Big|_{t=0}. \tag{10.12}$$

Also,

$$\rho(X)(f_1 f_2) = \rho(X)(f_1)f_2 + f_1\rho(X)(f_2).$$

This shows that $\rho(X)$ is a vector field on M, that is, an element of $V(M)$. We can sum up these ideas in the following theorem.

THEOREM 10.3

Suppose the Lie group G is a transformation group on a manifold M. Equation (10.11) defines a representation of G by linear transformations in $F(M)$, and (10.12) defines a mapping of **G**, the set of all one-parameter subgroups of G, into $V(M)$.

Suppose $t \to g(t)$ is a one-parameter subgroup of G and $X \in V(M)$ is the vector field on M defined by (10.12). Then each orbit $t \to g(t)p$ of the one-parameter group is an integral curve of the vector field $-X$.

Proof. The first part of the statement is evident. To prove the second, suppose $\sigma(t) = g(t)p, f \in F(M)$:

$$\sigma'(t)(f) = \frac{d}{dt} f(\sigma(t)) = \frac{d}{dt} f(g(t)p)$$

$$= \lim_{\Delta t \to 0} f(g(\Delta t)g(t)p) - f(g(t)p)$$

$$= -X(f)(g(t)p). \qquad \text{Q.E.D.}$$

There are three standard ways to make G act on G itself (strictly speaking, G acts on M, where M is the underlying manifold structure on the space of points making up G), namely:

(i) *Left translation:*   Given $g \in G$, L_g denotes the diffeomorphism $h \to gh$ on G.

(ii) *Right translation:*   Given $g \in G$, R_g denotes the diffeomorphism $h \to hg^{-1}$ of G.

(iii) *Adjoint action:*   Given $g \in G$, Ad g denotes the diffeomorphism $h \to ghg^{-1}$.

Notice that for fixed $g \in G$, L_g and R_g commute, and Ad $g = L_g R_g$.

Definition

A vector field X on G is *left* (*right*) *invariant* if

$$L_g^*(X(f)) = X(L_g^*(f)) \qquad \text{for all } f \in F(g), \quad \text{all } g \in G.$$
$$R_g^*(X(f)) = X(R_g^*(f)) \qquad \text{for all } f \in F(G), \quad \text{all } g \in G.$$

For each one-parameter subgroup $X \in \mathbf{G}$, let X_L be the vector field on G that is the infinitesimal generator of the one-parameter group $t \to R_{\exp(tX)}$. Thus X_L is a left-invariant vector field on M. Similarly, let X_R be the infinitesimal generator of the one-parameter subgroup $t \to L_{\exp(tX)}$. It is right invariant.

THEOREM 10.4

The mappings $X \to X_L$ and X_R are 1-1 onto maps from the set of one-parameter subgroups to the set of left- and right-invariant vector fields on G.

Proof. We shall work with the left-invariant vector fields. The proof for the right-invariant fields is similar.

Suppose first that two one-parameter subgroups $t \to g_1(t)$ and $t \to g_2(t)$ give rise to the same element X_L. Now both

$$t \to g_1(t) \qquad \text{and} \qquad t \to g_2(t)$$

are integral curves of the vector field $-X_L$ (by Theorem 10.3). Since both begin at e, they must coincide, that is, $g_1(t) = g_2(t)$ for all t. This proves that $X \to X_L$ is 1-1.

To show it is onto, proceed as follows: Let Y be a left-invariant vector field on G. We shall first show that the integral curve of Y beginning at e can be extended over $(-\infty, \infty)$. Suppose otherwise, that is, that $\sigma: (a, b) \to G$ is an integral curve of Y which cannot be extended over a large interval. Now the following geometric property of left-invariant vector fields is inherent in this definition:

If $t \to \gamma(t)$ is an integral curve of Y, if $g \in G$, then $t \to g\gamma(t) = L_g(\gamma(t))$ is an integral curve of Y.

Thus, for $t_0 \in (a, b)$, the curve $t \to \sigma(t_0)^{-1}\sigma(t)$ is an integral curve of Y, which is equal to e for $t = t_0$. By uniqueness of integral curves,

$$\sigma(t_0)^{-1}\sigma(t) = \sigma(t - t_0) \qquad \text{for } a \leq t \leq b.$$

This shows that the size of the neighborhood of t_0 in which there exists a solution of the differential equations defining the integral curves of Y remains bounded away from zero as t_0 approaches b, which gives the desired contradiction.

Then let $\sigma(t)$, $-\infty < t < \infty$, be the curve in G that is the integral curve of Y beginning at e for $t = 0$. Since the t_0 used above can be any real number,

$$\sigma(t_0 + t) = \sigma(t) \cdot \sigma(t_0);$$

that is, $t \to \sigma(t)$ is a one-parameter subgroup of G and hence defines an element of **G**, which we call X. The left invariance of Y then proves that

$$-X_L = Y. \qquad\qquad\qquad \text{Q.E.D.}$$

Remarks. It is more customary to *define* the Lie algebra of a Lie group as the set of left-invariant vector fields. (For example, this is the procedure adopted by Chevalley [1] and Helgason [1].) While this is most convenient for the purpose of proving the main theorems in the foundations of Lie group theory, it is slightly awkward when considering Lie groups as transformation groups, since the identification of the Lie algebra with the set of one-parameter subgroups is better adapted to the geometric intuition. At any rate, Theorem 10.4 and Exercise 6 shows that this is compatible with the definition we have chosen.

There is an action of G on the underlying vector space of **G** that is also called the *adjoint action* of G. (Strictly speaking, it should be called the infinitesimal version of the *adjoint action* of G on **G**, but it is customary to confuse this point.) It can be most readily defined as follows:

> For $g \in G$, $X \in \mathbf{G}$, the one-parameter subgroup represented by Ad $g(X)$ is just
>
> $$t \to \text{Ad } g(\exp(tX)) = g \exp(tX)g^{-1}$$

It is readily verified that for each $g \in G$, Ad g considered as a mapping $\mathbf{G} \to \mathbf{G}$ is a *Lie algebra isomorphism*. Thus "Ad" also stands for a linear representation of G by automorphisms of **G**. This can be symbolized by the relation:

$$\text{Ad } g(\exp tX) = \exp(t(\text{Ad } g(X))) \qquad \text{for } g \in G, \quad X \in \mathbf{G}, \quad -\infty < t < \infty.$$

If G acts on a manifold M, we then also have the important formula

$$\begin{aligned} g \cdot \exp(tX) \cdot p &= g \cdot \exp(tX) \cdot g^{-1} \cdot gp \\ &= \text{Ad } g(\exp(tX)) \cdot gp \\ &= \exp(t(\text{Ad } g(X))) \cdot gp. \end{aligned}$$

It seems to be inevitable in Lie group theory that each symbol has at least two possible meanings. For example, we have seen the two meanings of "Ad." So far, we have been working with one fixed meaning of "exp." However, there is another related meaning.

Definition

Let G be a Lie group and let G denote its Lie algebra. The *exponential mapping*, denoted also by "exp," is the mapping: $G \to G$ defined as follows:

For $X \in G$, $\exp(X)$ is the value at $t = 1$ of the one-parameter subgroup of **G** determined by X.

This completes our listing of the general facts relating a single Lie group to its Lie algebra. However, for geometric purposes it is most important to know the relation between the Lie subgroups of a Lie group and the Lie subalgebras of its Lie algebra.

Definition

Let G be a Lie group. A *Lie subgroup* of G is defined by a pair (typically denoted by (H, ϕ)) such that H is a Lie group, and ϕ is a submanifold map: $H \to G$, that is a homomorphism of the group structures on H and G.

As usual in the theory of submanifolds, it is convenient to often suppress explicit mention of the map ϕ, for the sake of notational simplicity, and write $H \subset G$. However, it is quite important to keep in mind that the topology that makes H into a Lie group is not necessarily the topology induced from G. In addition, we shall usually say "subgroup" instead of "Lie subgroup," since subgroups in the purely algebraic sense will not be considered.

A subgroup H of G defines a (Lie) subalgebra, denoted typically by **H**, of **G**. For, every one-parameter subgroup of H can be regarded as a one-parameter subgroup of G, defining the inclusion $\mathbf{H} \subset \mathbf{G}$. It is obvious from the definition that all Jacobi brackets of elements of **H** again lie in **H**, so that it is a subalgebra; we say that **H** *corresponds* to H. One of the main theorems of Lie theory is Theorem 10.5.

THEOREM 10.5

Let G be a connected Lie group. The correspondence $H \to \mathbf{H}$ sets up a 1-1 correspondence between connected subgroups of G and the subalgebras of **G**.

Proof. First we shall show that every subalgebra **H** of **G** arises in this way from a connected subgroup of G. For this purpose it is most convenient to regard the Lie algebra of G as the set of left-invariant vector fields on G. Thus **H** can be regarded as a subalgebra of $V(G)$; hence it defines a completely integrable vector-field system on G. This system is invariant under left translation by G; hence it is everywhere nonsingular. Let H be its maximal connected integral submanifold passing through the identity element of G.

Next we show that H is a subgroup of G in the purely algebraic sense. Let $h \in H$. We want to prove that $h^{-1} \in H$. From Exercise 11 [part (a)], we know that h can be written at least one way in the form

$$h = \exp(X_1) \cdots \exp(X_n) \qquad \text{for some choice } X_1, \ldots, X_r \in \mathbf{H}.$$

Now $\exp(X)^{-1} = \exp(-X)$; hence $h^{-1} \in H$. Next we prove that $h_1 h_2 \in H$ if $h_1, h_2 \in H$. By left invariance, $L_{h_1}(H)$ is an integral submanifold of H passing through h_1; hence it must be contained in H, whence $h_1 h_2 \in H$.

Consider the map $H \times H \to G$ defined by $(h_1 h_2) \to h_1^{-1} h_2$. Its image is contained in H. By Theorem 9.4 it can be factored through a mapping $H \times H \to H$, that is, the map $(h_1, h_2) \to h_1^{-1} h_2$ is differentiable in terms of the manifold structure on H. This defines it as a Lie group. Clearly, the submanifold map $H \to G$ defines it as a Lie subgroup of G, and by its very construction the corresponding subalgebra is $\mathbf{H}$.

Suppose H_1 is another connected subgroup of G whose corresponding Lie subalgebra of G is $\mathbf{H}$. Using the fact that a connected Lie group is generated by any neighborhood of the identity, we see that H_1 and H are identical as point-sets in G. Using Theorem 9.4 again, we see that the identity map $H_1 \to H$ is differentiable. Turning the argument around, the identity map $H \to H_1$ is differentiable; that is, H and H_1 are identical as Lie subgroups of G.   Q.E.D.

Thus we begin to see how the algebraic properties of the Lie algebra reflect the algebraic properties of the groups. There is a group of useful theorems giving sufficient conditions that subgroups in the algebraic sense be Lie subgroups:

> Let H be a subgroup in the algebraic sense of a Lie group G such that every element of H can be joined to the identity element by a (broken) C^∞ path lying completely within H. Then, H is a Lie subgroup of G.

For the proof, we refer to Kobayashi-Nomizu [1, p. 275].

> Let H be a subgroup in the algebraic sense of a Lie group G that is a closed subset of G. Then H is a Lie subgroup of G. Further, the topology on H is that induced from G, and H is a regularly embedded submanifold of G.

For the proof, we refer to Helgason [1, Theorem 2.3, p. 605].

These subgroups are the most important in the geometric applications. We shall call them *closed subgroups*. They arise geometrically in the following way: Suppose that a Lie group G acts as a transformation group on a mani-fold M. Let $p \in M$, and let H be defined as follows:

$$H = \{g \in H : gp = p\},$$

where H is called the *isotropy subgroup* of G at p. That it is a closed subgroup of G follows from the fact that the mapping $G \times M \to M$ is continuous. The subset $Gp = \{gp : g \in G\} \subset M$ is called the *orbit* of G at p. It can be identified with the *space of left cosets* of G by H, which is denoted by G/H, defined as:

An element of G/H is the subset of the form gH for one choice of $g \in G$. G/H is also called the *homogeneous space* of G with *isotropy subgroup H*. The coset eH is called the *origin* of G/H. The map $G \to G/H$ sending $g \in G$ into gH is called the *projection* of G into G/H. Each $g_0 \in G$ induces a trans-formation of G/H as follows: $g_0 \cdot (gH) = (g_0 g)H$. (In other words, G acts on G/H in such a way that the projection map $G \to G/H$ commutes with the action of G on itself by left translation and on G/H.) Notice that H is then the set of $g \in G$ such that the transformation defined by g on G/H leaves the origin invariant. We shall state the basic theorems concerning these ideas, referring again to Helgason [1, Chap. 2, Sects. 3–4] for the proofs.

Theorem. Let H be a closed subgroup of a Lie group G. G/H can be made into a manifold so that the projection map $G \to G/H$ is a maximal rank, onto mapping. The fibers† of the projection are the left cosets of H, and they are also integral manifolds of the left-invariant vector-field system on G deter-mined by H.

(In fact, $G \to G/H$ is a principal fiber bundle with H as structure group, referring to Auslander-Mackenzie [1] for this notion.)

Theorem. Suppose a Lie group G acts as a transformation group on a manifold M, and that the subgroup H is the isotropy subgroup of G at a point $p \in M$. Then the mapping $G/H \to Gp$, which assigns to gH the point gp,‡ defines G/H as a submanifold of M whose set of points is the orbit to p.

(Thus, when we speak of the orbits as "submanifolds," we mean their manifold structure inherited from G/H.)

As a bonus from these general theorems, we obtain a way of proving that various spaces are manifolds, without the necessity of going through the details of exhibiting an atlas of coordinate systems. One such important example is the Grassman manifolds, which we do as an illustration. Let V be

---

† If $\phi : M \to B$ is a map of M into B, the inverse image of a point of B is called the fiber above that point.

‡ Notice that this map is well defined, since if g and g_1 define the same coset, $gg_1^{-1} \in H$; hence $gp = g_1 p$.

a real, finite dimensional vector space. Let $A(V)$ be the group of linear automorphisms of V. It can be easily proved that $A(V)$ is a Lie group such that the mapping $A(V) \times V \to V$ defines it as a Lie transformation group on V. (For example, choosing a basis for V identifies V with R^n ($n = \dim V$) and identifies $A(V)$ with $GL(n, R)$, the group of all $n \times n$ invertible real matrices. In the exercises, we go over the Lie group generalities for $GL(n, R)$ and the other "classical" groups.)

For each integer p, $0 < p < n = \dim V$, let $G^p(V)$ be the set of p-dimensional linear subspaces of V (the *Grassman manifold*). $A(V)$ acts on $G^p(V)$ in an obvious algebraic way: If W is a p-dimensional subspace of V, that is, a "point" of $G^p(V)$, and if $a \in A(V)$, then aW is just the subspace $a(W)$. It is quite simple linear algebra to prove that $A(V)$ acts transitively on $G^p(v)$. Let W_0 be a fixed element of $G^p(V)$. Then the isotropy subgroup of $A(V)$ at W is $A(V, W)$, defined as

$$A(V, W_0) = \{a \in A(V): a(W_0) = W_0\}.$$

It is clearly a closed subgroup of $A(V)$, identifying $G^p(V)$ with $A(V)/A(V, W_0)$, hence giving it a manifold structure. Of course a similar procedure would be followed for vector spaces over the complex numbers.

We shall leave the general theory of Lie groups at this point.

Exercises

1. Show that the solution of (10.2) does indeed define $\exp(tA)$ as a one-parameter group of linear transformations on V.

2. Show that $\exp(A)\exp(B) = \exp(A + B) = \exp(B)\exp(A)$ if $AB = BA$, with $\exp(A)$ as defined by (10.2). If $[A, B]$ merely commutes with A and B, work out the formula connecting $\exp(A + B)$, $\exp(A)$, $\exp(B)$.

3. Prove (10.4) if V is finite dimensional.

4. Work out the formal details of (10.7).

5. Show that (10.6) and (10.7) hold if A and B are finite dimensional operators, that is, carry out the needed estimates. (In fact, the same estimates hold if A and B are bounded operators in a Hilbert space.)

6. Let G be a Lie group, and let $X \to X_L$ be the isomorphic mapping of **G**, the set of one-parameter subgroups of G, onto the set of left-invariant vector fields. Suppose ρ is a representation of G by linear transformations on a vector space V. For each $X \in \mathbf{G}$, let $\rho(X)$ be the infinitesimal generator of the

one-parameter group of linear transformations $t \to \rho(\exp(tX))$. Suppose that $X, Y \in \mathbf{G}$. Prove *directly* that

$$X_L + Y_L = \rho(X) + \rho(Y), \qquad [X_L, Y_L] = \rho([X_L, Y_L]).$$

This result can be interpreted as follows: Using Theorem 10.4, $\mathbf{G}$ can be identified with $\mathbf{G}_L$, the set of left-invariant vector fields on $\mathbf{G}$. Now $\mathbf{G}_L$ is a subalgebra of $V(G)$. Use this identification to make $\mathbf{G}$ into a Lie algebra. Then the exercise shows that $X \to \rho(X)$ is a Lie algebra homomorphism.

7. Show that dim $\mathbf{G}$ = dim G.

8. Prove that, for $X \in \mathbf{G}$, the vector field on G, which is the infinitesimal generator of the one-parameter group $t \to \mathrm{Ad}(\exp(tX))$, is $X_L + X_R$.

9. Prove that, for $X \in \mathbf{G}$, $X_L(e) = -X_R(e)$, whose e is the identity element of G.

10. For $X \in \mathbf{G}$, prove that $\exp(X)$ is the value at $t = 1$ of the integral curve of the vector fields $-X_L$ or X_R that begins at e.

11. Prove the following facts:

  (a) exp, considered as a map $\mathbf{G} \to G$, is differentiable.
  (b) $\exp_*$, its differential, is an isomorphism $\mathbf{G}_0 \to G_e$.

(If V is a neighborhood of 0 in G such that exp restricted to V is a diffeomorphism, then $U = \exp(V)$ is called a *canonical neighborhood* of e in G. The coordinate system in U, obtained by pulling back via $\exp^{-1}$ a Euclidean coordinate system for $\mathbf{G}$, is called a *canonical coordinate system* for U.)

  (c) If G is connected and $-X \in V$ for all $X \in V$, then every element of G can be written as the product of a finite number of elements chosen from $U = \exp(V)$.
  (d) If G is connected, it is Abelian if and only if $[X, Y] = 0$ for all $X, Y \in \mathbf{G}$; that is, $\mathbf{G}$ is an Abelian Lie algebra.

12. Suppose that $X_1, \dots, X_n$ is a basis for the vector space $\mathbf{G}$. Define a map $\phi: \mathbf{G} \to G$ as follows: If $X = x_1 X_1 + \cdots + x_n X_n$, then $\phi(X) = \exp(x_1 X_1) \cdots \exp(x_n X_n)$. Prove that ϕ is also a diffeomorphism in a neighborhood of $X = 0$. The coordinate system obtained in this way for the corresponding neighborhood of e is called a *canonical coordinate system of the second kind*.

13. The Lie algebra $\mathbf{G}$ is said to be *nilpotent* if, for n sufficiently large, $\mathrm{Ad}\, X_p \cdots \mathrm{Ad}\, X_n = 0$ for any n-tuple of elements $X_1, \dots, X_n$ of elements of $\mathbf{G}$. Prove that $\exp: \mathbf{G} \to G$ and the map ϕ of Exercise 12 have everywhere nonzero Jacobian in this case.

14.   If G is connected, show that every element $g \in G$ can be written in the form $\exp(Y_1) \cdots \exp(Y_m)$ for some choice $Y_1, \ldots, Y_m$ of elements of **G**.

The following exercises will elucidate the "classical groups."

15.   Let V be a finite dimensional real vector space. Prove that the set of invertible linear transformations is a Lie group, denoted by $GL(V)$. Its Lie algebra is $E(V)$, the space of all linear operators $V \to V$. Similarly, if V is a complex vector space, with $GL(V, C)$ the group of all complex-linear isomorphisms: $V \to V$, its Lie algebra is $E(V, C)$, the complex-linear operators $V \to V$. If $V = R^n$, then $GL(V, R)$ becomes $GL(n, R)$, the group $n \times n$ real invertible matrices. Similarly, if $V = C^n$, $GL(V, C)$ is $GL(n, c)$, the group of $n \times n$ complex invertible matrices.

16.   Suppose V is a vector space; $B(\ ,\ )$ is a bilinear, scalar-valued form on V. Let G be the group of isomorphisms: $V \to V$ such that $B(gv, gu) = B(v, u)$ for all $v, u \in V$; that is, G is the subgroup of $GL(V)$ that preserves the form B. Prove that **G** consists of the operators $A : V \to V$ such that

$$B(Au, v) + B(u, Av) = 0.$$

The other "classical" matrix groups (in addition to $GL(n, R)$, $GL(n, C)$) can be obtained in this way. First suppose that V is a real vector space of dimension n, and $B(\ ,\ )$ is a symmetric, positive definite form. G is then essentially $0(n, R)$, the real orthogonal matrices. Show that its Lie algebra consists of the skew-symmetric $n \times n$ real matrices.

If V is a complex vector space, $B(\ ,\ )$ a nondegenerate symmetric complex-linear form G is essentially $0(n, C)$, the $n \times n$ complex-orthogonal matrices.

If V is a real vector space of dimension n, if $B(\ ,\ )$ is a symmetric bilinear form that, when brought to "normal form," has p-plus and $(n - p)$-minus signs, G is denoted by $GL(p, n - p)$.

If B is a nondegenerate skew-symmetric form, then G is denoted by $Sp(n, C)$ and $Sp(n, R)$, according to whether the form is real or complex. Determine its Lie algebra.

Suppose V is a complex-vector space, but the form $B(\ ,\ )$ is *Hermitian bilinear*; that is, it is bilinear as a real form, and in addition,

$$B(cu, v) = cB(u, v) \qquad \text{for } u, v \in V, \quad c \in C,$$

$$B(u, cv) = cB(u, v).$$

If $B(v, v) > 0$ for all $v \in V$, the group of complex-linear automorphisms preserving B is denoted by $U(B)$. In terms of matrices, it can be identified with $U(n)$, the group of $n \times n$ complex unitary matrices. Determine its Lie algebra.

If V is direct sum of complex subspaces $V_1 \oplus V_2$, with

$$B(V_1, V_2) = 0; \qquad B(v_1, v_1) > 0; \qquad B(v_1, v_2) < 0; \qquad \text{for } v_1 \in V_1, \quad v_2 \in V_2,$$

and

$$\text{complex dim } V_1 = p, \qquad \dim V_2 = q,$$

then $U(B)$, when realized as a matrix group, is denoted by $U(p, q)$. Determine its Lie algebra.

17.   Let $SL(n, R)$ and $SL(n, C)$ be the subgroup of determinant 1 matrices. Show that their Lie algebra are the $n \times n$ matrices of trace zero.
Define:

$$SO(n, R) = O(n, R) \cap SL(n, R)$$

$$SO(n, C) = O(n, C) \cap SL(n, C)$$

$$SU(n) = U(n) \cap SL(n, C)$$

18.   Prove that $SL(n, R)$, $GL(n, C)$, $SL(n, C)$, $SO(n, R)$, $O(n, C)$, $SO(n, C)$, $U(n)$, $SU(n)$ are all connected. However, $GL(n, R)$, $O(n, R)$ are disconnected and have two components. Find the formula for the dimension of each of these groups.

11 Classical Mechanics of Particles and Continua

Mechanics of a Single Particle

Our aim in this chapter is to give a survey of some topics in mechanics that are of interest from a geometer's point of view.

Let us start off at the most elementary level, with Newton's law of motion for a particle moving in Euclidean 3-space, which we denote by R^3. Conforming with the notations in books on mechanics, points of R^3 are denoted by $\mathbf{r}$. The Euclidean dot product is

$$\mathbf{r} \cdot \mathbf{r}'.$$

It is a symmetric, positive-definite bilinear form. The vector, or cross product is $\mathbf{r} \times \mathbf{r}'$. It will be assumed that the reader is familiar with the rules of this Euclidean vector algebra and analysis.

Consider a particle moving with time t, analytically given by a curve $t \rightarrow \mathbf{r}(t)$. If m is its mass and if $\mathbf{F}(\mathbf{r}, \dot{\mathbf{r}}, t)$ is its force law, Newton's equation of motion is

$$m \frac{d^2 \mathbf{r}}{dt^2} = \mathbf{F}\left(\mathbf{r}, \frac{d\mathbf{r}}{dt}, t\right). \tag{11.1}$$

This force law $\mathbf{F}$ is then essentially a mapping $T(R^3) \times R \rightarrow R^3$, which must be prescribed by the physical theory with which one is involved. The main physical theories (for example, gravitation, electromagnetism, and fluid mechanics) provide a distinctive way of prescribing a force law.

Note how strongly the vector-space structure of R^3 enters into the equation. First, the solutions for the force-free case are straight lines. Second, to equate both sides of (11.1), we are relying on the fact that the tangent vector to the wave, $d\mathbf{r}/dt$, can be identified with a vector in R^3 itself, a characteristic property of vector spaces.

Notice that the theory is "covariant" under the group of affine transformations of R^3; that is, if $\phi \colon R^3 \rightarrow R^3$ is of the form

$$\phi(\mathbf{r}) = A(\mathbf{r}) + \mathbf{a},$$

where A is a linear transformation: $R^3 \rightarrow R^3$, $a \in R_3$, and if $\mathbf{r}'(t) = \phi(\mathbf{r}(t))$

is the transformed motion, then

$$m \frac{d^2 \mathbf{r'}}{dt^2} = \mathbf{F'}\left(\mathbf{r'}, \frac{d\mathbf{r'}}{dt'} t\right),$$

with

$$\mathbf{F'}(\mathbf{r'}, \mathbf{r'}, t) = A\mathbf{F}(\phi^{-1}(\mathbf{r'}), A^{-1}\mathbf{r}, t) \tag{11.2}$$

Here, "covariance" is a rather vague term of course: If the solutions of (11.1) are subjected to an arbitrary diffeomorphism R^3, (11.1) is transformed into *some* second-order differential equation, but of a considerably more complicated type than (11.2). Thus the criterion of "covariance" can be regarded as esthetic; one could pinpoint the affine group by requiring that the diffeomorphism preserve the force laws that are linear in the indicated variable. After the equations are recast into the form of the Euler equations of the calculus of variations, or the Hamilton equations of Hamilton–Jacobi theory, there will be revealed a more subtle "covariance" with respect to a much larger group. (Perhaps one can look upon this as the physical reason for introducing these mathematical elaborations into mechanics.)

The metric structure of R^3 so far has played no role. It enters, for example, with the idea of "energy." The kinetic energy T is defined by

$$T = \frac{1}{2} m \left| \frac{d\mathbf{r}}{dt} \right|, \tag{11.3}$$

with $|d\mathbf{r}/dt|^2$ defined as $(d\mathbf{r}/dt) \cdot (d\mathbf{r}/dt)$. Then

$$\frac{d}{dt} T = \mathbf{F}\left(\mathbf{r}, \frac{d\mathbf{r}}{dt}, t\right) \cdot \frac{d\mathbf{r}}{dt}, \tag{11.4}$$

Suppose that $\mathbf{F}$ is independent of $\dot{\mathbf{r}}$ and t. Equation (11.4) suggests that we use $\mathbf{F}$ to define a 1-differential form ω on R^3 by requiring that

$$\omega(v) = \mathbf{F}(\mathbf{r}) \cdot v,$$

for each $\mathbf{r} \in \mathbf{R}^3$, each $v \in R_\mathbf{r}^3$, which is identified with $\mathbf{R}^3$ itself. Then, if $\omega = -dV$, where $V \in F(R^3)$, we see that

$$\frac{d}{dt}\left(T\left(\mathbf{r}(t), \frac{d\mathbf{r}}{dt}, t\right) + V(\mathbf{r}(t))\right) = 0,$$

that is, the "total energy" $E = T + V$ is constant along the motion or, as the physicists say, is a "conserved quantity." The (local) condition for the existence of such a potential-energy function V is, of course, that $d\omega = 0$, which means in the language of Euclidean vector analysis that the curl of the vector field $\mathbf{F}$ is zero.

The conservation "laws" of momentum and angular momentum are also readily introduced:

$$\mathbf{p}, \text{ the linear momentum, } = m\,\frac{d\mathbf{r}}{dt},$$

$$\mathbf{L}, \text{ the angular momentum, } = \mathbf{r} \times \mathbf{p};$$

$$\frac{d\mathbf{p}}{dt} = \mathbf{F}, \qquad \frac{d\mathbf{L}}{dt} = \mathbf{r} \times \mathbf{F}.$$

Systems of Particles

Suppose we are given s particles, each moving in 3-space, subject to given external forces and to mutual interaction forces. Suppose $\mathbf{r}_1(t), \ldots, \mathbf{r}_s(t)$ are their paths of motion, with masses $m_1, \ldots, m_s$. Newton's equations of motion then look something like this:

$$m_1\,\frac{d^2\mathbf{r}_1}{dt^2} = \mathbf{F}_1\left(\mathbf{r}_1, \ldots, \mathbf{r}_s, \frac{d\mathbf{r}_1}{dt}, \ldots, \frac{d\mathbf{r}_s}{dt}, t\right)$$

$$\vdots$$

$$m_s\,\frac{d^2\mathbf{r}_s}{dt^2} = \mathbf{F}_s\left(\mathbf{r}_1, \ldots, \mathbf{r}_s, \frac{d\mathbf{r}_1}{dt}, \ldots, \frac{d\mathbf{r}_s}{dt}, t\right).$$

Introduce indices $1 \le a, b, \ldots \le s$.

The total kinetic energy T is given by

$$T = \sum_a \frac{1}{2}\, m_a \left|\frac{d\mathbf{r}_a}{dt}\right|^2, \qquad \frac{dT}{dt} = \sum_a \mathbf{F}_a \cdot \frac{d\mathbf{r}_a}{dt}.$$

Again a potential function $V(\mathbf{r}_1, \ldots, \mathbf{r}_s)$ can be introduced by the condition

$$\frac{d}{dt}\, V(\mathbf{r}, (t), \ldots, \mathbf{r}_s(t)) = -\sum_a \mathbf{F}_a \cdot \frac{d\mathbf{r}_a}{dt}$$

for *each* curve $t \to (\mathbf{r}_1(t), \ldots, \mathbf{r}_s(t))$ in R^{3s}. Conservation of total energy $E = T + V$ will result.

Total momentum

$$\mathbf{p} = \mathbf{p} + \cdots + \mathbf{p}_m = \sum_a m_a \cdot \frac{d\mathbf{r}_a}{dt}$$

and total angular momentum

$$\mathbf{L} = \mathbf{L}_1 + \cdots + \mathbf{L}_s = \sum_a \mathbf{r}_a \times \mathbf{p}_a$$

can be now introduced. These quantities are most useful if the forces $\mathbf{F}_a$ are of a special type, namely,

$$\mathbf{F}_a = \sum_b \mathbf{F}_{ab},$$

where $\mathbf{F}_{ab}$, for $b \neq a$, is interpreted as the force that the bth particle exerts on the ath particle, and $\mathbf{F}_{aa}$ is interpreted as the action of the external forces on the ath particle. Then

$$\frac{d}{dt}\mathbf{p} = \sum_a \mathbf{F}_a = \sum_{a,b} \mathbf{F}_{ab}. \tag{11.5}$$

This suggests the simplifying condition

$$\mathbf{F}_{ab} = -\mathbf{F}_{ba} \qquad \text{for } a \neq b. \tag{11.6}$$

(It is just the quantitative version of Newton's law: "Action = reaction".) With this condition,

$$\frac{d}{dt}\mathbf{p} = \sum_a \mathbf{F}_{aa}. \tag{11.7}$$

The right-hand side is the sum of the external forces. In particular, total momentum is conserved if the system is isolated, that is, if there are no external forces.

Turn now to total angular momentum:

$$\frac{d\mathbf{L}}{dt} = \sum \mathbf{r}_a \times \frac{d\mathbf{p}_a}{dt} = \sum_a \mathbf{r}_a \times \mathbf{F}_a = \sum_{a,b} \mathbf{r}_a \times \mathbf{F}_{ab}$$

$$= \sum_{a<b} (\mathbf{r}_a - \mathbf{r}_b) \times \mathbf{F}_{ab} + \sum_a \mathbf{r}_a \times \mathbf{F}_{aa}.$$

This suggests the simplifying condition

$$(\mathbf{r}_a - \mathbf{r}_b) \times \mathbf{F}_{ab} = 0 \qquad \text{for } a \neq b, \tag{11.8}$$

which means that $\mathbf{F}_{ab}$ points along the line joining $a \neq b$; that is, the forces of interaction are directed along the line joining $\mathbf{r}_a$ to $\mathbf{r}_b$. Again the underlying geometry enters in a strong way at this point. With (11.7) satisfied, we have

$$\frac{d}{dt}\mathbf{L} = \sum_a \mathbf{r}_a \times \mathbf{F}_{aa}. \tag{11.9}$$

Again the right-hand side involves only the external forces. Equations (11.7) and (11.9) then express precisely the desirable features of linear and angular momentum. In turn, they arise from Lie groups acting on Euclidean space, in a way we shall describe later.

Constrained Motion

As in the preceding section, consider a system of particles moving according to the laws of motion, (11.5). The motion of the individual particles, $r_1(t), \ldots, r_s(t)$, can be consolidated into a single curve $r(t) = (r_1(t), \ldots, r_s(t))$ in R^{3s}. Suppose we regard the particles as being constrained to be on a submanifold N of R^{3s}. Again the problem is indeterminate until we prescribe, from other physical reasoning, how this effects the force law. "D'Alembert's principle" gives the relevant information. (See Goldstein [1] for a fuller discussion of this topic.)

Suppose $F_1, \ldots, F_r$ would be the forces if there were no constraint. Then, consider the vectors:

$$m_1 \frac{d^2 r_1}{dt^2} - F_1, \ldots, m_r \frac{d^2 r_s}{dt^2} - F_s.$$

They would be zero if there were no constraints. Thus they should be interpreted as the "forces of the constraint." They can be considered together as giving a vector in R^{3s}. D'Alembert's principle now asserts that this vector, considered as a tangent vector to the point of R^{3s} given by $r(t) = (r_1(t), \ldots, r_s(t))$, is *perpendicular* to the submanifold of constraint N. Again, Euclidean geometry enters into one of the basic assumptions of dynamics. (We keep emphasizing this point because it is just the understanding of the basic "principles of interaction" that constitute the main unsolved problems of elementary particle physics.)

This, in turn, suggests that we reformulate the equations (11.5) so as to put the Euclidean geometry of R^n more in the foreground. Consider $r = (r_1, \ldots, r_r)$ and $\dot{r} = (\dot{r}_1, \ldots, \dot{r}_s)$ as vectors of R^{3s}. Consolidate the force function appearing on the right-hand side of (11.5) into a function $F: R^{3s} \times R^{3s} \times R \to R^{3s}$:

$$F(r, \dot{r}, t) = (F_1(r_1, \ldots, r_s, \dot{r}_1, \ldots, \dot{r}_s, t), \ldots).$$

Then (11.5) takes the form

$$m \frac{d^2 r}{dt^2} = F\left(r, \frac{dr}{dt}, t\right) \qquad (11.10)$$

where m, instead of being a scalar as for the motion of a single particle, is an operator: $R^{3s} \to R^{3s}$; that is,

$$m(r_1, \ldots, r_s) = (m_1 r_1, \ldots, m_s r_s).$$

The momentum p is now the vector: $m(dr/dt)$. The kinetic energy T is now given by

$$T = \frac{1}{2}\left(m\frac{d\mathbf{r}}{dt}\right) \cdot \left(\frac{d\mathbf{r}}{dt}\right),$$

where dot product ($\cdot$) is that which is usual for R^{3s}; that is,

$$(\mathbf{r}_1, \ldots, \mathbf{r}_s) \cdot (\mathbf{r}_1', \ldots, \mathbf{r}_s') = \mathbf{r}_1 \cdot \mathbf{r}_1' + \cdots + \mathbf{r}_s \cdot \mathbf{r}_s';$$

$$m\frac{d^2\mathbf{r}}{dt^2} - \mathbf{F}\left(r, \frac{d\mathbf{r}}{dt}, t\right) \qquad (11.11)$$

is perpendicular to the tangent subspace $N_{\mathbf{r}(t)}$ to N in R^{3s}.

There are various techniques available for finding explicitly the equations of motion implicit in (11.11). One method proceeds via the calculus of variations: If the equations of motion, (11.10), can be interpreted as the Euler equations of a variational problem, the problem can be regarded as a special case of a "Lagrange problem" obtained by putting constraints on the curves (that is, that they lie on N) that are in competition to give a stationary value to the Lagrangian. However, in the simplest case, where the forces are derivable from a potential $V(\mathbf{r})$, there is a more direct method available for writing down the explicit equations of motion as a system of Hamiltonian equations. We shall present this method, leaving the details of the calculation as an exercise.

Suppose the submanifold N is locally describable by functions $\mathbf{r}(q_1, \ldots, q_n)$, where $q = (q_1, \ldots, q_n)$ is a point in a domain D of R^n. Choose indices $i, j, k, \ldots$ running from 1 to n. Suppose the potential function V, when restricted to N, becomes a function $V(q_1, \ldots, q_n)$ of these variables. The curve $t \to \mathbf{r}(t)$ defines a curve $t \to q(t)$ such that

$$\mathbf{r}(t) = \mathbf{r}(q(t)).$$

Now T takes the form

$$T(q(t)) = G_{ij}(q(t))\frac{dq_i}{dt}\frac{dq_j}{dt},$$

where $G_{ij}(q)$ are functions of $q_1, \ldots, q_n$. Further, the $n \times n$ matrix function of $q = (q_1, \ldots, q_n)$, $G = (G_{ij})$, is nonsingular; that is, G^{-1} exists.

We introduce new functions of t:

$$p_i(t) = G_{ij}(q(t))\frac{dq_j}{dt}. \qquad (11.12)$$

These variables, $p = (p_1, \ldots, p_n)$, are defined as the *momenta* of the particles defined by the constraints. Consider E, the total energy $T + V$. It is a function

of the variables $q_1, \ldots, q_n, (dq_1/dt), \ldots, (dq_n/dt)$. Equation (11.12) enables us
to describe it also as a function of $q_1, \ldots, q_n, p_1, \ldots, p_n$. Explicitly,

$$E = (G^{-1}(q))_{ij}\, p_i\, p_j + V(q_1, \ldots, q_n). \qquad (11.13)$$

Now one can verify by straightforward but tedious calculations that
equations (11.1) are equivalent to the following *Hamiltonian equations*:

$$\frac{dq_i}{dt} = \frac{\partial E}{\partial p_i}(p(t), q(t)); \qquad \frac{dp_i}{dt} = -\frac{\partial E}{\partial q_i}(p(t), q(t)). \qquad (11.14)$$

We shall investigate such equations in more detail in Part 2 and find a
deeper reason why (11.13) and (11.14) take this simple form.

Continuum Mechanics

Suppose we have s particles of mass $m_1, \ldots, m_s$ moving in R^3. Let $\mathbf{r}_1(t)$,
$\ldots, \mathbf{r}_s(t)$ be the position curves as these particles evolve in time. Suppose G
is a group of transformations acting on R^3. Suppose that there is a curve
$t \to g(t)$ in G such that

$$\mathbf{r}_1(t) = g(t)\mathbf{r}_1(0),$$
$$\vdots$$
$$\mathbf{r}_s(t) = g(t)\mathbf{r}_s(0).$$

Suppose also that

$$g r_a(0) = r_a(0) \qquad \text{for } 1 \le a \le s$$

implies that g is the identity element of G. Then the different possible positions
of the particles may be identified with the group G itself. As Arnold [2] has
recently emphasized, this enables one to interpret certain ideas in mechanics
in terms of the differential geometry of the underlying manifold of G.

In this section, we carry out a part of this program for the case of fluid
motion. Here one thinks of a particle at every point of R^3, and G as the group
of all diffeomorphisms of R^3. We shall aim to derive the standard "Eulerian"
description of continuum mechanics (see Prager [1]).

In fact it is useful to be even more general. Suppose M is a manifold and
$t \to g(t)$ is a one-parameter family of diffeomorphisms of M. For each value of
t, define a vector field $X_t \in V(M)$ as follows:

> For $p \in M$, $X_t(p)$ is the tangent vector to the curve
> $u \to g(u)g(t)^{-1}p$ at $u = t$.

Physically, X_t is the "Eulerian" velocity field corresponding to the "fluid motion" defined by $g(t)$; that is, $X_t(p)$ is the velocity vector of the particle that, at time t, is at the point p.

Let us compute X_t in terms of its action on functions on M. For $f \in F(M)$,

$$X_t(f)(p) = \frac{d}{du} f(g(u)g(t)^{-1} p)\Big|_{u=t} = \frac{d}{du}(g(u)g(t)^{-1})(f)(p)\Big|_{u=t}$$

$$= \frac{d}{du} g(t)^{-1*}g(u)^*(f)(p)\Big|_{u=t} g(t)^{-1*}\left(\frac{d}{du} g(u)^*(f)(p)\right);$$

or

$$g(t)^*(X_t(f))(p) = \frac{d}{du} g(u)^*(f)(p)\Big|_{u=t} = \frac{\partial}{\partial t}(g(t)^*(f))(p);$$

or

$$g(t)^*(X_t(f)) = \frac{\partial}{\partial t}(g(t)^*(f)); \tag{11.15a}$$

or

$$X_t(f) = g(t)^{-1*} \frac{\partial}{\partial t}(g(t)^*(f)) \qquad \text{for } f \in F(M). \tag{11.15b}$$

On the other hand, one can form the "Lagrangian" velocity field Y_t: $Y_t(p)$ is the "velocity" vector of the particle that at time $t = 0$ was at p. Analytically, for $f \in F(M)$,

$$Y_t(f)(p) = \frac{\partial}{\partial t}(g(t)^*(f)(p)),$$

or

$$Y_t(f) = \frac{\partial}{\partial t} g(t)^*(f). \tag{11.16}$$

Hence

$$X_t(f) = g(t)^{-1*}(Y_t(f)) \qquad \text{for } f \in F(M). \tag{11.17}$$

We can express the "conservation of mass" in this form. Suppose ω is a fixed-volume element differential form on M, and $\rho(p, t)$ is the density function of mass; that is, if D is a domain in M, then $\int_D \rho_t \omega$ is the total mass of the "fluid" in the region 0 at *time t*, where ρ_t is the function $p \to \rho(p, t)$ on M.

Then "conservation of mass" in integral form is the relation

$$\int_{g(t)D} \rho_t \omega = \int_D \rho_0 \omega. \tag{11.18}$$

From Chapter 7, we see that the left-hand side of this relation is equal to

$$\int_D g(t)^*(\rho_t \omega) = \int_D \rho_0 \omega. \qquad (11.19)$$

Since the right-hand side of (11.18) is independent of t, we can differentiate (11.19) with respect to t and set the result equal to zero:

$$\int_D \frac{\partial}{\partial t} (g(t)^*(\rho_t \omega)) = 0. \qquad (11.20)$$

Now, if θ is a differential form,

$$\frac{\partial}{\partial t} (g(t)^*(\theta)) = Y_t(\theta) = g(t)^*(X_t(\theta)), \qquad (11.21)$$

where $Y_t(\theta)$ denotes the Lie derivative of the form θ by the vector field Y_t. (See the exercises for the proof of this: Note that (11.16) and (11.17) assert this when θ is a 0-form.) Hence

$$\frac{\partial}{\partial t} (g(t)^*(\rho_t \omega)) = g(t)^*(X_t(\rho_t \omega)) + g(t)^* \left(\frac{\partial}{\partial t} (\rho_t) \omega \right)$$

and (11.20) takes the form:

$$\int_D g(t)^* \left(X_t(\rho_t \omega) + \frac{\partial}{\partial t} (\rho_t) \omega \right),$$

which equals

$$\int_{g(t)D} X_t(\rho_t \omega) + \frac{\partial}{\partial t} (\rho_t) \omega.$$

Since D is an arbitrary open set, this can be true only if the integrand is zero; that is,

$$X_t(\rho_t \omega) + \frac{\partial}{\partial t} (\rho_t) \omega = 0. \qquad (11.22)$$

This is the *equation of continuity*. We leave to the exercises the task of writing out what this means for $M = R^3$, and show there that it reduces to the form of the continuity equation that one finds in books on fluid mechanics (for example, Prager [1]).

Suppose now that we want to write down the "equations of motion" for the fluid. In Prager's book [1] one finds a clear description of how to do this for Euclidean space; that is, $M = R^3$. Since, as an exercise in differential geometry, we would like to continue to work with a general manifold, let us adopt one simple way of freeing the argument from Euclidean geometry.

Let θ be a 1-differential form on M. Suppose that W is a vector field on M. Let ω continue to be a volume-element differential form on M. Then, if D is a domain in M, $\int_D \theta(W)\omega$ can be considered as the "θ-component of the total effect of the vector field W on the domain D."

Suppose that F is a vector field representing the "volume" forces on a domain D; that is, $\int_D \rho\theta(F)\omega$ is the "θ-component of the volume forces acting on the domain D." (ρ is a function on M giving the density of mass. We are working here at a fixed time. In essence, we are analyzing the "kinematics" for forces.) The discipline of continuum mechanics can also encounter forces that come from the region surrounding a bit of fluid, expressed analytically by the "stress tensor." We shall not present the analysis of the physical idea, but only state how this can be phrased in differential geometric language.

Let T be a tensor field on M representing this stress. At $p \in M$, T is a skew-symmetric $(m-1)$-multilinear mapping $M_p \times \cdots \times M_p \to M_p (m = \dim M)$. Thus, for $p \in M$, $v_1, \ldots, v_{m-1} \in M_p$, $\theta(T(v_1, \ldots, v_{m-1}))$ is an $(m-1)$-covector on M. We can then consider the symbol $\theta(T)$ defining, for each θ, an $(m-1)$-differential form on M. (In fact we can also regard T as defined by an $F(M)$-linear map $F^1(M) \to F^{m-1}(M)$ of 1-forms into $(m-1)$-forms. Physically, $T(v_1, \ldots, v_{m-1})$ should be thought of as the "stress" force exerted on the piece of hypersurface that is tangent to the vectors $v_1, \ldots, v_{m-1}$. Thus, if D is a domain in M with boundary ∂M, $\int_{\partial D} \theta(t)$ should be thought of as the total θ-component of the stress force on the domain D. This is equal, by Stokes' theorem, to $\int_D d\theta(t)$. Thus

$$\int_D (\rho\theta(F)\omega + d\theta(t)) \tag{11.23}$$

should represent the θ-component of the force acting on the domain D at a fixed time.

Now, we apply Newton's law of motion in the form:

"Rate of change of θ-component of momentum = forces acting."

Suppose a group of particles making up the fluid starts out at $t = 0$ to occupy the domain D. At time t, they will be in domain $g(t)D$. Their θ-component of total momentum will be

$$\int_{g(t)D} \theta(X_t)\rho_t \omega, \tag{11.24}$$

which is equal to

$$\int_D g(t)^*(\theta(X_t)\rho_t \omega). \tag{11.25}$$

Equation (11.21) tells us how to differentiate this with respect to t:

$$\frac{d}{dt} \int_D g(t)^*(\theta(X_t)\rho_t\,\omega) = \int_D g(t)^* \cdot (X_t(\theta(X_t)\rho_t\,\omega))$$

$$+ \int_D g(t)^*\left(\theta\!\left(\frac{\partial X_t}{\partial t}\right)\rho_t\,\omega + \theta(X_t)\frac{\partial \rho_t}{\partial t}\,\omega\right)$$

$$= \int_{g(t)D}\left(X_t\!\left(\theta(X_t)\rho_t\,\omega + \theta\!\left(\frac{\partial X_t}{\partial t}\right)\rho_t\,\omega\right)\right.$$

$$\left. + \theta(X_t)\frac{\partial \rho_t}{\partial t}\,\omega\right).$$

Equating this to the expression (11.23) for the force acting on this bunch of particles gives the identity:

$$\int_{g(t)D}(\rho_t\,\theta(F_t)\omega + d(\theta(T(Z_t)(Z\lrcorner\,\omega))) = \int_{g(t)D} X_t(\theta(X_t)\rho_t\,\omega)$$

$$+ \theta\!\left(\frac{\partial X_t}{\partial t}\right)\rho_t\,\omega + \theta(X_t)\frac{\partial \rho_t}{\partial t}\,\omega. \quad (11.26)$$

Since this is to hold for all domains D, we have

$$\rho_t\,\theta(F_t)\omega + d\theta(T_t) = X_t(\theta(X_t)\rho_t\,\omega)$$

$$+ \theta\!\left(\frac{\partial X_t}{\partial t}\right)\rho_t\,\omega + \theta(X_t)\frac{\partial \rho_t}{\partial t}\,\omega. \quad (11.27)$$

This is the coordinate-free version of Euler's equations of fluid motion. Let us make it explicit for $M = R^3$, with coordinates (x_i), $i = 1, 2, 3$. Suppose

$$X_t = v_i(x, t)\frac{\partial}{\partial x_i}, \qquad \omega = dx_1 \wedge dx_2 \wedge dx_3,$$

$$\rho_t = \rho(x, t), \qquad \theta = dx_k, \qquad F = F_k\frac{\partial}{\partial x_k},$$

$$dx_k(T) = T_{ijk}(x, t)\, dx_i \wedge dx_j.$$

Suppose T_{ik} is defined by the condition

$$T_{ijk} = \tfrac{1}{2}\varepsilon_{ijl}\,T_{lk},$$

where ε_{ljk} is the 3-index, skew-symmetric tensor (with $\varepsilon_{123} = 1$). Now

$$d(\theta(T)) + \frac{1}{2}\frac{\partial T_{ijk}}{\partial x_h}\,dx_h \wedge dx_i \wedge dx_j = \frac{1}{2}\left(\varepsilon_{hij}\frac{\partial T_{ijk}}{\partial x_h}\right)\omega$$

$$= \frac{1}{2}\,\varepsilon_{hij}\,\varepsilon_{ijl}\frac{\partial T_{lk}}{\partial x_h}\,\omega$$

$$= \delta_{hl}\frac{\partial T_{lk}}{\partial x_h}\,\omega = \frac{\partial T_{ik}}{\partial x_i}\,\omega. \qquad (11.28)$$

Now

$$X_t(\omega) = \frac{\partial v_i}{\partial x_i}\,\omega.$$

Hence (11.27) becomes

$$\rho F_k + \frac{\partial T_{ik}}{\partial x_i} = v_i\frac{\partial}{\partial x_i}(v_k\rho) + v_k\rho\frac{\partial v_i}{\partial x_i}$$

$$+ \frac{\partial v_k}{\partial t}\rho + v_k\frac{\partial\rho}{\partial t}. \qquad (11.29)$$

This is the fundamental dynamical equation of continuum mechanics. Proceeding further requires the development of additional physical ideas concerning the relation between the stress tensor and the kinematic data. We shall leave it at this point.

Exercises

1. Prove (11.21).

2. Work out the explicit form for the equation of continuity, (11.22), for the case of fluid motion in R^3.

3. Work out the equations of motion of a rigid body (that is, a system of particles constrained to move in such a way that the distances between individual particles remains constant) by using d'Alembert's principle or the equation (11.9) for rate of change of angular momentum, or both. Compare with the more indirect approach that uses the calculus of variations and "moving frames" given in Chapters 16 and 33.

Part **2** THE HAMILTON–JACOBI THEORY
AND CALCULUS OF VARIATIONS

12 Differential Forms and Variational Problems

Although we are concerned in this book only with the relatively simple theory of variational problems with one independent variable, in this chapter we shall briefly describe a general method for dealing with the multiple integral problems. It follows Cartan's general approach to geometric problems; the idea is to "prolong" a variational problem given on a space to one defined by differential forms on a space sitting over the given one. This "standard" type of variational problem will be in optimally simple form; hence it will be called a *canonical variational problem*. We shall see that Stokes' formula can be used in a very systematic manner to derive the first and second variation formula for this sort of variational problem.

To describe a canonical variational problem, we should be given the following objects:

(a) A manifold M.
(b) An r-differential form θ on M.
(c) A set of differential forms, denoted by I, on M which forms a differential ideal; that is, an ideal in the algebraic sense with respect to the exterior algebra structure on all differential forms of M and, in addition, which is closed under exterior differentiation d.
(d) A manifold N with boundary ∂N. The dimension of N is r. N should be oriented, and should induce an orientation on ∂N so that r-forms can be integrated over N.

(We shall be using in this chapter the theory of integration on manifolds described in Chapter 11 of Part 1. Thus ∂N does not have to be the whole point-set boundary of N, but just the $(r - 1)$-dimensional part so that Stokes' formula is valid.)

Let $E(N, M)$ be the space of submanifold maps of N onto M. Since N and M will be fixed throughout the discussion, we abbreviate $E(N, M)$ to E. Let $E(I)$ be the set of maps of E that are integral maps of the ideal I, that is, the set of submanifold maps $\phi : N \to M$ such that

$$\phi^*(\omega) = 0 \qquad \text{for all } \omega \in I.$$

The r-form θ defines a real-valued function L on E as follows: If ϕ is a submanifold map: $N \to M$, then

$$\mathbf{L}(\phi) = \int_N \phi^*(\theta).$$

113

The "problem" is to study the "critical points" L *restricted* to $E(I)$. The advantage of studying variational problems of this special type is that the first and second variation formulas are obtained very simply from Stokes' formula.

Now E should be considered as an infinite dimensional manifold. This can be done in a formal way by introducing a ring of functions on E. Rather than trace through the general formalism, we simply indicate the obvious geometric meaning of the "tangent space" to E. This is the only feature of its manifold structure that we shall actually use. For $\phi \in E$, the "tangent space" to E at ϕ, denoted by E_ϕ, is defined as follows: An element of E_ϕ is a map, typically denoted by **v**, of $N \to T(M)$ such that $\mathbf{v}(p) \in M_{\phi(p)}$ for all $p \in N$. Thus, as in Fig. 2, **v** is a "vector field" along the mapping, pointing outward into M;

FIGURE 2

that is, v is an "infinitesimal deformation" of ϕ. To make this precise, suppose that we are given a deformation of ϕ, that is, a one-parameter family of maps, $t \to \phi_t$, of $N \to M$, with $\phi_0 = \phi$. Define the infinitesimal deformation as an element $v \in E$ by the following formula:

For $p \in N$, $\mathbf{v}(p) =$ the tangent vector to the curve $t \to \phi_t(p)$ at $t = 0$.

There is another geometric way of looking at this:

$t \to \phi_t$ defines a "curve" in E, and $\mathbf{v} \in E$ is the "tangent vector" to this curve at $t = 0$.

The following formula (12.1) is the basic tool of this chapter, since it tells us how differential forms on M behave *to the first order* when they are dragged along by a deformation of ϕ. The reason that it is desirable to express geometric objects in terms of differential forms (rather than, say, other types of tensor fields) is that they do behave so simply.

$$\frac{\partial}{\partial t} \phi_t^*(\omega)\bigg\|_{t=0} = \phi^*(\mathbf{v} \lrcorner\, d\omega) + d\phi^*(\mathbf{v} \lrcorner\, \omega) \tag{12.1}$$

for each differential form ω on M.

There is a notational convention inherent in this formula. For $p \in N$, $\mathbf{v}(p) \lrcorner\, \omega$ is the contraction of the form $\omega(\phi(p))$ by the tangent vector $\mathbf{v}(p)$; hence it is a form on the tangent space to M at $\phi(p)$ of one lower degree than ω.

$\phi^*(\mathbf{v}(p) \lrcorner \omega)$ is the pullback of this form to give a form on the tangent space to N at p as p varies over N; this gives a differential form on N (which we denote by $\phi^*(\mathbf{v} \lrcorner \omega)$), to which d may be applied. This is just the second term on the right-hand side of (12.1). The first term on the right-hand side is defined similarly, with $d\omega$ replacing ω. Note the similarity of this formula and the one involving ω, a vector field X, and Lie derivative of ω by X, namely,

$$X(\omega) = X \lrcorner d\omega + d(X \lrcorner \omega). \tag{12.2}$$

In fact this formula may be considered as a special case of (12.1); it is obtained when we choose $N = M$, ϕ as the identity mapping, and $t \to \phi_t$ as the one-parameter group of M generated by X.

Now we turn to the proof of (12.1). First (12.1) must be proved when ω is a 0-form, that is, a function, which we shall call f to keep things straight. The second term on the right-hand side of (12.1) is zero, since a form of degree 1 is, by convention, zero. The value of the right-hand side at a point $p \in N$ is

$$\mathbf{v}(p) \lrcorner dg,$$

which is

$$\mathbf{v}(p)(f),$$

which is, by the definition of $v(p)$,

$$\left. \frac{\partial}{\partial t} f(\phi_t(p)) \right\|_{t=0},$$

which is the left-hand side.

The next step in the proof of (12.1) is to show that if it is true for ω, it is true for $d\omega$. The left-hand side is now

$$\left. \frac{\partial}{\partial t} \phi_t^*(d\omega) \right\|_{t=0} = d \left(\left. \frac{\partial}{\partial t} \phi_t^*(\omega) \right\|_{t=0} \right).$$

The right-hand side is $d\phi^*(\mathbf{v} \lrcorner d\omega)$. They are equal if (12.1) is true for ω. The final step is to show that if (12.1) is true for ω_1 and ω_2, it is true for $\omega_1 \wedge \omega_2$. We leave it to the reader to do this tedious but straightforward calculation. Finally (12.1) is true in general, since any form can be built up from 0-forms by applying d and exterior product.

Return now to the variational problem defined by the differential ideal I of differential forms and the r-form θ. To study the behavior of $\phi \to L(\phi)$ $= \int_N \phi^*(\theta)$, let us suppose that $t \to \phi_t$ is a deformation of ϕ by a one-parameter family of maps of $N \to M$. Let $\mathbf{v} \in E$ be the corresponding infinitesimal deformation. Then

$$\frac{d}{dt}\mathbf{L}(\phi_t)\bigg|_{t=0} = \int_N \frac{d}{dt}\,\phi_t^*(\theta)\bigg|_{t=0}$$

$$= (\text{using (12.1)}) \int_N \phi^*(\mathbf{v} \lrcorner\, d\theta) + d\phi^*(\mathbf{v} \lrcorner\, \theta)$$

$$= (\text{using Stokes' formula}) \int_N \phi^*(\mathbf{v} \lrcorner\, d\theta) + \int_{\partial N} \phi^*(\mathbf{v} \lrcorner\, \theta). \quad (12.3)$$

This is the "first variation formula."

Now we are interested in the "critical points" of $\mathbf{L}$ restricted to $E(I)$. If $\phi \in E(I)$, that is, if $\phi^*(\omega) = 0$ for all $\omega \in I$, we must find the subspace of E_ϕ corresponding to deformations that also lie in $E(I)$. But the condition for this is also obvious from (12.1), namely,

$$\phi^*(\mathbf{v} \lrcorner\, d\omega) + d\phi^*(\mathbf{v} \lrcorner\, \omega) = 0 \qquad \text{for all } \omega \in I. \quad (12.4)$$

The set of $\mathbf{v} \in E$ satisfying (12.4)—the "linear variational equations" of the partial differential equations defining the integral submanifolds of I—can be thought of as the "tangent space" to $E(I)$ at the "point" ϕ, and will accordingly be denoted by $E(I)_\phi$. We can then say that a map $\phi: N \to M$ is an *extremal* of the variational problem if

$$\phi^*(\mathbf{v} \lrcorner\, d\theta) = 0 \qquad \text{for all } v \in E(I)_\phi. \quad (12.5)$$

We shall say that ϕ is an *extremal of the first kind* if (12.5) is true for *all* $\mathbf{v} \in E\phi$; that is, if

> $\phi^*(X \lrcorner\, d\theta) = 0$ for all vector fields X on M, that is,
> if ϕ is an integral manifold of the system of forms
> spanned by the $X \lrcorner\, d\theta$, with $X \in V(M)$. $\qquad (12.6)$

An extremal of the first kind, then, is one that is also an extremal of the variational problem obtained by retaining θ but throwing away I. As we shall see, it is the extremals of the first kind that admit the simplest type of a second variation formula.

We can now read off from the first variation formula the definition of the second basic idea, namely, that of transversality. The vector field $v \in E_\phi$ on M is *transversal to ϕ at the boundary (with respect to θ)* if

$$\phi^*(\mathbf{v} \lrcorner\, \theta)(p) = 0 \qquad \text{for all } p \in \partial N. \quad (12.7)$$

Hence we see that the first variation is zero if ϕ is an extremal and if v is transversal to ϕ at the boundary.

To show that there are situations where all extremals are of the first kind (hence that the theory of the second variation to be developed below is non-vacuous), let us look at the example that will be our main concern in this book.

Simple Integral Variational Problems

"Simple integral" means that dimension $N = 1$. Therefore, we may as well choose N as an interval of real numbers, which we shall normalize to $[0, 1]$. Then t will usually denote the parameter on this interval. In keeping with our earlier notation, maps of N into manifolds, that is, curves, will usually be denoted by σ.

Let B be a manifold of dimension n with indices $1 \leq j, \ldots, \leq n$. Let $T(B)$ be the tangent bundle of B, and let M be the Cartesian product $T(B) \times R$. A *Lagrangian* for B is a real-valued function on M, denoted usually by $L(v, t)$. Associated with a curve $t \to \sigma(t)$ in B, we define the number

$$\mathbf{L}(\sigma) \quad \text{as} \int_0^1 L(\sigma'(t), t)\, dt. \tag{12.8}$$

The "ordinary" problem is to study the critical points of this real-valued function on the space of paths of B. In (classical) Lagrange variational problems, we are, also given an additional set $g_1(v, t), \ldots, g_m(v, t)$ of real-valued functions on M, and we study the critical points of L restricted to the set of curves $t \to \sigma(t)$ in B that satisfy the "constraints":

$$g_a(\sigma'(t), t) = 0 \quad \text{for} \quad 0 \leq t \leq 1. \tag{12.9}$$

More generally, we can prescribe a *constraint subset* C of M (not necessarily defined by setting functions equal to zero; for example, in optimal control theory, subsets defined by inequalities appear) and consider the critical points of $\mathbf{L}$ restricted to curve $t \to \sigma(t)$ in B that satisfy

$$(\sigma'(t), t) \in C \quad \text{for} \quad 0 \leq t \leq 1. \tag{12.10}$$

Following Cartan's idea [1], such variational problems can be "prolonged" to canonical variational problems on M. It is most convenient to do this by using a local coordinate system x_j for B: It is usually readily verified that the objects defined are independent of the coordinates used. Define functions $\dot{x}_j$ on $T(M)$:

$$\dot{x}_j(v) = dx_j(v).$$

Thus the $\dot{x}_j$ are just the differentials of the coordinates relabeled and regarded as real-valued functions on $T(B)$; hence, also on $M = T(B) \times R$. We shall often use a vector notation:

$$x = (x_j); \quad \dot{x} = (\dot{x}_j).$$

L and the g_a then become functions $L(x, \dot{x}, t)$ and $g_a(x, \dot{x}, t)$. Define

$$\theta(L) = \frac{\partial L}{\partial \dot{x}_j} (dx_j - \dot{x}_j \, dt) + L \, dt$$

$$= \frac{\partial L}{\partial \dot{x}_j} dx_j - H \, dt, \tag{12.11}$$

with

$$H = L - \frac{\partial L}{\partial \dot{x}_j} \dot{x}_j$$

where $\theta(L)$ is called the *Cartan form* defined by the Lagrangian L. Consider (for the ordinary variational problem) the ideal I of forms generated by the differential forms $dx_j - \dot{x}_j \, dt$. Suppose we have a curve $t \to (x(t), \dot{x}(t), t) = \phi(t)$ in M. Suppose it annihilates the forms in I. Then

$$\frac{dx_j}{dt} = \dot{x}_j(t),$$

that is, $t \to \phi(t)$ is the tangent vector curve $t \to (\sigma'(t), t)$ to the "projected" curve $t \to x(t)$ in B. Conversely, the tangent vector curve to any curve in B annihilates the form in I. For such a curve, notice that

$$\theta(\sigma'(t), t) = \frac{\partial L}{\partial \dot{x}_j} (dx_j - \dot{x}_j \, dt)(\sigma'(t), t) + L(\sigma'(t), t) \, dt;$$

that is,

$$\int_N \phi^*(\theta(L)) = \int_0^1 L\left(x(t), \frac{dx}{dt}, t \right) dt = L(\sigma).$$

Thus, under the projection map $M \to B$, the spaces $E(I)$ and the curves in B correspond in a 1-1 way, and the real-valued function L corresponds to the real-valued function on $E(I)$ obtained by integrating $\theta(L)$.

Let us see what condition (12.6) means. First, $d\theta(L)$ is a 2-form, which we call ω. Notice it means only that

$$\phi'(t) \lrcorner \, \omega = 0 \qquad \text{for } 0 \leq t \leq 1. \tag{12.12}$$

Recall that it is the condition that $t \to \phi(t) = (\sigma'(t), t)$ be an extremal of the first kind. As we shall describe in the next chapter, this means that $t \to \phi(t)$ is a *characteristic curve* for ω, and will also lead to a description of $t \to \phi(t)$ in certain local coordinates for M, the *Hamilton equations*.

Now we shall work out the conditions for (12.12) in terms of the $(x, \dot{x}, t)$-coordinate system for M. Suppose that $t \to (x(t), \dot{x}(t), t)$ describes ϕ in these coordinates. Put

$$L_j = \frac{\partial L}{\partial x_j}; \qquad L_{n+j} = \frac{\partial L}{\partial \dot{x}_j}; \qquad L_t = \frac{\partial L}{\partial t}.$$

Then

$$d\omega = dL_{n+j} \wedge (dx_j - \dot{x}_j \, dt) + dL_n \wedge dt - L_{n+j} \, d\dot{x} \wedge dt$$

$$= dL_{n+j} \wedge (dx_j - \dot{x}_j \, dt) + L_j \, dx_j \wedge dt$$

$$= (dL_{n+j} + L_j \, dt) \wedge (dx_j - \dot{x}_j \, dt). \tag{12.13}$$

Suppose that $t \to x(t)$ is a curve in B. Then its tangent vector curve $t \to (x(t), (dx/dt), t)$ annihilates the forms $dx_j - \dot{x}_j \, dt$. Thus, (12.12) is satisfied. if and only if

$$\frac{d}{dt}\left(\frac{\partial L}{\partial \dot{x}_j}\left(x(t), \frac{dx}{dt}, t\right)\right) = \frac{\partial L}{\partial x_j}\left(x(t), \frac{dx}{dt}, t\right). \tag{12.14}$$

These are just the classical Euler–Lagrange equations, and will be familiar to the reader if he has looked at more traditional treatments (for example, Gelfand and Fomin [1]). The solutions of (12.14) are called the *extremals* of the variational problem. We have then shown that:

> The extremal curves in B are precisely those curves tangent to vector curves in $M = T(B) \times R$ and are characteristic curves of the 2-form ω.

The Second Variation for Extremals of the First Kind

Let us return to the study of general variational problems.

Now let $\phi: N \to M$ be a map on $E(I)$ that is an extremal of the first kind for the canonical variational problem defined by θ and I. Let $t \to \phi_t$ be a deformation of ϕ. We want to compute

$$\frac{d^2}{dt^2} L(\phi_t)\bigg|_{t=0} = \frac{d^2}{dt^2}\int_N \phi_t^*(\theta)\bigg|_{t=0}.$$

This will give us the second variation formula. Now it is clear geometrically that we are not interested in considering deformations for which the infinitesimal deformation $\mathbf{v} \in E_\phi$ is tangent to $\phi(N)$. Suppose then that

$$\mathbf{v}(p) \notin \phi_*(N_p) \qquad \text{for all } p \in N.$$

Then, for sufficiently small t, we can find a vector field $X \in V(M)$ such that
$$t \to \phi_t(p) \text{ is an integral curve of } X.$$

(Strictly speaking, we shall be calculating the second variation for deformations of this type, and then verifying that the result is independent of the actual choice of X.) Then, we can apply (12.1) again to obtain

$$\frac{d}{dt} L(\phi_t) = \int_{\partial N} \phi_t^*(X \lrcorner \theta) + \int_N \phi_t^*(X \lrcorner d\theta).$$

Hence, differentiating again and using (12.1), we have

$$\frac{d^2}{dt^2} L(\phi_t)\bigg|_{t=0} = \int_{\partial N} \phi^*(X \lrcorner d(X \lrcorner \phi)) + \int_N \phi^*(X \lrcorner d(X \lrcorner d\theta)). \quad (12.15)$$

We must now verify that the separation of the second variation formula into the two terms given by (12.15) has an intrinsic geometric meaning, that is, that it is independent of the extension of v to a vector field on M, provided ϕ is an extremal of the first kind and v is transversal to ϕ at the boundary.

Let us deal with the first term, that is, the boundary term. Consider the form

$$(X, Y) \to \phi^*(X \lrcorner d(Y \lrcorner \theta) + B \lrcorner d(X \lrcorner \theta)), \quad (12.16)$$

defined for vector fields that are transversal to the ϕ at the boundary. To show that it depends only on the values of X and Y on $\phi(\partial N)$, it suffices to note what happens when fX is substituted for X, where f is a function on M.

$$(fX, Y) \to \phi^*(f)\phi^*(X \lrcorner \theta) + \phi^*(f)\phi^*(Y \lrcorner d(X \lrcorner \theta))$$
$$+ \phi^*(Y \lrcorner (df \wedge (X \lrcorner \theta))).$$

Working out the third term, we have

$$\phi^*(Yf)\phi^*(X \lrcorner \theta) - \phi^*(df) \wedge \phi^*(Y \lrcorner X \lrcorner \theta).$$

Now, since X is transversal to ϕ at the boundary,

$$\phi^*(X \lrcorner \theta) = 0.$$

If f is constant on the submanifold, $\phi^*(df) = 0$. This shows that the form (12.16) depends only on the values of X and Y in the manifold ϕ.

Let us perform the analogous computation for the form

$$(X, Y) \to \phi^*(X \lrcorner d(Y \lrcorner d\theta) + Y \lrcorner d(X \lrcorner d\theta)). \quad (12.17)$$

Now

$$(fX, Y) \to \phi^*(f)\phi^*(X \lrcorner d(Y \lrcorner d\theta) + Y \lrcorner d(X \lrcorner d\theta))$$
$$+ \phi^*(Y \lrcorner (df \wedge (X \lrcorner d\theta))$$
$$= \phi^*(f)\phi^*(X \lrcorner d(Y \lrcorner d\theta) + Y \lrcorner d(X \lrcorner d\theta)) + \phi^*(Y(f))\phi^*(X \lrcorner d\theta)$$
$$- \phi^*(df) \wedge \phi^*(Y \lrcorner X \lrcorner d\theta).$$

Now $\phi^*(X \lrcorner d\theta) = 0$, since ϕ is an extremal of ω; hence we see again that the form (12.17) depends only on the values of X and Y on the submanifold ϕ.

In summary, we have split up the second variation formula into two terms, one involving integration over ∂N, the other involving integration over N. Both integrands involve first-order differential operators assigning differential forms on ∂N and N to pairs of elements of E_ϕ. (However, if dim $N = 1$, $\phi^*(df) = 0$, indicating that the boundary term depends only on the values of v at the points of ∂N. This is one reason for the simplicity of the 1-independent variable calculus of variations in comparison with the multiple integral problems.)

Finally, we mention another reason to be confident that the second variation formula always takes the form given by (12.15), even when $t \to \phi_t$ is not necessarily of the assumed form. Computation in local coordinates such as can be found, for example, in the classical literature, convinces one that the second variation can be written as the sum of two terms—one involving an integration over N, the other an integration over the boundary—and that each of the terms *depends only on the values of*

$$\mathbf{v} = \frac{\partial}{\partial t} \phi_t \bigg\|_{t=0} \qquad \text{on } N.$$

Hence, in computing $(d^2/dt^2)L(dt)\|_{t=0}$, we can choose *any* deformation $t \to \phi_t$ whose infinitesimal deformation is $\mathbf{v}$: In particular, if $\mathbf{v}$ can be exhibited as being restricted to $\phi(N)$ of a vector field X on M, we can choose ϕ_t as the image under the one-parameter group generated by X.

We shall leave this approach to the calculus of variations and the second variational formula, and turn to more classical material.

13 Hamilton–Jacobi Theory

Classically, Hamilton–Jacobi theory is the study of the formal properties of the solutions of ordinary differential equations of the Hamilton type:

$$\frac{dx_i}{dt} = \frac{\partial H}{\partial y_i}(x(t), y(t), t), \qquad \frac{dy_i}{dt} = -\frac{\partial H}{\partial x_i}(x(t), y(t), t), \qquad (1 \leq i \leq n),$$

and of first-order partial differential equations of the Hamilton–Jacobi type:

$$\frac{\partial S}{\partial t}(x, t) = -H\left(x, \frac{\partial S}{\partial x}, t\right),$$

and of the "duality" between them.

We shall interpret Hamilton–Jacobi theory in the wider sense as the study of the characteristic curves and maximal integral submanifolds of a closed 2-differential form. As we saw in Chapter 12, this leads to the study of extremal curves of simple variational problems.

Let M be a manifold with a 2-differential form ω such that $d\omega = 0$.

Definition

A tangent vector-vector $v \in T(M)$ is a *characteristic vector* for ω if $v \lrcorner \omega = 0$. A vector field $X \in V(M)$ is a *characteristic vector field* if

$$X \lrcorner \omega = 0;$$

that is, if $X(p)$ is a characteristic vector for all $p \in M$. A curve $t \to \sigma(t)$ in M is a *characteristic curve* of ω if $\sigma'(t)$ is a characteristic vector for all t; that is, if $\sigma'(t) \lrcorner \omega(t) = 0$ for all t.

Let us study the algebraic properties of the characteristic vectors at a point $p \in M$. They form a subspace of M_p. Let $v_1, \ldots, v_m$ be a basis for M_p such that $v_1, \ldots, v_n$ form a basis for the characteristic vectors.

Let $\omega_1, \ldots, \omega_m$ be a dual basis for 1-covectors; that is,

$$\omega_i(v_j) = \delta_{ij} \qquad \text{for } 1 \leq i, \ j \leq m.$$

Then

$$\omega = a_{ij} \omega \wedge \omega_j \quad \text{at p.}$$

$$0 = v_a \lrcorner \omega = a_{ij} \omega_i(v_a)\omega_j \qquad \text{for } 1 \leq a \leq n,$$

122

or

$$0 = a_{aj}\omega_j;$$

hence,

$$a_{aj} = 0 \quad \text{or} \quad \omega = \sum_{i,\,j>n} a_{ij}\omega_i \wedge \omega_j.$$

Now the determinant of the matrix $(a_{ij})_{n+1 \le i,\,j \le m}$ must be nonzero. Otherwise there would be a characteristic vector of ω that is a combination of the $v_{n+1}, \ldots, v_n$. But this matrix is real and skew-symmetric; hence its eigenvalues are pure imaginary and come in nonzero complex-conjugate pairs. We conclude that:

$$m - n \text{ is an even number,}$$
$$\text{say, equal to } 2r.$$

Then

$$\omega^r = \det(a_{ij})\omega_{n+1} \wedge \cdots \wedge \omega_m \ne 0.$$

(ω^r means the exterior product of r copies of the 2-covector ω). Also, $\omega^{r+1} = 0$. Summing up, we have proved the following theorem

THEOREM 13.1

The dimension of the space of characteristic vectors at a point $p \in M$ is equal to $m - 2r$, where $m = \dim M$ and r is the greatest integer such that $\omega^r \ne 0$. Suppose $\omega_1, \ldots, \omega_m$ is a basis for covectors at p, and

$$\omega = \sum_{i,\,j=1}^{m} a_{ij}\omega_i \, r\omega_j.$$

Then $2r = $ rank of the matrix $(a_{ij})_{1 \le i,\,j \le m}$.

Now we show how the characteristic vector field and the characteristic curves of ω can be used to construct integral submanifolds for ω.

Definition

A submanifold $\phi: N \to M$ is said to be an *integral* submanifold for ω if $\phi^*(\omega) = 0$; that is, if ω restricted to the submanifold is zero.

Now suppose that $\phi: N \to M$ is an integral submanifold for ω and that $X \in V(M)$ is a characteristic vector field for ω; that is, its integral curves are characteristic curves of ω. For $p \in N$, $t \in R$, define $\delta(p, t)$ by requiring that:

(a) The curve $t \to \phi(p, t)$ is an integral curve of X.
(b) $\delta(p, 0) = \phi(p)$.

In another notation,

$$\delta(p, t) = \exp(tX)\phi(p).$$

Suppose that $\phi(N)$ is small enough so that this can be defined uniformly for $0 \le t \le a$. Then δ defines a map: $N \times [0, a] \to M$. It is a submanifold map (for a and N sufficiently small) if

$$X(\phi(p))\phi^*(N_p) \qquad \text{for all } p \in N,$$

that is, if X is not tangent to $\phi(N)$.

THEOREM 13.2

With these conditions satisfied, δ is an integral submanifold of ω. Geometrically, by passing through each point of the given integral submanifold the integral curve of X starting at that point, we obtain an integral submanifold of one greater dimension passing through the given submanifold.

Proof. The theorem is obviously of a purely local nature. We can suppose that coordinates (x_i), $1 \le i, j \le m$, are chosen so that $X = \partial/\partial x_1$:

$$X(\omega) = X \lrcorner d\omega + d(X \lrcorner \omega) = 0.$$

Suppose that $\omega = a_{ij} dx_i \wedge dx_j$. Then

$$0 = X(a_{ij}) dx_i \wedge dx_j = \frac{\partial a_{ij}}{\partial x_1} dx_i \wedge dx_j;$$

hence,

$$\frac{\partial a_{ij}}{\partial x_1} = 0.$$

Also, $X \lrcorner \omega = 0$; that is, $a_{1j} dx_j = 0$ or $a_{1j} = 0$. Then

$$\omega = \sum_{i, j \ge 2} a_{ij}(x_2, \ldots, x_n) dx_i \wedge dx_j.$$

From the explicit form $X = \partial/\partial x_1$, we see that

$$\delta^*(x_i) = \phi^*(x_i) \qquad \text{for } i \ge 2$$

(since the x_i, $i \ge 2$, remain constant on integral curves of X); hence, obviously,

$$\delta^*(\omega) = \phi^*(\omega) = 0.$$

THEOREM 13.3

Let ω be a closed 2-form on M whose rank is the same at every point of M. Then each point $p \in M$ has a neighborhood U and a coordinate system (y_i), $1 \le i, j, \ldots, \le n$, valid in U such that ω takes the following *canonical form in U*:

$$\omega = dy_1 \wedge dy_2 + \cdots + dy_{r-1} \wedge dy_r.$$

Proof. We proceed by induction on the dimension m of the space M. It is certainly (if vacuously) true for $m = 1$. Suppose, in the original coordinate system (x_i), that

$$\omega = a_{ij}\, dx_i \wedge dx_j.$$

Case 1 (2r < n, where 2r is the rank of ω)

Since the rank is constant, there is at least one nonzero characteristic vector field X. If the coordinate system is changed so that $X = \partial/\partial x_1$, then, as in the proof of Theorem 13.2,

$$\omega = \sum_{i,\, j \geq 2} a_{ij}(x_2, \ldots, x_n)\, dx_i \wedge dx_j;$$

that is, ω is a form in $(n-1)$ variables and the induction hypothesis can be applied.

Case 2 (2r = m)

Then $\det(a_{ij}(p)) \neq 0$. We may suppose, if U is small enough, that $\det(a_{ij}(q)) \neq 0$ for all $q \in U$.

Let f be any function in U such that df is never zero in U. Since the linear equations $a_{ij}(x)\lambda_j = c_i$ can be solved for (λ_j) whatever the (c_i), and the rank is constant when x varies, there is a vector field X in U such that $X \lrcorner \omega = df$.

Suppose that the coordinate system is chosen so that $X = \partial/dx_1$:

$$X(\omega) = X \lrcorner d\omega + d(X \lrcorner \omega)$$

$$= d(df) = 0$$

$$= \frac{\partial a_{ij}}{\partial x_1} dx_1 \wedge dx_j;$$

hence,

$$\frac{\partial a_{ij}}{\partial x_1} = 0.$$

Also, $a_{1j}\, dx_j = \tfrac{1}{2}\, df$; hence

$$\omega = dx_1 \wedge d\left(-\frac{f}{2}\right) + \sum_{i,\, j \geq 2} a_{ij}(x_2, \ldots, x_n)\, dx_i \wedge dx_j.$$

Now

$$0 = X \lrcorner (X \lrcorner d\omega) = X(f) = \frac{\partial f}{\partial x_1}.$$

Hence, by at most changing variables in $(x_2, \ldots, x_m)$ space, we may suppose that $-(f/2) = x_2$; that is,

$$\omega = dx_1 \wedge dx_2 + \sum_{i, j \geq 2} a_{ij}(x_2, \ldots, x_m) \, dx_i \wedge dx_j.$$

Now $\omega' = \sum_{k, j \geq 2} a_{ij} \, dx_i \wedge dx_j$ is closed also. Its rank is everywhere $\leq m - 1$; since m is even, it is $\leq m - 2$. It cannot be less than $m - 2$ at any point, for otherwise the value of ω at that point could be written in terms of at most $(m - 1)$–1-covectors, which would contradict that ω^m is everywhere $\neq 0$. Thus ω' is a form in a space of $(m - 1)$ variables $(x_{2m}, \ldots, x_m)$ always of rank $(m - 2)$. By induction hypotheses, there are $(m - 2)$ functionally independent functions $y_1, \ldots, y_{m-2}$ of the variables $(x_2, \ldots, x_m)$ such that

$$\omega' = dy_1 \wedge dy_2 + \cdots + dy_{m-3} \wedge dy_{m-2}.$$

At no point can dx_2 be written in terms of $dx_1, dy_1, \ldots, dy_{m-2}$, for otherwise ω would not be of rank m at that point. Thus the functions $(x_1, x_2, y_1, \ldots, y_{m-2})$ are such that their differentials $dx_1, dx_2, dy_1, \ldots, dy_{m-2}$ are everywhere linearly independent; hence they form a new coordinate system in which ω obviously has the desired canonical form.   Q.E.D.

Theorem 13.4

Let ω be a closed 2-form on a manifold M. Suppose that ω is of rank $2r$; that is, $\omega_p{}^r \neq 0$ for all $p \in M$, but $\omega^{r+1} = 0$. Then:

(a)   An integral submanifold of ω can at most be of dimension $m - r$. Let us say that an integral submanifold is maximal if it is of dimension $m - r$, that is, if it is of maximal dimension.

(b)   If $\phi : N \to M$ is a maximal integral submanifold of ω, then there is a local coordinate system (x_i), $1 \leq i, j, \ldots, \leq m$, for M such that

$$\omega = \sum_{i=1}^{r} dx_i \wedge dx_{r+i} \, ;$$

that is, ω is in canonical form and $\phi(N)$ is defined locally by $0 = x_1 = \cdots = x_r$.

(c)   If $\phi : N \to M$ is any maximal integral submanifold of ω, then there is a unique vector-field system H on N, with $\dim H_p = n - r$ for all $p \in N$, having the property that if $t \to \sigma_1(t)$ is an integral curve of H, $t \to \phi(\sigma_1(t))$ is a characteristic curve of ω.

Proof.   Let C be the vector-field system on M consisting of the characteristic vector fields of ω; that is

$$C = \{X \in V(M) : X \lrcorner \, \omega = 0\}.$$

Since the dimension of the characteristic vectors of ω at a point is constant on

M, equal to $m - 2r$, C is a nonsingular vector-field system; that is, every point $p \in M$ is a maximal point, and

$$\dim C_p = m - 2r \qquad \text{for all } p \in M.$$

Notice that $[C, C] \subset C$; that is, C is a completely integrable vector-field system. Suppose we first choose the coordinate system (x_i), using the Frobenius integrability theorem, so that the vector fields $(\partial/\partial x_{2r+1}), \ldots, (\partial/\partial x_m)$ are a base for C (possibly making M smaller, of course).

For $X \in C$, $X(\omega) = X \lrcorner d\omega + d(X \lrcorner \omega) = 0$. Suppose then that

$$\omega = a_{ij}\, dx_i \wedge dx_j.$$

Then

$$a_{ij} = 0 \qquad \text{for } i, j \geq 2r + 1,$$

$$\frac{\partial a_{ij}}{\partial x_k} = 0 \qquad \text{for } k \geq 2r + 1, \quad \text{all } i, j.$$

Hence ω can be written as a form in the variables $x_1, \ldots, x_{2r}$; that is,

$$\omega = \sum_{i,\, j \leq 2r} a_{ij}(x_1, \ldots, x_r)\, dx_i \wedge dx_j.$$

This form in r-variables can have no characteristic vectors; hence $\omega^r \neq 0$. By Theorem 13.2, any integral submanifold $\phi: N \to M$ of maximal dimension is obtained locally by taking a maximal integral submanifold of this form in r-variables and "adding" the variables $(x_{r+1}, \ldots, x_m)$ to it. Thus, to prove part (a), it suffices to suppose that $m = 2r$, which we shall proceed to do.

Now, looked at more abstractly, $\phi: N \to M$ is an integral submanifold if and only if

$$\omega_{\phi(p')}(u, v) = 0 \qquad \text{for all } u, v, \in \phi^*(N_{p'}), \quad \text{all } P' \in N.$$

The fact that $m = 2r$, that is, that there are no characteristic vectors, implies that for each $p \in M$, the skew-symmetric bilinear form in M_p—$(u, v) \to \omega_p(u, v)$—is nondegenerate. Hence the fact that $\dim \phi^*(N_p) \leq r$ will follow from the following lemma from linear algebra.

LEMMA 13.5

Let V be a real vector space of dimension $2r$, and let $(u, v) \to \omega(u, v)$ be a nondegenerate skew-symmetric bilinear form on V. Let T be a linear subspace of V such that $\omega(u, v) = 0$ for all $u, v \in T$. Then, $\dim T \leq r$.

Proof. Let $(u, v) \to \langle u, v \rangle$ be any positive-definite symmetric quadratic form on V. For fixed $v \in V$, there must then be a vector $J(v) \in V$ such that

$$\omega(u, v) = \langle u, J(v) \rangle \qquad \text{for all } u \in V.$$

(Since the linear form $u \to \omega(u, v)$ belongs to the dual space of V, and it is known that $\langle\,,\,\rangle$ can be used to set up an isomorphism between V and its dual space.)

Clearly, $v \to J(v)$ is a linear transformation of V into itself that must be an isomorphism, lest ω be degenerate. Suppose dim $T > r + 1$. Then $T \cap J(T)$ would be a nonzero subspace of V; say $v \in T \cap J(T)$, $v \neq 0$, and $v = J(u)$, for some $u \in T$. Then

$$0 \neq \langle v, v \rangle = \langle v, j(u) \rangle$$

$$= \omega(v, u) = 0, \qquad \text{contradiction.} \qquad \text{Q.E.D.}$$

Turn to (b) now. In a similar way as in (a), it suffices to prove (b) in case $m = 2r$; that is, there are no characteristics. We proceed in a way very similar to that used in the proof of Theorem 13.3, by induction on m. Suppose that f is a function on M such that $f = 0$ on $\phi(N)$, but that $df \neq 0$ in M (if necessary making M smaller). As in the proof of Theorem 13.3, there is a vector field X such that $X \lrcorner \omega = df$; hence $X(\omega) = 0$. Choose the coordinate system for X so that $X = \partial/\partial x_1$. If $\omega = a_{ij}\, dx_1 \wedge dx_j$,

$$\frac{\partial a_{ij}}{\partial x_1} = 0, \qquad a_{1j}\, dx_j = \frac{f}{2};$$

hence,

$$\omega = dx_1 \wedge d\left(-\frac{f}{2}\right) + \sum_{i,\, j \geq 2} a_{ij}\, dx_i \wedge dx_j.$$

As before, we can suppose that $x_2 - (-(f/2)$; hence

$$\omega = dx_1 \wedge ds_2 + \sum_{i,\, j \geq 2} a_{ij}\, dx_i \wedge dx_j.$$

Now $\phi^*(x_2) = 0 = \phi^*(f)$, by construction; hence ϕ is also an integral submanifold of the form $\sum_{i,\, j \geq 2} a_{ij}\, dx_i \wedge dx_j$. As in the proof of Theorem 13.3, this form must everywhere in M have rank $m - 2$; hence the induction hypothesis may be applied.

Part (c) now follows from (b): For if

$$\omega = \sum_{i=1}^{r} dx_i \wedge dx_{r+i'},$$

with $x_{r+1} = 0 = \cdots = x_m$ defining $\phi(N)$ locally, then the vector fields $(\partial/\partial x_{2r+1}), \ldots, (\partial/\partial x_m)$ span C, the characteristic vector-field system of ω. Now, by inspection, the vector fields $(\partial/\partial x_{2r+1}), \ldots, (\partial/\partial x_m)$ are *tangent* to the submanifold $x_{r+1} = 0 = \cdots = x_{2n}$; that is, their integral curves starting at one point of the submanifold remain on the submanifold. Abstractly, this means that

$$C_{\phi(p)} \subset \phi_*(N_{p'}) \qquad \text{for all } p \in N.$$

C "by restriction" defines the vector-field system H on N' required for the proof of (c).

THEOREM 13.6

Let ω be a closed 2-form on the manifold M, and let θ be a 1-form such that $d\theta = \omega$. Suppose that $\phi: N \to M$ is a submanifold of M that is also an integral submanifold of θ, that is, $\phi^*(\theta) = 0$.

Let X be a characteristic vector field of ω that is not tangent to $\phi(N)$ at any point, and such that

$$X(\theta) = f\theta \quad \text{for some } f \in F(M).$$

Let $\delta: N \times [0, a]$ be the submanifold map constructed above; that is, for fixed p, $t \to \delta(p, t)$ is an integral curve of X, reducing to $\phi(p)$ at $t = 0$. Let ϕ_t be the submanifold map: $p \to \delta(p, t) = \phi_t(p)$. Then:

(a) δ is an integral submanifold of ω.
(b) For each t, ϕ_t is an integral submanifold of θ.

Proof. (b) is a consequence of Theorem 13.2, since ϕ is also, of course, an integral submanifold of ω. Now $X(\theta) = X \lrcorner d\theta + d(X(\theta)) + d(X(\theta))$, since X is characteristic $d\theta$. It suffices to prove (b) locally: We can then suppose that the coordinate system (x_i), $1 \le i, j, \ldots, \le n$, has been chosen so that $X = \partial/\partial x_1$. Then there exists a $g \in F(M)$ such that $X(g\theta) = 0$ and such that g is everywhere $\ne 0$. For g must satisfy

$$\frac{\partial g}{\partial x_1} \theta + gf\theta = 0 \quad \text{or} \quad \frac{\partial g}{\partial x_1} + gf = 0,$$

and it is evident that (locally) such a g can be found. Suppose $g\theta = a_i \, dx_i$. Hence $\partial a_i/\partial x_1 = 0$. We see, using the explicit form of the integral curves of X, that $\phi_t^*(x_i) = \phi^*(x_i)$ for $i > 1$,

$$\phi_t^*(x_1) = \phi^*(x_1) + t.$$

Thus, holding t constant,

$$\phi_t^*(g\theta) = \phi_t^*(a_i(x_2, \ldots, x_n)) \, d(\phi_t^*(x_i))$$

$$= a_1(x_2, \ldots, x_n) \, d(x_1 + t)$$

$$+ \sum_{i \geq 1} a_i(x_2, \ldots, x_n) \, dx_i$$

$$= \phi^*(g\theta) = 0. \qquad \text{Q.E.D.}$$

Now we shall indicate the relation of this general theory to Hamilton–Jacobi theory in the usual sense, namely, the study of the Hamilton ordinary differential equations and the Hamilton–Jacobi partial differential equations.

We change notations: M will be a domain in R^{2n+1}, $1 \leq i, j, \ldots, \leq n$. A point of M will be denoted by (x, y, t), $x = (x_i)$, $y = (y_i)$. In physical problems, the x_i are coordinates of configuration space, the y_i the coordinates of momentum space, t the coordinate of time. (The reader will more frequently in physics books see x and y replaced respectively by q and p.) Suppose that $H(x, y, t)$ is a real-valued function on M. A closed 2-form ω in M is said to be in *Hamiltonian form* with *Hamiltonian H* if

$$d\omega = dy_i \wedge dx_i - dH \wedge dt.$$

The following special notation is useful in the computations in Hamilton–Jacobi theory and the calculus of variations:

$$H_i(x, y, t) = \frac{\partial H}{\partial x_i}(x, y, t), \qquad H_{n+i} = \frac{\partial H}{\partial y_i}, \qquad H_t = \frac{\partial H}{\partial t},$$

$$H_{i, j} = \frac{\partial^2 H}{\partial x_i \, \partial x_j}, \qquad H_{i, n+j} = \frac{\partial^2 H}{\partial y_j \, \partial x_i}, \qquad \text{etc.}$$

Thus,

$$dH = H_i \, dx_i + H_{n+i} \, dy_i + H_t \, dt.$$

THEOREM 13.7

Let ω be the 2-form given by

$$\omega = dy_i \wedge dx_i - dH \wedge dt.$$

Then:

(a)   Rank $\omega = 2n$, dimension of characteristic vectors $= 1$.
(b)   There is exactly one characteristic vector field X such that $X(t) = 1$, namely,

$$X = \frac{\partial}{\partial t} + H_{n+i} \frac{\partial}{\partial x_i} - H_i \frac{\partial}{\partial y_i}. \tag{13.1}$$

X also satisfies: $X(H) = H_t$.

(c)   A curve in M that is a characteristic curve of X can be written in the form $(t, x(t), y(t))$. The functions $x(t)$, $y(t)$ are determined as solutions of the Hamilton equations with Hamiltonian H:

$$\frac{dx_i(t)}{dt} = H_{n+i}(x(t), y(t), t); \qquad \frac{dy_i(t)}{dt} = -H_n(x(t), y(t), t). \tag{13.2}$$

Proof.   Suppose $v \in T(M)$ is a nonzero tangent vector to M that is a characteristic tangent vector to ω. Then

$$0 = v \lrcorner \omega = v(y_i) \, dx_i - v(x_i) \, dy_i - v(H) \, dt + v(t)(H_i \, dx_i + H_{n+i} \, dy_i + H_t \, dt).$$

First we must have $v(t) \neq 0$: for otherwise, $0 = v(y_i) = v(x_i)$; hence v is identically zero.

Thus v can be normalized so that $v(t) = 1$; hence

$$v(y_i) = -H_i, \qquad v(x_i) = H_{n+i},$$

that is, v is uniquely determined; hence the space of characteristic vectors is one-dimensional. Working backward, we see that (13.1) provides an everywhere $\neq 0$ characteristic vector field. That (13.2) gives the integral curves of X follows, of course, from the very definition for vector field.

Now, we turn to a similar geometric interpretation of the *Hamilton–Jacobi partial differential equation* with Hamiltonian H:

$$\frac{\partial S}{\partial t} + H\left(x_i, \frac{\partial S}{\partial x_i}, t\right) = 0$$

and to an explanation of the "duality" between this single equation and the Hamilton system (13.2).

THEOREM 13.8

Let ω be the 2-form $dy_i \wedge dx_i - dH \wedge dt$. Suppose, for simplicity, that H is defined over all (x, y, t)-space so that ω is defined over all of R^{2n+1}. Let $\pi: R^{2n+1} \to R^{n+1}$ be the projection map of (x, y, t) on (x, t). Let D be a convex domain of R^{n+1}, and $S(x, t)$ a function defined on D. Associate with D the map: $\phi_S: D \to R^{2n+1}$, defined as follows:

$$\phi_S(x, t) = \left(x_i, \frac{\partial S}{\partial x_i}, t\right).$$

(Thus $\phi_S^*(x_i) = x_i$, $\phi_S^*(y_i) = \partial S/\partial x_i$, $\phi_S^*(t) = t$.) Then

(a) $\phi_S^*(\omega) = 0$; that is, ϕ_S is an integral submanifold of ω if

$$\frac{\partial S}{\partial t} + H\left(x, \frac{\partial S}{\partial x}, t\right) = 0; \tag{13.3}$$

that is, $S(x, t)$ is a solution of the Hamilton–Jacobi partial differential equation.

(b) Conversely, any map $\phi: D \to R^{2n+1}$ that is a cross-section map for π, that is, satisfies $\pi\phi = $ identity, and that is an integral submanifold of ω arises in this way as ϕ_S for some function S on D that is a solution of (13.3).

(c) If $S(x, t)$ is a solution of (13.3) defined in D, consider the vector field

$$Y = \frac{\partial}{\partial t} + H_{n+i}\left(x, \frac{\partial S}{\partial x}, t\right)\frac{\partial}{\partial x_i}$$

$$= \frac{\partial}{\partial t} + \phi_S^*(H_{n+i})\frac{\partial}{\partial x_i}. \tag{13.4}$$

The integral curves of Y are of the form $(t, x(t))$, where $x(t)$ is a solution of the system of ordinary differential equations:

$$\frac{dx_i}{dt} = H_{n+i}\left(x(t), \frac{\partial S}{\partial x}(x(t), t\right).$$ (13.5)

Each of these integral curves is the projection under π of a characteristic curve of ω.† Explicitly, for a solution $x(t)$ of (13.5), the curve $t \to (x(t), y_i(t) = (\partial S/\partial x_i)(x(t), t), t)$ is a characteristic curve of ω, that is, is a solution of the Hamilton equations. Equivalently, we may say that ϕ maps every integral curve of Y into an integral curve of X.

Proof. Let $\theta = y_i \, dx_i - H \, dt$. Then

$$\phi_S{}^*(\theta) = \phi_S{}^*(y_i) \, d\phi_S{}^*(x_i) - \phi_S{}^*(H) \, d\phi_S{}^*(t)$$

$$= \frac{\partial S}{\partial x_i} \, dx_i - \phi_S{}^*(H) \, dt$$

$$= dS - \left(\frac{\partial S}{\partial t} + \phi_S{}^*(H)\right) dt.$$

Thus, if S is a solution of (13.3), that is, $(\partial S/\partial t) + \phi_S{}^*(H) = 0$, then

$$\phi_S{}^*(d\theta) = d \, dS = 0.$$

This proves (a). Conversely, suppose that $\phi: D \to R^{2n+1}$ is a cross-section map such that $\phi^*(\omega) = 0$. Now $\omega = d\theta$; hence

$$d(\phi^*(\theta)) = 0.$$

Suppose $S(x, t)$ is a function on D such that

$$dS = \phi^*(\theta) = \phi^*(y_i) \, dx_i - \phi^*(H) \, dt.$$

(Since a cross-section map: $D \to R^{2n+1}$ is characterized by the conditions $\phi^*(x_i) = x_i$, $\phi^*(t) = t$); hence: $\phi^*(y_i) = \partial S/\partial x_i$, that is, $\phi = \phi_S$. This proves (b).

Turn to (c) and note that

$$0 = X \lrcorner \omega = X \lrcorner \, d\theta = X(\theta).$$

Since proving (c) involves a general relation between mappings and vector fields, it is worth our while to put down the general condition.

---

† For the Hamiltonians arising from the calculus of variations, the integral curves of Y form what is known as an "extremal field."

Lemma 13.9

Let $\alpha: M \to M'$ be a mapping between manifolds. Let X and X' be vector fields on, respectively, M and M'. Then α maps every integral curve of X into an integral curve of X' if and only if

$$\alpha^*(X(f)) = X\alpha^*(f) \qquad \text{for all } f \in F(M'), \qquad (13.6a)$$

or

$$\alpha_*(X(p)) = X(\alpha(p)) \qquad \text{for all } p \in M. \qquad (13.6b)$$

Proof. Suppose $\sigma(t)$, $0 \le t \le b$, is an integral curve of $\sigma_1(t) = \alpha\sigma(t)$. Then, $\sigma_1'(t) = X(\sigma_1(t))$; that is, for $f \in F(M')$,

$$\frac{d}{dt} f(\sigma_1(t)) = X(\sigma_1(t))(f) = X(f)(\sigma_1(t)).$$

But

$$\frac{d}{dt} f(\sigma_1(t)) = \frac{d}{dt} f(\alpha\sigma(t)) = \frac{d}{dt} \alpha^*(f)(\sigma(t))$$

$$= \sigma'(t)(\alpha^*(f)) = X'(\sigma(t))(\alpha^*(f))$$

$$= X(\alpha^*(f))(\sigma(t)).$$

$$X(f)(\sigma_1(t)) = X(f)(\alpha\sigma(t)) = \alpha^*(X(f))(\sigma(t)).$$

Since $\sigma(0)$ can be any point of M, we get condition (b), and also condition (a), as

$$X(\alpha^*(f))(p) = \alpha^*(X(f))(p) \qquad \text{for all } p \in M.$$

The steps we have gone through are reversible, to prove the converse.

Q.E.D.

Returning to X given by (13.1) and Y given by (13.4), we verify the condition (13.6) (it suffices to verify (13.6) when f varies over any basis for the functions):

$$\phi_S^*(X(x_i)) = \phi_S^*(H_{n+i}) = \phi_S^* Y(x_i) = Y(\phi_S^*(x_i)).$$

$$Y(\phi_S^*(y_i)) = Y\left(\frac{\partial S}{\partial x_i}\right)$$

$$= \frac{\partial^2 S}{\partial t \, \partial x_i} + \phi_S^*(H_{n+j}) \frac{\partial^2 S}{\partial x_i \, \partial y_i}$$

$$= \frac{\partial}{\partial x_i} \left(-H\left(x, \frac{\partial S}{\partial x}, t\right)\right) + \phi_S^*(H_{n+i}) \frac{\partial^2 S}{\partial x_i \, \partial x_j}$$

(using the fact that S satisfies (13.3))

$$= -H_i\left(x, \frac{\partial S}{\partial x}, t\right) - H_{n+j}\left(x, \frac{\partial S}{\partial x}, t\right) \frac{\partial^2 S}{\partial x_i \, \partial x_j}$$

$$+ H_{n+j}\left(x, \frac{\partial S}{\partial x}, t\right) \frac{\partial^2 S}{\partial x_j \, \partial x_i}$$

$$= -\phi_S^*(H_i) = \phi_S^*(X(x_i)).$$

$$\phi_S^*(X(t)) = \phi_S^*(1) = 1 = Y(t) = Y(\phi_S^*(t)). \qquad \text{Q.E.D.}$$

Let us now turn to the problem of actually solving the Hamilton–Jacobi equation

$$\frac{\partial S}{\partial t} + H\left(x, \frac{\partial S}{\partial x}, t\right) = 0. \tag{13.7}$$

THEOREM 13.10

Suppose that the domain $D \subset R^{2n+1}$ is sufficiently small, that $S^0(x)$ is a function defined in a domain D' of R^n (that is, x-space) such that the point $(x, y = (\partial S^0/\partial x_i)(x), \ t = 0)$ belongs to D whenever $x \in D'$. Then, if D is sufficiently small, there exists an $a > 0$ and a unique solution $S(x, t)$ of (13.7), defined for $x \in D', \ 0 \le t \le a$, such that

$$S(x, 0) = S^0(x).$$

Further, for $x^0 \in D$, let $(x(t), y(t)), \ 0 \le t \le a$, be the solution of the Hamilton equations:

$$\frac{dx_i}{dt} = H_{n+i}(x, y, t), \qquad \frac{dy_i}{dt} = -H_i(x, y, t), \tag{13.8}$$

with $x(0) = x^0, \ y(0) = (\partial S^0/\partial x_i)(x^0)$. Then $(x(t), y(t))$ must also satisfy

$$\frac{dx_i}{di} = H_{n+i}\left(x(t), \frac{\partial S}{\partial x}(x(t), t)\right), \qquad y_i(t) = \frac{\partial S}{\partial x_i}(x(t), t). \tag{13.9}$$

That is, $t \to (x(t), t)$ is an integral curve of the vector field defined by (13.4) on (x, t)-space. For $T \in [0, a]$,

$$S(x(T), T) = S^0(x^0) + \int_0^T \left[y_i(t) \frac{dx_i(t)}{dt} - H(x(t), y(x), t) \right] dt. \tag{13.10}$$

Proof. This theorem is really nothing more than a realization of Theorem 13.2. Let ϕ^0 be the mapping $D' \to D$ that assigns $(x, y = ((\partial S/\partial x_i)(x), 0))$ to $x \in D'$. Then

$$\phi^{0*}(y_i \, dx_i - H \, dt) = \frac{\partial S}{\partial x_i} \, dx_i = dS;$$

hence ϕ^0 defines D' as an integral submanifold of the 2-form

$$\omega = dy_i \wedge dx_i - dH \wedge dt.$$

We have seen that the characteristic curves of ω are essentially defined as the solutions of the Hamilton equations (13.9). By Theorem 13.2 there is an integral submanifold $\delta \colon D' \times [0, a] \to D$ such that $\delta(x, 0) = \phi^0(x)$ for $x \in D'$, and such that for each $x^0 \in D$, $t \to \delta(x^0, t)$ is a characteristic curve of ω.

Let $p \colon D \to R^{n+1}$ be the "standard" projection that assigns (x, t) to the point $(x, y, t) \in D$. Consider the map $p\delta \colon D' \times [0, a] \to R^{n+1}$. If a is sufficiently small, this map has nonzero Jacobian. Suppose D' and a are chosen small enough so that there is a domain $D'' \subset R^{n+1}$ and an inverse map $(p\delta)^{-1} \colon D'' \to D' \times [0, a]$. Let $\phi = \delta(p\delta)^{-1}$, a map $D'' \to R^{2n+1}$. Then

$$p\phi = p\delta(p\delta)^{-1} = \text{identity map};$$

that is, ϕ is a cross section map $D'' \to R^{2n+1}$, and is an integral submanifold of ω. Then $d\phi^*(y_i \, dx_i - H \, dt) = 0$; hence

$$\phi^*(y_i) \, dx_i - \phi^*(H) \, dt = dS \qquad (13.11)$$

for some function $S(x, t)$ defined for $(x, t) \in D''$. ($\phi^*(x_i) = x_i$ and $\phi^*(t) = t$ because of the cross section property of ϕ; that is, $p\phi = $ identity map.) Thus

$$\frac{\partial S}{\partial x_i} = \phi^*(y_i), \qquad \frac{\partial S}{\partial t}(x, t) = -H(\phi(x, t)) = -H\left(x, \frac{\partial S}{\partial x_i}(x, t), t\right);$$

that is, S satisfies the Hamilton–Jacobi equation. We now show that $S(x, 0) = S^0(x) + \text{constant}$. We see that $\phi(x, 0) = \phi^0(x)$. Thus

$$d(S(x) - S^0(x)) = 0.$$

We have already seen in Theorem 13.7 that (13.9) does define a characteristic curve of ω starting at $(x^0, y(0) = ((\partial S/\partial x_i)(x^0)), 0) = \phi^0(x^0)$; hence it must agree with the curve $t \to \delta(x^0, t)$.

Finally we prove (13.10). By (13.11),

$$S(x(T), T) - S(x(0), 0) = \int_0^T \left[\frac{d}{dt} S(x(t), t)\right] dt$$

$$= \int_0^T \left[\phi^*(y_i)(x(t), t)\frac{dx_i}{dt} - \phi^*(H)(x(t), t)\right] dt$$

$$= \int_0^T \left[y_i(t)\frac{dx_i}{dt} - H(x(t), y(t), t)\right] dt. \qquad \text{Q.E.D.}$$

Equation (13.10) has an interpretation in terms of the "action" that has a certain importance in physics. In general, if $(x(t), y(t))$, $0 \le t \le T$, is a curve in (x, y)-space, the number

$$\int_0^T \left[y_i(t) \frac{dx_i}{dt} - H(x(t), y(t), t) \right] dt \qquad (13.12)$$

is called the *action* along the curve. In problems in mechanics, $x_i(t)$ and $y_i(t)$ describe, respectively, how the position and momentum coordinates of a particle (or system of particles) changes in time. The function H gives the value of the energy, so that (13.12) assigns a definite number to each possible trajectory of the physical system. The "principle of least action" requires that the trajectory actually followed is one that minimizes this value of the action. It is easily seen that these curves are contained among the solutions of the Hamilton equations (13.8). In quantum mechanics (according to the viewpoint of Feynman) there is a "smearing out" of this one definite trajectory that minimizes the action, and possible trajectories are given weights determined by the action, and by Planck's constant h, in such a way that as $h \to 0$, this "smearing" peaks up to concentrate at the one definite minimizing trajectory. This would give a marvelously geometric picture of the "correspondence principle" (that is, of the sense in which quantum mechanics reduces to classical mechanics as Planck's constant goes to zero) if Feynman's ideas could be made more rigorous.

This finishes our discussion of the part of Hamilton–Jacobi theory that can be stated in terms of precise theorems. Much more material, harder to formulate as theorems, has been developed in the long history of the subject. This is mainly motivated by the role that Hamilton–Jacobi theory has played in physical applications, particularly in celestial mechanics, geometrical optics, and in the foundations of quantum mechanics. It is almost an obligatory task for anyone interested in these physical applications to read this supplementary material. We shall limit ourselves here to several remarks that fit in particularly well with the differential-form point of view.

First we ask what is meant by "solving" the Hamilton equations. We have seen in Part 1 that "solving" a system of ordinary differential equations may be interpreted geometrically as finding a change of coordinates so that the vector field whose integral curves solve the differential equations is in these new coordinates a vector field whose integral curves are in some sense "known." We can make a similar interpretation of the problem of "solving" the Hamilton equations.

Suppose that $\omega = dy_i \wedge dx_i - dH \wedge dt$. If a new coordinate system (x_i', y_i', t') can be found so that

$$\omega = dy_i' \wedge dx_i', \qquad (13.13)$$

we can say that ω is in *canonical form* in the coordinate system. Since ω

remains the same, the characteristic curves of ω are geometrically the same, but the coordinates of these curves in the " new " coordinate system satisfy the Hamilton equations with Hamiltonian *zero*. That is, the (x_i', y_i') are constant along the integral curves; hence, when expressed in terms of the " old " coordinates, they are a set of $2n$ functionally independent integral functions of the original Hamilton equations. Hence these original Hamilton equations can be regarded as " solved." We can then say that solving them is more or less equivalent to throwing ω into canonical form.

In Theorem 13.3 we have one method for writing ω in canonical form. However, this is not a really practical method for doing so: For example, it applies to any 2-form of constant rank and does not really take advantage of the fact that ω is initially in a relatively simple form. There is another method, due to Jacobi, for doing this. This method works by solving the Hamilton–Jacobi partial differential equation and that seems particularly well adapted (at least as well as anything else) to the equations of celestial mechanics, particularly the 2-body problem. We now explain this method.

We have seen that a single solution $S(x, t)$ of

$$\frac{\partial S}{\partial t} + H\left(x, \frac{\partial S}{\partial x}, t\right) = 0 \tag{13.14}$$

determines an n-parameter family of solutions of the Hamilton equations, obtained by finding the integral curves of the vector field

$$\frac{\partial}{\partial t} + H_{n+i}\left(x, \frac{\partial S}{\partial x}, t\right)\frac{\partial}{\partial x_i}$$

in (x, t)-space. Thus an n-parameter family $S(x, t; a_1, \ldots, a_n)$ of solutions of (13.4) that depends " essentially " on the parameters, that is, satisfies

$$\det\left(\frac{\partial S}{\partial x_i \, \partial a_j}\right) \neq 0, \tag{13.15}$$

should in principle determine the full $2n$-parameter family of solutions of the Hamilton equations. An n-parameter family of solutions of (13.14) satisfying (13.15) is called a *complete solution* of (13.14). Jacobi's trick consists in the observation that, given a complete solution, the reduction of ω to canonical form can be made directly without solving any differential equations, as follows:

Introduce a " new " space R^{4n+1} of variables (x, y, t, a, b), $a = (a_i)$, $b = (b_i)$, etc. Consider the form

$$\Omega = dy_i \wedge dx_i - dH \wedge dt + db_i \wedge da_i$$
$$= d(y_i \, dx_i - H \, dt + b_i \, da_i).$$

Consider $S(x, t; a)$ as a function of *all* the indicated $2n + 1$ variables. Then

$$dS(x, t; a) = \frac{\partial S}{\partial x_i}\, dx_i + \frac{\partial S}{\partial t}\, dt + \frac{\partial S}{\partial a_i}\, da_i$$

$$= \frac{\partial S}{\partial x_i}\, dx_i - H\left(x, \frac{\partial S}{\partial x}, t\right) dt + \frac{\partial S}{\partial a_i}\, da_i.$$

Consider the submanifold defined by the relations

$$y_i - \frac{\partial S}{\partial x_i} = 0, \qquad b_i - \frac{\partial S}{\partial a_i} = 0. \qquad (13.16)$$

Notice first that the differentials of the functions on the left-hand side of relations (13.16) are everywhere linearly independent; hence the relations do define a bonafide $2n + 1$-dimensional submanifold of R^{4n+1}.

We next show that the projection of this submanifold on (x, y, t)-space has nonzero Jacobian. For this it suffices to show that every form on the submanifold can be written in terms of the dx_i, dy_i, and dt.† Clearly, this is an integral submanifold of Ω. Now, on the submanifold,

$$db_i = \frac{\partial^2 S}{\partial x_j\, \partial a_i}\, dx_j + \frac{\partial^2 S}{\partial a_i\, \partial t}\, dt + \frac{\partial^2 S}{\partial a_i\, \partial a_j}\, da_j,$$

$$dy_1 = \frac{\partial^2 S}{\partial x_i\, \partial a_j}\, da_j + \frac{\partial^2 S}{\partial x_i\, \partial x_j}\, dx_j + \frac{\partial^2 S}{\partial x_i\, \partial t}\, dt.$$

By (13.15), da_i can be restricted to the submanifold, then be expressed in terms of dy and dx, and thus so can db_i. This shows that the projection on (x, y, t)-space has nonzero Jacobian.

Then, locally, the submanifold defined by (13.16) can be written as the graph of a mapping $\phi : (x, y, t) \rightarrow (a(x, y, t))$ of $R^{2n+1} \rightarrow R^{2n}$. We have

$$\phi^*(da_i \wedge db_i) = \omega;$$

hence ϕ is the required mapping, sending ω into canonical form (if a_i and b_i are redefined as x_i', y_i').

Of course one point to all this is that (at least for some of the Hamiltonians occurring in the simpler problems of classical mechanics) a complete solution

---

† If $\phi : V \rightarrow V'$ is a linear transformation between vector spaces of the same dimension, to prove that ϕ is an isomorphism it suffices to prove that the dual map ϕ^* of linear forms: $V'^* \rightarrow V^*$ is *onto*.

of the Hamilton–Jacobi equation can be found (after a possible change in variables of x-space) in the additive form

$$S(x_1, \ldots, x_n; a_1, \ldots, a_n) = S_1(x_1, a_1) + \cdots + S_n(x_n, a_n)$$

by the method of separation of variables, so useful in elementary theoretical physics. However, the Hamilton–Jacobi equation is highly nonlinear, and solutions of this type seem to be even more accidental than are the solutions that can be obtained from the usual *linear* partial differential equations of theoretical physics.

Our second remark is concerned with "perturbation theory" in the special sense that it is used in celestial mechanics. However, a few remarks about perturbation theory in general might be in order.

Let D be a domain in an R^n, and let X be a vector field in D. Let X^ε be a one-parameter family of vector fields in D reducing to X when $\varepsilon = 0$. Suppose also that, for simplicity, the coefficients of X^ε depend on ε in a real analytic way. The simplest example would be $X^\varepsilon = X + \varepsilon Y$, where Y is another vector field. In general, "perturbation theory" is concerned with studying how the integral curves of X^ε are related to those of X as $\varepsilon \to 0$. In terms of the nineteenth century, pre-Poincaré view of differential equations, this was a purely computational problem, limited only by one's ability to compute formal expansions in ε. Research since Poincaré has shown that this is a hopelessly naive view. (It is of a different order of difficulty, for example, from the results in divergent series; modern research has shown here that, by and large, the formal classical work can be cleaned up.) Existence theorems for the type of expansions one is trying to find must be proved and are usually quite difficult, at least for physically realistic situations.

The typical problem of this type is that of perturbing periodic integral curves. An integral curve $\sigma(t)$, $-\infty < t < \infty$, is periodic or closed with period T if $\sigma(t + T) = \sigma(t)$ for all t. It suffices, in view of the uniqueness theorem for integral curves, to show that $\sigma(T) = \sigma(0)$ (but $\sigma(t) \neq \sigma(0)$ for $0 < t < T$). Given such a periodic integral curve, does there exist a periodic curve σ_ε with period $T(\varepsilon)$ for ε sufficiently close to 0, reducing to the σ and T as $\varepsilon \to 0$?

Let us return now to Hamilton–Jacobi theory. Suppose we have a one-parameter family of Hamiltonian functions, say, $H(x, y, t) = H^0(x, y, t) + \varepsilon H^1(x, y, t)$. Suppose the Hamilton equations with Hamiltonian H^0 can be "solved," say by the method of Jacobi given above, and H^1 is regarded as a "small" perturbing "energy" applied to the "known" system with Hamiltonian H^0. The typical example in celestial mechanics is that where H^0 describes the motion of the sun and earth, the "solvable" 2-body problem, and where H^1 describes the perturbation on the earth, by, say, Venus. (Or, to be modern, replace sun by earth, earth by satellite, Venus by the Moon.) Intuitively, the effect can be visualized as a " slow " change in the elliptical orbit of the earth, that is, the "parameters" describing the orbit that would be constant were there no perturbation to change slowly with time.

Analytically, this can be interpreted as follows:

$$dy_i \wedge dx_i - dH \wedge dt = (dy_i \wedge dx_i - dH^0 \wedge dt) + dH^1 \wedge dt.$$

Being able to solve the system with Hamiltonian H^0 means that we can find functions (x_i', y_i') on (x, y, t)-space such that

$$dy_i \wedge dx_i - dH^0 \wedge dt = dy_i' \wedge dx_i'.$$

Now (x_i', y_i', t) forms a new coordinate system; for, holding $t = $ constant, we have $dy_i' \wedge dx_i' = dy_i \wedge dx_i$; hence the Jacobian, for fixed t, of the map going from (x, y) to $(x'(x, y, t), y'(x, y, t))$ is 1. Thus

$$dy_i \wedge dx_i - dH \wedge dt = dy_i' \wedge dx_i' + dH^1 \wedge dt.$$

When H^1 is expressed as a function of the new coordinates, the characteristic curves of the form, that is, the Hamilton equations with " total " Hamiltonian H, are described by Hamilton equations in the primed coordinates with Hamiltonian H^1: The effects of the unperturbed system have been completely taken into account, and the variations of the "constants" (x_i', y_i') of the unperturbed motion due to the " perturbation " H^1 are very simply taken into account.

Our third topic will be to discuss in more generality some of the underlying "transformation" properties of the Hamilton equations that we have used in the first two topics. Suppose, then, that we are given two separate systems. Consider two spaces of variables (x_i, y_i, t) and (x_i', y_i', t') with Hamiltonians H and H' given on both. A mapping ϕ from unprimed to the primed space such that

$$\phi^*(dy_i' \wedge dx_i' - dH' \wedge dt') = dy_i \wedge dx_i - dH \wedge dt \qquad (13.17)$$

will have the following property:

> Given a curve $(x(t), y(t))$ in unprimed space (that is, solutions of the Hamiltonian H), the image curve $\phi(x(t), y(t))$ will, after reparametrization by the level surface of the function t', be a solution of the Hamilton equations with Hamiltonian H'.

Thus a ϕ satisfying (13.17) sets up a correspondence between solutions of the two Hamilton equations; however, the sense of "time" may not be preserved in this transformation, and the Hamiltonian H' may bear a quite complicated relation to H.

Now, clearly of special importance in all this are the transformations of (x, y) to (x', y')-space above, such that

$$\phi^*(dy_i' \wedge dx_i') = dy_i \wedge dx_i. \tag{13.18}$$

Such a transformation is called a *canonical transformation*. If $H'(x', y', t)$ and $H(x, y, t)$ are functions such that $\phi^*(H') = H$, by (13.18) ϕ carries solutions of the Hamilton equations with Hamiltonian H into solutions for the Hamiltonian H'. If we regard ϕ as a mapping of the same space onto itself, the canonical transformation with an inverse† forms a group. This group may be regarded as permuting the Hamiltonian systems. In classical language, a Hamiltonian system of ordinary differential equations is a Lie system with respect to the group of canonical transformations (just as a linear system of differential equations defined by a vector field of the form

$$X = \frac{\partial}{\partial t} + A_{ij}(t)x_j \frac{\partial}{\partial x_i}, \qquad 1 \le i, j, \ldots, \le n,$$

is a Lie system with respect to the group of all transformations of (x, t)-space of the form $(x, t) \rightarrow (a(t)x, t)$, where $a(t) = (a_{ij}(t))$ is an $n \times n$ matrix function of t).

We defer further study of the group of canonical transformations until later.

Exercises

1. Work out the solution of the Hamilton–Jacobi equation for the case where $H(x, y)$ is of the form: $\frac{1}{2}y_i y_i + V(r)$ with $r^2 = x_i x_i$, $(1 \le i \le 3)$.

Work out the solution of the Kepler problem in the celestial mechanics (that is, the case $V(r) = 1/r$) in as complete a form as possible.

2. Let $H(x, y)$, $H'(x, y)$ be two Hamiltonians. Show by means of Jacobi's "complete solution" method that locally there is a canonical transformation taking one into the other. If, for example, H' is a function of y alone, discuss what this means for the problem of "solving" the Hamilton equations for Hamiltonian H. Can you think of any "global" reasons why this canonical transformation may not exist globally? For example, discuss the Kepler problem from this global point of view. Also, discuss globally the simple case where x and y are one-dimensional vectors.

---

† Since $\phi^*(dx_i' \wedge dy_i' \wedge \cdots \wedge dx_n') = dx_i \wedge dy_i \wedge \cdots \wedge dy_n$, a canonical transformation always has Jacobian equal to 1; hence it has at least a local inverse.

14 Extremal Fields
and Sufficient Conditions for a Minimum

Let B be a manifold. We have said that a *Lagrangian* for B is a real-valued function $L: T(B) \times R \to R$, which enables us to define a real-valued function

$$\sigma \to L(\sigma) = \int_0^1 L(\sigma'(t), t)\, dt$$

on the space of curves of B. For theoretical purposes, it is most convenient to study *homogeneous, time-independent* Lagrangians. This means that

$$L \text{ is a function } L(v) \text{ of } v \in T(B) \text{ alone;} \qquad (14.1a)$$

$$L(\lambda v) = \lambda L(v) \qquad \text{for } \lambda > 0. \qquad (14.1b)$$

Condition (14.1b) guarantees that the function $t \to L(\sigma)$ is independent of the parametrization of the curves. In the development of this chapter (we are following Carathéodory's ideas [2], as modified slightly by Hermann [1]), we shall consider such Lagrangians, indicating later how nonhomogeneous ones are handled also.

Introduce local coordinates (x_j) for B and $(x_j, \dot{x}_j)$ for $T(B)$ as explained in Chapter 12. Then L becomes a function $L(x, \dot{x})$, satisfying the homogeneity condition

$$L(x, \lambda \dot{x}) = \lambda L(x, \dot{x}).$$

Differentiating both sides of this relation gives Euler's relations:

$$L(x, \dot{x}) = L_{n+j}(x, \dot{x})\dot{x}_j, \qquad (14.2)$$

$$L_{n+j}(x, \dot{x})\dot{x}_j = 0, \qquad (14.3)$$

$$L_{n+j}(x, \lambda \dot{x}) = L_{n+j}(x, \dot{x}). \qquad (14.4)$$

(Recall that

$$L_{n+j} = \frac{\partial L}{\partial \dot{x}_j}, \qquad L_j = \frac{\partial L}{\partial x_j}, \qquad \text{etc.)}$$

Now

$$\theta(L) = L_{n+j}\, dx_j - (L - L_{n+j}\dot{x}_j)\, dt$$

$$= L_{n+j}\, dx_j;$$

142

using (14.2), $\theta(L)$ becomes a form on $T(B)$ alone. Hence, in dealing with such homogeneous Lagrangians, we can take M as $T(B)$ and omit explicit "time" dependence.

When considering constraints, it is appropriate to consider homogeneous ones also. Thus K will be a subset of $T(B)$ such that

$$\lambda v \in K \qquad \text{for all } v \in K, \text{ all } \lambda > 0.$$

In the traditional versions of the Lagrange variational problem, K is defined by equations on $T(B)$:

$$g_a(v) = 0 \qquad \text{for } 1 \le a \le m,$$

with

$$g_a(\lambda v) = \lambda g_a(v) \qquad \text{for } \lambda > 0.$$

Definition

An *extremal field* for the homogeneous variational problem is defined by a pair (W, X) consisting of a real-valued function W on B and a vector field $X \in V(B)$ such that

$$X(W) = 1 = L(X(b)) \qquad \text{for all } b \in B. \tag{14.5a}$$

That is,

$$\frac{d}{dt} W(\sigma(t)) = L(\sigma'(t))$$

along any integral curve $t \to \sigma(t)$ of X. (This is just a normalizing condition.)

$$X(b) \in K \qquad \text{for all } b \in B. \tag{14.5b}$$

For each $b \in B$, $L(X(b))$ is a relative minimum function $v \to L(v)$, where v varies over the vectors $v \in B_b$ satisfying $v \in K$, $v(W) = 1$. $\tag{14.5c}$

THEOREM 14.1

Let $\sigma(t)$, $0 \le t \le a$, be an integral curve of X. If $\sigma_1(t)$, $0 \le t \le a$ is any nearby† curve to $\sigma(t)$, with $W(\sigma(0)) = W(\sigma_1(0)), W(\sigma_1(1)) = W(\sigma(1))$, whose tangent vector curve belongs to the constraint-set, that is, $\sigma_1'(t) \in K$ for $0 \le t \le a$, then

$$\mathbf{L}(\sigma) = \int_0^a L(\sigma'(t))\, dt \le \mathbf{L}(\sigma_1) = \int_0^a L(\sigma_1'(t))\, dt.$$

† The precise meaning of "nearby" will be made clear in the proof.

If, further, for each $b \in B$, $X(b)$ is the only minimal point of $L(v)$, with v subject to the conditions listed in (14.5c), then $\mathbf{L}(\sigma) < \mathbf{L}(\sigma_1)$, unless σ_1 differs from σ only by a change of parametrization.

Proof. We can suppose without loss of generality that $W(\sigma(0)) = 0$ $W(\sigma(a)) = 1$. Then, by (14.5a), $W(\sigma(t)) = t$; that is, σ is parametrized by the value of the W on the level surface of W it lies on. (Think of the successive level surfaces of W as "wave fronts," and the integral curves of X as the "rays" corresponding to these wave fronts.)

If $(d/dt)W(\sigma_1(t)) > 0$, the parametrization of σ_1 can be changed so that $W(\sigma_1(t)) = t$ also, that is, so that σ_1 is parametrized by the level surface of W it lies on. Let us then make precise the condition that σ_1 be "nearby" to σ by requiring that:

(a) $(d/dt)W(\sigma_1(t)) > 0$; that is, the function W is always strictly increasing on σ_1. Thus the values of W can be introduced as a parametrization for σ_1; that is, we can suppose that $W(\sigma_1(t)) = t$, $0 \leq t \leq 1$.

(b)   For each $t \in [0, a]$, $\sigma_1'(t)$ (which now satisfies $\sigma_1'(t)(W) = 1$ and $\sigma_1'(t) \in K$) is sufficiently close to $X(\sigma_1(t))$ so that property (14.5c) holds; that is, $L(X(\sigma_1(t))) \leq L(\sigma_1'(t))$.

Thus,

$$L(\sigma_1'(t)) \geq L(X(\sigma_1(t)))$$

$$= 1 = L(X(\sigma(t))) = L(\sigma'(t)),$$

whence

$$\mathbf{L}(\sigma_1) = \int_0^a L(\sigma_1'(t))\, dt \geq \int_0^a 1\, dt$$

$$\geq \int_0^a L(\sigma'(t))\, dt \geq \mathbf{L}(\sigma). \qquad \text{Q.E.D}$$

Thus we have found a method (Carathéodory's) for proving that certain curves give a minimum to a given variational problem by solving an infinite succession (parametrized by the level surfaces of W) of finite dimensional minimization problems. Actually, the method is an abstraction of a method that had been implicit from the beginning of the calculus of variations. Carathéodory simply stood the classical reasoning on its head and put the motivation into, first, making the method clear; and second, into carrying out the analytical details necessary to show that there is a "plentiful" (local) supply of such extremal fields, and to find the conditions that a single curve be embeddable as an integral curve of an extremal field.

At every point of the domain, we have a vector $X(b)$, which are the "rays" corresponding to the curve fronts $W = $ constant. $X(b)$ represents the "optimal" direction to go when a curve is at point b. Since σ is an integral curve of X, it is always going optimally; (14.5c) expresses this "optimality". Any other curve going from $\sigma(0)$ to the surface $W = W(\sigma(1))$ would at some point violate this optimality; hence it would give a larger value to $L(\sigma_1)$.

Let us now work out the conditions (14.5) more explicitly in the case of the constraint-set K defined by equations:

$$g_a(x, \dot{x}) = 0.$$

Introduce the abbreviations:

$$g_{a,i} = \frac{\partial g_a}{\partial x_i}, \quad g_{a,n+i} = \frac{\partial g_a}{\partial \dot{x}_i}, \quad \text{etc.} \quad W_i = \frac{\partial W}{\partial x_i}, \quad \text{etc.}$$

Suppose that $W(x)$ and $X \equiv A_i(x)(\partial/\partial x_i)$ define an extremal field. Fix $x^0 \in D$. We shall carry out the minimization of (14.5c), using in the usual way the Lagrange multiplier rule. Introduce real constants λ, λ_a: set up the function $\dot{x} \to L(x^\circ, \dot{x})$, add the constraint functions multiplied by the multiplier of constants

$$\dot{x} \to L(x^0, \dot{x}) + \lambda(W_i(x^0)\dot{x}_i - 1) + \lambda_a g_a(x^0, \dot{x}),$$

and express the fact that $\dot{x}_1 = A_i(x^0)$ is to be a critical point for this unconstrained function of $\dot{x}$; that is,

$$L_{n+i}(x^0, A(x^0)) + \lambda W_i(x^0) + \lambda_a g_{a,n+i}(x^0, A(x^0)) = 0.$$

Now we want x^0 to vary. It is not too unreasonable to suppose that the λ and λ_a will also vary with x; that is,

$$L_{n+i}(x, A(x)) + \lambda(x)W_i + \lambda_a(x)g_{a,n+i}(x, A(x)) = 0. \tag{14.6}$$

By (14.5a), we have $W_i A_i = 1$. The Euler relations for homogeneous functions give

$$L_{n+i}(x, \dot{x})\dot{x}_i = L(x, \dot{x}), \quad g_{a,n+i}(x, \dot{x})\dot{x}_i = g_a(x, \dot{x}).$$

By (14.5b), $g_a(x, A(x)) = 0$; hence $g_{a,n+i}(x, A(x))A_i(x) = g_a(x, A(x))$. Multiplying (14.6) by $A_i(x)$ and adding, using the Euler relations, we have

$$0 = L(x, A(x)) + \lambda(x) = 1 + \lambda(x).$$

Thus (14.6) simplifies to

$$\frac{\partial W}{\partial x_i}(x) = L_{n+i}(x, A(x)) + \lambda_a(x)g_{a,n+i}(x, A(x)),$$

or

$$dW = L_{n+i}(x, A(x))\, dx_i = \lambda_a(x)g_{a,n+i}(x, A(x))\, dx_i. \tag{14.7}$$

We want to describe this relation more geometrically. Now $\theta(L) = L_{n+i}\, dx_i$. Consider (λ_a) as the coordinates of a space R^m, and consider the space of the variables $(x_i, \dot{x}_i, \lambda_a)$ as $T(B) \times R^m$. Then X and the functions $(\lambda_a(x))$ together define a cross-section mapping $\Phi: B \to K \times R^m$. Notice that (14.7) can be rewritten as

$$dW = \Phi^*(\theta(L) + \lambda_a \theta(g_a)). \tag{14.8}$$

Applying d to both sides, we have

$$0 = \Phi^*[d(\theta(L) + \lambda_a \theta(g_a))]. \tag{14.9}$$

Thus Φ, considered as a map of $B \to K \times R^m$, defines a submanifold of $K \times R^m$ such that the 2-form, $\omega = d(\theta(L) + \lambda_a \theta(g_a))$, on $K \times R^m$ is identically zero when restricted to this submanifold. Thus the (partial) differential equations defining the extremal field can be defined in this "geometric" way.

Conversely, consider an n-dimensional submanifold of $K \times R^m$ such that ω is zero on this submanifold and such that the forms $dx_1, \ldots, dx_n$ are independent on the submanifold. Notice now that if B is sufficiently small, the cross-section map $\Phi: B \to K \times R^m \subset T(B) \times R^m$ and the function W on D satisfying (14.8) can be reconstructed. For suppose that the submanifold is realized as a map $\phi: B' \to K \times R^m$, where B' is a domain of R^m such that

$$\phi^*(\omega) = 0, \qquad \phi^*(dx_1 \wedge \cdots \wedge dx_n) \neq 0.$$

Then the composite map $B' \to K \times R^m \to B$ has nonzero Jacobian (if coordinates of B' are $t_1, \ldots, t_n$, ϕ satisfies

$$\phi^*(dx_1 \wedge \cdots \wedge dx_n) = J(t)(dt_1 \wedge \cdots \wedge dt_n)).$$

Hence, if B' is small enough, an inverse map exists; that is, we can identify B' with B and suppose that ϕ is a cross-section map $x \to (X(x), \lambda_a(x))$, where $X(x) \in K$, and $(\lambda_a(x)) \in R^m$.

$$0 = \phi^*(\omega) = \phi^*(d(\theta(L) + \lambda_a \theta(g_a))) = d\phi^*(\theta(L) + \lambda_a \theta(g_a));$$

hence there is a function W with

$$dW = \phi^*(\theta(L) + \lambda_a \theta(g_a));$$

that is, if ϕ is identified with Φ, we have just (14.8).

This discussion may be summed up by saying:

> There is a 1-1 correspondence between extremal fields of the variational problem defined by the homogeneous Lagrangian $L(x, \dot{x})$ and the homogeneous constraint function $g_a(x, \dot{x}) = 0$ and n-dimensional integral submanifolds of the 2-form $d(\theta(L) + \lambda_a \theta(g_a))$ on $(K \times R^m)$ $(=$ subset of $(x_i, \dot{x}_i, \lambda_a)$ defined by $g_a = 0)$ which have the property that $dx_1 \wedge \cdots \wedge dx_n$ is nonzero on the submanifold.

Of course one source of imprecision in this statement is that in our working of our way backward to define X, $X(x)$ is only a critical point, not necessarily a relative minimum, of the function $v \to L(v)$ when v runs over those $v \in D_{x^0}$ such that $v \in K$, $v(w) = 1$. It is usual in classical treatments to impose a priori conditions on the second derivatives $L_{n+i, n+j}$, $g_{a, n+i, n+j}$ of L and g_a, guaranteeing that the Hessian form of this function is positive. Such a condition is usually called a *Legendre condition*, but there is really no point in our writing it down explicitly here.

THEOREM 14.2

If $\Phi: x \to (x, \dot{x} = A(x), \lambda_a(x))$ is an integral map of $B \to K \times R^m$ such that $\Phi^*(d(\theta(L) + \lambda_a \theta(g_a))) = 0$, if X is the associated vector field, that is, $X = A_i(\partial/\partial x_i)$, then an integral curve $x(t)$ of X has the following property:

The curve $t \to (x(t), (d/dt)x(t) = \dot{x}(t), \lambda_a(x(t)))$ is a characteristic curve of the 2-form $d(\theta(L) + \lambda_a \theta(g_a))$. A necessary condition that a given curve $t \to x(t)$ in B be embeddable in an extremal field is then that there be functions $(\lambda_a(t))$, called Lagrange multipliers, so that the curve

$$t \to \left(x(t), \frac{d}{dt} x(t), \lambda_a(t) \right)$$

is a characteristic curve of this 2-form.

Proof. Let $\sigma(t)$, $0 \le t \le 1$, be an integral curve of X, and let $\sigma_1(t) = \Phi(\sigma(t)) = (\sigma_1'(t), \lambda_a(\sigma(t)))$ be the image curve in $K \times R^m$. Let $\theta = L_{n+i} dx_i + \lambda_a g_{a, n+i} dx_i = \theta(L) + \lambda_a \theta(g_a)$.

$$\sigma_1'(t) \lrcorner d\theta = \frac{d}{dt} [(L_{n+i} + \lambda_a g_{a, n+i})(x(t)), \lambda_a(x(t))] \, dx_i$$

$$- \frac{d}{dt} x_i(t) \, d(L_{n+i} + \lambda_a g_{a, n+i}).$$

Taking $\partial/\partial \dot{x}_j$ of (14.2), we have

$$L_{n+i, n+j}(x, \dot{x})\dot{x}_i + L_{n+j} = L_{n+j} \quad \text{or} \quad L_{n+i, n+j}(x, \dot{x})\dot{x}_j = 0.$$

We remark now that $\sigma_1'(t) \lrcorner d\theta$, as a 1-covector at the point $\sigma_1(t)$, contains nonzero terms only in the dx_i-terms. For since $\sigma(t)$ is an integral curve of $X = A_i(\partial/\partial x_i)$,

$$\frac{d}{dt} x(t) = A(x(t)).$$

The coefficient of $\sigma_1'(t) \lrcorner d\theta$ involving $d\dot{x}_j$ is then

$$\frac{d}{dt}(x_i(t))L_{n+i, n+j}\left(x, \frac{dx}{dt}\right) + \lambda_a g_{a, n+i, n+j}\left(x, \frac{dx}{dt}\right) = 0$$

by the Euler relations.

The coefficient of $d\lambda$ is

$$\frac{d}{dt} x_i(t) g_{a, n+i}\left(x, \frac{d}{dt} x(t)\right) = g_a\left(x, \frac{dx}{dt}\right) = 0,$$

since $\sigma'(t) \in K$; that is, $g_a(\sigma'(t)) = 0$.

Now we remark that the 1-covector $\sigma_1'(t) \lrcorner d\theta$ is zero when pulled back to B by Φ^*; that is, $\Phi^*(\sigma_1'(t) \lrcorner d\theta = 0$. To prove this, let $v \in B_{\sigma(t)}$.

$$\Phi^*(\sigma_1'(t) \lrcorner d\theta)(v) = (\sigma_1'(t) \lrcorner d\theta(\Phi_*(v)) = d\theta(\sigma_1'(t), \Phi_*(v))$$

$$= d\theta(\Phi_*(\sigma'(t), \Phi_*(v)) = \Phi^* d\theta)(\sigma'(t), v) = 0.$$

These two remarks clearly force $\sigma_1'(t) \lrcorner d\theta = 0$; that is, $t \to \sigma_1(t) = \Phi(\sigma(t))$ is a characteristic curve of the 2-form $d(\theta(L) + \lambda_a\theta(g_a))$, as required. The fact that $t \to (x(t), (dx/dt), \lambda_a(t))$ is a characteristic curve of $d(\theta(L) + \lambda_a\theta(g_a))$ leads to an interpretation of the *Lagrange variational rule*: Construct the Lagrangian

$$L'(x, \dot{x}, t) = L(x, \dot{x}) + \lambda_a(t)g_a(x, \dot{x}).$$

Notice that the curves $t \to (x(t), (dx/dt), \lambda_a(t))$ that are characteristic curves of $d(\theta(L) + \lambda_a\theta(g_a))$ and satisfy the constraints $g_a = 0$ are also characteristic curves of $d\theta(L')$; that is, they are the extremals of the ordinary variational problem that are defined by L' that happen to satisfy the constraints.

Linear Lagrangians and Convex Inequality Constraints

Suppose now that $L: v \to L(v)$ is a linear function on $T(B)$ with B a domain of R^m. Thus, in terms of coordinates $(x_i, \dot{x}_i)$ for $T(b)$, $1 \le i, j, \ldots, \le n$, $L(x, \dot{x})$ must have the form

$$L(x, x) = a_i(x)x_i.$$

Further, we shall suppose that K is defined as the set of $(x, \dot{x}) \in T(B)$ such that $g_a(x, \dot{x}) \le 0$, $1 \le a, b, \ldots, \le m$, where, for each $x \in B$, the Hessian matrix $(g_{a, n+i, n+j}(x, \dot{x}))$ is positive semidefinite. (Thus, the g_a are convex functions when restricted to each tangent space.)

Suppose that W and $X = A_i(\partial/\partial x_i)$ are, respectively, functions and vector fields in D that define an extremal field in B for the variational problem. By (14.5a),

$$X(W) = 1 = a_i(x)A_i(x), \qquad g_a(x, A(x)) \le 0.$$

For each $x \in B$, $\dot{x} = A(x)$ is the minimum value of the function $\dot{x} \to A_i(x)\dot{x}_i$ when $\dot{x}$ varies in a neighborhood of $A(x)$, subject to the condition

$$W_i(x)\dot{x}_i = 1, \qquad g_a(x, \dot{x})) \le 0.$$

Note first that we cannot have $g_a(x, A(x)) < 0$ for all a; that is, $A(x)$ cannot be in the interior of the constraint set. For otherwise the function $\dot{x} \to L(x, \dot{x})$ would be a linear function that has a relative minimum on an *open* subset of a space R^{n-1} (after the constraint $W_i(x)\dot{x}_1 = 1$ is taken into account), which is impossible.

Suppose, then, that $g_a(x, A(x)) = 0$ for $1 \le a \le p$, but that $g_a(x, A(x)) < 0$ for $p + 1 \le a \le m$.

Let us use a geometric terminology. Let K^x be the subset of $\dot{x}$ such that $(x, \dot{x}) \in K$. Thus K^x is that part of the constraint-set lying over the point x. It is a convex subset of B_x. Think of the subset of K^x consisting of those $\dot{x}$ satisfying

$$g_a(x, \dot{x}) = 0, \quad 1 \le a \le p, \quad g_a(x, \dot{x}) < 0, \quad p + 1 \le a \le n,$$

as a *face* of the convex set K^x. We also call the face *nondegenerate* if the rank of the matrix $(g_{a, n+i}(x, \dot{x}))$ is, for all $(x, \dot{x})$ on the face and for $1 \le a \le p$, $1 \le i \le n$, equal to n, that is, is of maximal rank. We shall then say that this is an $(n - p)$ *dimensional face* of the convex set K^x.

Continue to regard $x \in B$ as fixed. We now show that the linear forms

$$\dot{x} \to W_i(x)\dot{x}_i, \qquad \dot{x} \to g_{a, n+i}(x, A(x))\dot{x}_i, \qquad 1 \le a \le p, \qquad (14.10)$$

are *linearly independent*.

Suppose otherwise: By the hypothesis that the matrix $(g_{a, n+i}(x, A(x)))$ has maximal rank, the forms $\dot{x} \to g_{a, n+i}(x, A(x))\dot{x}_i$ are linearly independent. There must then be a relation of the form

$$W_i(x) = \sum_{a=1}^{p} \lambda_a g_{a, i}(x, A(x)).$$

Then

$$1 = W_i(x)A_i(x) = \sum_{a=1}^{p} \lambda_a g_{a, i}(x, A(x))A_i(x)$$

$$= \sum_{a=1}^{p} \lambda_a g_a(x, A(x)) = 0,$$

which is a contradiction.

Let $v \in B_x$ and consider the line segment $t \to X(x) + tv$, $-1 \le t \le 0$. If the following conditions are satisfied, the whole segment lies in K^x, for t sufficiently close to zero, and satisfies the normalizing constraint $v(W) = 1$:

$$W_i(x)\dot{x}_i(v) = 0. \tag{14.11a}$$

$$\frac{d}{dt} g_a(X(x) + tv)\Big|_{t=0} = g_{a,\,n+i}(x, A(x)), \quad \dot{x}_i(v) \le 0 \quad \text{for } 1 \le a \le p. \tag{14.11b}$$

The minimal property of $X(x) = (x, A(x))$ requires that

$$L(v) = a_i(x)\dot{x}_i(v) \ge 0$$

for all vectors $v \in B_x$ satisfying (14.11). The first condition this imposes is that the form $\dot{x} \to a_i(x)\dot{x}_i$ or $v \to L(v)$ can be written as a linear combination of the forms in (14.10); that is,

$$a_i(x)\dot{x}_i = \sum_{a=1}^{p} \lambda_a g_{a,\,n+i}(x, A(x))\dot{x}_i + \lambda(W_i(x)\dot{x}_i), \tag{14.12a}$$

$$a_i(x) = \sum_{a=1}^{p} \lambda_a g_{a,\,n+i}(x, A(x)) + \lambda W_i(x). \tag{14.12b}$$

For the forms of (14.10) are linearly independent: If they are extended to a basis of linear forms, if the form $\dot{x} \to a_i(x)\dot{x}_i$ is expressed in terms of this basis, if the coefficients of the forms other than those in (14.10) were nonzero, there would be a $v \in B_x$ satisfying (14.11)—in fact (14.11b) could be zero—but $L(v)$ could have arbitrary sign, which would give a contradiction.

Using the Euler homogeneity relations again, we see that the λ occurring in (14.12a) must be 1. Thus, finally, the minimization property requires that the λ_a, $1 \le a \le p$, occurring in (14.12) be ≤ 0. We can thus extend the λ_a to $1 \le a \le m$ by requiring that $\lambda_a \le 0$.

All this has been for a fixed value $x \in B$. If, when x varies, $X(x)$ always lies on a nondegenerate $(n - p)$-dimensional face, the λ_a can be chosen as functions of x, $\lambda_a(x)$, $1 \le a \le m$, and we then have

$$dW = a_i \, dx_i - \sum_{a=1}^{p} \lambda_a(x)g_{a,\,n+i}(x, A(x)) \, dx_i.$$

Note that $\theta(L) = L_{n+i} \, dx_i = a_i \, dx_i$. Again this means that the mapping $\Phi: x \to (X(x), -\lambda_a(x))$ of $B \to C \times R^m$ is an integral submanifold of

$$d(\theta(L) + \lambda_a \theta(g_a)),$$

so that the extremal fields are determined by the same sorts of differential equations as those for the variational problems (14.5a) involving equality constraints, but in addition the integral submanifolds of this 2-form must satisfy an *inequality* condition, namely: The functions λ_a on $K \times R^m$ must be ≥ 0 on the integral submanifold. This may be described as the "non-singular" part of the theory. One obvious sort of singularity may happen when $x \to X(x)$ lies on faces of different dimensions as x varies over B. In problems of the theory of optimal control, this phenomenon has great importance, since it corresponds to "switching," but its general theory seems to be much more difficult.

It is traditional in treatises in the calculus of variations to spend consider-able effort in developing the various necessary and sufficient conditions for extremals of variational problems to give minima. However, this is not a sub-ject of active interest in differential geometry (except in the special case of a Riemannian metric, which we shall develop later with other methods), and we shall not go into more details here. Our aim in this chapter has been only to present Carathéodory's brilliant idea in as clear a form as possible. In the next chapter, we shall present further material of a classical nature that is useful in classical mechanics.

Exercises

1. Prove (14.2) through (14.4).

2. Suppose L is a Lagrangian on a manifold M, and N is a submanifold. Suppose the constraints-set K consists of the $v \in T(M)$ that are tangent to N. What does the Lagrange variational rule say about the extremals?

3. Show that Newton's equations of motion for a system of particles (Chapter 11), for forces derivable from a potential, at least, can be written directly as the Euler equations for a Lagrangian. What is the relation of d'Alembert's principle to the Lagrange variation rule?

4. Discuss the case of "nonholonomic" constraints in classical mechanics (for example, the case of a friction-free sphere rolling on a plane) from the point of view of the Lagrange variational rule. Is there a generalization of d'Alembert's principle to this case?

5. For a simple variational problem (that is, with no constraints) work out the Legendre condition.

6. Consider a simple case where such a Legendre condition is not satisfied in a uniform way; for example, the case of a pseudo-Riemannian metric in the plane (see Part 3). Discuss the possible minimizing properties of geodesics (that is, extremals), using Carathéodory's method.

15 The Ordinary Problems of the Calculus of Variations

In this chapter, we present the more classical approach to the most important special case of the general variational problem, whose theory has been already outlined. One may regard much of this material as constituting the mathematical content of classical mechanics; some will be a repetition (for the sake of clarity) of material already given.

Let D be a domain in R^n, the space of variables x_i, $1 \leq i, j, \ldots n$. For $x \in D$, let D_x be the tangent vector space to D at x. Let

$$T(D) = \bigcup_{x \in D} D_x$$

be the tangent bundle to D considered as a domain in R^{2n} with coordinates $(x_i, \dot{x}_i)$, where $\dot{x}_i$ are the functions on $T(D)$ defined as

$$\dot{x}_i(v) = v(x_i) \qquad \text{for} \quad v \in T(D).$$

Consider R, the real numbers, as parametrized by t. A *Lagrangian* on D is a real-valued function L on $T(D) \times R$. If $\sigma : [a, b] \to D$,

$$\mathbf{L}(\sigma) = \int_a^b L(\sigma'(t), t) \, dt.$$

The function $\sigma \to \mathbf{L}(\sigma)$ defines a function on the space of curves in D, and the extremal curves of L, in general, are the curves that in some sense are critical "points" for this function. However, in this simplest case, the *first variation formula* gives a rationale for a more explicit definition of the extremals as solutions of the Euler equations.

Let us derive the Euler equations and the first variation formula in the standard way. Suppose $\sigma(t)$ is defined in coordinates by $x(t) = (x_i(t))$. Then

$$\mathbf{L}(\sigma) = \int_a^b L\left(x(t), \frac{dx}{dt}(t), t\right) dt.$$

Suppose that σ_s, $0 \leq s \leq 1$, is a deformation of σ, that is, a one-parameter family of curves with $\sigma_0 = \sigma$. If in coordinates, $\sigma_s = x(t, s) = (x_i(t, s))$; if $v(t) \in D_{\sigma(t)}$ is, for each $t \in [a, b]$, the tangent vector to the curve $s \to \sigma_s(t)$ at $s = 0$, then

$$\dot{x}_i(v(t)) = \frac{\partial x_i}{\partial s}(t, 0).$$

152

The tangent vector field $t \to v(t)$ along σ is called the *infinitesimal deformation* corresponding to the given deformation $s \to \sigma_s$ of σ. Put $v_i(t) = (\partial x_i/\partial s)(t, 0)$.†

$$\mathbf{L}(\sigma_s) = \int_a^b L\left(x(t, s), \frac{\partial x}{\partial t}(t, s)t\right) dt.$$

$$\frac{d}{ds}\mathbf{L}(\sigma_s) = \int_a^b \left[L_i\left(x(t, s), \frac{\partial x}{\partial t}(t, s), t\right)\frac{\partial x_i}{\partial s}(t, s) + L_{n+i}\frac{\partial^2 x_i}{\partial t\,\partial s}\right] dt$$

and after the second term on the right-hand side is integrated by parts,

$$\frac{d}{ds}\mathbf{L}(\sigma_s) = \int_a^b \left[L_i\frac{\partial x_i}{\partial s} - \frac{\partial}{\partial t}\left(L_{n+1}(x(t, s), \frac{\partial x}{\partial t}(t, s), t)\right)\frac{\partial x_i}{\partial s}(t, s)\right] dt$$

$$+ L_{n+i}\left(x, \frac{\partial x}{\partial t}, t\right)\frac{\partial x_i}{\partial s}\bigg|_{t=a}^{t=b}.$$

Hence

$$\frac{d}{ds}\mathbf{L}(\sigma_s)\bigg|_{s=0} = -\int_a^b \left[\frac{d}{dt}\left(L_{n+i}\left(x(t), \frac{dx(t)}{dt}, t\right)\right) - L_i\left(x(t), \frac{dx(t)}{dt}, t\right)\right]v_i(t)\, dt$$

$$+ L_{n+i}\left(x(t), \frac{dx(t)}{dt}, t\right)v_i(t)\bigg|_{t=a}^{t=b}. \tag{15.1}$$

The *first variation formula* leads us to consider curves that satisfy the following system of second-order differential equations, the *Euler equations*:

$$\frac{d}{dt}\left(L_{n+1}\left(x(t), \frac{dx(t)}{dt}, t\right)\right) - L_i\left(x(t), \frac{dx}{dt}, t\right) = 0. \tag{15.2}$$

We depart slightly from the general point of view and regard an *extremal* of the variational problem as a curve satisfying (15.2); thus (15.2) is to be regarded as a system of differential equations to be investigated for its own sake. Of course the relation of the two notions of "extremal curve" is obvious from (15.1). For example, if $\sigma_s(a) = \sigma_0(a)$, $\sigma_s(b) = \sigma_0(b)$, that is, if σ_s is a deformation with fixed end points, then $v_i(a) = 0 = v_i(b)$; hence $(d/ds)\mathbf{L}(\sigma_s)|_{s=0} = 0$. Conversely, if $(d/ds)\mathbf{L}(\sigma_s)|_{s=0}$ is true for every deformation with fixed end points, then (15.2) is satisfied (see any classical book on the calculus of variations). However, (15.1) contains information about deformations that may not have fixed end points: For example, if σ satisfies (15.2) and if each of the "boundary terms"—that is, the last two terms on the right-hand

† It is convenient to use a subscript notation for partial derivatives:

$$L_i = \frac{\partial L}{\partial x_i}, \quad L_{n+i} = \frac{L\partial}{\partial \dot{x}_i}, \quad L_{n+i,j} = \frac{\partial^2 L}{\partial \dot{x}\,\partial x_j}, \quad \text{etc.}$$

side of (15.1)—vanishes, then the left-hand side vanishes. We shall see a little later on what the vanishing of these last two terms means geometrically.

After these classical comments, we proceed to a more intrinsic, "geometric" characterization of the solution of the Euler equations as the projection into D of the characteristic curves of a certain closed 2-form on $T(D) \times R$.

Define the *Cartan 1-form* $\theta(L)$ associated with L as a 1-form on $T(D) \times R$ as

$$\theta(L) = L_{n+i}\, dx_i - (L_{n+i}\dot{x}_i - L)\, dt \left(= \frac{\partial L}{\partial \dot{x}_i}\, dx_i - \left(\frac{\partial L}{\partial \dot{x}_i}\dot{x}_i - L\right) dt\right). \quad (15.3)$$

Given a curve $\sigma(t)$, $a \le t \le b$, in D, we can consider its *extended curve* $\dot{\sigma}(t) = (\sigma'(t), t)$ in $T(D) \times R$: In other words, $\dot{\sigma}$ is the graph of the tangent vector curve of σ. $\theta(L)$, as a 1-differential form on $T(D) \times R$, defines a *Lagrangian* on $T(D) \times R$.

(a) $\mathbf{L}(\sigma) = \theta(\mathbf{L})(\dot{\sigma})$; that is, the value of the function defined by the Lagrangian L on the curve σ is equal to the value on the Lagrangian $\theta(L)$ defined on $T(D) \times R$ on the curve $\dot{\sigma}$. Explicitly:

$$\int_a^b L\left(x(t), \frac{dx(t)}{dt}, t\right) dt = \int_a^b \left[y_i(t)\frac{dx_i}{dt} - H\left(x(t), \frac{dx}{dt}, t\right)\right] dt, \quad (15.4)$$

where y_i are the functions $\partial L/\partial \dot{x}_i$ on $T(D) \times R$,

$$y_i(t) = y_i(\dot{\sigma}(t)) = L_{n+1}\left(x(t), \frac{dx}{dt}, t\right),$$

and H is the function $(\partial L/\partial \dot{x})\dot{x}_i - L$ on $T(D) \times R$.

(b)   The curve σ is a solution of the Euler equations (15.2); that is, is an extremal of L if and only if

$$\dot{\sigma} = \left(x(t), \frac{dx(t)}{dt}, t\right)$$

is a characteristic curve of the 2-form $d\theta(L)$ on $T(D) \times R$. Thus, since $\theta(L) = y_i\, dx_i - H\, dt$, if the functions (x_i, y_i, t) form a new coordinate system for $T(D) \times R$, that is, of

$$\det(L_{n+1, n+j}) \ne 0, \quad (15.5)$$

then σ is an extremal of L if and only if its extended curve, when written in the new coordinates as $(x_i(t), y_i(t), t)$, is a *solution* of the *Hamilton equations* with Hamiltonian H:

$$\frac{dx_i}{dt} = \frac{\partial H}{y_i}(x(t), y(t), t), \qquad \frac{dy_i}{dt} = -\frac{\partial H}{\partial x_i}(x(t), y(t), t).$$

All except the remark about the Euler equations being equivalent to Hamilton's has been proved in Chapter 12. Note that

$$dy_i = L_{n+i, \, n+j} \, d\dot{x}_j + L_{n+1, \, n+j} \, dx_j + L_{n+i, \, t} \, dt.$$

Now the (x_i, y_i, t) define a new coordinate system (at least locally) for $T(D) \times R$ if and only if the $d\dot{x}_j$ can be expressed in terms of the dx_i, dy_i, and dt. This is so if and only if (15.5) is verified. Given this condition in the new coordinate system, $d\theta(L)$ is in Hamiltonian form $dy_i \wedge dx_i - dH \wedge dt$ with Hamiltonian function $H = L_{n+i} \dot{x}_i - L$ when expressed in the new coordinates.† We can now refer to our work in Chapter 13 to complete the description of the extremals as solutions of the Hamilton equations.

A Lagrangian L satisfying (15.5) is said to define a *regular, nonparametric* (or *nonhomogeneous*) variational problem. In such problems, the extremal curves come with their "own" parametrization, in the sense that the parametrization cannot be freely changed without destroying the extremal curve property. Thus this sort of variational problem is the appropriate one for defining the time evolution of physical systems in Newtonian physics, where "time" is "given" absolutely for the whole system, from the "outside," as it were. A brief indication of at least the formal relation with Newton's laws of motion might be in order.

The type of Lagrangian satisfying (15.5) for which the Euler equations are as simple as possible is one of the following form (assuming no explicit time dependence in L):

$$L(x, \dot{x}) = \tfrac{1}{2} m \dot{x}_i \dot{x}_i - V(x), \tag{15.6}$$

where m is a constant, $V(x)$ is a function on D, $n = 1, 2,$ or 3;

$$L_{n+1} = m \dot{x}_i, \qquad L_i = -\frac{\partial V}{x_i},$$

$$\frac{d}{dt} \left(L_{n+1} \left(x(t), \frac{dx}{dt} \right) \right) - L_i = m \frac{d^2 x_i}{dt^2} + \frac{\partial V}{\partial x_i}.$$

Recall Newton's law for motion of a particle: Force "vector" = mass $\times$ "acceleration vector." This will be formally identical with the Euler equations if we identify m with mass, $(d^2 x_i/dt^2)$ with the acceleration vector, and $(-\partial V/\partial x_i)$ with the "force" vector. Thus $V(x)$ is to be regarded as the potential function giving rise to the "force" vector. Newton's laws are implicitly based on the Euclidean nature of the underlying space, in particular on the "unnatural" identification between vector fields and differential forms. It

† In other words, H may be regarded as function $H(x_i, y_i, t)$ of the indicated $2n + 1$ variables such that, identically in $(x, \dot{x}, t)$,

$$H(x_i, L_{n+i}(x, \dot{x}, t), t) = L_{n+j}(x, \dot{x}, t)\dot{x}_j - L(x, \dot{x}, t).$$

seems more natural, then, to regard the "force" vector field as a differential form, namely as $-dV$.

Continuing, we see that the $\dot{x}_i$ are to be regarded as the coordinates of the velocity of the particle. L then has the form: (kinetic energy $-$ potential energy). Then $y_i = L_{n+i} = m\dot{x}_i$ are the coordinates of the *linear momentum* of the particle.

$$\dot{x}_i = \frac{y_i}{m},$$

$$H = L_{n+i}\dot{x}_i - L = m\dot{x}_i\dot{x}_i - \tfrac{1}{2}m\dot{x}_i\dot{x}_i + V(x)$$

$$= \tfrac{1}{2}m\dot{x}_i\dot{x}_i + V(x)$$

$$= \text{(potential + kinetic) energy} = \text{total energy}. \tag{15.7}$$

Thus the formal study of regular, nonparametric variational problems may be regarded as a generalization of the material that goes under the name of "classical mechanics." This has the great advantage of replacing the Newtonian theory, which is really "covariant" only under the group of orthogonal transformations, by an apparatus that is covariant under the much bigger group of *all* transformations of the underlying space D.

We now want to make precise this "covariance" of the Euler equations under arbitrary transformations of the domain D. We shall be able to do even more, namely, to develop covariance with respect to arbitrary mappings of one domain $D \subset R^n$ into another $D' \subset R^m$.

Suppose, then, that D is a domain in R^n with coordinates (x_i), $1 \le i, j, \ldots \le n$, that D' is a domain in R^m, with coordinates (z_a), $1 \le a, b, \ldots \le m$, and that ϕ is a map: $D \to D'$. Suppose $\phi_a(x) = z_a$ are the functions defining the mapping; that is,

$$\phi^*(z_a) = \phi_a.$$

There is a mapping $\phi_*: T(D') \to T(D)$ of the tangent bundles assigning $\phi_*(v) \in D'_{\phi(x)}$ to each $v \in D_x$. If $(z_a, \dot{z}_a)$ and $(x_i, \dot{x}_i)$ are respectively the standard coordinates on $T(D)$ and $T(D')$, respectively, then recall that

$$(\phi_*)^*(z_a) = \phi_z(x), \qquad (\phi_*)^*(\dot{z}_a) = \frac{\partial \phi_a}{\partial x_j}\dot{x}_j. \tag{15.8}$$

THEOREM 15.1

Let D and D' be domains in, respectively, R^n and R^m, $\phi: D \to D'$ a map between them, $\phi_*: T(D) \to T(D')$ the prolonged map to tangent vectors. Consider ϕ_* as a map also of $T(D) \times R \to T(D') \times R$ by mapping

$$\phi_*(v, t) = (\phi_*(v), t) \qquad \text{for} \quad v \in T(D), t \in R;$$

that is, $(\phi_*)^*(t) = t$. Let L and L' be, respectively, functions on $T(D) \times R$ and $T(D') \times R$ defining Lagrangians on D and D' such that $(\phi_*)^*(L') = L$. Then:

(a) If $\sigma(t)$, $a \le t \le b$, is a curve in D, if $\sigma_1(t) = \phi(\sigma(t))$ is the transformed curve in D' under ϕ, then

(b) $\mathbf{L}(\sigma) = \mathbf{L}'(\sigma_1)$, $(\phi_*)^*(\theta(L')) = \theta(L)$.

Proof. (a) Follows more or less from the definitions. The basic geometric property of ϕ_* is

$$\sigma_1'(t) = \phi_*(\sigma'(t));$$

hence,

$$\mathbf{L}'(\sigma_1) = \int_a^b L'(\sigma_1'(t)) \, dt = \int_a^b L'(\phi_*(\sigma'(t))) \, dt$$

$$= \int_a^b (\phi_*)^*(L')(\sigma'(t)) \, dt$$

$$= \int_a^b L(\sigma'(t)) \, dt = \mathbf{L}(\sigma).$$

(b) This requires a little more computation:

$$dL = L_{n+1} \, d\dot{x}_i + L_i \, dx_i + L_t \, dt$$

$$= (\phi_*)^*(dL') = (\phi_*)^*(L'_{n+a} \, d\dot{z}_a + L'_a \, dz_a + L'_t \, dt)$$

$$= (\phi_*)^*(L'_{n+a}) \, d\!\left(\frac{\partial \phi_a}{x_j} \dot{x}_j\right) + (\phi_*)^*(L'_a) \, d\phi_a + (\phi_*)^*(L'_t) \, dt$$

$$= (\phi_*)^*(L'_{n+a}) \frac{\partial \phi_a}{\partial x_j} \, d\dot{x}_j + \cdots$$

(the unwritten terms involve dx_j and dt). Hence,

$$L_{n+j} = (\phi_*)^*(L'_{n+a}) \frac{\partial \phi_a}{\partial x_j}.$$

$$(\phi_*)^*(dz_a - \dot{z}_a \, dt) = d\phi_z - \frac{\partial \phi_a}{\partial x_j} \dot{x}_j \, dt$$

$$= \frac{\partial \phi_a}{\partial x_j} \, dx_j - \frac{\partial \phi_a}{\partial x_j} \dot{x}_j \, dt$$

$$= \frac{\partial \phi_a}{\partial x_j} (dx_j - \dot{x}_j \, dt).$$

Now

$$(\phi_*)^*(\theta(L')) = (\phi_*)^*[L'_{n+a}(dz_a - \dot{z}_a \, dt) + L' \, dt]$$

$$= (\phi_*)^*(L'_{n+a}) \frac{\partial \phi_a}{\partial x_j}(dx_j - \dot{x}_j \, dt) + L \, dt$$

$$= L_{n+j}(dx_j - \dot{x}_j \, dt) + L \, dt = \theta(L). \qquad \text{Q.E.D.}$$

COROLLARY 1

If $\phi_*(T(D)) = T(D')$, then ϕ carries an extremal of L into an extremal of L'.

Proof. The proof consists in putting together three general remarks.

(a) If E and E' are domains, $\varphi: E \to E'$ is a map such that $\phi_*(T(E)) = T(E')$; that is, ϕ is a maximal rank mapping. If w' is a closed 2-form on E', and if $v \in T(E)$ is a characteristic vector of $\varphi^*(w)$, then $\varphi_*(v)$ is a characteristic vector of w.

For the proof, suppose that $v \in E_y$, $y \in E$. Let $u' \in E'_{\psi(y)}$. We must show that $w(\varphi_*(v), u') = 0$. But by hypothesis there exists a vector $u \in E_y$ such that $\varphi_*(u) = u'$. Then

$$w(\varphi_*(v), u') = w(\varphi_*(v), \varphi_*(u')) = \varphi^*(w)(v, u') = 0.$$

(b) If $\phi_*(T(D)) = T(D')$, then $(\phi_*)_*: T(T(D)) \to T(T(D))$ is onto, that is, ϕ_* is a maximal rank mapping of $T(D)$ or $T(D')$.

We shall use the standard coordinates $(x_i, \dot{x}_i)$, $(z_a, \dot{z}_a)$ for, respectively, $T(D)$ and $T(D')$, $1 \le i, j, \ldots, \le n; 1 \le a, b, \ldots, \le m$. To show that a mapping of vector spaces is onto is equivalent to showing that the dual mapping on covectors is 1-1. Thus, suppose that there is a covector on $T(D')$ mapped into zero by $(\phi_*)^*$; say,

$$0 = (\phi_*)^*(\lambda_a \, dz_a + \lambda_{m+a} \, d\dot{z}_a)$$

$$= \lambda_a \frac{\partial \phi_a}{\partial x_i} \, dx_i + \lambda_{m+a} \, d\left(\frac{\partial \phi_a}{\partial x_i} \dot{x}_i\right)$$

$$= \lambda_a \frac{\partial \phi_a}{\partial x_i} \, dx_i + \lambda_{m+a} \frac{\partial^2 \phi_a}{\partial x_j \, \partial x_i} x_i \, dx_j + \lambda_{m+a} \frac{\partial \phi_a}{\partial x_i} \, d\dot{x}_i.$$

Now that ϕ is maximal rank means that the rank of the matrix $(\partial \phi_a / \partial x_i)$ is everywhere m. Then

$$\lambda_{m+a} \frac{\partial \phi_a}{\partial x_i} \, d\dot{x}_i = 0; \quad \text{hence,} \quad \lambda_{m+a} \frac{\partial \phi_a}{\partial x_i} = 0,$$

hence,

$$\lambda_a \frac{\partial \phi_a}{\partial x_i} dx_i = 0, \quad \text{hence,} \quad \lambda_a \frac{\partial \phi_a}{\partial x_i} = 0, \quad \text{hence,} \quad \lambda_a = 0.$$

(c) If $\sigma(t)$ is a curve in D, if $\sigma_1(t) = \phi(\sigma(t))$ is the transformed curve under ϕ, then the image of the curve $t \to (\sigma'(t), t)$ under the map ϕ_* is the curve $t \to (\sigma_1'(t), t)$.

This follows from the very definition of the map $\phi_* : T(D) \times R \to T(D') \times R$.

COROLLARY 2

Let $X = A_i(\partial/\partial x_i)$ be a vector field on D. Define the prolonged vector field $\dot{X}$ on $T(D) \times R$ as

$$\dot{X} = A_i \frac{\partial}{\partial x_i} + \frac{\partial A_i}{\partial x_j} \dot{x}_j \frac{\partial}{\partial \dot{x}_i} + \frac{\partial}{\partial t}.$$

Then

$$\dot{X}(\theta(L)) = \theta(\dot{X}(L)). \tag{15.9}$$

Proof. This could be verified by a similar direct computation, but it is more constructive to reduce it to Theorem 15.1 by a geometric argument. Suppose, for simplicity, that X generates a one-parameter group of transformations of $D, s \to T_s$; that is, for $x^0 \in D, s \to T_s(x^0)$ is an integral curve of X. In particular,

$$\frac{\partial}{\partial t} T_s^*(x_i) = X(T_s^*(x_i)) = A_j \frac{\partial}{\partial x_j} (T_s^*(x_i)).$$

Now, from the geometric meaning, $s \to T_{s*}$ is also a one-parameter transformation group on $T(D)$. Extend T_s to $T(D) \times R$ by

$$(T_{s*})^*(t) = t + s.$$

Finally, then, $s \to T_{s*}$ is a one-parameter group of transformations of $T(D) \times R$. We want to show that $\dot{X}$ is the infinitesimal generator of this group:

$$\frac{d}{ds}(T_{s*})^*(x_i)\Big|_{t=0} = \frac{d}{ds}(T_{s*})(x_i)\Big|_{s=0} = A_i,$$

$$(T_{s*})^*(\dot{x}_i) = \frac{\partial(T_{s*}(x_i))}{\partial x_j} \dot{x}_j,$$

$$\frac{\partial}{\partial s}(T_{s*})^*(\dot{x}_i) = \frac{\partial}{\partial s}\left(\frac{\partial(T_{s*}(x_i))}{\partial x_j}\right)\dot{x}_j;$$

hence,

$$\frac{\partial}{\partial s}(T_{s*})^*(\dot{x}_i)\Big|_{s=0} = \frac{\partial}{\partial x_j}\left(\frac{\partial}{\partial s}(T_{s*}(x_i))\Big|_{s=0}\right)\dot{x}_j$$

$$= \frac{\partial A_i}{\partial x_j}\dot{x}_j\,;$$

$$\frac{\partial}{\partial s}(T_{s*})^*(t)\Big|_{s=0} = 1.$$

This verifies the indicated form of $\dot{X}$. Finally, to prove (15.9),

$$\dot{X}(\theta(L)) = \frac{\partial}{\partial s}(T_{s*})^*(\theta(L))\Big|_{s=0} = \frac{\partial}{\partial s}\,\theta(T_{s*})^*(L)\Big|_{s=0}$$

$$= \theta\frac{\partial}{\partial s}(T_{s*})^*(L)\Big|_{s=0} = \theta(\dot{X}(L)).$$

As useful as these nonparametric Lagrangians are for understanding classical mechanics from a " higher" point of view, for theoretical purposes it is more convenient (as we saw in Chapter 14) to have Lagrangians whose extremal curves *can* be freely reparametrized. In physics this corresponds to giving up the Newtonian picture of "time" as an "independent" variable with a different status from the "dependent" space and velocity coordinates.

We first show that the extremals of a Lagrangian L on D are independent of the parametrization if

(a) L is a function on $T(D)$ alone; that is, L is time-independent;
(b) $L(\lambda v) = \lambda L(v)$ for $\lambda > 0$.

Proof.   Let $\sigma(t)$, $a \le t \le b$, and $\sigma_1(\tau)$, $\alpha \le \tau \le \beta$, be curves differing only by change in parametrization. By definition, this means that there is a real-valued function $t(\tau)$, $\alpha \le \tau \le \beta$, such that $t'(\tau) > 0$, $\tau(\alpha) = a$, $\tau(\beta) = b$, and $\sigma_1(\tau) = \sigma(t(\tau))$ for $\alpha \le \tau \le \beta$.

$$\mathbf{L}(\sigma_1) = \int_\alpha^\beta L(\sigma_1'(\tau))\,d\tau = \int_\alpha^\beta L(\sigma'(t(\tau)t'(\tau))\,d\tau$$

$$= \int_\alpha^\beta L(\sigma'(t(\tau)))t'(\tau)\,d\tau = \int_a^b L(\sigma'(t))\,dt = \mathbf{L}(\sigma).$$

On the other hand, we can start with an arbitrary time-dependent Lagrangian $L(x_1, \ldots, x_n, \dot{x}_1, \ldots, \dot{x}_n, t)$; and by introducing another pair of dependent variables $x_{n+1} = t$, $\dot{x}_{n+1} = \dot{t}$, and a Lagrangian L_i, then by the formula

$$L_1(x_1, \ldots, x_{n+1}, \dot{x}_1, \ldots, \dot{x}_{n+1}) = L\left(x_1, \ldots, x_n, \frac{\dot{x}_1}{\dot{x}_{n+1}}, \ldots, \frac{\dot{x}_n}{\dot{x}_{n+1}}, x_{n+1}\right) \dot{x}_{n+1},$$

we convert the time-dependent, parametrization-dependent variational problem in n variables to a time-independent, parametrization-independent
problem in $(n + 1)$ variables.

To verify that this formula actually does this, notice that L_1 so defined is
homogeneous, and that $\mathbf{L}_1(\sigma_1) = \mathbf{L}(\sigma)$, where $\sigma = (x_i(t))$, and $\sigma_1 = (x_i(t), t)$
is the "graph" of σ in $(n + 1)$-space.

We shall work from now on with such a time-independent, homogeneous
Lagrangian $L(x_i, \dot{x}_i)$. Then L satisfies the Euler homogeneous function relations, which will play an important role. To derive them, start with

$$L(x, \lambda\dot{x}) = \lambda L(x, \dot{x}). \tag{15.10a}$$

Differentiate with respect to λ:

$$L_{n+1}(x, \lambda\dot{x})\dot{x}_i = L(x, \dot{x}). \tag{15.10b}$$

Differentiate again with respect to λ and set $\lambda = 1$.

$$L_{n+1, n+j}(x, \dot{x})\dot{x}_i \dot{x}_j = 0. \tag{15.10c}$$

Differentiate (15.10a) with respect to $\dot{x}_i$:

$$L_{n+1}(x, \lambda\dot{x})\lambda = \lambda L_{n+1}(x, \dot{x}) \quad \text{or} \quad L_{n+1}(x, \lambda\dot{x}) = L_{n+1}(x, \dot{x}). \tag{15.10d}$$

Applying $\partial/\partial\lambda$ to (15.10d), we have

$$L_{n+1, n+j}(x, \dot{x})\dot{x}_j = 0. \tag{15.10e}$$

Then

$$\theta(L) = L_{n+i}\, dx_i - (L_{n+i}\dot{x}_i - L)\, dt$$
$$= L_{n+1}\, dx_i - 0,$$

by (15.10b). Thus $\theta(L)$ is a form on $T(D)$ alone, and we can in effect ignore
the additional explicit "time" variable and consider extremals as characteristic curves of the 2-form $d\theta(L)$ on $T(D)$. In addition, note that by
(15.10e), $\det(L_{n+i, n+j}) = 0$; hence the functions $y_i = L_{n+i}$ are not functionally independent.

However, if $(n - 1)$ of them are functionally independent, that is, if

$$\text{rank}(L_{n+i, n+j}(v)) = n - 1 \quad \text{for all} \quad v \in T(D). \tag{15.11a}$$

then we say that L defines a *regular* homogeneous variational problem.

Another way of putting this condition is as follows:

Whenever (b_j) are numbers such that

$$L_{n+i,\,n+j}(x, \dot{x})b_j = 0, \tag{15.11b}$$

then we must have $b_j = a\dot{x}_j$ for some real number a.

For (15.11b) just expresses the fact that the nullity of the matrix $(L_{n+i,\,n+j})$ is 1, equivalent to the fact that the rank is $n - 1$.

Suppose from now on that L satisfies this regularity condition. The general theory of homogeneous variational problems expounded in Chapter 14 is applicable, with no constraints; that is, $K = T(B)$. Modifying slightly the general theory (since we may want to also consider extremals that do not minimize **L**), we say that an *extremal field* for the variational problem is defined by a vector field $X: D \to T(D)$ such that

$$X^*(d\theta(L)) = 0, \qquad X^*(L) > 0 \text{ at all points of } D. \tag{15.12}$$

(We are using the characterization of vector fields as mappings $D \to T(D)$ such that $X(x) \in D_x$ for all $x \in D$, that is, as cross-section maps.) Equation (15.10b) implies that

> If $X \in V(D)$ defines an extremal field, so does fX, for
> each positive function f on D. (15.13)

Suppose that $X = A_i(\partial/\partial x_i)$, and that W is a function on D such that $X^*(\theta(L)) = dW$; that is,

$$dW = L_{n+i}(x, A(x))\, dx_i. \tag{15.14}$$

Then

$$X(W)(x) = L_{n+1}(x, A(x))A_i(x) = L(x, A(x))$$
$$= X^*(L)(x) \qquad \text{for } x \in D.$$

Hence we can normalize X by multiplying by a positive function so that

$$X(W) = 1 = L(X(x)) \qquad \text{for all } x \in D.$$

We shall call such a function (defined up to an additive constant) the *characteristic function* associated with the extremal field.

THEOREM 15.2

Suppose that X is a vector field on D that defines an extremal vector field for the variational problem defined by a homogeneous regular Lagrangian L on D; that is, X satisfies (15.12). Suppose that W is a function on D such that $X^*(\theta(L)) = dW$. Then:

(a)   The integral curves of X are extremals of L.

(b)   Let σ and σ_1 be curves beginning and ending on the same level surface of W whose tangent vector curves are sufficiently close together. Suppose further that σ is an integral curve of X and that the following condition is satisfied:

> The symmetric matrix $(L_{n+i,\,n+j}(\sigma'(t)))$ is positive semidefinite.
$$(15.15)$$

Then $\mathbf{L}(\sigma) < \mathbf{L}(\sigma_1)$. Equality holds only if σ_1 is also an integral curve of X.

Proof.   Part (a) is a consequence of Theorem 15.1. To prove Part (b) we will show that, for each $x \in D$, $L(v) > L(X(x))$ for each $v \in D_x$ that is sufficiently close to $X(x)$, and that satisfies $v(W) = 1$, $v \neq X(x)$. If, say,

$$X = A_i \frac{\partial}{\partial x_i}, \qquad \dot{x}_i(v) = v_i,$$

then

$$\frac{d}{dt}(L(x, A(x) + t(v - A(x)))) = L_{n+i}(v_i - A_i(x)).$$

$$\frac{d^2}{dt^2} L(x, A(x) + t(v - A(x)))|_{t=0} = L_{n+i,\,n+j}(x, A(x))(v_i - A_i(x))(v_j - A_j(x)).$$

We know that $(d/dt)(L(x, A(x) + t(v_i - A(x))))|_{t=0} = 0$, from the very definition of extremal vector field. Now, $(d^2/dt^2)L(x, A(x) + tv)|_{t=0} \geq 0$. We want to prove that it is > 0. Suppose, otherwise, that is, it $= 0$. Then, by (15.11b), $v_i - A_i(x) = \rho A_i(x)$. The condition

$$1 = \frac{\partial W}{\partial x_i}(x)v_i = \frac{\partial W}{\partial x_i}(x)A_i(x)$$

forces $\rho = 0$; contradiction.   Q.E.D.

We see that extremal vector fields are very useful if they can be found. Now we indicate how the general method given in Chapter 13 for finding integral manifolds can be adapted to finding integral manifolds of the special 1-form $d\theta(L)$.

Let $\sigma(t)$, $a \leq t \leq b$, be a curve in D, and let us look for necessary conditions that σ is the integral curve of an extremal vector field X. The first condition that comes to mind is that σ is to be an extremal itself, that is, a solution of the Euler equations. Let W be the function on D such that $X^*(\theta(L)) = dW$. At most adding a constant to W, we can suppose that $W(\sigma(a)) = 0$. Suppose that

$\phi \colon D' \to D$ is a submanifold of D such that W is equal to zero on $\phi(D')$. Then, for $x \in D$,

$$dW = L_{n+i}(X(x))\, dx_i.$$

Hence, for $x \in \phi(D')$ and for a tangent vector $v \in D_x$ that is tangent to $\phi(D')$ at x, we have

$$v(W) = L_{n+i}(X(x))v(x_i) = 0.$$

Forgetting for the moment how we arrived at this relation, let us make a general definition.

Definition

Let $L \colon T(D) \to R$ define a homogeneous, regular Lagrangian on D. Suppose that u and v are tangent vectors to a point $x \in D$; u is said to be *perpendicular* to v (with respect to the Lagrangian L) if

$$L_{n+i}(u)\dot{x}_i(v) = 0. \qquad (15.16)$$

If V is a subspace of D_x, we say that v is *perpendicular* to V (with respect to L) if v is perpendicular to all vectors $u \in V$. If $\phi \colon D' \to D$ is a submanifold of D such that $x \in \phi(D')$, we say that v is *perpendicular to the submanifold* if v is perpendicular to the tangent space of the submanifold at x. If a χ is a vector field on the submanifold ϕ, that is, χ is a map assigning a vector $\chi(x) \in D_x$ to each $x \in \phi(D)$, we say that χ is a *perpendicular vector field* to ϕ if $\chi(x)$ is perpendicular to the tangent space to $\phi(D)$ at each point $x \in \phi(D)$.

This relation is a generalization of the ordinary relation of perpendicularity for vectors in Euclidean spaces. However, notice that this relation is not necessarily symmetric, as it is for Euclidean geometry; that is, if v is perpendicular to u, u is not necessarily perpendicular to v. It is also easily seen that this definition is independent of the coordinate system.

Returning now to the extremal vector field X, its associated characteristic function W, and its integral curve $\sigma(t)$ with $W(\sigma(0)) = 0$, we see that $\sigma'(0) = X(\sigma(0))$ is perpendicular to any submanifold $\phi \colon D' \to D$ on which W is zero, and the vector field on the submanifold obtained by restricting X is also perpendicular to the submanifold. Note also that the map $D' \to T(D)$, which assigns $X(\phi(x'))$ to each $x \in D'$, is an integral submanifold of the 1-form $\theta(L)$. Now we are prepared to apply the general theory of Chapter 13 concerning integral submanifolds of 1- and 2-forms to reverse this reasoning and give a condition that an isolated extremal curve of L can be embedded as an integral curve of a vector field.

THEOREM 15.3

Let D be a domain of R^n, with a homogeneous, regular Lagrangian L. Let $\phi \colon D' \to D$ be a submanifold of D of dimension $n - 1$, and let $\sigma \colon [0, 1] \to D$ be an extremal curve such that $\sigma(0)$ lies on $\phi(D')$ and such that its tangent vector $\sigma'(0)$ is perpendicular there to $\phi(D')$, and such that $L(\sigma'(0)) = 1$. Then, if D is sufficiently small, there is a unique extremal vector field X such that:

(a) σ is an integral curve of X.
(b) If W is the function on D such that $X^*(\theta(L)) = dW$, then $W = 0$ on $\phi(D')$.

Thus, an isolated extremal curve of L can be embedded (locally) in an extremal field in many ways—every choice of a hypersurface to which it is initially perpendicular defines such a field. We shall arrange our proof of Theorem 15.3 in a series of lemmas so that the reader can see at least the beginning steps of attempting to embed σ in an extremal field if its initial perpendicular submanifold is of lower dimension than $n - 1$. We shall not complete this project here, partly because we do not know the answer (except for Riemannian manifolds, where it can be done).

LEMMA 15.4

Let D be a domain with a homogeneous regular Lagrangian L. Let $\phi: D' \to D$ be a submanifold of dimension m of D. Let $P(\phi)$ be the set of tangent vectors $u \in T(D)$ to points $x \in \phi(D')$ such that $L(u) = 1$, u is perpendicular to $\phi(D)$. Then $P(\phi)$ is a submanifold of $T(D)$ of dimension $(n - 1)$, and is an integral submanifold of the 1-form $\theta(L)$. A vector $v \in P(\phi)$ is not tangent to $\phi(D')$.

Proof. It suffices to prove the lemma in the case that D is as small as we please. Let $X_a = A_i^a(\partial/\partial x_i)$, $1 \le a, b, \ldots, \le m$, be everywhere linearly independent vector fields in D such that the X_a are tangent to $\phi(D')$ and that their values at each point of $\phi(D')$ define a basis for its tangent space. A vector $u = (\dot{x})$ is perpendicular to $\phi(D')$ at x if

$$L_{n+i}(x, \dot{x})A_i^a(x) = 0.$$

We add the equation $L(x, \dot{x}) = 1$, and must show that these equations are of maximal rank. Thus we must show that the rank of the $n \times (m + 1)$ matrix

$$\begin{pmatrix} L_{n+i, n+j}(x, \dot{x})A_i^a(x) \\ L_{n+j}(x, \dot{x}) \end{pmatrix}$$

is equal to $m + 1$. Suppose, then, that there is a relation of the form

$$\lambda L_{n+j}(x, \dot{x}^0) + \lambda_a L_{n+1, n+j}(x, \dot{x}^0)A_i^a(x) = 0.$$

Multiplying by $\dot{x}_j$ and using the Euler relation (15.10b) and (15.10c), we have

$\lambda = 0$. Since now $L_{n+i,\,n+j}(x,\dot{x})(\lambda_a A_i{}^a(x)) = 0$, since L is regular, we must have relations of the form $\lambda_a A_i{}^a(x) = \rho x_i{}^0$, whence

$$0 = L_{n+i}(x,\dot{x}^0)\lambda_a A_i^a(x) = \rho L_{n+i}(x,\dot{x})\dot{x}_i = \rho.$$

Finally, then, $\lambda_a X^a(x) = 0$, whence $\lambda_a = 0$.

Now suppose $v \in P(\phi) \cap D_x$ is tangent to $\phi(D)$. We must then have relations of the form

$$v = \gamma_a X^a(x), \qquad L_{n+i}(x,\dot{x}(v))A_i^a(x) = 0;$$

hence,

$$0 = L_{n+i}(x,\dot{x}(v))A_i^a(x)\gamma_a = L_{n+i}(x,\dot{x}(v))\dot{x}(v)$$

$$= L(x,\dot{x}(v)) = 1, \qquad \text{contradiction.}$$

LEMMA 15.5

Let L be a regular homogeneous Lagrangian on a domain D and let $v \in D_{x^0}$, for $x^0 \in D$, satisfy $L(v) = 1$. Then, if a is sufficiently small, there is a unique extremal curve $\sigma(t)$, $0 \leq t \leq a$, satisfying $\sigma(0) = x^0$, $\sigma'(0) = v$, $L(\sigma'(t)) = 1$ for $0 \leq t \leq a$. Further, a can be chosen uniformly as v varies over a compact subset of the subset of $T(D)$ defined by $L = 1$.

Proof. If $x(\sigma(t)) = x(t)$, it must satisfy

$$\frac{d}{dt}L_{n+i}\!\left(x(t),\frac{dx}{dt}\right) = L_i\!\left(x(t),\frac{dx}{dt}\right)$$

$$= L_{n+i,\,j}\frac{dx}{dt} + L_{n+i,\,n+j}\frac{d^2 x_j}{dt^2},$$

$$\frac{d}{dt}L\!\left(x(t),\frac{dx}{dt}\right) = L_j\frac{dx_j}{dt} + L_{n+j}\frac{d^2 x_j}{dt^2} = 0.$$

We must show that these equations are equivalent to a system of differential equations of the form

$$\frac{d^2 x_i}{dt^2} = F_i\!\left(x(t),\frac{dx}{dt}\right).$$

To do this, it suffices to prove that the $n \times (n+1)$ matrix

$$\begin{pmatrix} L_{n+i,\,n+j} \\ L_{n+j} \end{pmatrix}$$

has rank n at every point $(x,\dot{x})$ where $L(x,\dot{x}) = 1$. Suppose, then, that there is a relation of the form

$$\lambda L_{n+j} + \lambda_i L_{n+i,\,n+j} = 0.$$

Proceed as in the proof of Lemma 15.3. Multiply by $\dot{x}_j$, and use the Euler relations to infer that $\lambda = 0$. Then, since rank $(L_{n+i,\,n+j}) = n - 1$, there is a relation of the form $\lambda_i = \rho \dot{x}_i$. In particular, the nullity is 1; hence the rank is n.

LEMMA 15.6

Let L be a regular, homogeneous Lagrangian on a domain D. Then the 2-form $d\theta(L)$ restricted to the submanifold $L = 1$ has rank $2(n - 1)$. In particular, at each $v \in T(D)$ with $L(v) = 1$, there is a unique (up to scalar multiple) tangent vector to v that is a characteristic vector of the 2-form $d\theta(L)$ and is tangent to the hypersurface $L = 1$.

Proof.

$$d\theta(L) = L_{n+i,\,n+j}\, d\dot{x}_j \wedge dx_i + L_{n+i,\,j}\, dx_j \wedge dx_i.$$

We shall prove that

$$(L_{n+i,\,n+j}\, d\dot{x}_j\, d\dot{x}_j \wedge dx_i)^{n-1} \wedge dL \neq 0. \tag{15.17}$$

This will obviously prove that $(d\theta(L))^{n-1} \neq 0$ when restricted to $L = 1$, as required, since the second term for $d\theta(L)$ will contribute no term in $d\dot{x}_j$. Note that when $d\dot{x}_j$ and dx_j are subject to the same linear transformations with constant coefficients, $(L_{n+i,\,n+j}(v))$ changes as the matrix of a quadratic form. Hence, in trying to prove that

$$(L_{n+i,\,n+j}\, d\dot{x}_j \wedge dx_i)^{n-1}_v \neq 0,$$

there is no loss of generality to suppose that the symmetric matrix $(L_{n+i,\,n+j}(v))$ is diagonal, with eigenvalues $(\lambda_1, \ldots, \lambda_{n-1}, 0)$. (There is only one zero eigenvalue, since we know that rank $(L_{n+i,\,n+j}) = n - 1$.) Then

$$(L_{n+i,\,n+j}\, d\dot{x}_j \wedge dx_i)^{n-1}_v = (\lambda_1\, d\dot{x}_1 \wedge dx_1 + \cdots + \lambda_{n-1}\, d\dot{x}_{n-1} \wedge dx_n)^{n-1}$$

$$= \lambda_1 \cdots \lambda_{n-1}\, d\dot{x}_1 \wedge dx_1 \wedge \cdots \wedge d\dot{x}_{n-1} \wedge dx_{n-1}.$$

Now $dL = L_i\, dx_i + L_{n+i}\, dx_i$. Now $L_{n+i,\,n+j}(v)\dot{x}_j(v) = 0 = \lambda_i\, \dot{x}_i(v)$ (no summation), whence $\dot{x}_i(v) = 0$ for $i < n$. But, $1 = L_{n+i}(v)\dot{x}_i(v) = L_{2n}(v)x_{2n}(v)$. This proves (15.17) and hence the lemma.

Now we can turn to the proof of Theorem 15.3. Let $x^0 = \sigma(0) \in \phi(D')$, and let $v^0 = \sigma'(0)$. By hypothesis, v^0 is perpendicular to $\phi(D')$. By Lemma 15.4, if D is sufficiently small, there is a mapping $\chi: \phi(D') \to T(D)$ such that for each $x \in \phi(D')$, $\chi(x) \in D_x$ is a vector that is perpendicular to $\phi(D')$ and such that $L(\chi(x)) = 1$. Thus, the mapping χ is an integral manifold of $\theta(L)$; hence also an integral manifold of $d\theta(L)$. By Lemma 15.4, $\chi(x)$ is not tangent to $\phi(D')$ for $x \in \phi(D')$. By Lemma 15.5, the characteristic curve of $d\theta(L)$ beginning at $\chi(x)$ and lying on $L = 1$ is the tangent vector curve to the extremal of L beginning at x and tangent there to v. In particular, the unique (up to a scalar multiple) characteristic vector field of $d\theta(L)$ is not tangent to the submanifold of $T(D)$ defined by χ; hence Theorem 13.2 can be applied to construct an n-dimensional integral manifold of $d\theta(L)$ passing through the one already defined by χ. Project this integral submanifold down to D: This amounts to constructing, for a and D sufficiently small, a map $\delta: D' \times [0, a] \to \bar{D}$ having the following properties:

(a) $\delta(x', 0) = \phi(x')$ for $x' \in D'$.

(b)   For each x', the curve $t \to \delta(x', t)$ is an extremal of L. The tangent vector to this curve at $t = 0$ is $\chi(\phi(x'))$. L has the value 1 on its tangent vector field.

(c)   Construct the mapping $X: D' \times [0, a] \to T(D)$ by assigning to each $(x', t') \in D' \times [0, a]$ the tangent vector to the curve $t \to \delta(x', t)$ at t. Then X is an integral manifold of $d\theta(L)$.

Notice now, since $\chi(x)$ is not tangent to $\phi(D')$ for $x \in \phi(D')$, that the mapping δ has nonzero Jacobian; that is, no nonzero tangent vector to $D' \times [0, a]$ can be mapped into 0 by δ (if a is sufficiently small). Hence we can suppose, if D is taken small enough, that $\delta(D' \times [0, a]) = D$, and that δ has an inverse map. Having made this identification, it should be clear that the map X is the extremal vector field of L that we are looking for.

As a bonus from this proof, we obtain the following geometric-physical picture of how the extremal field is constructed: For $t \in [0, a]$, let $\phi_t: D' \to D$ be the map assigning $\delta(x', t)$ to each $x' \in D'$. We construct the map $\chi_t: \phi_t(D') \to T(D)$ by assigning $X(x', t')$ to each $\phi_t(x')$. By Theorem 13.6, each map χ_t is an integral submanifold of $\theta(L)$; that is, for $x \in \phi_t(D')$, $\chi_t(x)$ is perpendicular to $\phi_t(D')$.

Mapping $t \to \phi_t$ defines a " wave " traveling through D, guided along by the " rays " that are the integral curves of X. If—as in geometrical optics defined by Fermat's principle—$L(\sigma)$, for a curve σ, represents the time a light ray takes to move along the curve, the surfaces $\phi_t(D')$ represent the wave fronts at time t for light rays starting at $t = 0$ on $\phi(D')$. W, the characteristic function of the extremal field, is defined by the condition that its value of $\phi_t(D')$ is t, that is, the time needed for the beam of light rays to get from the initial surface. Thus, inverting the historical order, we arrive at the picture that guided Hamilton in discovering " Hamilton–Jacobi theory."

Exercises

1.   Prove that Euler's equations (15.2) are necessary conditions for an extremal.

2.   Take a variational problem of minimal complexity (for example, a

Lagrangian $L(x, \dot{x}, t)$, where x is a real number). Discuss carefully the differentiability properties of extremals. One interesting question: If the curve is only C^1, the notion of extremal is well defined. However, Euler's equation (15.2) requires it and L to be C^2. How does one modify things? Under what conditions does a C^1 extremal have to be C^2. What are the conditions that an extremal be piecewise C^2?

16 Groups of Symmetries of
Variational Problems: Applications to Mechanics

The role played by transformation groups that leave a variational system invariant can often be best understood from the more abstract, manifold point of view. Hence we shall pause to show how the basic machinery of the calculus of variations can be formulated in coordinate-free terms for manifolds. As a bonus, we shall obtain a useful way of developing the differential equation for extremals in terms of an arbitrary basis of differential forms, which has great advantages in certain types of calculations.

Let M be a manifold; $F(M)$ denotes its ring of (C^{∞}) real-valued functions, $V(M)$ the set of its vector fields, $T(M) = \bigcup_{p \in M} M_p$ its tangent bundle. A *Lagrangian* on M is just a real-valued function on $T(M) \times R$, usually denoted by a letter such as L. (R = the real numbers, usually parametrized by t.) Such a function enables one to define a real-valued function $\sigma \to \mathbf{L}(\sigma)$ on curves σ in M. If σ is a map: $[a, b] \to M$, then

$$\mathbf{L}(\sigma) = \int_a^b L(\sigma'(t), t)\, dt,$$

where $t \to \sigma'(t) \in M_{\sigma(t)}$ is the tangent vector field to σ. As in Chapter 12, one defines the extremals of L as the curves σ that have the property that σ is a " critical point " of $\mathbf{L}$ restricted to the space of all curves going from $\sigma(a)$ to $\sigma(b)$. (For simplicity, we shall consider only *ordinary* variational problems in this chapter; that is, we shall impose no additional constraints that the tangent vector field to σ must satisfy.)

To give the Euler equations for the extremals in coordinate-free form, introduce the *Cartan 1-form* $\theta(L)$, a 1-differential form on $T(M) \times R$. This can be defined by using a coordinate system, as in Chapter 15. The reader may find it useful to see a more general definition in terms of an arbitrary basis $(\omega_1, \ldots, \omega_n)$ of differential 1-forms in an open set U of M. Adopt the following range of indices and summation convention:

$$1 \le i, j, \ldots \le n = \dim M.$$

Since no confusion is likely, let ω_i also denote the differential forms on the open subset of $T(M) \times R$ lying above U, obtained by pulling back via the projection map. Of course we must then denote by y_i the real-valued functions defined by ω_i on $T(M)$; hence also on $T(M) \times R$:

$$y_i(v) = \omega_i(v) \qquad \text{for } v \in T(M).$$

At any rate, (ω_i, dy_i, dt) forms a local basis for differential forms on $T(M) \times R$. Suppose, then, that

$$dL = L_i \omega_i + L_{n+i}\, dy_i + L_t\, dt.$$

Now

$$\theta(L) = L_{n+i}\omega_i - (L_{n+i}y_i - L)\, dt.$$

One immediately sees that this reduces to the 1-form, introduced in Chapter 15, by specializing to the case where $\omega_i = dx_i$, with $(x_1, \ldots, x_n)$ functions on U defining a coordinate system. As an independent check on this fact, let us verify that $\theta(L)$ remains unchanged when a different basis (ω_i') of 1-forms for U is used. Suppose that $\omega_i' = A_{ij}\omega_j$. Then also

$$y_i' = A_{\cdot j}y_j,$$

$$dL = L_i'\omega_i' + L_{n+i}'\, dy_i' + L_t'\, dt \equiv L_{n+i}'A_{ij}\, dy_j \qquad (\text{modulo } \omega_i, dt).$$

Hence,

$$L_{n+j} = L_{n+i}'A_{ij}.$$
$$\theta'(L) = L_{n+i}'\omega_i' - (L_{n+i}'y_i' - L)\, dt$$
$$= L_{n+i}'A_{ij}\omega_j - (L_{n+i}'A_{ij}y_j - L)\, dt$$
$$= L_{n+j}\omega_j - (L_{n+j}y_j - L)\, dt$$
$$= \theta(L),$$

which expresses the invariance of $\theta(L)$.

We state another property of $\theta(L)$: If $t \to \sigma(t)$, $a \leq t \leq b$, is a curve in M, if $t \to (\sigma'(t), t) = \gamma(t)$ is its extended curve in $T(M) \times R$, then

$$\int_a^b L(\sigma'(t), t)\, dt = \int_a^b \theta(L)(\gamma'(t))\, dt.$$

Thus, by "lifting" to the space $T(M) \times R$ sitting over M, we have converted a "nonlinear" Lagrangian L to a "linear" one, $\theta(L)$. (This procedure of lifting to a higher dimensional space to simplify the structure of a geometric object is typical of Cartan's entire approach to differential geometry.)

We now recognize that a curve $t \to \sigma(t)$ in M is an *extremal* for L; that is, it satisfies the Euler equations if and only if its extended curve $t \to (\sigma'(t), t) = \gamma(t)$ in $T(M) \times R$ is a characteristic curve for the differential form $d\theta(L)$, that is, satisfies

$$\gamma'(t) \lrcorner\, d\theta(L) = 0.$$

As we have seen in Chapter 13, the study of the characteristic curves of a closed 2-form is more or less identical with Hamilton–Jacobi theory.

Let us work out these conditions explicitly:

$$d\theta(L) = d(L_{n+i}(\omega_i - y_i\,dt) + L\,dt)$$
$$= dL_{n+i} \wedge (\omega_i - y_i\,dt) + L_{n+i}(d\omega_i - dy_i \wedge dt)$$
$$+ L_i\omega_i \wedge dt + L_{n+i}\,dy_i \wedge dt$$
$$= dL_{n+i} \wedge (\omega_i - y_i\,dt) + L_{n+i}\,d\omega_i + L_i\omega_i \wedge dt$$
$$= dL_{n+i} \wedge (\omega_i - y_i\,dt) + L_i\omega_i \wedge dt + L_{n+i}C_{jki}\omega_j \wedge \omega_k,$$

where the (C_{jki}) are the functions such that

$$d\omega_i = C_{jki}\omega_j \wedge \omega_k, \qquad C_{jki} + C_{kji} = 0.$$

Now

$$(\omega_i - y_i\,dt)(\gamma'(t)) = \omega_i(\sigma'(t)) - y_i(\gamma(t)) = 0,$$

$$dL_{n+i}(\gamma'(t)) = \frac{d}{dt}L_{n+i}(\sigma'(t), t), \qquad \text{etc.}$$

Hence the conditions that $\gamma(t) = (\sigma'(t), t)$ be a characteristic curve of $d\theta(L)$ are

$$\frac{d}{dt}L_{n+i}(\sigma'(t), t)(\omega_i - y_i\,dt) - L_i(\sigma'(t), t)\omega_i + L_i\,y_i\,dt + L_{n+i}C_{jki}\,y_j\,\omega_k = 0.$$

Now ω_i and dt are independent differential forms; hence these equations imply that the coefficient of ω_i is zero, that is:

$$\frac{d}{dt}L_{n+i}(\sigma'(t), t) - L_i(\sigma'(t), t) + L_{n+k}C_{jik}(\sigma'(t), t)\omega_j(\sigma'(t)) = 0.$$

These differential equations for σ are the *Euler(-Lagrange) equations* with respect to the basis $(\omega_1, \ldots, \omega_n)$. Notice, in case the $\omega_1, \ldots, \omega_n$ are the differentials of a set of coordinate functions $x_1, \ldots, x_n$ for M, that they reduce (since $C_{jik} = 0$) to the classical Euler equations

$$\frac{d}{dt}\frac{\partial L}{\partial \dot{x}_i} - \frac{\partial L}{\partial x_i} = 0$$

that were derived in Chapter 15. The more general equations are very useful in certain mechanical problems (for example, in rigid body dynamics) where a basis for differential forms can be found more readily than for a "natural" coordinate system.

If the variational problem is nonhomogeneous, that is, if extremals cannot be freely reparametrized, *regularity* of the variational problem is determined by the condition

$$\theta(L)^n = \theta(L) \wedge \cdots \wedge \theta(L) \neq 0.$$
$$\underset{n \text{ factors}}{\qquad\qquad}$$

Alternately, this can be expressed by the condition $\det(L_{n+i, n+j}) \neq 0$, where

$$dL_{n+i} \equiv L_{n+i, n+j} \, dy_j \qquad (\text{modulo } \omega_i, \, dt).$$

If the variational problem is time-independent and homogeneous, that is, if

$$L(\lambda v) = \lambda L(v) \qquad \text{for } \lambda > 0,$$

then $(L_{n+i} y_i - L) = 0$; hence $\theta(L)$ can be considered as a 1-form on $T(M)$. Regularity is now determined by the condition:

$$\text{Dimension of the characteristic vector of } \theta(L) = 2$$

or

$$\text{rank}(L_{n+i, n+j}) = (n-1).$$

An *extremal vector field* for the variational problem can now be defined as a cross-section mapping $\Phi \colon M \times R \to T(M) \times R$ assigning to each pair $(p, t) \in M \times R$ a tangent vector $\Phi(p, t) \in M_p$ such that

$$\Phi^*(d\theta(L)) = 0.$$

A function $S(p, t)$ on $M \times R$ such that

$$dS = \Phi^*(\theta(L))$$

is a *solution* of the *Hamilton–Jacobi partial differential equation* associated with the variational problem. The *rays* of an extremal field are the curves $\sigma(t)$ that are solutions of the system of ordinary differential equations:

$$\sigma'(t) = \Phi(\sigma(t), t).$$

They *are* extremals of the variational problem, as described above, but such n-parameter families of extremals play an important role in proving that extremals really do minimize, and are very important in physics (for example, in describing the wave-particle duality).

Let $\phi \colon N \to M \times R$ be a submanifold of $M \times R$. A " vector field " on N is a mapping $v \colon N \to T(M)$ such that $v(p) \in \phi(p)$ for $p \in N$. Such a vector field is *perpendicular* to N if $v^*(\theta(L)) = 0$. If Φ is an extremal vector field, with S the associated solution of the Hamilton–Jacobi equation, and N is a submanifold defined by $S = $ constant, then one sees that Φ restricted to N is such a perpendicular vector field.

Now suppose that L and L' are Lagrangians on manifolds M and M', that $\phi \colon M' \to M$ is a map, and $\phi_* \colon T(M') \to T(M)$ is the differential of ϕ. We shall also use ϕ_* to denote the map: $T(M') \times R \to T(M) \times R$, which acts identically on R. Suppose that

$$(\phi_*)^*(L) = L'.$$

Then, also, as we have proved in Chapter 15 (Theorem 15.1)

$$(\phi_*)^*(\theta(L)) = \theta(L').$$

For example, if ϕ is a diffeomorphism between M and M', it is clear that this implies that ϕ maps an extremal of L' into an extremal of L. If $M = M'$, $L = L'$, such a ϕ can be regarded as a *symmetry* of the variational problem. A Lie group G acting on M as diffeomorphisms of M can be regarded as a *group of symmetries* if each individual transformation is a symmetry. Now, the action of G on M can be *prolonged* to an action of G on $T(M) \times R$ by sending $\phi \in G$ into ϕ_*. (It is left to the reader to verify that this actually defines an action of G on $T(M) \times R$.) This action of G preserves $\theta(L)$; hence, also $d\theta(L)$. Now the Lie algebra of G also acts as a Lie algebra of vector fields on $T(M) \times R$, since the action of a Lie group on a manifold gives rise to an action of its Lie algebra as vector fields. For example, if an element X in the Lie algebra of G is realized as a vector field

$$X = A_i \frac{\partial}{\partial x_i}$$

on M (using a local coordinate system $x_1, \ldots, x_n$ for M), the *prolonged* vector field is

$$\dot{X} = A_i \frac{\partial}{\partial x_i} + \frac{\partial A_i}{\partial x_j} \dot{x}_j \frac{\partial}{\partial \dot{x}_i}$$

on $T(M) \times R$, as in Chapter 15.† Thus we shall *automatically* have

$$\dot{X}(\theta(L)) = 0, \qquad \dot{X}(d\theta(L)) = 0.$$

These basic geometric facts suggest that we split up the problem of discussing groups of symmetries into its "Hamiltonian" and "Lagrangian" components.

Symmetry Groups from the Point of View of Hamilton–Jacobi Theory

We shall now change our point of view. We regard Hamilton–Jacobi theory as the study of the characteristic curves of a closed 2-form, independently of whether the 2-form arises from a variational problem.

---

† With one slight modification, that is, we leave off $+(\partial/\partial t)$ in the definition of $\dot{x}$, thus regarding $\dot{x}$ as acting trivially on the time coordinate.

Let P be a manifold. (By choosing P, we mean to emphasize that the typical case is that where P is the "phase space" of a mechanical problem.) Let ω be a closed 2-form on P. Recall that a vector $v \in T(P)$ or vector field $X \in V(M)$ is the *characteristic* for ω if

$$v \lrcorner \omega = 0, \qquad X \lrcorner \omega = 0.$$

We suppose that the dimension of the characteristic vectors (or, equivalently, the rank of ω) is constant on P. A vector field $Y \in V(M)$ *leaves ω invariant* if $Y(\omega) = 0$.

THEOREM 16.1

Let ω be a closed 2-differential form of constant rank on P. Let

$$C = \{X \in V(P): X \lrcorner \omega = 0\}, \qquad I = \{Y \in V(P): Y(\omega) = 0\}.$$

Then

$$[I, I] \subset I, \qquad [C, I] \subset C.$$

In other words, C is an ideal in the Lie algebra I. The one-parameter transformation group generated by a $Y \in I$ permutes the characteristic curves of ω.

Proof. Most of this follows trivially from the rules of operation for vector fields and differential forms. For example, we prove $[C, I] \subset I$. For $X \in C$, $Y \in I$,

$$[X, Y] \lrcorner \omega = Y(X \lrcorner \omega) - X \lrcorner Y(\omega) = 0;$$

hence $[X, Y] \in C$.

To prove $C \subset I$, suppose $X \in C$. Then $X(\omega) = X \lrcorner d\omega + d(X \lrcorner \omega) = 0$. We leave the last remark as an exercise.

Now, in accordance with general group-theoretical principles, one should regard I as the Lie algebra of the transformation group of all diffeomorphisms ϕ of P that preserve ω, that is, that satisfy $\phi^*(\omega) = \omega$. The reader should be warned, however, that this group cannot be regarded as a Lie group. (Roughly, it cannot be described by a finite number of parameters.) Hence this relation between the group and Lie algebra will remain in the background as intuitive motivation.

Let $Y \in I$. Using another of the rules of operation concerning vector fields and forms, we have

$$0 = Y(\omega) = Y \lrcorner d\omega + d(Y \lrcorner \omega),$$

hence $d(Y \lrcorner \omega) = 0$. Thus the mapping $Y \to Y \lrcorner \omega$ sends I into the set of closed 1-forms on P. The kernel is C. Since C is an ideal, the image in the set of closed 1-forms inherits the Lie algebra structure associated with I/C.

What precisely is this image in the set of closed 1-forms? Notice that $\theta = Y \lrcorner \omega$ satisfies

$$X \lrcorner \theta = 0 \qquad \text{for all } X \in I. \tag{16.1}$$

Note another useful fact:

If ψ is a 1-form satisfying $d\psi = \omega$, and if $Y(\psi) = 0$, then

$$d(Y \lrcorner \psi) = - Y \lrcorner \omega. \tag{16.2}$$

Before proceeding further in these abstract directions, it may be helpful for the reader to see an example of what this means in more classical language.

EXAMPLE (THE POISSON BRACKET)

Suppose dim $P = 2n$, with coordinates $(q_1, \ldots q_n, p_1, \ldots, p_n)$.

$$\omega = dp_i \wedge dq_i \qquad (1 \leq i, j, \ldots, \leq n; \text{ summation convention in force}).$$

We choose this way of labeling coordinates on P so as to suggest the usual terminology in classical mechanics. P is " phase-space," the q are coordinates of "configuration space," and the p are coordinates of " momentum space." Let $Y \in I$.

$$Y \lrcorner \omega = Y(p_i) \, dq_i - Y(q_i) \, dp_i.$$

Since $d(Y \lrcorner \omega) = 0$, and P is a Euclidean space, by the Poincaré lemma there is a function $f \in F(P)$ such that

$$df = Y \lrcorner \omega \qquad \text{or} \qquad \frac{\partial f}{\partial q_i} = Y(p_i); \tag{16.3a}$$

$$\frac{\partial f}{\partial p_i} = - Y(q_i) \qquad \text{or} \qquad Y = - \frac{\partial f}{\partial p_i} \frac{\partial}{\partial q_i} + \frac{\partial f}{\partial q_i} \frac{\partial}{\partial p_i}. \tag{16.3b}$$

Suppose that we turn this around and, given $f \in F(P)$, define Y_f as a vector field on P by the formula (16.3). Then

$$Y_f(\omega) = d(Y_f \lrcorner \omega) + Y_f \lrcorner d\omega = d(df) + 0 = 0.$$

Thus, for $g \in F(P)$,

$$Y_f(g) = \frac{\partial f}{\partial q_i} \frac{\partial g}{\partial p_i} - \frac{\partial f}{\partial p_i} \frac{\partial g}{\partial q_i}. \tag{16.4}$$

The function on the right-hand side of 16.4 is classically called the *Poisson bracket* of the function f and g, and denoted by $\{f, g\}$. Now we have defined it so that

$$df = Y_f \lrcorner \, \omega. \tag{16.3c}$$

Then

$$d\{f, g\} = dY_f(g) = Y_f(dg) = Y_f(Y_g \lrcorner \, \omega) = [Y_f, Y_g] \lrcorner \, \omega.$$

Thus,

$$Y_{\{f, g\}} = [Y_f, Y_g]. \tag{16.5}$$

Equation (16.5) suggests that we regard $F(P)$ as some sort of algebra under the Poisson bracket operation $(f, g) \to \{f, g\}$, and (16.5) then says that the mapping $f \to Y_f$ is an *algebra homomorphism* of $F(P)$ onto the Lie algebra I.

In fact, we shall show that $F(P)$ under $\{ \ , \ \}$ is itself a Lie algebra, so that $f \to Y_f$ is a Lie algebra homomorphism. Skew symmetry: $\{f, g\} = -\{g, f\}$ of the Poisson bracket is obvious from (16.4).

It remains only to prove the Jacobi identity:

$$\{f, \{g, h\}\} = Y_f(\{g, h\}) = Y_f(Y_g(h)) = [Y_f, Y_g](h) + Y_g(Y_f(h))$$

$$= Y_{\{f, g\}}(h) + \{g, \{f, h\}\} = \{\{f, g\}, h\} + \{g, \{f, h\}\},$$

which is precisely the Jacobi identity.

There is an alternative definition of Poisson bracket in terms of exterior multiplication. Note that ω is a 2-form of maximal rank $2n$. Hence $\omega^n \neq 0$. (ω^n = exterior product of n copies of ω.) For $f, g \in F(P)$, $\omega^{n-1} \wedge df \wedge dg$ is a $2n$-form that then must be a multiple of ω^n, say,

$$\omega^{n-1} \wedge df \wedge dg = h\omega^n.$$

Let us find h by applying $Y_f \lrcorner$ to both sides:

$$Y_f \lrcorner \, \omega^{n-1} = (n-1)\omega^{n-2} \wedge df, \qquad Y_f \lrcorner \, \omega^n = n\omega^{n-1} \wedge df$$

(since $df \wedge \omega = (-1)^{2 \cdot 1}\omega \wedge df = \omega \wedge df$), and

$$Y_f \lrcorner \, df = Y_f(f) = \{f, f\} = 0.$$

Finally, then,

$$\omega^{n-1} \wedge df \cdot \{f, g\} = h \cdot n\omega^{n-1} \wedge df.$$

This suggests that we try to prove that $h = \{f, g\}/n$. Since they are functions, it suffices to prove that there is point-by-point equality.

Now, if $df = 0$ at a point, clearly both sides must be zero; hence, equality. If $df \neq 0$, $df \wedge \omega^{n-1}$ is not zero (exercise in exterior algebra; left to the reader); hence, equality again. Finally, then,

$$\omega^{n-1} \wedge df \wedge dg = \frac{\{f, g\}}{n} \omega^n. \tag{16.6}$$

Notice now that we have used only the coordinate system (p_i, q_i) to get the classical formula for Poisson bracket. Then we can sum up our results in coordinate-free form as follows:

THEOREM 16.2

Let P be a manifold of dimension $2n$, and let ω be a differential form on P of rank $2n$. Let I be the Lie algebra of vector fields on P that preserve ω. There is a linear onto mapping: $F(P) \to I$, denoted by $f \to Y_f$, satisfying (in fact, defined by) (16.3c). Defining the Poisson bracket of f; $g \in F(P)$, denoted by $\{f, g\}$, by (16.4) makes $F(P)$ into a Lie algebra such that the mapping onto I is a Lie algebra homomorphism with kernel the constant functions. Equation (16.6) provides an alternate definition for Poisson bracket in terms of exterior algebra.

The geometric properties of the Poisson bracket operation can be summed up as follows: Each $f \in F(P)$ gives rise (modulo the usual difficulties in extending integral curves of vector fields, which we shall ignore here) to a one-parameter group of diffeomorphisms on P that preserves the form ω. The condition $\{f, g\} = 0$ means that g is constant on the orbit of the group, that is, that g is an integral of the ordinary differential equations defining the orbit. If (q_i, p_i) is a coordinate system for P such that

$$\omega = dp_i \wedge dq_i$$

(that is, if ω is in canonical form with respect to the coordinate system), then the differential equations for the orbits of the group generated by f are just

$$\frac{dq_i}{dt} = -\frac{\partial f}{\partial p_i}, \qquad \frac{dp_i}{dt} = \frac{\partial f}{\partial q_i}.$$

These, it will be recognized, are just the Hamilton equations with Hamiltonian f.

Let us rephrase some of these results in a more informal way, which is useful in physics. We are *given* a "phase space" P and a 2-form of ω of maximal rank on P. The functions on P are the *observables* on phase space. With the help of ω, the observables can be made into a Lie algebra. There is a mapping that assigns a one-parameter group of ω-preserving transformations on P. (Classically, a ω-preserving diffeomorphism is called a *canonical transformation*.) This is not quite 1-1, but the kernel is unimportant (for classical mechanics); that is, just the constant functions. In physics, choosing a particular mechanical system with phase-space P amounts to choosing a distinguished observable H, to be called the *Hamiltonian* (or energy). The corresponding one-parameter transformation group on P is to be regarded as determining the evolution of the mechanical system with time: A one-parameter group of symmetries of the mechanical system with Hamiltonian H is determined by an "observable" f with $\{H, f\} = 0$.

The main point to keep in mind is this correspondence between "observables," that is, functions on phase space, and certain one-parameter groups of diffeomorphisms of phase space, called "canonical transformations." It is this structure that quantum mechanics has in common with classical mechanics, but in quantum theory the phase-space P must be regarded as being infinite dimensional.

As application of these ideas, we shall prove two simple theorems concerning the global properties of Hamiltonian systems. As above, let P be an even dimensional manifold, carrying a closed 2-form ω of maximal rank. For $f \in F(P)$, let Y_f be the vector field such that $df = Y_f \lrcorner \omega$. Then the Poisson bracket of f and g is

$$Y_f(g) = \{f, g\}.$$

Two functions f and g are said to be *in involution*† if $\{f, g\} = 0$. Thus, if f and $H \in F(P)$, f and H are in involution if f is an integral of Y_H, that is, if f is constant along the solutions of the Hamilton equations with Hamiltonian H. The next theorem due to Arnold [1] gives a good qualitative picture of the global conditions that a given Hamiltonian system must satisfy in order that it admit a "large" number of integrals that are in involution.

THEOREM 16.3

Suppose $\dim P = 2n$, and that n functions $f_1, \ldots, f_n$ are given on P that are in involution with each other and with H. Let Q be a connected component of

$$\{p \in P : f_1(p) = 0 = \cdots = f_n(p)\}.$$

Suppose that:

(a) Q is compact.
(b) The forms $df_1, \ldots, df_n$ are linearly independent at each point of Q.

Then Q is diffeomorphic to a torus, in such a way that Y_H goes over into a vector field on the torus generated by a one-parameter subgroup.‡

Proof. Suppose for the moment that just (b) is satisfied. Then $Y_{f_1}, \ldots, Y_{f_n}$ are vector fields on P that are tangent to Q and are linearly independent at every point of Q. Further, (b) guarantees that Q is a submanifold of P. Then $Y_{f_1}, \ldots, Y_{f_n}$ define a basis for vector fields on Q. Further, they commute, as

---

† This is the classical terminology, which probably should be changed because it is confusing to the modern reader. It comes from the classical theory of partial differential equations.

‡ That is, regarding the torus as the underlying space of a compact Abelian Lie group. Thus, either all integral curves of Y_H on Q are closed or they behave in the same way as do the one-parameter subgroups going off at an irrational angle.

is obvious from the condition that the $f_1, \ldots, f_n$ are all in involution. Then Y_H can be written in Q in the form

$$Y_H = g_1 Y_{f_1} + \cdots + g_n Y_{f_n}, \qquad \text{with} \quad g_1, \ldots, g_n \in F(Q).$$

Now the condition that Y_H commute with $Y_{f_1}, \ldots, Y_{f_n}$ forces $g_1 = $ constant, $\ldots, g_n = $ constant. Now, if Q is compact, the $Y_{f_1}, \ldots, Y_{f_n}$ generate a global connected Abelian Lie group of diffeomorphisms of Q; hence Q is the underlying manifold of a compact, connected Abelian Lie group, that is, a torus.   Q.E.D.

Now let P continue to be a manifold of even dimension, with a closed 2-form ω of maximal rank. Let D be an open subset of P whose boundary in P consists of a number of submanifolds of P. Let Y be a vector field defined in a neighborhood of D such that

(a) Y is tangent to the submanifolds constituting the boundary of D;
(b) $Y(\omega) = 0$.

Suppose, then, that there exists a function f such that $df = Y \lrcorner \omega$. (Recall that $d(Y \lrcorner \omega) = 0$, so there are certain topological restrictions to the global existence of this f.) Then the critical points of f that occur *inside* D are also zero points of Y. This can be exploited (see, for example, Theorem 16.4) to show the existence of zero points for Y if one knows for some a priori reason that the maxima and minima of f do not occur on the boundary. This can be made explicit as follows:

Let p be a point on the boundary of D in P. Let us extend the notion of tangent vector to D by saying that a tangent vector $v \in P_p$ *belongs to* D_p if there is a curve $t \to \sigma(t)$, with $\sigma(0) = p$, defined for sufficiently small t and lying in the closure of D, such that $\sigma'(0) = v$. Then, if such a p is also a critical point of f restricted to the closure of D,

$$v(f) = 0 = \omega(Y(p), v) \qquad \text{for all } v \in D_p.$$

This condition can, under suitable hypotheses on Y, often be used to conclude that $Y(p) = 0$. Now, we specialize.

THEOREM 16.4

Let D be the region between two concentric circles in the (x, y)-plane. Let $t \to \phi_t$ be a one-parameter semigroup area-preserving diffeomorphism of D such that:

> Each ϕ_t rotates the inner and outer boundary of D in opposite senses, with no fixed points on the boundary. Then the semigroup has at least two fixed points inside D.

Proof. Let Y be the vector field in D which is the infinitesimal generator of $t \to \phi_t$. The area-preserving condition requires that $Y(\omega) = 0$, where $\omega = dx \wedge dy$. Hence also, $d(Y(\omega)) = 0$. We want to assert the existence of a function in D such that

$$df = Y \lrcorner \omega = A\, dy - B\, dx, \qquad \text{where} \quad Y = A\frac{\partial}{\partial x} + B\frac{\partial}{\partial y}.$$

Now D is not simply connected, but the condition for the existence of f is seen to be that the integral of $Y \lrcorner \omega$ around a boundary circle be zero, or that the line integral of the vector field

$$X = A\frac{\partial}{\partial y} - B\frac{\partial}{\partial y}$$

around the boundary circle is zero. Now X and Y are perpendicular vector fields. Our assumptions on each ϕ_t guarantee that Y has the behavior indicated in Fig. 3, where D is the region between the two circles. The full arrows indicate Y, which is tangent to the two boundary circles. Hence X, represented by the dotted arrows, is perpendicular to the boundary circles, the line integral of X around each is zero, and such an f exists.

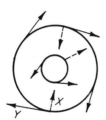

FIGURE 3

Now let p be a critical point of f restricted to the closure of D. Then

$$\omega(Y, X) = Y \lrcorner \omega(X) = A^2 + B^2.$$

At most changing Y to $-Y$, we can suppose that X always points *into* D on the boundary. Then p cannot be on the boundary, for otherwise

$$0 = X(f)(p) = df(X)(p) = Y \lrcorner \omega(X)(p) = A^2 + B^2(p),$$

which contradicts that $t \to \phi_t$ has no fixed points on the boundary. Hence, f has at least two critical points (namely, its maximum and minimum) inside D, which then must be fixed points for the semigroup. Q.E.D.

Remark. The famous Poincaré–Birkhoff fixed-point theorem asserts that a *single* area-preserving homeomorphism of D that rotates the boundary of D in opposite directions must have at least two fixed points. Thus, Theorem 16.4 is the infinitesimal, differentiable version of their theorem. The proof we have given of Theorem 16.4 is considerably simpler than any existing proof of the stronger theorem. (Notice that, even if the transformation is differentiable, Theorem 16.4 cannot be applied to a single one, since there is no reason to expect that it can be embedded in a whole semigroup. Perhaps this *is* true, but no doubt proving it would be considerably harder than proving the Poincaré–Birkhoff theorem.) It remains a challenge to topologists to formulate and prove a general fixed-point theorem including the Poincaré–Birkhoff theorem, whose proof now uses very special techniques.

This completes our discussion of the case where P is even dimensional, and where ω is of rank equal to the dimension of P.

Let us now return to the general case, where ω is a closed 2-form on P whose rank is constant. As we have seen, if $Y \in V(P)$ satisfies $Y(\omega) = 0$, then $d(Y \lrcorner \omega) = 0$. Now, if the Poincaré lemma applies, there is a function $f \in F(P)$ such that $df = Y \lrcorner \omega$. At any rate, we shall suppose that such a function exists. For example, this is so if the first Betti number of P is zero. Of course f is only really defined up to an additive constant, but this is not particularly bothersome.

THEOREM 16.5

Let ω be a closed 2-form on a manifold P of constant rank on a manifold P; let $Y \in V(P)$ and $f \in F(P)$ satisfy $Y(\omega) = 0$, $df = Y \lrcorner \omega$. Then f is a constant along all characteristic curves of ω.

Proof. If X is a characteristic vector field for ω, that is, if $X \lrcorner \omega = 0$, then

$$X(f) = df(X) = \omega(X, Y) = (X \lrcorner \omega)(Y) = 0. \qquad \text{Q.E.D.}$$

We see the general setting for the relation between one-parameter groups of symmetries and functions on phase space which are integrals of motion that is typical of all Hamiltonian mechanics. (Physicists usually know this as " E. Noether's theorem.")

THEOREM 16.6

Let ω, P, Y and f be as in Theorem 16.5. Then a point $p \in P$ is a critical point of f if and only if the integral curve of Y beginning at p is a characteristic curve of ω.

Proof. If $Y(p) = 0$, this is true (since a point curve must be considered as a characteristic curve of ω). Suppose, then, that $Y(p) \neq 0$. Since the theorem is a local one, we may suppose coordinates $(x_1, \ldots, x_r)$ have been chosen for P so that

$$Y = \frac{\partial}{\partial x_1}, \qquad x_1(p) = 0 = \cdots = x_r(p).$$

Thus, if

$$\omega = \sum_{1 \le i, j \le r} a_{ij}\, dx_i \wedge dx_j,$$

$Y(\omega) = 0$ forces

$$\frac{\partial a_{ij}}{\partial x_1} = 0, \qquad Y \,\lrcorner\, \omega = \sum_{2 \le j \le r} a_{1j}\, dx_j.$$

Hence, $df(p) = Y(p) \,\lrcorner\, \omega$ is zero if and only if $a_{1j}^*(0, \ldots, 0) = 0$, where $a_{ij}^*(\,, \ldots,)$ is the function on R^r such that $a_{ij}^*(x_1(p), \ldots, x_r(p)) = a_{ij}(p)$. But if $\sigma'(t) = Y(\sigma(t))$, $\sigma(0) = p$, then

$$x_i(\sigma(t)) = 0 \quad \text{if } i > 1; \qquad t \quad \text{if } i = 1.$$

$$\sigma'(t) \,\lrcorner\, \omega = \sum_{1 \le i, j \le r} a_{1j}(\sigma(t))\, dx_i(\sigma'(t))\, dx_j$$

$$= \sum_{2 \le j \le r} a_{1j}^*(t, 0, \ldots, 0)\, dx_j.$$

But $\partial a_{1j}/\partial x_1 = 0$ forces $a_{1j}^*(t, 0, \ldots, 0) = a_{1j}^*(0, \ldots, 0)$; hence $\sigma'(t) \,\lrcorner\, \omega = 0$ for all t if and only if $df(p) = Y(p) \,\lrcorner\, \omega = 0$. \hfill Q.E.D.

Return to the Calculus of Variations

M is a manifold of dimension m; L is a Lagrangian on M, that is, a real-valued function on $T(M)$; and $P = T(M) \times R$. (For simplicity, we consider only time-independent Lagrangians on M.) We may as well work with coordinates. Suppose x_i ($1 \le i, j, \ldots \le n = \dim M$; summation convention) is a coordinate system for M. Then $(x_i, \dot{x}_i, t)$ forms a coordinate system for P, with $\dot{x}_i(v) = dx_i(v)$, t the coordinate on R. The x_i are just the original x_i on M pulled up to $T(M)$ with no change in notation. The Cartan 1-form associated with L is then

$$\theta(L) = L_{n+i}\, dx_i - (L_{n+i}\dot{x}_i - L)\, dt,$$

ω is then $d\theta(L)$. A first source of symmetry vector fields of ω is obtained by taking a vector field on M, whose associated one-parameter group preserves the extremals of L, and prolonging to P:

$$X = A_i \frac{\partial}{\partial x_i}, \qquad Y = \dot{X} = A_i \frac{\partial}{\partial x_i} + \frac{\partial A_i}{\partial x_j} \dot{x}_j \frac{\partial}{\partial \dot{x}_i}.$$

We know that

$$Y(\theta(L)) = \theta(Y(L)).$$

We have seen earlier that $\exp(tX)$ permutes the extremals of L if and only if $\dot{X}(L) = 0$. Thus, if X is a vector field on M that generates "symmetries" of L, we are in position to apply (16.2), and Theorems 16.3 and 16.4. If

$$f_X = \theta(L)(\dot{X}) = L_{n+i} A_i,$$

then f_X is constant along the characteristic curves of $d\theta(L)$; that is, by Theorem 16.1,

$$f_X\left(x(t), \frac{dx}{dt}\right) = \text{constant}$$

for any curve $t \to x(t)$ in M that solves the Euler equations. We call f_X the function on P that is *conjugate* to the vector field X on M.

Now we can discuss where Theorem 16.4 is applicable. We must examine $df_X = d(L_{n+i} A_i)$ for critical points. But

$$d(L_{n+i} A_i) = L_{n+i, \, n+j} A_j \, d\dot{x}_j + (L_{n+i, \, j} A_i + L_{n+i} A_{i, \, j}) \, dx_j.$$

This is equal to zero at a point and forces

$$L_{n+i, \, n+j} A_j = 0, \tag{16.7a}$$

$$L_{n+i, \, j} A_i + L_{n+i} A_{i, \, j} = 0. \tag{16.7b}$$

These equations admit an immediate geometric interpretation in case L is a homogeneous regular Lagrangian, since then rank $(L_{n+i, \, n+j}) = m - 1$, and (A_j) must be a multiple of $(\dot{x}_j)$, say, $\lambda \dot{x}_j$. The second equation becomes

$$0 = L_{j, \, n+i}(x, \dot{x})\lambda \dot{x}_i + L_{n+i}(x, \dot{x}) \frac{\partial A_i}{\partial x_j}.$$

The Euler homogeneous function relations give

$$0 = \lambda L_j\left(x, \frac{A(x)}{\lambda}\right) + L_{n+i}\left(x, \frac{A(x)}{\lambda}\right) \frac{\partial A_i}{\partial x_j} = \frac{\partial}{\partial x_j} L(x, A(x)).$$

Returning to coordinate-free notations, these conditions mean that the point is a critical point of the function $q \to L(X(q))$ on M.

There is a similarly simple geometric answer to the question in case L is a nonhomogeneous, regular Lagrangian. In this case, however, (16.7) gives essentially a trivial answer. For regularity means that $\det(L_{n+i, \, n+j}) \neq 0$;

hence (16.7a) forces $A_j = 0$, that is, the point is a zero point of X. To get a more interesting answer, we must replace $\dot{X}$ by the vector field $\dot{X} + \partial/\partial t$:

$$\theta(L)\left(\dot{X} + \frac{\partial}{\partial t}\right) = L_{n+i}A_i - (L_{n+i}\dot{x}_i - L);$$

that is, we must just subtract from f_X the Hamiltonian function. The critical point conditions for this function become

$$L_{n+i,\,n+j}A_i = L_{n+i,\,n+j}\dot{x}_i, \tag{16.8a}$$

$$\frac{\partial}{\partial x_j}(L_{n+i}A_i - L_{n+i}\dot{x}_i + L) = 0. \tag{16.8b}$$

But (16.8a) and regularity forces $A_i = \dot{x}_i$; hence (16.8b) condenses to

$$L_{n+i}(x, A(x))\frac{\partial A_i}{\partial x_j} + \frac{\partial L}{\partial x_j}(x, A(x)) = 0 \quad \text{or} \quad \frac{\partial}{\partial x_j}(L(x, A(x))) = 0.$$

Hence, geometrically, we get essentially the same answer as in the homogeneous case. We can sum these computations up in the following coordinate-free form.

THEOREM 16.7

Let L be a regular Lagrangian on a manifold M, and let X be a vector field on M that generates a one-parameter group on M permuting the extremals of L; that is, X generates symmetries of L. Then the integral curve of X beginning at q_0 is an extremal of L if and only if q_0 is a critical point of the function $q \to L(X(q))$ on M.

A famous example of this theorem is provided by the particular solution given by Lagrange of the Newtonian 3-body problem, where the three bodies rotate uniformly at the vertices of an equilateral triangle.

Newtonian mechanics. A glance at a book on classical mechanics will convince the reader that most *Newtonian* problems correspond to Lagrangians of the form

$$L(x, \dot{x}) = \tfrac{1}{2}g_{ij}(x)\dot{x}_i\dot{x}_j + a_i(x)\dot{x}_i - V(x). \tag{16.9}$$

(As above, $x_1, \ldots, x_n$ continue to denote coordinates for M, usually the "configuration space.") In fact the $g_{ij}(x)$ are determined by the mass-distributions, the $(a_i(x))$ are components of the *vector potentials*, the $V(x)$ the *scalar potential*, of any force fields that may be present. (For example, problems of motion of charged particles usually involve the $a_i(x)$ in a nontrivial way, while in gravitational or electrostatic problems, only $V(x)$ is present.) In fact this possibility of separating the Lagrangian into the sum of terms involving, respectively, inertial masses, scalar potentials, and vector potentials seems to be characteristic of Newtonian physics and accounts for its simplicity by comparison, say, to Einsteinian physics.

Now let us compute the Hamiltonian function for the Lagrangian given by 16.9,

$$L_{n+i} = g_{ij}\dot{x}_j + a_i, \qquad L_{n+i,\,n+j} = g_{ij}.$$

Thus the variational problem (which is nonhomogeneous) is regular if and only if $\det(g_{ij}) \neq 0$, a condition that we shall suppose is verified.

Let us compute the Hamiltonian function. Put

$$y_i = L_{n+i} = g_{ij}\dot{x}_j + a_i.$$

$$\begin{aligned}
H &= L_{n+i}\dot{x}_i - L \\
&= g_{ij}\dot{x}_i\dot{x}_j - L + a_i\dot{x}_i \\
&= \tfrac{1}{2}g_{ij}\dot{x}_i\dot{x}_j + V(x) \\
&= \tfrac{1}{2}G_{ij}(y_i - a_i)(y_j - a_j) + V(x),
\end{aligned}$$

where $(G_{ij}(x))$ is the inverse matrix to $(g_{ij}(x))$.

Again, this simplicity of the Hamiltonian (that is, total energy) is characteristic of Newtonian physics.

A word as to *why* H is to be regarded as the total energy might be of interest. Most naively, $\tfrac{1}{2}g_{ij}\dot{x}_i\dot{x}_j$ is to be regarded as the "kinetic energy" ($\tfrac{1}{2}$ mass $\times$ (velocity)^2 in terms of elementary physics), and $V(x)$ is the potential energy, so that their sum is to be regarded as the "total energy." Of course, in elementary physics, V and hence H is defined only up to an additive constant. Now the Lagrangian L is time-independent; hence $\partial/\partial t$ is to be regarded as generating a symmetry group on P. The function

$$-\theta(L)\left(\frac{\partial}{\partial t}\right) \equiv H$$

is then to be regarded as the function that is "conjugate" to the symmetry $\partial/\partial t$.

Another more precise way of looking at this is to regard t as another dependent variable, say, $t = x_{n+1}$, and replace the Lagrangian $L(x_1, \ldots, x_n, \dot{x}_1, \ldots, \dot{x}_n)$ by the equivalent *homogeneous* Lagrangian

$$L'(x_1, \ldots, x_{n+1}, \dot{x}_1, \ldots, \dot{x}_{n+1}) = L\left(x_1, \ldots, x_n, \frac{\dot{x}_1}{\dot{x}_{n+1}}, \ldots, \frac{\dot{x}_n}{\dot{x}_{n+1}}\right)\dot{x}_{n+1}.$$

Then

$$L'_{n+1+i} = L_{n+i} \quad \text{for } 1 \le i \le n, \qquad L'_{2n+2} = \sum_{j=1}^{n} -L_{n+j}\frac{\dot{x}_j}{\dot{x}_{n+1}} + L.$$

$$\theta(L') = \sum_{i=1}^{n} L'_{n+1+i}\, dx_i + L'_{2n+2}\, dx_{n+1}$$

$$= \sum_{i=1}^{n} L_{n+i}\left(x, \frac{\dot{x}}{\dot{x}_{n+1}}\right) dx_i - \left(\sum_{i=1}^{n} L_{n+i}\left(x, \frac{\dot{x}}{\dot{x}_{n+1}}\right) - L\left(x, \frac{\dot{x}}{\dot{x}_{n+1}}\right)\right) dx_{n+1}$$

which is just $\theta(L)$ when we identify x_{n+1} with t, and $\dot{x}_{n+1}$ with dt/dt, that is, with 1.

Considered as a group on the configuration space of variables $(x_1, \ldots, x_n, t)$, the group generated by $\partial/\partial t$ is genuinely a group of symmetries for the Lagrangian L', and H is genuinely its conjugate function on phase space. This identification of the total energy with the function that is conjugate to time translation is most useful in relativistic and quantum mechanics, where the "elementary," operational ways of defining energy are not available in obvious form.

Of course this remark can be turned around and can be used to convince one that $\frac{1}{2}g_{ij}\dot{x}_i\dot{x}_j$ and $V(x)$ should be regarded as, respectively, the kinetic and potential energy. This indicates that the case where $V = 0 = a_i$ is to be regarded as the "free particle" case. Let X be a vector field on M that generates a group of symmetries of the "free particle" Lagrangian $L = \frac{1}{2}g_{ij}\dot{x}_i\dot{x}_j$. Thus, if $X = A_i(x)(\partial/\partial x_i)$, the conjugate function $g_{ij}A_i(x)\dot{x}_j$ can be regarded as the "momentum" function defined by X. For example, suppose that

$$g_{ij} = \delta_{ij}m, \qquad m = 3;$$

that is, L is the free Lagrangian appropriate to a particle of mass m moving in 3-space, R^3. It is easily seen that the generators of symmetries are of the form

$$X = (\alpha_i + \beta_{ij}x_j)\frac{\partial}{\partial x_i},$$

where α_i, β_{ij} are constants, and (β_{ij}) is a skew-symmetric matrix. Let us take, say, translation in the x_1-direction:

$$X = \frac{\partial}{\partial x_1}.$$

The conjugate momentum function is then $m\dot{x}_1$, that is, just the classical linear momentum in the corresponding direction.

Suppose now that

$$X = x_2 \frac{\partial}{\partial x_1} - x_1 \frac{\partial}{\partial x_2}.$$

Thus X generates the group of rotations about the x_3-axis. The conjugate momentum function is $m(x_2 \dot{x}_1 - x_1 \dot{x}_2)$, which is just the classical angular momentum.

These facts explain from our higher point of view the role that these momentum functions play in elementary physics. Further, giving these functions such a group-theoretic interpretation enables one to define the corresponding functions in the generalizations of classical mechanics; for example, Einsteinian and quantum mechanics.

The Equivalence of Homogeneous and Nonhomogeneous Lagrangians. The Principle of Maupertuis

Let $(x_1, \ldots, x_n)$ be a coordinate system for the manifold M, and let $L(x, \dot{x})$ be a time-independent homogeneous, regular Lagrangian for M. We now ask: How can the differential equations for the extremals of L be written in Hamiltonian form? One way is to give up the symmetry between all variables, and choose one, say, x_1, to parametrize the curves of M. The effect of this is to construct the Lagrangian

$$L'(x_1, \ldots, x_{n-1}, t, \dot{x}_1, \ldots, \dot{x}_{n-1}) = L\left(x_1, \ldots, x_{n-1}, t, \frac{\dot{x}_1}{\dot{x}_{n+1}}, \ldots, \frac{\dot{x}_n}{\dot{x}_{n+1}}, 1\right),$$

obviously leading both to rather awkward formulas and to difficulties from the global point of view. There is an alternate procedure that keeps the symmetry between the dependent variables; hence it is preferable both for esthetic reasons and because it carries over to manifolds.

The extremals of L are always the curves of M whose tangent vector curve in $(x, \dot{x})$-space is a characteristic curve for $d\theta(L)$, where

$$\theta(L) = L_{n+i} \, dx_i.$$

Now the obstacle in the way of writing the equations of the characteristic curves in Hamiltonian form is that the functions $L_{n+1}, \ldots, L_{2n}$ are not functionally independent. Indeed, since

$$\text{rank}(L_{n+i, \, n+j}) = n - 1$$

(by definition of regularity), we know by the implicit function theorem that there is a function $H(x_1, \ldots, x_n, y_1, \ldots, y_n)$ of $2n$-variables such that

$$H(x_1, \ldots, x_n, L_{n+1}(x, \dot{x}), \ldots, L_{2n}(x, \dot{x})) = 0 \qquad \text{identically.}$$

Define a mapping ϕ of $(x, \dot{x}, t)$-space to (x, y, t)-space by

$$\phi(x, \dot{x}) = \left(x, \frac{\partial L}{\partial \dot{x}}, t \right) = (x, y, t).$$

Then, since by construction of H, $\phi^*(H) = 0$, we have

$$\phi^*(y_i \, dx_i - H \, dt) = \theta(L).$$

Thus ϕ carries a characteristic curve of $d\theta(L)$ into a characteristic curve of $d(y_i \, dx_i - H \, dt)$ restricted to the submanifold: $H = 0$. We know from Chapter 13 that the characteristic curves of $d(y_i \, dx_i - H \, dt)$ are, after parametrization by t, just the solutions of the Hamilton equations with Hamiltonian $H(x, y)$. Hence the differential equations for extremal curve $x(t)$ of L can be written in Hamiltonian form:

$$\frac{dx}{dt} = H_y(x(t), y(t)), \qquad \frac{dy}{dt} = -H_x(x(t), y(t)), \tag{16.10}$$

subject to the subsidiary condition

$$H(x(t), y(t)) = 0. \tag{16.11}$$

Now suppose that $L'(x, \dot{x})$ is another Lagrangian on M, in fact nonhomogeneous and regular. Suppose in addition that this same function H is the Lagrangian for L'; that is,

$$H\left(x, \frac{\partial L'}{\partial \dot{x}} \right) = \frac{\partial L'}{\partial \dot{x}} \dot{x} - L'.$$

We also know that (16.10), without the subsidiary condition, describes the differential equations for the extremals of L. We can immediately draw several conclusions.

(a)   Every extremal curve of L can be parametrized so that it is an extremal of L'. This parametrization $t \to x(t)$ is determined by the condition

$$H\left(x(t), \frac{\partial L'}{\partial \dot{x}} \left(x(t), \frac{dx}{dt} \right) \right) = 0.$$

(b)   Every curve $x(t)$ of L' that satisfies

$$H\left(x(t), \frac{\partial L'}{\partial \dot{x}} \left(x(t), \frac{dx}{dt} \right) \right) = 0$$

is also an extremal curve for L.

We now want to turn these remarks around and suppose that L' is given. We know that $H(x, y)$ can be constructed according to the usual rules and that every extremal of curve $t \to x(t)$ of L satisfies (16.10), with

$$y(t) = \frac{\partial L'}{\partial \dot{x}}\left(x(t), \frac{dx}{dt}\right) \quad \text{and} \quad H(x(t), y(t)) = \text{constant} \quad \text{(say, } C\text{).}$$

Suppose now that we can find a one-parameter family $e \to L^e$ of homogeneous, regular Lagrangians on x-space such that

$$H\left(x, \frac{\partial L^e}{\partial \dot{x}}(x, \dot{x})\right) = e \quad \text{identically on } (x, \dot{x}).$$

We conclude:

(a′) For each choice of e, the extremals of L^e can be parametrized so as to be extremals of L'.

(b′) If $t \to x(t)$ is an extremal of L', with

$$e = H\left(x, \frac{\partial L'}{\partial x}\left(x, \frac{dx}{dt}\right)\right),$$

then it is also an extremal of L^e.

This reduction of the problem of finding the extremals of a nonhomogeneous Lagrangian to the problem of finding the extremals of a one-parameter family of homogeneous Lagrangians is sometimes known as the *isoenergetic reduction*. (Notice that if L' is the Lagrangian of a Newtonian-mechanical problem, H is just the energy.) This circle of ideas forms what may be called the *Principle of Maupertuis*.

Let us descend from these generalities to find examples of Lagrangians that actually occur in Newtonian physics. Let us consider a Lagrangian of the form

$$L' = \sqrt{V(x)g_{ij}(x)\dot{x}_i\dot{x}_j} + a_i\dot{x}_i.$$

The condition for regularity is seen to be

$$\det(g_{ij}) \neq 0, \qquad V \neq 0,$$

and we shall suppose without further comment that these conditions are fulfilled.

$$L'_{n+i} = \frac{\sqrt{V}g_{ij}\dot{x}_j}{\sqrt{g_{ij}\dot{x}_i\dot{x}_j}} + a_i.$$

Let $H(x, y) = G_{ij}(x)(y_i - a_i)(y_j - a_j) - V(x)$, where (G_{ij}) is the inverse matrix to (g_{ij}). Then

$$H\left(x, \frac{\partial L'}{\partial \dot{x}}\right) = \frac{V}{g_{ij}\dot{x}_i\dot{x}_j} G_{kl} g_{hk_1} \dot{x}_{k_1} g_{ll_1} \dot{x}_{l_1} - V(x) = 0.$$

As we have seen above, this function $H(x, y)$ is the Hamiltonian for the following nonhomogeneous Lagrangian:

$$L = \tfrac{1}{2}g_{ij}\dot{x}_i\dot{x}_j + V(x) + a_i\dot{x}_i.$$

Thus an extremal of L', say, $t \rightarrow x(t)$, that satisfies

$$H\left(x(t), \frac{\partial L}{\partial \dot{x}}\left(x(t), \frac{dx}{dt}\right)\right) = 0 = L_{n+i}\frac{dx_i}{dt} - L \quad \text{or} \quad \tfrac{1}{2}g_{ij}\frac{dx_i}{dt}\frac{dx_j}{dt} - V(x(t)) = 0$$

is an extremal of L. For example, if $a_i = 0$, $V = \tfrac{1}{2}$, this means that the extremals of L' that satisfy

$$L'\left(x, \frac{dx}{dt}\right) = 1$$

are extremals of L'^2. Now, in this case L' defines a *Riemannian metric* on M (see Part 3). The condition $L'(x, (dx/dt)) = 1$ means that the curve $t \rightarrow x(t)$ is parametrized by arc length. (This equivalence between the variational problem defined by L' and L'^2 is used as a simplifying technique by Milnor [1]. Notice, however, that it is quite special and is linked to the quadratic nature of the Lagrangian.)

Conversely, suppose that we start off with L given. The time independence of L implies that, for each extremal curve, $t \rightarrow x(t)$:

$$\tfrac{1}{2}g_{ij}\frac{dx_i}{dt}\frac{dx_j}{dt} - V - a_i\frac{dx_i}{dt} = \text{constant}.$$

This constant can be absorbed in V. The result is that the integral curves of L for which this constant has the value e are integral curves of the homogeneous Lagrangian

$$L^e = \sqrt{(V + e)g_{ij}\dot{x}_i\dot{x}_j} + a_i\dot{x}_i.$$

The most interesting case is where $a_i = 0$. Then this "isoenergetic reduction process" tells us that all integral curves with a given value of "energy" are *geodesics* (that is, extremals) of a certain Riemannian metric or configuration space. As we shall see in Part 3, the theory of geodesics on a Riemannian manifold has a much richer geometric background than a random variational problem.

The Transition from Newtonian to Einsteinian† Mechanics
via the Calculus of Variations

The aim of this section is to show how some standard facts of special relativity theory can be derived (following rather closely to Levi-Civita's ideas [1]) from the formalism of the calculus of variations.

To give the essentials of the method, it suffices to suppose that M is one-dimensional, so that the Newtonian picture is of a particle of mass m moving on a line with coordinate x and potential energy $V(x)$. The Newtonian Lagrangian is, of course, just

$$L = \tfrac{1}{2} \dot{x}^2 - \frac{V(x)}{m} .$$

This Lagrangian is of the nonhomogeneous, regular type, so that its extremals come with their own parametrization. This parameter, of course, is identified with the physical time.

Now L defines a whole class of Lagrangians, as $V(x)$ runs over the class of suitable functions. Let ϕ be a transformation of (x, t)-space into itself which "preserves" the class in the following sense: Given L and ϕ, there is a Lagrangian L' of the same class, that is,

$$L' = \tfrac{1}{2} \dot{x}^2 - \frac{V'(x)}{m} ,$$

so that if $t \to (x(t), t)$ is an extremal of L, $t \to \phi(x(t), t)$ is an extremal of L'.

Now it is easily seen that this requires that $\phi^*(dt) = dt$. That is, $\phi^*(t) = t + \text{constant}$: $(\phi_*)^*(L') = L$. To determine the explicit possibilities for ϕ, suppose $\phi^*(x) = f(x, t)$. Then

$$(\phi_*)^*(L') = \frac{1}{2} \left(\frac{\partial f}{\partial x}\right)^{2 \cdot 2} x - V'(f(x, t)) = 2L,$$

for some constant α, or

$$\frac{\partial f}{\partial x} = \pm 1 \quad \text{or} \quad f = \pm x + g(t).$$

---

† We believe it would be more accurate from the geometric point of view to replace the standard name "relativistic mechanics" by "Einsteinian mechanics." For example, the beginner often is led to believe (in the numerous bad expositions of the theory) that classical Newtonian mechanics is not "relativistic." However, it is covariant under a perfectly good group, namely, the Galilean group. In fact, the main effect of the Einsteinian revision is to replace covariance under this group by covariance under another group, the Lorentz group. (Of course Einstein himself in his own popularizations is always very good on this point.)

The condition

$$\frac{V'(f(x, t))}{m} = \frac{V(x)}{m}$$

forces $g(t) = \beta = $ constant.
 Finally, then, we see that ϕ must be of the form

$$\phi(x, t) = (\pm x + \alpha, t + \beta).$$

Hence the symmetry group is the group of "rigid motions" of the real line. We also see that the symmetry group permuting this class of Lagrangians is the symmetry group of the Lagrangian for the *free* Lagrangian.
 Now let us look at the symmetry group for the *extremals* of the free Lagrangian. We are looking for maps ϕ of (x, t)-space into itself which permute the extremals of

$$L = \tfrac{1}{2}\dot{x}^2.$$

ϕ is of the form

$$\phi(x, t) = (f(x, t), t + \beta).$$

The extended transformation of ϕ is

$$\phi_*: (x, \dot{x}, t) \to \left(f(x, t), \frac{\partial f}{\partial x} \dot{x} + \frac{\partial f}{\partial t}, t + \beta \right).$$

Now $\theta(L) = \dot{x}\, dx - \tfrac{1}{2}\dot{x}^2\, dt$; hence

$$(\phi_*)^*(\theta(L)) = \left(\frac{\partial f}{\partial x} \dot{x} + \frac{\partial f}{\partial t} \right)\left(\frac{\partial f}{\partial x} dx + \frac{\partial f}{\partial t} dt \right) - \frac{1}{2}\left(\frac{\partial f}{\partial x} \dot{x} + \frac{\partial f}{\partial t} \right)^2 dt.$$

Setting the coefficient of $d\dot{x} \wedge dt$ in $\phi^*(d\theta(L)) - d\theta(L)$ equal to zero gives

$$\frac{\partial f}{\partial x}\frac{\partial f}{\partial t} - \left(\frac{\partial f}{\partial x}\dot{x} + \frac{\partial f}{\partial t} \right)\frac{\partial f}{\partial x} = -\dot{x}.$$

This implies, since $(x, \dot{x}, t)$ are independent variables,

$$\frac{\partial f}{\partial x} = \pm 1 \qquad \text{or} \qquad \frac{\partial f}{\partial x} = \pm x + g(t).$$

Hence,

$$(\phi_*)^*(\theta(L)) = \left(\pm \dot{x} + \frac{dg}{dt} \right)(\pm dx + dg) - \frac{1}{2}\left(\pm \dot{x} + \frac{dg}{dt} \right)^2 dt.$$

Setting the coefficient of $dx \wedge dt$ in $d(\phi_*)^*(\theta(L)) - d\theta(L)$ equal to zero gives

$$\frac{d^2g}{dt^2} = 0 \qquad \text{or} \qquad g(t) = \gamma t + \alpha.$$

Finally, then, ϕ is of the form $(x, t) \rightarrow (\pm x, \gamma t + \alpha, t + \beta)$. This is a *Galilean transformation*. Its defining property can be put more physically in the following way:

> If $s \rightarrow (x(s), t(s))$ is a curve in space-time, let $((dx/ds)/(dt/ds))$ be the velocity of the curve. The Galilean transformations permute the curves of constant velocity. The coefficient γ is the increment given to the velocity. The new coordinates for space-time introduced by a Galilean transformation then represent physically a coordinate system moving at constant velocity with respect to the old.

The Einstein modification of this scheme is an attempt to allow transformations of space-time that permit a more thorough "mixing" of the space and time variables, that is, that dethrone time from the absolute position it holds in Newtonian physics. Now an arbitrary transformation on (x, t)-space would send a Lagrangian of the form

$$L = \tfrac{1}{2} \dot{x}^2 - \frac{V(x)}{m}$$

into a Lagrangian on (x, t)-space in the form $L'(x, t, \dot{x}, \dot{t})$, but clearly it would be of a rather unrecognizable type.

Following Levi-Civita [1, p. 292], we can modify the Lagrangian L to get a Lagrangian L^* that *does* have a more reasonable transformation law under space-time transformations.

Consider a given extremal of L, and let c be a positive real number that is very large in comparison with the velocity of the given extremal. Let us first modify L to

$$L - c^2 = -c^2 \left(1 - \frac{\tfrac{1}{2} \dot{x}^2}{c^2} + \frac{V(x)}{mc^2} \right).$$

This is harmless, since it does not affect the extremals of L. In a neighborhood of the tangent vector-field $t \rightarrow (t, x(t), (dx/dt))$ of the given extremal,

$$1 - \frac{\tfrac{1}{2} \dot{x}^2}{c^2} + \frac{V(x)}{c^2} \quad \text{is close to} \quad \sqrt{1 - \frac{\dot{x}^2}{c^2} + 2V(x)}.$$

Thus, if we replace L by

$$L^* = -c^2 \sqrt{1 - \frac{\dot{x}^2}{c^2} + \frac{2V(x)}{mc^2}} = -c \sqrt{c^2 - \dot{x}^2 + \frac{2V(x)}{m}},$$

we can be confident that the extremal of L^* having the same end points as $t \to x(t)$ will be " close " to $t \to x(t)$.†

What is the significance of the Lagrangian L^*? Notice that L^* is in fact closely related to the *homogeneous* Lagrangian

$$L^{**} = \sqrt{\left(c^2 + \frac{2V(x)}{m}\right)\dot{t}^2 - \dot{x}^2}.$$

In fact the extremals of L^{**}, which are a priori of the form

$$s \to (x(s), t(s)),$$

are, when reparametrized by t, just the extremals of L^*. Now L^{**} is a Lagrangian whose extremals are *geodesics* (extremals) of a pseudo-Riemannian metric (of Lorentz type) on space-time. Such Lagrangians have a very simple transformation law under changes of variable in space-time. Thus, at the expense of introducing this new sort of " Lorentzian " or (which is more just historically) *Minkowskian* geometry for space-time, we have " geometrized " the problem of allowing " mixing " transformations of space and time. Notice another fact that is of interest for the later extension to general relativity: The coefficients of the metric determined by L^{**} depend, in case $V(x) \neq 0$, on the *mass* of the particle. Crudely, the massiveness of the particle actually affects the geometry.

Let us return for a moment to L^* and compare it to L. We know how to define the *energy* and *momentum* of the Newtonian system by applying the variational formalism to L; namely,

$$\text{energy} = -m\theta(L)\left(\frac{\partial}{\partial t}\right), \qquad \text{momentum} = m\theta(L)\left(\frac{\partial}{\partial x}\right).$$

This also makes sense with L replaced by L^*. Let us compute and see what happens.

$$\frac{\partial L}{\partial \dot{x}} = \frac{c\dot{x}}{\sqrt{c^2 - \dot{x}^2 + 2V(x)/m}}.$$

$$\theta(L) = \frac{c\dot{x}}{\sqrt{c^2 - \dot{x}^2 + 2V(x)/m}}\, dx - H\, dt.$$

---

† The analogy is with the following fact about extrema of functions in finite dimensional spaces: If q^0 is a critical point of the real-valued function $q \to F(q)$, and if the critical point is nondegenerate, then for small ε, the function $q \to F(q) + \varepsilon G(q)$ will have a critical point that is close to q^0. In this finite dimensional situation, this can be proved by use of the implicit function theorem, but the matter is more delicate for functions on infinite dimensional spaces such as those that occur in the calculus of variations.

with

$$H = \frac{c\dot{x}^2}{\sqrt{c^2 - \dot{x}^2 + 2V(x)/m}} + c\sqrt{c^2 - \dot{x}^2 + 2V(x)/m}$$

$$= \frac{c(c^2 + 2V(x)/m)}{\sqrt{c^2 - \dot{x}^2 + 2V(x)/m}} = \frac{c^2 + 2V(x)/m}{\sqrt{1 - (\dot{x}^2/c^2) + (2V(x)/mc^2)}}.$$

Thus the "energy" is

$$\frac{mc^2 + 2V(x)}{\sqrt{1 - (\dot{x}^2/c^2) + (2V(x)/mc^2)}};$$

and the momentum is

$$\frac{m\dot{x}}{\sqrt{1 - (\dot{x}^2/c^2) + (2V(x)/mc^2)}}.$$

Several famous conclusions follow from these calculations: First notice that if $V(x) = 0$, the energy differs by an additive constant from what it is in the Newtonian case; namely,

$$\text{energy} = mc^2.$$

Further notice that if $t \to x(t)$ is an extremal, then $\dot{x}(t) = dx/dt$, the *velocity* of the particle in the usual sense. If (as we shall see in a moment) c should be identified with the velocity of light in a vacuum, then as long as the velocity of the particle is small compared with this velocity of light and $V(x)$ is small compared with mc^2, there should be no substantial difference from the Newtonian energy (except for the additive constant); hence the motion should also not differ substantially from the Newtonian motion. (Of course this is built into our construction, but it is nice to see precisely how it is reflected on the equations of motion.)

Finally note that if one wants to write

$$\text{momentum} = \text{mass} \times \text{velocity},$$

the mass of the particle must be identified not with its Newtonian m, but with

$$\frac{m}{\sqrt{1 - (\dot{x}^2/c^2) + (2V(x)/mc^2)}}.$$

Thus the mass of a moving particle may vary with time, particularly if $V(x)$ is small compared with mc^2, and $(dx/dt)/c$ is close to 1; the mass blows up. Since the energy must be a constant of motion, we see that a particle moving by this Lagrangian never can (if $V(x)$ is small compared with mc^2) approach the velocity of light (from below). Finally, let us write the Euler–Lagrange equations of motion:

$$\frac{d}{dt}\frac{\partial L}{\partial \dot{x}} = \frac{\partial L}{\partial x},$$

or

$$\frac{d}{dt}\frac{c\dot{x}}{\sqrt{c^2 - \dot{x}^2 + (2V(x)/m)}} = \frac{-c(dV/dx)}{m\sqrt{c^2 - x^2 + (2V(x)/m)}},$$

or

$$\frac{d}{dt}\frac{mc\dot{x}}{\sqrt{c^2 - \dot{x}^2 + (2V(x)/m)}} = \frac{-(dV/dx)}{\sqrt{1 - (\dot{x}^2/c^2) + (2V(x)/mc^2)}}.$$

Notice that the Newtonian law of motion,

$$\text{mass} \times \text{acceleration} = \text{force},$$

makes no kind of sense. But, if the Newtonian law is rewritten in the form

$$\text{derivative of momentum} = \text{force},$$

it does make sense in Einsteinian mechanics, with the force

$$\frac{-(dV/dx)}{\sqrt{1 - (\dot{x}^2/c^2) + (2V(x)/mc^2)}}.$$

Now $-(dV/dx)$ is the Newtonian force. We shall leave Einsteinian mechanics at this point, having described how the basic laws of elementary physics might be modified.

Let us now return to the homogeneous Lagrangian L^{**} in (x, t)-space whose extremals, when parametrized by t, are those of L^*. We shall consider only the force-free Lagrangian, so

$$L^{**} = \sqrt{c^2\dot{t}^2 - \dot{x}^2}.$$

Let us look for the *symmetries* of L^{**}, that is, the transformations ϕ of space $\times$ time into itself such that $(\phi_*)^*(L^{**}) = L^{**}$. If

$$\phi^*(x) = f(x, t), \qquad \phi^*(t) = g(x, t),$$

then

$$(\phi_*)^*(\dot{x}) = \frac{\partial f}{\partial x}\dot{x} + \frac{\partial f}{\partial t}\dot{t}, \qquad (\phi_*)^*(\dot{t}) = \frac{\partial g}{\partial x}\dot{x} + \frac{\partial g}{\partial t}\dot{t};$$

hence,

$$c^2 \left(\frac{\partial g}{\partial x} \dot{x} + \frac{\partial g}{\partial t} \dot{t} \right)^2 - \left(\frac{\partial f}{\partial x} \dot{x} + \frac{\partial f}{\partial t} \dot{t} \right)^2 = c^2 \dot{t}^2 - \dot{x}^2.$$

Thus,

$$\left(c \frac{\partial g}{\partial x} \right)^2 - \left(\frac{\partial f}{\partial x} \right)^2 = -1, \qquad \left(c \frac{\partial g}{\partial t} \right)^2 - \left(\frac{\partial f}{\partial t} \right)^2 = c^2, \qquad c^2 \frac{\partial g}{\partial x} \frac{\partial g}{\partial t} = \frac{\partial f}{\partial x} \frac{\partial f}{\partial t}.$$

Differentiating the first relation with respect to t and the second with respect to x,

$$c^2 \frac{\partial g}{\partial x} \frac{\partial^2 g}{\partial x \partial t} - \frac{\partial f}{\partial x} \frac{\partial^2 f}{\partial x \partial t} = 0, \qquad c^2 \frac{\partial g}{\partial t} \frac{\partial^2 g}{\partial x \partial t} - \frac{\partial f}{\partial t} \frac{\partial^2 f}{\partial x \partial t} = 0.$$

Thus, either

$$\frac{\partial^2 g}{\partial x \partial t} = 0 = \frac{\partial^2 f}{\partial x \partial t} \qquad \text{or} \qquad c^2 \frac{\partial f}{\partial x} \frac{\partial g}{\partial t} = \frac{\partial f}{\partial t} \frac{\partial g}{\partial x}.$$

The second possibility is impossible: For example, it leads to

$$\frac{\partial f / \partial x}{\partial g / \partial x} = \frac{\partial g / \partial x}{\partial f / \partial x} \qquad \text{or} \qquad \left(\frac{\partial f}{\partial x} \right)^2 = \left(\frac{\partial g}{\partial x} \right)^2,$$

which leads to $c^2 = 0$.

The first possibility leads to

$$f(x, t) = h(x) + h_1(t), \qquad g(x, t) = k(x) + k_1(t).$$

Substituting this back in, leads to

$$c^2 \left(\frac{dk}{dx} \right)^2 - \left(\frac{dh}{dx} \right)^2 = -1, \qquad c^2 \frac{dk}{dx} \frac{dk_1}{dt} - \frac{dh}{dx} \frac{dh_1}{dt} = 0,$$

$$c^2 \left(\frac{dk_1}{dt} \right)^2 - \left(\frac{dh_1}{dt} \right)^2 = c^2.$$

Using the first two gives

$$\left(\frac{dh}{dx} \right)^2 \frac{dk_1}{dt} - \frac{dh}{dx} \frac{dk}{dx} \frac{dk_1}{dt} = \frac{dk_1}{dt}.$$

This identity forces

$$\frac{dk_1}{dt} = \alpha_1 = \text{constant},$$

or k_1 is a linear function of t.

Similarly, working on the rest of the relations, we see that f and g are linear functions of x and t, say,

$$\phi^*(x) = a_{11}x + a_{12}t + a, \qquad \phi^*(t) = a_{21}x + a_{22}t + b.$$

The relations the constants must satisfy are found by substituting back in

$$c^2 a_{21}^2 - a_{11}^2 = -1, \qquad c^2 a_{22}^2 - a_{12}^2 = c^2, \qquad c^2 a_{21} a_{22} - a_{11} a_{12} = 0.$$

These conditions define the affine linear transformation as the *Lorentz group*.† Several very important physical facts can be read off from the properties of the Lorentz transformations.

First let us examine what happens as $c \to \infty$. Let us suppose that the matrix

$$\begin{pmatrix} a_{11} & a_{12} \\ a_{21} & a_{22} \end{pmatrix}$$

depends on c and that each element goes to a finite limit as $c \to \infty$. Let

$$\begin{pmatrix} a'_{11} & a'_{12} \\ a'_{21} & a'_{22} \end{pmatrix}$$

be the limit matrix. It follows from the first and second relation that $a'_{21} = 0$, $a'_{22} = \pm 1$. Now it is readily seen that the determinant of every Lorentz transformation is ± 1. This relation also holds in the limit:

$$1 = (a'_{11} a'_{22} - a'_{21} a'_{12})^2 = a'^2_{11} a'^2_{22} = a'^2_{11}.$$

Finally, then, we see that the " limit " of a Lorentz transformation as $c \to \infty$ is one of the form

$$x \to \pm x + vt + a \quad \text{(with } v = a'_{12}), \qquad t \to \pm t + b.$$

Notice that this is a Galilean transformation! Hence we may say that the " limit " as $c \to \infty$ of the Lorentz group, the symmetry group of Einsteinian physics, is the Galilean group, the symmetry group of Newtonian physics. Thus we have a more sophisticated group-theoretical way of describing the transition. A variant of the same sort of reasoning can be used to describe the transition from quantum to classical mechanics.

Now, let $s \to (x(s), t(s))$ be a curve in space-time. We agreed earlier to call

$$\frac{dx/ds}{dt/ds} = v(s)$$

the *velocity* of the curve. We saw that the Galilean group was characterized by

---

† Of course "space" is usually three-dimensional, so that what is usually called the Lorentz group is the analogous group acting on (x_1, x_2, x_3, t)-space.

the property of giving a constant increment v to the velocity of all curves in space-time. Let us examine a Lorentz transformation from the same point of view.

Now the transformed curve is

$$s \to (a_{11}x(s) + a_{12}t(s) + a, \ a_{21}x(s) + a_{22}t(s) + b).$$

Hence the transformed velocity is

$$\frac{a_{11}(dx/ds) + a_{12}(dt/ds)}{a_{21}(dx/ds) + a_{22}(dt/ds)} = \frac{a_{11}v(s) + a_{12}}{a_{21}v(s) + a_{22}}.$$

Notice that if $v(s) = 0$, then the transformed curve has velocity a_{12}/a_{22}. This number, then, should be an interesting invariant of the Lorentz transformation; in fact, it would be physically just the velocity of the new coordinate system defined by the Lorentz transformation with respect to the old.

Let $\beta = a_{12}/a_{22}$ be this invariant. Now β seems completely to determine the transformation. (This version of the Lorentz group is just one-dimensional.) One finds explicitly that

$$a_{11} = \frac{1}{\sqrt{1 - (\beta^2/c^2)}}, \qquad a_{21} = \frac{\beta}{c^2\sqrt{1 - (\beta^2/c^2)}},$$

$$a_{22} = \pm\frac{1}{\sqrt{1 - (\beta^2/c^2)}}, \qquad a_{12} = \pm\frac{\beta}{\sqrt{1 - (\beta^2/c^2)}}.$$

(The sign $\pm$ is determined by the sign of the determinant $(a_{11}a_{22} - a_{12}a_{21})$.) Substituting this back into the expression for the transformed velocity, we see that it is

$$\frac{(a_{11}/a_{22})v(s) + \beta}{(a_{21}/a_{22})v(s) + 1} \le \frac{\pm v(s) + \beta}{\pm(v(s)\beta/c^2) + 1}.$$

Thus we see explicitly how the transformation law for velocities in Newtonian physics must be modified. Notice also that the condition that the transformation be real is $\beta^2 < c^2$. Then

$$\frac{v + \beta}{v(\beta/c^2) + 1} \quad \text{cannot be greater or equal to } c \text{ if } v < c.$$

For then there would be (by continuity) a v such that

$$v + \beta = c\left(\left(\frac{v\beta}{c^2}\right) + 1\right) = v\left(\frac{\beta}{c}\right) + c, \quad \text{or} \quad v = \frac{c - \beta}{1 - (\beta/c)} = c.$$

Hence it is impossible to take a velocity less than c and transform it to be greater than c. In effect, c is an upper bound for the velocities possible in our world. Further, the same argument (when reversed) shows that the result of applying a Lorentz transformation to a motion of velocity c is *again* a motion of velocity c. These motions (physically, they are the paths of light rays, as we shall see in a moment) then have a distinguished role, both as a limiting possibility for the motions of velocity less than c and as possessing the property that their velocity is invariant under Lorentz transformation. (This latter property is just the mathematical statement of the result of the famous Michelson–Morley experiment, which initiated the "relativistic" revolution in physics.)

Another way of labeling these notions serves to introduce us to the notions of general relativity. Change our previous notations slightly, and let L be the following Lagrangian on (x, t)-space:

$$L = c\dot{t}^2 - \dot{x}^2.$$

In terms of the jargon to be introduced in Part 3, L defines a pseudo-Riemannian metric of Lorentz type, or a *Lorentz metric*, for short, on (x, t)-space. The curves whose velocities are less than c are then just those on whose tangent vectors L has a *positive* value. Such curves are also said to be *timelike*. The curves on whose tangent vectors L has a negative value are *spacelike*, while those for which L has the value zero are *lightlike*. Since the Lorentz group preserves L, it is geometrically obvious that it permutes timelike, spacelike, or lightlike curves.

The route we have taken in developing the "Special Theory of Relativity" by generalizing Newtonian mechanics is not historically the way it was discovered, nor is it even the most important from the general physical point of view. Actually, the main clue in the minds of the discoverers of the theory—Einstein, Lorentz, and Poincaré (listed in alphabetical order)—was that the Lorentz group, not the Galilean group, permuted the solutions of Maxwell's equations of electromagnetism. In fact, in Whittaker's judgment [2], Poincaré rather than Einstein deserves most of the credit, since he saw most clearly that it was just this property of the Lorentz transformation that was involved. (Of course, as one of the two or three greatest figures in mathematics—indeed in all of science—in the nineteenth century, this is not surprising. As in so many other things, Poincaré was far ahead of his time, for this group-invariance point of view has only recently been absorbed into the mainstream of physics.)

While it would be too great a detour to describe Maxwell's equations here, perhaps it is worthwhile to give a primitive, one-dimensional version of the argument. First, we must describe what is meant by a *wave*. Restricting ourselves to 1-space dimension x, it may be described as a real-valued function $S(x, t)$. For a fixed t and constant α, the points $S(x, t) = \alpha$ may be called the *wave fronts* at time t. A curve $t \to x(t)$ is a *ray* if

$$S(x(t), t) = \text{constant for all } t.$$

Thus the ray is a curve following along the wave front. (In our one-dimensional situation, of course it is more or less uniquely determined.) The velocity $(dx/dt)(t)$ of the ray may be called the *velocity* of the wave at time t and point $t(t)$. Now the curves describing ordinary light waves in a vacuum are those satisfying the *wave equation*:

$$\frac{\partial^2 S}{\partial x^2} = \frac{1}{c^2}\frac{\partial^2 S}{\partial t^2}.$$

Suppose ϕ is a Lorentz transformation of (x, t)-space into itself. We leave it to the reader to verify, but it is seen that:

If S is a solution of the wave equation, so is $\phi^*(S)$.

This is what is meant by the Lorentz transformation "permuting" the solutions of the wave equation or, more loosely, *preserving* the wave equation.

Suppose now that $t \to x(t)$ is a ray associated with a given wave $S(x, t)$. Then

$$\frac{\partial S}{\partial x}(x(t), t)\frac{dx}{dt} + \frac{\partial S}{\partial t}(x(t), t) = 0.$$

First we assume without proof a proof of the uniqueness of the wave equation: If $S(x, t)$ is a solution, and $S(x, 0) = (\partial S/\partial t)(x, 0)$ for all x, then S is identically zero. (See Courant-Hilbert [1, p. 441] for a simple proof.) Thus, if $f(\ )$ and $g(\ )$ are functions of one variable such that

$$S(x, 0) = f(x) + g(x), \qquad \frac{\partial S}{\partial t}(x, 0) = c(f'(x) - g'(x)), \qquad f'(0) = 0,$$

then

$$S(x, t) = f(x + ct) - g(x - ct).$$

(Clearly, such functions can be found.)

Now this "general" solution represents a superposition of curves traveling to the left and right on the x-axis. Clearly, only waves traveling strictly in one direction will possess a genuine "wave velocity" and a system of rays. Suppose, for example, that

$$S(x, t) = f(x - ct).$$

Then

$$\frac{d}{dt}f(x(t) - ct) = 0 \qquad \text{or} \qquad f'(x - ct)\cdot\left(\frac{dx}{dt} - c\right) = 0,$$

or

$$\frac{dx}{dt} = c \qquad \text{or} \qquad x = ct + \alpha.$$

Thus we have completed our limited discussion of the connection between c as the "wave velocity" of light waves and as the constant occurring as an upper bound for velocities (and in $E = mc^2$) in Einsteinian mechanics.

Special Relativity and Lie Group Theory

In the preceding section we developed the elements of what is usually known as the Theory of Special Relativity from the point of view of generalizing Newtonian mechanics so as to replace the symmetry group of classical mechanics (the Galilean group) by another group (the Lorentz group), which permits some mixing between space and time. It is appropriate to call this and its later extensions to general relativity, which generalize the Newtonian theory even further, "Einsteinian mechanics." In this way of developing the theory, Lie group theory plays only a subsidiary role, and mechanics (or the calculus of variations) is basic. We shall now present an alternate approach based more directly on Lie group theoretical considerations.

We shall still consider a space-time which, as used throughout the Theory of Special Relativity, is a manifold covered with a single coordinate system, diffeomorphic to Euclidean space. For the moment, we shall continue to suppose that space is only one-dimensional and that (x, t) are the coordinates on this space-time manifold.

As in the preceding section, the *velocity* of a curve $s \to (x(s), t(s))$ in space-time is, as a function of its parameter,

$$s \to \frac{dx/ds}{dt/ds} = v(s).$$

We saw that both the Galilean and Lorentz groups had the property that they permuted the curves with constant velocity. We shall now show that these are essentially the only possibilities if we want this and a reasonable physical property to hold.

Suppose ϕ is a diffeomorphism of space-time, with

$$\phi^*(x) = f(x, t), \qquad \phi^*(t) = g(x, t).$$

Then, if $s \to \phi(x(s), t(s))$ is the transformed curve,

$$x(\phi(x(s), t(s))) = \phi^*(x)(x(s), t(s)) = f(x(s), t(s)).$$

Thus we see that the transformed curve is

$$s \to (f(x(s), t(s)), g(x(s), t(s))).$$

The velocity of the transformed curve is then

$$\frac{(d/ds)(f(x(s),\,t(s)))}{ds(g(x(s),\,t(s)))} = \frac{(\partial f/\partial x)(dx/ds) + (\partial f/\partial t)(dt/ds)}{(\partial g/\partial x)(dx/ds) + (\partial g/\partial t)(dt/ds)} = \frac{(\partial f/\partial x)v(s) + (\partial f/\partial t)}{(\partial g/\partial x)v(s) + (\partial f/\partial t)}.$$

Hence, if we want to be constant whenever $v(s)$ is constant, it is clear that the coefficients must be constant; that is, f and g must be linear† functions of x and t, say,

$$\phi^*(x) = a_{11}x + a_{12}t, \qquad \phi^*(t) = a_{21}x + a_{22}t,$$

so that the velocity of the transform of a curve moving with constant velocity v is

$$v' = \frac{a_{11}v + a_{12}}{a_{21}v + a_{22}}.$$

As before, it is convenient to put $\beta = a_{12}/a_{22}$, the velocity of the transform of a curve with zero velocity, so that

$$v' = \frac{(a_{11}/a_{22})v + \beta}{(a_{21}/a_{22})v + 1}.$$

Now, when β approaches zero, one expects (for physical reasons, if none other) that v' approaches v. This indicates that the coefficients of v in the numerator and denominator should be‡ functions of β, say,

$$v' = \frac{\alpha(\beta)v + \beta}{\gamma(\beta)v + 1},$$

with $\alpha(0) = 1$, $\gamma(0) = 0$.

We now determine α and γ by imposing the condition that the transformations we are considering form a *group*, which again is obviously physical. Suppose that β_1 is the parameter of another such transformation and that the result of composing the two transformations is a third transformation characterized by parameter β_2. A direct computation shows that

$$\begin{pmatrix} \alpha(\beta_2) & \beta_2 \\ \gamma(\beta_2) & 1 \end{pmatrix} = \begin{pmatrix} \alpha(\beta_1) & \beta_1 \\ \gamma(\beta_1) & 1 \end{pmatrix} \begin{pmatrix} \alpha(\beta) & \beta \\ \gamma(\beta) & 1 \end{pmatrix}.$$

First notice that $\beta_2 = \alpha(\beta_1)\beta + \beta_1$. Comparing the other two terms in the product, we have

$$\alpha(\alpha(\beta_1)\beta + \beta_1) = \alpha(\beta_1)\alpha(\beta) + \beta_1,$$

$$\gamma(\alpha(\beta_1)\beta + \beta_1) = \gamma(\beta_1)\alpha(\beta) + \gamma(\beta).$$

† For convenience, we shall consider only homogeneous transformations.
‡ More accurately, one expects that the transformations belong to a group. The condition that the transformations approach the identity as $\beta \to 0$ requires that the group be one-dimensional.

Differentiate these relations with respect to β and then set $\beta = 0$:

$$\alpha'(\beta_1)\alpha(\beta_1) = \alpha(\beta_1)\alpha'(0),$$

$$\gamma(\beta_1)\alpha(\beta_1) = \gamma(\beta_1)\alpha'(0) + \gamma'(0).$$

Also differentiate the first relations with respect to β, and then set $\beta_1 = 0$:

$$\alpha(\beta)(\alpha'(0)\beta + 1) = \alpha'(0)\alpha(\beta) + 1.$$

From this last relation, we have, after setting $\beta = 0$,

$$1 = \alpha'(0) + 1 \quad \text{or} \quad \alpha'(0) = 0.$$

Now changing β_1 to β, we have the following differential equations determining α and γ:

$$\alpha'(\beta)\alpha(\beta) = 0, \qquad \gamma'(\beta)\alpha(\beta) = \gamma'(0).$$

Now $\alpha(\beta) = 0$ is ruled out, since $\alpha(0) = 0$. Hence

$$\alpha'(\beta) = 0 \quad \text{or} \quad \alpha(\beta) = 1.$$

Thus, putting $\gamma'(0) = 1/c^2$, we have†

$$\gamma(\beta) = \frac{\beta}{c^2}.$$

This gives the law of transformation for velocities that we obtained earlier for the Lorentz group:

$$v' = \frac{v + \beta}{(\beta/c^2)v + 1}.$$

Now, we must determine the whole matrix

$$\begin{pmatrix} a_{11} & a_{12} \\ a_{21} & a_{22} \end{pmatrix}.$$

As before, the conditions that this belong to a group and that it approach the identity as $\beta \to 0$ require that the coefficients be functions of β also. Thus

$$\frac{a_{12}(\beta)}{a_{22}(\beta)} = \beta, \qquad \frac{a_{11}(\beta)}{a_{22}(\beta)} = \alpha(\beta) = 1, \qquad \frac{a_{21}}{a_{22}} = \gamma(\beta) = \frac{\beta}{c^2}.$$

Now, from the fact that $\alpha(\beta) = 1$, that is, $\beta_2 = \beta_1 + \beta$, we see that

$$\beta \to \begin{pmatrix} a_{11}(\beta) & a_{12}(\beta) \\ a_{21}(\beta) & a_{22}(\beta) \end{pmatrix}$$

is a one-parameter group of 2×2 real matrices.

† We include the possibility $\gamma'(0) = 0$ by possibly allowing $c = \infty$.

One more relation is needed to determine the matrix elements completely. This can be obtained by the following considerations: Let $D(\beta) = a_{11}a_{22} - a_{21}a_{12}$ be the determinant of the matrix. As for any one-parameter group of matrices, we have

$$D(\beta + \beta_1) = D(\beta)D(\beta_1);$$

hence,

$$D'(\beta) = D'(0)D(\beta).$$

Hence,

$$D(\beta) = e^{D'(0)\beta}.$$

We want to conclude that $D'(0) = 0$. We must impose an additional physical condition to do so: Let $s \to (x(s), t(s))$ be any curve in space-time. The " time-interval " along the curve, say over the interval $0 \le s \le 1$, is just $t(1) - t(0)$. The transformed curve is

$$s \to (a_{11}x(s) + a_{12}t(s), a_{21}x(s) + a_{22}t(s)).$$

The " time interval " along this curve,† say, for $0 \le s \le 1$, is then just

$$a_{21}x(1) + a_{22}t(1) - a_{21}x(0) - a_{22}t(0).$$

Now this is in general *not* the same time interval as the original curve. Of course, as $\beta \to 0$, the time intervals become the same, namely,

$$a_{21}x(1) - a_{21}x(0) + t(1)(a_{22} - 1) - t(0)(a_{22} - 1) \to 0$$

as $\beta \to 0$. However, it is reasonable to suppose even more: namely, that this difference divided by β approaches zero as $\beta \to 0$. This requires, of course, that

$$\frac{da_{21}}{d\beta}(0) = \frac{da_{22}}{d\beta}(0).$$

It is readily verified that this condition leads to $D'(0) = 0$; hence

$$D(\beta) = 1 = a_{11}a_{22} - a_{12}a_{21} = a_{22}^2 - \frac{\beta^2}{c^2}a_{22}^2,$$

or

$$a_{22} = \frac{1}{\sqrt{1 - (\beta^2/c^2)}}, \qquad a_{12} = \frac{\beta}{\sqrt{1 - (\beta^2/c^2)}},$$

$$a_{11} = \frac{1}{\sqrt{1 - (\beta^2/c^2)}}, \qquad a_{21} = \frac{\beta}{c^2\sqrt{1 - (\beta^2/c^2)}}.$$

† Mathematically, " time " is just a real-valued function on our manifold so that the " time interval " for the end points of two curves is just the difference of the values of this " time function " at the end points.

By reversing the reasoning of the preceding section, it is seen that these conditions show that ϕ is a Lorentz transformation. Thus we have succeeded in characterizing the Lorentz transformations by means of reasonable conditions.

This method bypasses mechanics. We can now reintroduce it in the following way. Suppose a particle of mass m moves along a curve in space-time. Its Newtonian energy and momentum are, respectively,

$$E(s) = m\left(\frac{dx/ds}{dt/ds}\right)^2, \qquad M(s) = m\,\frac{dx/ds}{dt/ds}.$$

Considered as a function on velocity space, with the coordinate v,

$$E(v) = \tfrac{1}{2}mv^2, \qquad M(v) = mv.$$

Now a Galilean transformation ϕ of parameter β introduces the translation $s \to v + \beta$ on velocity space. Thus

$$\phi^*(E)(v) = m(v + \beta)^2 = \frac{mv^2}{2} + mv\beta + \frac{m\beta^2}{2}$$

$$= E(v) + \beta M(v) + \frac{m\beta^2}{2}.$$

$$\phi^*(M)(v) = mv + m\beta = M(v) + m\beta.$$

Thus,

$$\phi^*(E) = E + \beta M + \frac{m\beta^2}{2}, \qquad \phi^*(M) = M + m\beta.$$

This computation indicates the following group-theoretic interpretation of energy and momentum:

> The transform of any one of the functions E, M and the constant function under a Galilean transformation is a linear combination with constant coefficients of the functions themselves. Thus the mapping
>
> $$\beta \to \begin{pmatrix} 1 & \beta & m\beta^2 \\ 0 & 1 & m\beta \\ 0 & 0 & 1 \end{pmatrix}$$
>
> defines a linear representation of the Galilean group by 3×3 real matrices.

Perhaps it is worthwhile to pause and describe the general background of this sort of phenomenon. Suppose that a Lie group G acts on a manifold P. The space $F(P)$ of all real-valued C^∞ functions on P forms a vector space under pointwise addition and multiplication by real scalars. The action of G on P defines a linear representation of G into the group of linear transformations on $F(p)$.

For $f \in F(P)$, $g \in G$, the transform of f by g is defined just as $g^*(f)$. Now $F(P)$ is, of course, infinite dimensional. However, there may be linear subspaces of $F(P)$ that are finite dimensional and invariant under G and hence define a finite dimensional representation of G. The case where P is the velocity space used above; G is the Galilean group (which is just the translation group on velocity space); and the subspace of $F(P)$ is spanned by E, M; and 1 is the case considered above. Now, in general, it is a very difficult problem to decompose completely the representation of G on $F(P)$. (Such a decomposition would be known as the "Plancherel theorem" for the action of G on P.) However, the cases where it can be accomplished are very important: For example, if P is the group G itself, with a compact G acting on itself by left translation, then the resulting decomposition is the *Peter–Weyl theorem*. The case where P is the 2-sphere in 3-space, with G the group $S0(3, R)$ of rotations, is very important in quantum mechanics. The irreducible finite dimensional subspaces $F(P)$ are generated by letting G act on the *spherical harmonics*.

One further general remark will be useful to us in extending these considerations to special relativity. Let $f_1, \ldots, f_n$ be linearly independent functions on P that are transformed among themselves by the action of G. Explicitly,

$$g^*(f_i) = a_{ij}(g)f_j, \qquad 1 \le i, j, \ldots \le n \quad \text{(summation convention)}.$$

The mapping $g \to (a_{ij}(g))$ then just defines a linear representation of G by $n \times n$ real matrices. (This is just the matrix representation obtained by choosing the basis $f_1, \ldots, f_n$ in the space of functions spanned by $f_1, \ldots, f_n$.) We know from general Lie theory that there is then at the "infinitesimal" level a corresponding linear representation of the Lie algebra of G by $n \times n$ real matrices (Lie bracket going into the commutator $ab - ba$). This can be obtained explicitly as follows: Recall that an element of the Lie algebras of G is a one-parameter subgroup of G, say, $t \to g(t)$. It, acting on P, has an infinitesimal generator X, which is a vector field on P. This correspondence defines a Lie algebra homomorphism of **G** into $V(M)$. Explicitly,

$$X(f) = \frac{\partial}{\partial t} g(t)^*(f)\Big|_{t=0}, \qquad \text{for } f \in F(M).$$

We then see that

$$X(f_i) = \left(\frac{d}{dt} a_{ij}(g(t))\Big|_{t=0}\right) f_j = a_{ij}(X)f_j.$$

The mapping $X \to (a_{ij}(X))$ is the desired linear representation of **G** by $(n \times n)$ real matrices.

Returning to the case where P is velocity space, G the Galilean group, we see that these infinitesimal relations take the form

$$X(E) = \frac{\partial E}{\partial v} = 2M, \qquad X(M) = \frac{\partial M}{\partial v} = m, \qquad X(1) = 0.$$

Note that we can separate out the roles played by E and M by additional relations:

$$X^2(M) = 0 = X^3(E), \qquad X^2(E) \neq 0.$$

Now turn to the Lorentz group. It, too, acts on velocity space:

$$v \to \frac{v + \beta}{(\beta/c^2)v + 1}.$$

Its Lie algebra is also one-dimensional: The infinitesimal generator is then

$$X(f) = \frac{\partial}{\partial \beta} f\left(\frac{v + \beta}{(\beta/c^2)v + 1}\right)\Bigg|_{\beta = 0} = f'(v) \cdot \left(1 - \frac{v^2}{c^2}\right), \qquad X = \left(1 - \frac{v^2}{c^2}\right)\frac{\partial}{\partial v}.$$

Now, in the Galilean case,

$$X\begin{pmatrix} E \\ M \\ 1 \end{pmatrix} = \begin{pmatrix} 0 & 1 & 0 \\ 0 & 0 & m \\ 0 & 0 & 0 \end{pmatrix}\begin{pmatrix} E \\ M \\ 1 \end{pmatrix}.$$

The trick now is to replace this matrix by

$$\begin{pmatrix} 0 & 1 & 0 \\ 1/c^2 & 0 & m \\ 0 & 0 & 0 \end{pmatrix}.$$

It is not possible here to explain in detail why this is the correct modification. However, it is related to the fact that in higher dimensions the Lorentz group is a semisimple Lie group, while the Galilean group is not. (Notice that the matrix

$$\begin{pmatrix} 0 & 1 & 0 \\ 1/c^2 & 0 & m \\ 0 & 0 & 0 \end{pmatrix}$$

has three distinct eigenvalues, namely, $\lambda = 0$, $\lambda = \pm(1/e)$, while

$$\begin{pmatrix} 0 & 1 & 0 \\ 0 & 0 & 1 \\ 0 & 0 & 0 \end{pmatrix}$$

has only $\lambda = 0$ as a multiple eigenvalue. The effect of the perturbation by c is to "split apart" these eigenvalues.) Now E and M satisfy the following conditions:

$$X(E) = M, \qquad X(M) = \frac{1}{c^2} E + m.$$

Hence $X^2(M) = (1/c^2)M$. This enables us to determine M explicitly by a change of variable:

$$u = \frac{c}{2} \log\left(\frac{c+v}{c-v}\right).$$

Notice that

$$\left(1 - \frac{v^2}{c^2}\right) \frac{d}{dv}\left(\frac{c}{2} \log\left(\frac{c+v}{c-v}\right)\right) = 1.$$

Let $M^*(u)$, $E^*(u)$ be the functions such that

$$M^*(u(v)) = M(v), \qquad E^*(u(v)) = E(v).$$

Thus, by this change of variable, X goes over to $\partial/\partial u$, and M^*, E^* satisfy

$$\frac{d^2 M^*}{du^2} = \frac{1}{c^2} M^*, \qquad \frac{dE^*}{du} = M^*.$$

Hence,

$$M^*(u) = a_1 e^{u/c} + a_2 e^{-u/c}, \qquad E^*(u) = b + c(a_1 e^{u/c} - a_2 e^{-u/c}).$$

Now

$$e^{u/c} = \exp\left[\log\left(\frac{c+v}{c-v}\right)^{1/2}\right],$$

$$M(v) = a_1\left(\frac{c+v}{c-v}\right)^{1/2} + a_2\left(\frac{c-v}{c+v}\right)^{1/2}$$

$$= \frac{a_1(c+v) + a_2(c-v)}{(c^2 - v^2)^{1/2}}.$$

Now we clearly want

$$M(0) = 0 = a_1 + a_2;$$

hence,

$$M(v) = \frac{2a_1 v/c}{[1 - (v^2/c^2)]^{1/2}}.$$

Now

$$E^*(u) = b + ca_1(e^{u/c} + e^{-u/c}),$$

or

$$E(v) = b + ca_1\left[\left(\frac{c + v}{c - v}\right)^{1/2} + \left(\frac{c - v}{c + v}\right)^{1/2}\right]$$

$$= b + ca_1\left[\frac{2c}{(c^2 - v^2)^{1/2}}\right] = b + \frac{2a_1 c}{[1 - (v^2/c^2)]^{1/2}}.$$

We can determine the integration constant b by using the relation

$$X(M)(0) = \frac{1}{c^2} E(0) + m = \frac{1}{c^2}(b + 2a_1 c) + m$$

$$= \frac{\partial M}{\partial v}(0) = \frac{2a_1}{c},$$

or $b = -mc^2$.

To determine a_1, it seems necessary to impose an additional condition: For example, it seems reasonable that as $v \to 0$, relativistic effects should subside and that $\partial M/\partial v$ should approach its Newtonian value m. But $(\partial M/\partial v)(0) = 2a_1/c$. Finally, then,

$$M(v) = \frac{mv}{[1 - (v^2/c^2)]^{1/2}}, \qquad E(v) = -mc^2 + \frac{mc^2}{[1 - (v^2/c^2)]^{1/2}}.$$

Now we have determined M and E partly by requiring that they reduce to the Newtonian values as $c \to \infty$. However, there is nothing sacred about $E = \frac{1}{2}mv^2$ in the Newtonian case; $\frac{1}{2}mv^2 +$ constant would serve just as well. However, since no particular constant serves to simplify anything, we usually are content to let it be zero. It is quite different, however, in the relativistic case. Notice that redefining E as E', where

$$E' = \frac{mc^2}{[1 - (v^2/c^2)]^{1/2}},$$

gives the following law of transformations under infinitesimal Lorentz transformations:

$$X(M) = \frac{1}{c^2} E', \qquad X(E') = M.$$

This is obviously a considerably simpler transformation law than our original choice of E. Notice, for example, that the transformation law *no longer involves* m, but is determined completely by the underlying geometry. In fact, let us compare this transformation law to the transformation law satisfied by the functions x and t on space-time.

We have seen that a Lorentz transformation on space-time can be written in terms of β as follows:

$$(x, t) \to \left(\frac{x}{[1 - (\beta^2/c^2)]^{1/2}} + \frac{t\beta}{[1 - (\beta^2/c^2)]^{1/2}} , \right.$$

$$\left. \frac{\beta x}{c^2[1 - (\beta^2/c^2)]^{1/2}} + \frac{t}{[1 - (\beta^2/c^2)]^{1/2}} \right).$$

Hence the infinitesimal generator is the vector field (which we shall also call X, since it, too, is identified with the generator of the Lie algebra of the Lorentz group):

$$X = t\frac{\partial}{\partial x} + \frac{x}{c^2}\frac{\partial}{\partial t}, \quad \text{or} \quad X(x) = t, \quad X(t) = \frac{x}{c^2}.$$

Hence the functions $\dot{x}$ and t transform under a Lorentz transformation precisely in the same way as do M and E'. This suggests the following geometric construction: Let $s \to (x(s), t(s)) = \sigma(s)$ be a curve in space-time, with velocity function $v(s) = (dx/ds)/(dt/ds)$. Define a vector field along σ by assigning to $\sigma(s)$ the tangent vector

$$E'(v(s))\frac{\partial}{\partial t} + M(v(s))\frac{\partial}{\partial x}.$$

This is the "momentum-energy" vector field along the curve.

This vector field has the following "covariance" property:

> If curves σ and σ_1 correspond under a Lorentz transformation, the momentum-energy vector fields also correspond under the same Lorentz transformation.

Notice that this behavior of energy and momentum *together* has no analog in Newtonian physics!

Variational Problems Admitting Given Groups of Symmetries

As we remarked in Part 1, there is often a connection between being able to solve a given system of differential equations by "quadratures," and the differential equations admitting a symmetry group of a certain algebraic structure, although it is difficult to make this precise. The differential equations arising from variational problems have a special structure, and this leads to a further interesting relation to possible symmetry groups. Lacking a general theory, we shall restrict ourselves to sufficiently illustrative remarks.

Let M be a manifold with a Lagrangian L given on M. Let $\theta(L)$ be the Cartan 1-form on $T(M) \times R = P$. A vector field Y on P generates a *symmetry group* of L if $Y(d\theta(L)) = 0$. Suppose that $Y_1, \ldots, Y_r$ are vector fields on P satisfying this condition. Choose functions $f_1, \ldots, f_r$ on P such that

$$df_\alpha = -Y_\alpha \lrcorner d\theta(L) \qquad \text{for } \alpha = 1, \ldots, r.$$

Then the f_α are constant on the characteristic curves of $d\theta(L)$; that is, they are "integrals of motion," in the classical sense, of the extremals of L. For each choice $\mathbf{c} = (c_1, \ldots, c_r)$ of real constants, consider the "submanifold" of P defined by

$$P^\mathbf{c} = \{p \in P : f_1(p) = c_1, \ldots, f_r(p) = c_r\}. \tag{16.12}$$

(Of course this need not be a submanifold. Most of our discussion will be only "generic," ignoring the possible singularities that may arise, and is intended only to cover the high points of the theory.)

Thus the problem of finding the characteristic curves of $d\theta(L)$ can be "reduced" to the problem of finding the characteristic curves of $d\theta(L)$ restricted to each of the submanifolds $P^\mathbf{c}$. Since this is a manifold of lower dimension, we have succeeded in reducing the difficulty involved in solving the differential equations that define the characteristic curves of $d\theta(L)$. However, this remark is independent of the algebraic structure of the Lie algebra generated by $Y_1, \ldots, Y_r$. Do certain algebraic structures lead to a further simplification?

Choose indices $1 \leq \alpha, \beta, \ldots \leq r$, and the summation convention. Then

$$[Y_\alpha, Y_\beta] = k_{\alpha\beta\gamma} Y_\gamma.$$

The $k_{\alpha\beta\gamma}$ are the *structure constants* of the Lie algebra generated by the $Y_1, \ldots, Y_r$. If Y is a vector field, then

$$Y(f_\alpha) = df_\alpha(Y) = d\theta(L)(Y, Y_\alpha).$$

If $Y(d\theta(L)) = 0$, and if $Y(f_\alpha)$ is expressible as a linear combination of $(f_1 - c_1), \ldots, (f_r - c_r)$, then Y is tangent to the submanifold $P^\mathbf{c}$ and hence provides an *additional* symmetry for the characteristic curves of $d\theta(L)$ that lie on $P^\mathbf{c}$.

In particular, the Y-elements in the Lie algebra generated by $Y_1, \ldots, Y_r$ that are tangent to $P^\mathbf{c}$ form a *subalgebra* that can be computed in a purely algebraic fashion. (For example, if the algebra as generated by $Y_1, \ldots, Y_r$ is Abelian, this subalgebra is the whole algebra.) This subalgebra acts as symmetries on the differential equations determining the characteristic curves of $d\theta(L)$ that lie on $\mathbf{P}^c$. The whole algorithm can then be iterated, with the sub-algebra acting on $\mathbf{P}^c$ instead of the whole algebra acting on P. If the process ends with a problem of finding the characteristic curves of a 2-form on a two-dimensional submanifold of P, we shall have succeeded in "integrating the characteristic curves of $d\theta(L)$ (hence the extremal curves of L) by quadratures," in the classical terminology.

As illustrations, let us consider an example of structure for the Lie algebra. First let us suppose $m = 2$:

$$[Y_1, Y_2] = kY_2.$$

(The Lie algebra is then *solvable*.) We shall also suppose that $Y_1(f_2) = kf_2$. Suppose $Y = a_1 Y_1 + a_2 Y_2$:

$$Y(f_1) = -a_2 kf_2, \qquad Y(f_2) = a_1 kf_2.$$

where Y is tangent to $\mathbf{P}^c$ if $c_2 = 0$.

Thus, we see in the non-Abelian case ($k \neq 0$) that we can expect that only a one-parameter family of the submanifolds $\mathbf{P}^c$ will admit a further group of symmetries.

All this applies if the Y are prolongations of vector fields on M that generate groups of symmetries of the extremals of L. However, the technique of finding *normal forms* for the vector fields is more useful for practical purposes in this case.

Suppose, then, that $X_1, \ldots, X_r$ are vector fields on M such that

$$\dot{X}_\alpha(L) = 0, \qquad \alpha = 1, \ldots, r.$$

First suppose that

$$[X_\alpha, X_\beta] = 0, \qquad 1 \leq \alpha, \beta \leq r, X_1(q), \ldots, X_r(q)$$

are linearly independent for all $q \in M$. Then, it is easily seen by an extension of the argument used in Chapter 8, that coordinates $(x_1, \ldots, x_n)$ can be chosen for the open set of M that we are working in, so that

$$X_1 = \frac{\partial}{\partial x_1}, \ldots, X_r = \frac{\partial}{\partial x_r}.$$

Then, also,

$$\dot{X}_1 = \frac{\partial}{\partial x_1}, \ldots, \dot{X}_r = \frac{\partial}{\partial x_r}.$$

We conclude that L in the coordinates is a function $L(x_{r+1}, \ldots, x_m, \dot{x}_1, \ldots, \dot{x}_m)$. In classical language, the coordinates $(x_1, \ldots, x_r)$ are *ignorable*. Now

$$\theta(L) = L_{n+i} dx_i - H dt, \qquad \text{with} \quad H = L_{n+i} \dot{x}_i - L.$$

We conclude that $\theta(L)(\dot{X}_1) = L_{n+1}, \ldots, \theta(L)(\dot{X}_r) = L_{n+r}$ are constant along the characteristic curves of $d\theta(L)$. H is a function $H(x_{r+1}, \ldots, x_n, y_1, \ldots, y_n)$. Then put $y_i = L_{n+i}$, and set $y_1 = c_1, \ldots, y_r = c_r$. The Hamilton equations for $x_{r+1}(t), \ldots, x_n(t), y_{r+1}(t), \ldots, y_n(t)$ are then, for $i = r + 1, \ldots, n$,

$$\frac{dx_i}{dt} = H_{n+i}(x_{r+1}(t), \ldots, x_n(t), c_1, \ldots, c_r, y_{r+1}(t), \ldots, y_n(t)),$$

$$\frac{dy_i}{dt} = -H_i(x_{r+1}, \ldots, x_n, c_1, \ldots, c_r, y_{r+1}, \ldots, y_n).$$

If $(x_{r+1}(t), \ldots, x_n(t), y_{r+1}(t), \ldots, y_n(t))$ is a solution of this Hamiltonian system in $2(n - r)$ variables (for each value of $(c_1, \ldots, c_r)$), then $x_1(t), \ldots, x_r(t)$ are determined by

$$x_i(t) = \int H_{n+i}(x_{r+1}(t), \ldots, x_n(t), c_1, \ldots, c_r, y_{r+1}(t), \ldots, y_n(t)) \, dt$$

$$\text{for } i = 1, \ldots, r.$$

Of course this is ideal if $(n - r) = 2$ because the resulting reduced Hamiltonian system can, of course, be further solved "by quadratures," since the Hamiltonian H is still available to us as an integral of motion.

For each value of $\mathbf{c} = (c_1, \ldots, c_r)$ is there a Lagrangian R^c on $x_{r+1}, \ldots, x_n$-space whose extremal curves are the curves in $x_{r+1}, \ldots, x_n$-space that occur as the projection of solutions of the reduced Hamiltonian system?

We mention the classical procedure for finding such an R:

$R^c(x_{r+1}, \ldots, x_n, \dot{x}_{r+1}, \ldots, \dot{x}_n)$ is the function such that

$$R^{(L_{n+1}(x, \dot{x}), \ldots, L_{n+r}(x, \dot{x}))}(x_{n+1}, \ldots, x_n, \dot{x}_{r+1}, \ldots, \dot{x}_n) = L(x, \dot{x}) - \sum_{i=1}^{r} L_{n+i} \dot{x}_i.$$

R is called the *Routhian*. We refer to Whittaker [1], for a fuller discussion and for the solution of many problems using Routh's method.

Integrals of the Type of "Total Angular Momentum"

Let M be a manifold on which a Lagrangian is given. We have discussed the general principle that the integrals of motion are associated with vector fields on $T(M)$, leaving $d\theta(L)$ invariant. One source of such vector fields that we have exploited is obtained by taking a vector field on M, which generates a group M permuting the extremals of L and prolonging it to $T(M)$. However, there is the possibility of groups acting on $T(M)$, leaving $d\theta(L)$ invariant, which do not arise as prolongations of vector fields on M. In this section, we present one method of obtaining such symmetries. It will also give us an opportunity to illustrate our earlier statement, namely, that it is often useful to work with a basis for differential forms on an M that does not arise from a coordinate system.

Suppose, then, that ω_i $(1 \le i, j, \ldots \le n = \dim M$; summation convention) is a basis for 1-forms on M, with

$$d\omega_i = c_{jki}\,\omega_j \wedge \omega_k .$$

As before, we consider ω_i as forms on $T(M)$, pulling them up with the dual of the projection map $T(M) \to M$ without any special notation. Then y_i denotes the functions $v \to y_i(v) = \omega_i(v)$ on $T(M)$. If $L \in F(T(M))$ is the Lagrangian $dL = L_i\,\omega_i + L_{n+i}\,dy_i$, then

$$\theta(L) = L_{n+i}\,\omega_i - H\,dt, \qquad \text{with} \quad H = L_{n+i}\,y_i - L.$$

Let X be a vector field on $T(M) \times R$ such that

$$X(t) = 0 = X(H) = X(L_{n+i}).$$

Then

$$X \lrcorner\, d\theta(L) = -\omega_i(X)\,dL_{n+i} + L_{n+i}\,c_{jki}\,\omega_j(X)\omega_k .$$

X will generate symmetries of the characteristic curves of $d\theta(L)$ if $d(X \lrcorner\, d\theta(L)) = 0$. There is one important case (to which we shall restrict ourselves) where such a choice can be made:

$$\omega_j(X) = L_{n+j}.$$

Suppose, for example, we *assume* that (c_{jki}) is skew-symmetric in all three indices, and that L is a nonhomogeneous, regular Lagrangian; that is, $\det(L_{n+i,\,n+j}) \ne 0$. Thus $X \lrcorner\, d\theta(L) = -L_{n+j}\,dL_{n+i}$. Hence, with these assumptions, $I = L_{n+i}L_{n+i}$ is an integral of the characteristic curves of $d\theta(L)$. We have not yet established that such an X exists. Now

$$0 = X(H) = X(L_{n+i})y_i + L_{n+i}X(y_i) - L_i\,\omega_i(X) - L_{n+i}X(y_i)$$
$$= -L_i L_{n+i} .$$

Thus the relations

$$L_i L_{n+i} = 0 \qquad \text{and} \qquad c_{jki} + c_{jik} = 0$$

must be considered as the conditions for the existence of this new integral of motion, which in the classical rotating rigid body problem is the integral of "total angular momentum."

Rigid Bodies Treated Group-Theoretically

The configuration space for a rigid body in Euclidean 3-space, with one point fixed, is just the group of 3×3 real orthogonal matrices of determinant 1. (For consider the fixed point of the body as the center of the coordinate system, and consider a fixed orthogonal coordinate system. The position of the body is evidently determined by the position of another orthogonal coordinate system fixed in the body. Two such coordinate systems are related by a 3×3 orthogonal matrix. Since the moving coordinate system can be deformed into its original fixed position, and an orthogonal matrix always has determinant ± 1, it is clear that we are interested only in orthogonal matrices of determinant 1.)

The traditional treatment of rigid-body dynamics usually is designed to mask the fact that the configuration space is the manifold of 3×3 real orthogonal matrices, that is, the underlying manifold of a Lie group. To restore some balance to this situation, we shall treat things strictly from the group-theoretical point of view, purposely looking for variational problems that can be solved easily by using symmetry principles. We shall mention only very briefly the relation to the traditional rigid-body problems.

Let G be a Lie group. We have defined the *Lie algebra* of G, usually denoted by **G**, as the set of one-parameter subgroups of G, and have justified the name " Lie algebra " by showing how the sum and Jacobi bracket of two one-parameter groups may be defined. If G acts a group of diffeomorphisms on a manifold M, we have also seen that, as the " infinitesimal version " of the action, **G** acts a Lie algebra of *vector fields* on M. The two most obvious examples of such an action are the action of G on itself by left and right translation. If a basis for **G** is chosen, the corresponding vector fields on G defined by these two actions form two bases for vector fields (" absolute parallelisms ") on G, and are, respectively, right- and left-invariant vector fields on G.

The basis of 1-forms dual to the basis of left- (or right) invariant vector fields on G is a basis for the vector space of left- (or right) invariant differential 1-forms on G.† Conversely, giving a basis of left- (or right) invariant 1-forms on G seems to fix the basis of left- (or right) invariant vector fields by duality.

Most Lie groups can be realized simply as subgroups of $GL(n, R)$, the group of all real $n \times n$ invertible matrices. Hence, a basis for its left- or right-invariant vector fields can usually be most easily found by finding a basis for left- or right-invariant vector fields on $GL(n, R)$, and then finding the subspace of these vector fields that are tangent to G. The general theory then tells

† A differential form on a Lie group that is invariant under left or right translation is often called a *Cartan–Maurer* form.

us that this subspace defines a basis for the left- or right-invariant vector fields on G.

We must compute the left- and right-invariant differential forms on $GL(n, R)$. Choose the following range of indices and summation conventions, $1 \leq i, j, \ldots \leq n$; x_{ij} will denote the functions on $GL(n, R)$ which assign the entry in the ith row and jth column to a matrix in $GL(n, R)$. Thus the whole matrix is (x_{ij}). The functions that assign the (i, j)th entry to the inverse matrix of an element of $GL(n, R)$ are denoted x_{ij}^{-1}. Thus

$$x_{ij} x_{jk}^{-1} = \delta_{ik} = x_{ij} x_{jk}^{-1}.$$

Now the following forms define a basis for left-invariant forms,

$$\omega_{ij} = x_{ik}^{-1} \, dx_{kj}, \tag{16.13}$$

while the following forms define a basis for right-invariant ones,

$$\omega_{ij} = dx_{ik} x_{kj}^{-1}. \tag{16.14}$$

The *orthogonal group*, $0(n, R)$, consists of all matrices whose inverse is equal to its transpose, and is thus a closed subgroup of $GL(n, R)$. $S0(n, R)$, the *rotation group*, consists of all orthogonal matrices of determinant 1. (Recall that the orthogonality condition requires that the determinant be ± 1.) Hence, from the general theory of Lie groups sketched in Chapter 10, one deduces that:

(a) $0(n, R)$ is a closed Lie subgroup of $GL(n, R)$.
(b) $S0(n, R)$ is the connected component containing the identity of $0(n, R)$; hence it is an invariant closed Lie subgroup of $0(n, R)$.

(Prove these facts directly, as an exercise!)

Now $0(n, R)$, as a submanifold of $GL(n, R)$, is determined by the relations

$$x_{ki} x_{kj} = \delta_{ij}.$$

Differentiating these relations, we have, on $S0(n, R)$,

$$dx_{ki} x_{kj} + x_{ki} \, dx_{kj} = 0.$$

Restricting to $S0(n, R)$ (with ω_{ij} and ω'_{ij} given by (16.13) and (16.14),

$$\omega_{ij} = x_{ki} \, dx_{kj} = -x_{kj} \, dx_{ki} = -\omega_{ji}.$$

Similarly, one proves that (ω'_{ij}) are skew-symmetric in i and j. Now it is readily verified by counting that

$$\dim S0(n, R) = \frac{n(n-1)}{2},$$

that is, just the numbers of pairs (i, j), with $1 \le i < j \le n$. We conclude:

> The ω_{ij} (resp. ω'_{ij}) with $1 \le i < j \le n$ are, when restricted to $SO(n, R)$ from $GL(n, R)$ (where they were originally defined by (16.13), (16.14)), form a basis for the left-invariant (right-invariant) 1-forms on $SO(n, R)$.

Let us now return to the case $n = 3$. We have seen that $SO(3, R)$ would be identified with the configuration space of a rigid body moving in three-dimensional Euclidean space with one point fixed, say, the origin. Recall that this is obtained by choosing a *fixed* orthonormal basis $(e_1{}^0, e_2{}^0, e_3{}^0)$ of R^3, and choosing one orthonormal basis (e_1, e_2, e_3) that is fixed in the body. There is a unique orthogonal matrix (x_{ij}) such that $e_i = x_{ij} e_j{}^0$. This allows us to identify the given "configuration" of the body with the matrix (x_{ij}). Now a physical motion of the body as a function of time is determined by functions of time: $e_i(t)$. This allows us to define the curve $(x_{ij}(t))$ in $SO(3, R)$ by

$$e_i(t) = x_{ij}(t) e_j{}^0.$$

What sort of Lagrangians on $SO(3, R)$ are suited to describe the (Newtonian) dynamics of rigid-body motion with no external motion? By general principles (or perhaps, more truthfully, because it is the type we are used to), the Lagrangian should be, at each point q of configuration space, a quadratic form on the tangent vectors to that point. Further, the general symmetry of Newtonian mechanics under rigid motions tells us that this Lagrangian should be invariant under *left translation* on $SO(3, R)$, since applying a left translation just means rotating each element of the rigid body by the same rotation.

These two conditions severely restrict the choice of Lagrangian. To express this analytically, let us take advantage of the fact that

$$\dim SO(n, R) = \frac{n(n-1)}{2} = n \quad \text{(only for } n = 3\text{)}.$$

Thus the tangent space to $SO(3, R)$ at a point, say, the identity element, can be identified with R^3. To do this explicitly, put

$$\omega_{12} = \omega_1, \qquad \omega_{13} = \omega_2, \qquad \omega_{23} = \omega_3.$$

Then $(\omega_1, \omega_2, \omega_3)$ form a basis for left-invariant forms on $SO(3, R)$. Let (y_1, y_2, y_3) be these forms regarded as functions on $T(SO(3, R))$. Evidently, then, the Lagrangian L representing a possible force-free rigid-body motion must be of the form

$$L = I_{ij} y_i y_j,$$

with *constants* I_{ij} forming a symmetric matrix. Of course this matrix is nothing but the *moment of inertia* matrix of the body. We can obviously exploit the freedom to choose the fixed bases $(e_1{}^0, e_2{}^0, e_3{}^0)$ by choosing it so that the matrix (I_{ij}) takes a diagonal form; that is,

$$I_{ij} = 0 \quad \text{if } i \neq j, \qquad = I_i \quad \text{if } i = j.$$

The axes moving the body are then the *principal axes* of the body, and L takes the form

$$L = I_1 y_1{}^2 + I_2 y_2{}^2 + I_3 y_3{}^2.$$

In accordance with general principles, the Lagrangian for a motion under forces derived from a potential function V defined on configuration space is then just

$$L = \tfrac{1}{2}(I_1 y_1{}^2 + I_2 y_2{}^2 + I_3 y_3{}^2) - V.$$

Then a curve $\sigma(t)$ is an extremal of L if it satisfies the general *Euler equations* (with respect to the basis of 1-forms) that were derived in the beginning of this chapter, namely,

$$\frac{d}{dt} L_{n+i}(\sigma'(t)) - L_i(\sigma'(t)) + c_{jki} L_{n+k}(\sigma'(t)))\omega_j(\sigma'(t)) = 0.$$

The first step in making these more explicit is to find $d\omega_i$:

$$d\omega_{ij} = d(x_{ki}\, dx_{kj}) = dx_{ki} \wedge dx_{kj} = dx_{ki} \wedge \delta_{kk_1} dx_{k_1 j}$$

$$= dx_{ki} x_{kj_1} x_{k_1 j_1} \wedge dx_{k_1 j}$$

$$= \omega_{ij_1} \wedge \omega_{j_1 j}.$$

Now

$$d\omega_1 = d\omega_{12} = \omega_{13} \wedge \omega_{32} = -\omega_{13} \wedge \omega_{23} = -\omega_2 \wedge \omega_3.$$

$$d\omega_2 = d\omega_{13} = \omega_{12} \wedge \omega_{23} = \omega_1 \wedge \omega_3.$$

$$d\omega_3 = d\omega_{23} = \omega_{13} \wedge \omega_{32} = -\omega_1 \wedge \omega_2.$$

This gives the following values of the nonzero components of (c_{jki}), the *structure constants* of the Lie group $SO(3, R)$:

$$c_{123} = -1, \qquad c_{132} = 1, \qquad c_{231} = -1.$$

Suppose $dV = V_i \omega_i$. Then

$$L_i = -V_i, \qquad L_{n+i} = I_i y_i \qquad \text{(no summation)}.$$

If $y_i(t) = \omega_i(\sigma'(t))$, the Euler equations take the form

$$I_1 \frac{dy_1}{dt} = y_2 y_3 (I_3 - I_2) + V_1, \qquad (16.15a)$$

$$I_2 \frac{dy_2}{dt} = -y_1 y_3 (I_3 - I_1) + V_2, \qquad (16.15b)$$

$$I_3 \frac{dy_3}{dt} = y_1 y_2 (I_2 - I_1) + V_3. \qquad (16.15c)$$

These equations are given in every textbook on rigid-body mechanics. (Notice, then, that the configuration space variables do not appear except in the potential. The problem of finding the extremals $\sigma(t)$ can be divided into two parts: First find $y_i(t)$ by solving the three-dimensional system (16.15); then find $\sigma(t)$ as solution of the second three-dimensional system:

$$\omega_i(\sigma'(t)) = y_i(t).$$

Except in the most trivial cases, solving (16.15) involves the theory of elliptic functions. (In fact, the applications to rigid-body problems were the principal impetus to the development of the theory of elliptic functions in the first half of the nineteenth century.)

Let us suppose that $V = 0$, and inquire about the possible existence of integrals of motion of the system (16.15) that arise because of the underlying group invariance. First, the Hamiltonian

$$H = L_{n+i} y_i - L = \tfrac{1}{2} I_i y_i^2 = L$$

is such an integral. (It is also the *total energy* in the case of rotating rigid bodies.) We shall now look systematically for more integrals of the characteristic curves of $d\theta(L)$ that are functions of $y_1, \ldots, y_n$ alone.

Now let us look for a function f of $(y_1, \ldots, y_n)$ alone, and a vector field Y on $T(SO(3, R))$ such that

$$df = Y \lrcorner d\theta(L) = Y \lrcorner (dL_{n+i} \wedge \omega_i + L_{n+i} c_{jki} \omega_j \wedge \omega_k - dH \wedge dt),$$

and $Y(t) = 0$.

As conditions we have

$$Y(L_{n+k}) + L_{n+i} c_{jki} \omega_j(Y) = 0, \qquad (16.16a)$$

$$Y(H) = 0, \qquad (16.16b)$$

$$df = dL_{n+i} \omega_i(Y). \qquad (16.16c)$$

Now, if Y satisfies these conditions,

$$Y(d\theta(L)) = d(Y(\theta(L))) = d(dY \lrcorner d\theta(L)) + d(\theta(L)(Y))$$
$$= ddf + dd(\theta(L)(Y)) = 0,$$

so that Y generates a one-parameter group that permutes the characteristic curves of $d\theta(L)$.

Conversely, if a vector field Y on $T(SO(3, R))$ satisfies

$$Y(t) = 0 \quad (16.16a; 16.16b) \qquad \text{and} \qquad dL_{n+i} \wedge d\omega_i(Y) = 0, \qquad (16.17)$$

then such an f exists, is an integral of the characteristic curves of $d\theta(L)$, and is a function of $y_1, \ldots, y_n$ alone. Writing out the condition of (16.17) in more detail, we have

$$L_{n+j, n+j} \, dy_j \wedge d\omega_i(Y) = 0 \qquad (16.18)$$

(since L is a function of $y_1, \ldots, y_n$ alone).

Now L is a regular, nonhomogeneous Lagrangian; that is, $\det(L_{n+i, n+j}) \neq 0$. The conditions then become:

$$\omega_i(Y) \text{ is a function of } y_1, \ldots, y_n \text{ alone.}$$

We shall not go into a deep analysis of these conditions here. Consider the simplest choice, namely,

$$\omega_i(Y) = a_{ij} y_j, \quad \text{with constant } a_{ij}; \qquad Y(y_i) = 0.$$

The condition on Y then becomes

$$L_{n+i, n+j} a_{ik} \, dy_j \wedge dy_k = 0.$$

Now

$$L_{n+i, n+j} = \begin{cases} 0 & \text{if } i \neq j \\ I_i & \text{if } i = j. \end{cases}$$

Thus,

$$\sum_{i, k} I_i a_{ik} \, dy_i \wedge dy_k = 0 \qquad \text{or} \qquad I_i a_{ik} = I_k a_{ki} \quad \text{(no summation)}.$$

Condition (16.16a) requires that

$$\sum_{i, j, l} I_i y_i c_{jki} a_{jl} y_l = 0.$$

Now (c_{jki}) is skew-symmetric in *all* three indices. Then this condition can be realized by choosing

$$a_{ji} = \begin{cases} 0 & \text{if } i \neq j \\ I_i y_i & \text{if } i = j \quad \text{(no summation)}. \end{cases}$$

It is then clear that *all* desired conditions are satisfied.† Then

$$\omega_i(Y) = I_i \, y_i \qquad \text{(no summation)};$$

hence,

$$df = \sum_i I_i^2 y_i \, dy_i \qquad \text{or} \qquad 2f = (I_1 y_1)^2 + (I_2 y_2)^2 + (I_3 y_3)^2. \qquad (16.19)$$

This is obviously an integral of (16.15) independent of the energy integral $I_1 y_1^2 + I_2 y_2^2 + I_3 y_3^2$ (unless, of course, $I_1 = I_2 = I_3$, which is the trivial case, since the right-hand side of (16.15) is identically zero anyway). Physically, it is the integral of *total angular momentum* for the rigid body, and the reader will readily verify that it is the integral found by more general arguments in the preceding section. These two integrals enable one to reduce (16.15) (remember that $V = 0$) to three separated first-order differential equations for y_1, y_2, y_3, which can be solved with elliptic functions. In fact, as we show later, following Tricomi [1], these equations can be used to define the Jacobi elliptic functions and derive their principal properties.

The Euler Angles for a Rotating Rigid Body

We have seen that the Euler equations for the extremals of a left-invariant variational problem on $S0(3, R)$ (or any Lie group for that matter) split up in two parts: To find an extremal curve $\sigma(t)$, first one solves for $y_i(t) = \omega_i(\sigma'(t))$, for $i = 1, 2, 3$ ($\omega_1, \omega_2, \omega_3$ a convenient basis for left-invariant forms) then finds σ itself. Of course the question arises exactly how to describe curves on $S0(3, R)$ in explicit terms, since it is a compact manifold and hence cannot be covered by a single-coordinate system. At least two methods can be used. First, we have defined the left-invariant form as

$$\omega_{ij} = x_{ik}^{-1} \, dx_{kj} \qquad (1 \le i, j, k, \dots \le 3; \text{ summation convention})$$

where x_{ij} are the functions on $S0(3, R)$ which to every matrix assign its (i, j)th entry. Of course the x_i functions x_{ij} are bound by the orthogonality conditions $x_{ij} x_{kj} = \delta_{ik}$. In principle, these relations could be solved for three independent functions to define a coordinate system for a piece of the manifold, but we can be certain that this would be too awkward to be of much value. However, if the "momentum" functions $y_{ij}(t) = \omega_{ij}(t)$ have already

---

† In making these choices, we must confess that we have been guided by knowing the answer via the analogy with rigid-body dynamics. The reader is invited to try to work out the necessary conditions to a conclusion.

been found, the functions $x_{ij}(\sigma(t))$ that actually describe the extremal are obtained as solutions of

$$\frac{d}{dt} x_{ij}(\sigma(t)) = x_{ik}(\sigma(t)) y_{kj}(t).$$

Now these form a system of linear, ordinary, time-dependent differential equations for the functions $t \to x_{ij}(\sigma(t))$, so there are certainly methods available to solve them, although they, too, may probably not be too practical for computations or for predicting the qualitative properties of the extremals.

The second method proceeds by introducing a coordinate system for a piece of $S0(3, R)$ that is well adapted to describing the group structure of $S0(3, R)$ (hence is also well adapted to the physics, since the physics and the group theory more or less coincide), namely, the *Euler angles*. They can be described group-theoretically. Consider the set of matrices:

$$\begin{pmatrix} \cos \theta_1 & \sin \theta_1 & 0 \\ -\sin \theta_1 & \cos \theta_1 & 0 \\ 0 & 0 & 1 \end{pmatrix} = A(\theta_1), \qquad -\infty < \theta_1 < \infty. \qquad (16.20)$$

They form a one-parameter subgroup of $S0(3, R)$; in fact, each one just represents a rotation about the x_3-axis of angle θ_1. Similarly, consider the one-parameter group of rotations about the x_1-axis:

$$\begin{pmatrix} 1 & 0 & 0 \\ 0 & \cos \theta_2 & \sin \theta_2 \\ 0 & -\sin \theta_2 & \cos \theta_2 \end{pmatrix} = B(\theta_2), \qquad -\infty < \theta_2 < \infty. \qquad (16.21)$$

It is seen now that each orthogonal matrix (of determinant 1) can be written as a product, $A(\theta_1)B(\theta_2)A(\theta_3)$, of three about the two axes. It can be verified that this representation is unambiguous for a certain open subset of $S0(3, R)$ and for $\theta_1, \theta_2, \theta_3$ suitably restricted. Thus $\theta_1, \theta_2,$ and θ_3 serve as a *coordinate system* for a piece of $S0(3, R)$. In fact, a suitable (but tedious) calculation shows that

$$\omega_1 = \sin \theta_2 \sin \theta_3 \, d\theta_1 + \cos \theta_3 \, d\theta_2, \qquad (16.22a)$$

$$\omega_2 = \sin \theta_2 \cos \theta_3 \, d\theta_1 - \sin \theta_3 \, d\theta_2, \qquad (16.22b)$$

$$\omega_3 = \cos \theta_2 \, d\theta_1 + d\theta_3. \qquad (16.22c)$$

Notice, for example, that these forms are not independent for $\theta_1 = 0 = \theta_2 = \theta_3$, so the Jacobian of the map

$$(\theta_1, \theta_2, \theta_3) \to A(\theta_1)B(\theta_2)A(\theta_3)$$

is zero at $\theta_1 = 0 = \theta_2 = \theta_3$. Now, the Lagrangian of the left-invariant variational problem is just

$$L = I_1(\sin\theta_2 \sin\theta_3 \dot\theta_1 + \cos\theta_3 \dot\theta_2)^2 + I_2(\sin\theta_2 \cos\theta_3 \dot\theta_1 - \sin\theta_3 \dot\theta_2)^2$$
$$+ I_3(\cos\theta_2 \dot\theta_1 + \dot\theta_3)^2.$$

Thus θ_1 does not appear explicitly in L. In fact, this is just the coordinate system chosen so that the infinitesimal generator of left translation by $A(\theta)$ is just $\partial/\partial\theta_1$. Note that the infinitesimal generator of *right* translation by $A(\theta)$ is just $\partial/\partial\theta_3$. Thus the condition that the rigid body be symmetric about the x_3-axis is that the Lagrangian not depend on θ_3 either. Clearly, the condition for this is $I_1 = I_2$.

Let us now compute the Hamiltonian for the Lagrangian $L = I_1 y_1^2 + I_2 y_2^2 + I_3 y_3^2$. Suppose the L_{n+i} and L'_{n+i} are such that

$$dL = L_{n+i}\, dy_i + \cdots; \qquad dL = L'_{n+i}\, d\theta_i + \cdots.$$

Now $L_{n+i} = 2I_i y_i$ (no summation). The $\dot\theta_i$ are related to $\dot y_i$ by solving (16.22) and making the substitutions $\omega \to \dot y$, $d\theta \to \dot\theta$.

$$\dot\theta_1 = \frac{\sin\theta_3 y_1 + \cos\theta_3 y_2}{\sin\theta_2}, \qquad \dot\theta_2 = \cos\theta_3 y_1 - \sin\theta_3 y_2,$$

$$\dot\theta_3 = y_3 - \cot\theta_2(\sin\theta_3 y_1 + \cos\theta_3 y_2).$$

Thus,

$$L_{n+1} = L'_{n+1}\frac{\sin\theta_3}{\sin\theta_2} + L'_{n+2}\cos\theta_3 - L'_{n+3}\cot\theta_2\sin\theta_3,$$

$$L_{n+2} = L'_{n+1}\frac{\cos\theta_3}{\sin\theta_2} - L'_{n+2}\sin\theta_3 - L'_{n+3}\cot\theta_2\cos\theta_3,$$

$$L_{n+3} = L'_{n+3}.$$

Now, if $p_i = L_{n+i}$, the Hamiltonian H is just L written in terms of the p (since L is a quadratic Lagrangian):

$$H = \frac{1}{4}\frac{p_1^2}{I_1} + \frac{p_2^2}{I_2} + \frac{p_3^2}{I_3}.$$

If $p_i' = L'_{n+i}$, we know from earlier work that the Hamiltonian for L in the $\theta_1, \theta_2, \theta_3$ coordinate system is obtained by simply substituting in the values of $p_i = L_{n+i}$ in terms of $p_i' = L'_{n+i}$:

$$H = \frac{1}{4I_1}\left(p_1'\frac{\sin\theta_3}{\sin\theta_2} + p_2'\cos\theta_3 - p_3'\cot\theta_2\sin\theta_3\right)^2$$
$$+ \frac{1}{4I_2}\left(p_1'\frac{\cos\theta_3}{\sin\theta_2} - p_2'\sin\theta_3 - p_3'\cot\theta_2\cos\theta_3\right)^2 + \frac{1}{4I_3}p_3'^2.$$

For example, look again at the case $I_1 = I_2$; that is, suppose that the variational problem is invariant under left and right translation by $A(\theta)$. Then

$$H = \frac{1}{4I_1}\left(\frac{p_1'^2}{\sin^2\theta_2} + p_2'^2 + p_3'^2\cot^2\theta_2 - 2p_1'p_3'\frac{\cos\theta_2}{\sin^2\theta_2}\right) + \frac{1}{4I_3}p_3'^2.$$

As predicted by the general theory, the Hamiltonian does not depend on θ_1 and θ_3, so p_1' and p_3' are constants, say, C_1 and C_2. Then the Hamilton equations for θ_2, p_2' give

$$\frac{d\theta_2}{dt} = \frac{1}{2I_1}p_2'.$$

Also, we know from "conservation of energy" (that is, the fact that the Hamiltonian is a constant of motion) that

$$\frac{1}{4I_1}\left(\frac{C_1^2}{\sin^2\theta_2} + 4I_1^2\left(\frac{d\theta_2}{dt}\right)^2\right.$$

$$\left. + C_3^2\cot^2\theta_2 - 2C_1C_3\frac{\cos\theta_2}{\sin^2\theta_2}\right) + \frac{1}{4I_3}C_3^2 = \text{constant} = E,$$

or

$$\left(\frac{d\theta_2}{dt}\right)^2 = -\frac{1}{4I_1^2\sin^2\theta_2}$$

$$\times (C_1^2 + C_3^2\cos^2\theta_2 - 2C_1C_3\cos\theta_2) + \frac{E - (C_3^2/4I_3)}{I_1}.$$

Change variables to $x = \cos\theta_2$. Then

$$I_1^2\left(\frac{dx}{dt}\right)^2 = \left(E - \frac{C_3^2}{4I_3}\right)I_1(1 - x^2) - \tfrac{1}{4}(C_1 - C_3 x)^2,$$

which can certainly be solved in elementary terms without elliptic functions. The most important point is to compute the roots of the second-degree polynomial on the right-hand side. The solution will then oscillate between these limits. If our rigid body is a top, θ_2 will measure the angle between its x_3-axis (in a coordinate system fixed in the top) and the fixed space x_3-axis. This leads to the typical rising and falling motion of the top. In fact, we see that we can add a potential-energy term of the form $V(\cos\theta_2)$ to our Lagrangian without affecting this qualitative picture of the motion. By the general principles, this merely adds $V(\cos\theta_2)$ to the Hamiltonian: p_1' and p_3' remain constants of motion, and $x(t)$ is again determined by an equation of the form

$$\left(\frac{dx}{dt}\right)^2 = f(x).$$

Hence the solution will oscillate between two roots of $f(x)$ if it starts out between them. For example, if $V(\cos \theta_2) = \alpha \cos \theta_2$ (corresponding to the example of the "heavy symmetrical top," which is found in every textbook on rigid-body mechanics; for example, Goldstein [1]), the effect is to make $f(x)$ a *cubic* polynomial in x, requiring the introduction of elliptic functions.

Once we have found $x(t) = \cos \theta_2(t)$, the other Euler angles θ_1, θ_3 can be found by a quadrature from the Hamilton equations:

$$\frac{d\theta_1}{dt} = \frac{\partial H}{\partial p_1'} = \frac{1}{4I_1}\left(\frac{2C_1 - 2C_3\,x(t)}{1 - x^2(t)^2}\right),$$

$$\frac{d\theta_3}{dt} = \frac{\partial H}{\partial p_3'} = \frac{1}{4I_1}\left(\frac{2C_3\,x^2 - 2C_1 x}{1 - x^2}\right) + C_3.$$

We can now summarize the qualitative features of our discussion: We have considered variational problems of Newtonian type on a manifold M that admits a relatively large group, namely, left and right translation by $S0(3, R)$. However, the largest Abelian subgroups of this group are just two-dimensional. The Euler angles define a coordinate system in which one of these two-dimensional Abelian subgroups takes its normal form, this form being the natural coordinate system for discussing variational problems that admit the Abelian groups as symmetry groups. (All these two-dimensional Abelian groups are conjugate within the big group, so the seemingly arbitrary choice of one of them really does not matter. In terms of the theory of compact Lie groups, these two-dimensional Abelian subgroups are *Cartan subgroups* of $S0(3, R) \times S0(3, R)$.) These variational problems are "integrable by quadratures," and in fact form most of the classical problems of rigid-body mechanics that have been found to be "integrable by quadratures" (except for the case discovered by S. Kovalewska, which does not seem to be explicable group-theoretically; see Golubev [1] for a full discussion). The case of a variational problem admitting left translation by $S0(3, R)$ as a symmetry group (the rigid body with no external forces) seems to be a typical problem admitting a non-Abelian group of symmetries, a class of problems on which more research needs to be done. (The maximal Abelian subgroup of $S0(3, R)$ are just one-dimensional, that is, the one-parameter subgroup, so that left invariance provides only a one-dimensional Abelian group of symmetries, which is not enough for "integrability by quadratures.") In fact, the group-theoretic properties of $S0(3, R)$ are connected with the basic properties of the elliptic functions, as we have tried to show in Chapter 17, but it is not yet possible to put this connection into definitive form.

Finally, we want to describe how the parametrization of $S0(3, R)$ by the Euler angles fits into the general theory of Lie groups, particularly the theory of symmetric spaces. (In this paragraph, we shall be using Helgason's book [1] as a basic reference, and shall assume that the reader is familiar with the general notions found there.) Let G be a connected Lie group, and let $s: G \to G$ be an automorphism of G such that $s^2 = $ identity. (s is then called an *involutive automorphism*.) Let

$$K = \{g \in G: s(g) = g\}.$$

Then K is a closed subgroup of G, called a *symmetric subgroup* of G, and G/K is called a *symmetric homogeneous space*.

We shall deal here with the case: K compact. (G/K is then called a *Riemannian* symmetric homogeneous space.) Now s defines an automorphism of $\mathbf{G}$, the Lie algebra of G, that will also be denoted by s. For example, this can be seen by identifying $\mathbf{G}$ with the set of one-parameter subgroups of G. If $t \to g(t)$ is such a one-parameter subgroup, its transform by s is the one-parameter subgroup, that is, $t \to sg(t)$. We see, then, that

$$s^2(X) = X \qquad \text{for all } X \in \mathbf{G}.$$

Since s is a linear transformation of $\mathbf{G}$, we can split $\mathbf{G}$ as the direct sum $\mathbf{K} \oplus \mathbf{P}$, with

$$\mathbf{K} = \{X \in \mathbf{G}: s(X) = X\}, \qquad \mathbf{P} = \{X \in \mathbf{G}: s(X) = -X\}.$$

From the fact that s is an automorphism of $\mathbf{G}$, we see that

$$\text{Ad } K(\mathbf{P}) \subset \mathbf{P}, \qquad [\mathbf{P}, \mathbf{P}] \subset \mathbf{K}.$$

Thus Ad K induces a linear representation on $\mathbf{P}$ (which is essentially equivalent to the linear isotropy group of the homogeneous space G/K). Let $\mathbf{A}$ be a maximal Abelian subalgebra of $\mathbf{P}$. One basic theorem of the theory of symmetric spaces is that

$$\text{Ad } K(\mathbf{A}) = \mathbf{P}.$$

$\mathbf{A}$ is called a *Cartan subalgebra* of the symmetric space G/K. (All maximal Abelian subalgebras of $\mathbf{P}$ are conjugate under Ad K.)

Now let $P = \exp(\mathbf{P}) \subset G$. The exponential map of $\mathbf{G} \to G$ usually has singularities. Thus it is a remarkable fact that P can be shown to be a closed submanifold of G. In fact P is the connected component containing the identity of

$$\{g \in G: s(g) = g^{-1}\}.$$

Elements of P are called *transvections* of the symmetric space G/K. Let $A = \exp(\mathbf{A}) \subset P$. Again it can be shown that A is a closed submanifold of P (diffeomorphic to a multidimensional torus if G is compact, to a Euclidean space if G is noncompact, and if $\mathbf{K}$ is a maximal compact subgroup of G). In a sense, this "flat" submanifold A is the "core" of the symmetric space; many of the important geometric and group-theoretic facts about G/K can be reconstructed from knowledge of A and a certain finite group acting on A, the *Weyl group*.

(The Weyl group can be defined as follows: Let $N(A, K)$ and $C(A, K)$ be, respectively, the normalizer and centralizer of A in K; that is,

$$N(A, K) = \{k \in K : \text{Ad } k(A) = A\}$$

$$C(A, K) = \{k \in K : kak^{-1} = a \text{ for all } a \in A\}.$$

Then $C(A, K)$ and $N(A, K)$ are closed subgroups of K, $C(A, K)$ is a normal subgroup of $N(A, K)$, and the Weyl group is the quotient group $N(A, K)/C(A, K)$. A more geometric way of looking at this is to notice that each $k \in N(A, K)$ induces a transformation, namely, Ad k, on A, and $C(A, K)$ is just the subgroup of those elements that act trivially on A.)

Now the relation Ad $K(\mathbf{A}) = \mathbf{P}$ implies Ad $K(A) = P$. Further, it can be proved that

$$G = P \cdot K.$$

Thus,

$$G = KPK^{-1}K = KPK,$$

that is, the map $\alpha : K \times A \times K \to G$ such that $\alpha(k, a, k') = kpk'$ for $kpk' \in K$, $a \in A$ is *onto* G.

Now $C(A, K)$ can be made to act as a transformation group on $K \times A \times K$ as follows:

$$c \cdot (k, a, k') = (kc^{-1}, a, ck') \qquad \text{for } c \in C(A, K), \quad k, k' \in K, \quad a \in A.$$

Notice that

$$\alpha(c \cdot (k, a, k')) = \alpha(kc^{-1}, a, ck') = kc^{-1}ack' = kac^{-1}ck' = \alpha(k, a, k');$$

that is, α maps each orbit of $C(A, K)$ into a point. Also, $C(A, K)$ acts on $K \times A \times K$ in such a way that no element except the identity transformation has a fixed point. Hence the orbit space $C(A, K)/K \times A \times K$ is a manifold; α passes to the quotient to define a map of the orbit space onto G, which we shall denote by $\bar{\alpha}$. Now the orbit space and G have the same dimension: α is not quite a diffeomorphism (this would be impossible topologically, if for no other reason), but the points of G that are regular with respect to $\alpha\dagger$ are sufficiently plentiful in the sense that their complement in G is the union of a finite number of submanifolds of lower dimension.

$\dagger$ If $\phi : M \to M'$ is a map of manifolds of the same dimension, a point $p' \in M'$ is regular with respect to ϕ if ϕ has nonzero Jacobian at each point of $\phi^{-1}(p')$. If ϕ is onto, a basic general theorem on the theory of manifolds says that the complement in M' of the set of regular elements is of measure zero.

As an example, we can apply this construction to the case $G = S0(3, R)$, $K =$ one-parameter group of rotation about the x_3-axis. Explicitly,

$$K = \left\{ \begin{pmatrix} \cos\theta & \sin\theta & 0 \\ -\sin\theta & \cos\theta & 0 \\ 0 & 0 & 1 \end{pmatrix} = A(\theta) : 0 \le \theta < 2\pi \right\}.$$

We want to exhibit the involutive automorphism of G that exhibits K as a symmetric subgroup and G/K as a symmetric homogeneous space.† Since K is a one-parameter group, a reasonable choice is just Ad of an element of K of order 2; namely,

$$s(g) = A(\pi)gA(-\pi) \qquad \text{for} \quad g \in S0(3, R).$$

We shall leave it to the reader to show that this choice does the job. Let us compute P:

$$P = \{g \in G : A(\pi)gA(-\pi) = g^{-1}\}.$$

Consider for the moment that matrices define linear transformations on 3-vectors, a 3-vector denoted by v. Any rotation in 3-space admits one and up to a constant multiple only one invariant vector, say, $g \cdot v = v$. Then

$$A(\pi)g = A(\pi)v = g^{-1}A(\pi)v \qquad \text{or} \qquad g(A(\pi)v) = A(\pi)v.$$

Thus,

$$A(\pi)v = \pm v.$$

Case 1 $A(\pi)v = v$

Then v is the same invariant vector as the whole one-parameter group $\theta \to A(\theta)$; hence g commutes with each $A(\theta)$, or

$$g^2 = A(-2\pi) = \text{identity matrix}.$$

Case 2 $A(\pi)v = -v$

Then v is perpendicular to the invariant vector of the one-parameter group $\theta \to A(\theta)$, that is, lies in the (x_1, x_2)-plane.

Since we are interested only in the connected component of P containing the identity element, we see that Case 2 is the only relevant one, and P can be

---

† In fact, G/K is just the two-sphere (that is, a Riemannian manifold of constant curvature). This fits in with the alternate geometric definition of a Riemannian symmetric space (modulo certain global complications) as a Riemannian manifold whose sectional curvatures are invariant under parallel translation.

considered as the set of rotations about axes lying in the (x_1, x_2)-plane. In particular, it contains the one-parameter group

$$\theta \to B(\theta) = \begin{pmatrix} 1 & 0 & 0 \\ 0 & \cos\theta & \sin\theta \\ 0 & -\sin\theta & \cos\theta \end{pmatrix}$$

of rotations about the x_1-axis. Now the centralizer of A in K is the identity; hence the map $(\theta_1, \theta_2, \theta_3) \to A(\theta_1)B(\theta_2)A(\theta_3)$, which defined the Euler angle parametrization of $S0(3, R)$, is essentially just the construction $\alpha: K \times A \times K \to G$ outlined for the general symmetric case.† (Another more qualitative way of putting this is to say that in this case K and A turn out to be one-dimensional (in fact, circles); hence $K \times A \times K$ can be described by three angular parameters. The specific choices we made are unimportant, since any two choices are related by a conjugacy.)

Exercises

1. Prove the last statement of Theorem 16.1.

2. Suppose ϕ is a diffeomorphism of R^{2n} such that $\phi^*: F(R^{2n}) \to F(R^{2n})$ is a Lie algebra homeomorphism relative to Poisson bracket. Prove that ϕ is a canonical transformation.

3. Investigate (using Theorem 16.6 and (16.7)) the solution of the two- and three-body problems of celestial mechanics that are also orbits of one-parameter groups of symmetries.

4. Verify the formula given for the "Routhian."

5. Suppose G is a Lie group and (ω_i), $1 \le i \le n$, are a basis for the left-invariant form on G. Let y_i be the functions on $T(G)$ such that

$$y_i(v) = \omega_i(v) \qquad \text{for } v \in T(G).$$

Let $L = I_i y_i^2$ define a Lagrangian and a variational problem on G. Work out the general conditions that a polynomial $f(y_i, \ldots, y_n)$ be an integral of motion. (*Hint:* Is there a relation with the Casimir operators of the universal-enveloping algebra of the Lie algebra of G? See Hermann [8] for the notion.)

6. Prove Formula (16.22).

† I owe these remarks concerning the general setting of the Euler angle construction to C. C. Moore.

17 Elliptic Functions

Unaccountably, the theory of elliptic functions has virtually disappeared from recent mathematics or physics literature, despite the fact that it is amazingly rich in structure, theorems, and mathematical or physical intuition. Of course we cannot hope to give the subject the systematic treatment it needs, and shall limit ourselves to some properties that follow from the fact that they can be *defined* as the functions describing rigid-body motion. Our treatment by means of differential equations then follows up an idea briefly sketched by Tricomi in his book on differential equations [1, pp. 19–26]. The most readily accessible treatment of elliptic functions along classical lines can be found in Whittaker and Watson [1], although they neglect the geometric side of the theory.

Recall that the problem of motion of a rotating rigid body with no external forces leads to differential equations of the form:

$$I_1 \frac{dy_1}{dt} = (I_3 - I_2)y_2 y_3, \tag{17.1a}$$

$$I_2 \frac{dy_2}{dt} = (I_1 - I_3)y_1 y_3, \tag{17.1b}$$

$$I_3 \frac{dy_3}{dt} = (I_2 - I_1)y_1 y_2. \tag{17.1c}$$

We have seen that the underlying rigid-body problem has two algebraic integrals, namely, those of "energy" and "total angular momentum":

$$I_1 y_1^2 + I_2 y_2^2 + I_3 y_3^2 = c \quad (= \text{constant}) \tag{17.2}$$

$$I_1^2 y_1^2 + I_2^2 y_2^2 + I_3^2 y_3^2 = m \quad (= \text{constant}). \tag{17.3}$$

It can easily be verified directly from (17.1) that (17.2) and (17.3) are indeed integrals; that is, they are constant along solutions of (17.1). We shall suppose that $I_1 \neq I_2 \neq I_3 \neq 0$. We have already seen that if this were not satisfied (for example, if two of the I were equal), then (17.1) could be solved in terms of sines and cosines. If, on the other hand, one of the I is zero, it is clear that

(17.1) can be solved in terms of exponentials. Finally, we are not necessarily assuming that the I are positive (as they are in the rigid-body problem).

One of the variables can be eliminated from (17.2) and (17.3) to obtain algebraic relations among the other two:

$$(I_1 I_2 - I_2{}^2)y_2{}^2 + (I_1 I_3 - I_3{}^2)y_3{}^2 = I_1 c - m, \tag{17.4}$$

$$(I_2 I_1 - I_1{}^2)y_1{}^2 + (I_2 I_3 - I_3{}^2)y_3{}^2 = I_2 c - m, \tag{17.5}$$

$$(I_3 I_1 - I_1{}^2)y_1{}^2 + (I_3 I_2 - I_2{}^2)y_2{}^2 = I_3 c - m. \tag{17.6}$$

These can be substituted into (17.1) to actually "solve" (17.1). For example,

$$\frac{dy_1}{dt} = \sqrt{(\alpha y_1{}^2 - \beta)(\gamma y_1{}^2 - \delta)}$$

for suitable constants α, β, γ, δ, or

$$\int \frac{dy_1}{\sqrt{(\alpha y_1{}^2 - \beta)(\gamma y_1{}^2 - \delta)}} = t + \text{constant}.$$

The integral on the left is an "elliptic integral," so this solution does us little good in practice. In fact we are usually interested in the reverse process, namely, inverting an elliptic integral to make it part of a system of the type of (17.1).

The remarkable property of system (17.1) is that any system of solutions $(y_1(t), y_2(t), y_3(t))$ satisfies an algebraic "addition formula" that is independent of I_1, I_2, I_3, namely,

$$\frac{y_2(t) + y_2(s)}{y_1(t)y_3(s) + y_3(t)y_1(t)} = \frac{y_2(s + t) + y_2(0)}{y_1(s + t)y_3(0) + y_3(s + t)y_1(0)}. \tag{17.7}$$

Two similar identities are obtained by permuting y_1, y_2, and y_3. Further, (17.4) through (17.6) can be used to obtain an algebraic formula connecting, say, $y_2(s + t)$ to $y_i(t)$ and $y_i(s)$, for $i = 1, 2, 3$.

To prove (17.7), one has only to apply the differential operator $(\partial/\partial t) - (\partial/\partial s)$ to the left-hand side of (17.7) to verify by direct computation that it vanishes when combined with (17.1) through (17.6); hence it is a function of $(s + t)$. The function given on the right-hand side is obtained by setting $t = 0$.

The solutions of (17.1) with special choices of the adjustable parameters have explicit names—the *Jacobian elliptic functions*:

$$y_1(t) = \operatorname{sn} t, \qquad y_2(t) = \operatorname{cn} t, \qquad y_3(t) = \operatorname{dn} t. \tag{17.8}$$

For

$$\frac{I_3 - I_2}{I_1} = 1, \qquad y_1(0) = 0;$$

$$\frac{I_1 - I_3}{I_2} = -1, \qquad y_2(0) = 1;$$

$$\frac{I_3 - I_1}{I_3} = -k^2, \qquad y_3(0) = 1.$$

Putting these values in (17.2) through (17.7) gives the classical addition formulas for the Jacobian elliptic functions, the treatment of which can be found in complete detail in all the reference books. For example,

$$sn(s + t) = \frac{sn(s)cn(t)\,dn(t) + cn(s)sn(t)\,dn(s)}{1 - k^2 sn^2(s)sn^2(t)},$$

where k is a free parameter, so really the Jacobian functions depend on t and k, but it is customary to express this explicitly.

Let us return to the study of system (17.1).

LEMMA 17.1

If any two functions among those constituting a solution $(y_1(t), y_2(t), y_3(t))$ of (17.1) vanish for one value of t, then the three functions are constant.

Proof. Let us suppose, say, that $y_1(t_0) = 0 = y_2(t_0)$. Then, if $(y_1{}^*(t), y_2{}^*(t),$ the $y_3{}^*(t))$ are defined as follows:

$$y_1{}^*(t) = 0, \qquad y_2{}^*(t) = 0, \qquad y_3{}^*(t) \equiv y_3(t_0).$$

Notice that they define a solution of (17.1) which satisfies the same initial conditions at $t = t_0$ as does our original solution. By the uniqueness theorem for ordinary differential equations, they must coincide.   Q.E.D.

In studying the properties of a system of differential equations such as (17.1), it is often a good practice to start by finding how the system behaves when transformed by various groups of transformations of the underlying space. We shall now do so, considering only the simplest group that seems interesting. (A more systematic treatment would be very interesting, but would carry us too far afield.)

Let us begin by rewriting the differential equations (17.1) as a Pfaffian system:

$$0 = \omega_1 = I_1\,dy_1 - (I_3 - I_2)y_2\,y_3\,dt, \qquad (17.9a)$$

$$0 = \omega_2 = I_2\,dy_2 - (I_1 - I_3)y_1 y_3\,dt, \qquad (17.9b)$$

$$0 = \omega_3 = I_3\,dy_3 - (I_2 - I_1)y_1\,y_2\,dt. \qquad (17.9c)$$

We shall consider only the group of linear transformations of (y_1, y_2, y_3, t)-space that are dilations, that is, that multiply the coordinates by constants. Thus, if ϕ is such a transformation,

$$\phi^*(t) = A\,dt, \qquad \phi^*(y_i) = A_i y_i \qquad \text{for } i = 1, 2, 3 \quad \text{(no summation)}.$$

Consider another system of the same form as (17.9):

$$\omega_1' = I_1'\,dy_1 - (I_3' - I_2')y_2\,y_1\,dt, \tag{17.10a}$$
$$\omega_2' = I_2'\,dy_1 - (I_1' - I_3')y_1\,y_3\,dt, \tag{17.10b}$$
$$\omega_3' = I_3'\,dy_3 - (I_2' - I_1)y_1\,y_3\,dt. \tag{17.10c}$$

The condition that ϕ carry the integral curves of (17.10) into integral curves of (17.9) is that the $\phi^*(\omega)$ be linear combinations of the ω', that is, that we have a relation of the form

$$\phi^*(\omega_i) = \sum_{j=1}^{3} \alpha_{ij}\,\omega_j' \qquad \text{for } i = 1, 2, 3.$$

Comparing the coefficients of the dy, we have

$$\alpha_{ij} = 0 \quad \text{if } i \neq j, \qquad A_i I_i = \alpha_{ii} I_i',$$

or

$$\alpha_{ii} = \frac{A_i I_i}{I_i'} \qquad \text{(no summation)}.$$

Thus,

$$I_1'(I_3 - I_3)A_2\,A_3\,A = A_1 I_1(I_3' - I_2'), \tag{17.11a}$$
$$I_2'(I_1 - I_3)A_1 A_3\,A = A_2 I_2(I_1' - I_3'), \tag{17.11b}$$
$$I_3'(I_2 - I_1)A_1 A_2\,A = A_3 I_3(I_2' - I_3'). \tag{17.11c}$$

Notice that if the I and I' are prescribed, one of the A^1, A_2, A_3, A can be prescribed arbitrarily. If $I_1 = I_1'$, $I_2 = I_2'$, I_3', then (17.11) holds if and only if

$$A_1{}^2 = A_2{}^2 = A_3{}^2, \qquad A = \frac{A_1}{A_2 A_3}. \tag{17.12}$$

Now, obviously system (17.1) is preserved under time translation. Thus, if one function of a triple (y_1, y_2, y_3) that solves (17.1) vanishes at some value of t, then combining a permutation of y_1, y_2, y_3, a transformation of type (17.11) and a time translation will send the given solution into the Jacobian elliptic functions (possibly needing complex values for the parameters of the transformation). Thus, the first problem is to find those solutions.

LEMMA 17.2

Let $(y_1(t), y_2(t), y_3(t))$ be a nonconstant solution of (17.1) defined for $a \le t \le 2b$ such that $y_1(a) = y_1(b) = 0$. Then, both y_2 and y_3 must have a zero in the interval $a < t < 2b$.

Proof. Suppose otherwise: For example, suppose that $y_2(t) \ne 0$ for $a \le t \le 2b$. Without loss in generality we may suppose that $a = 0$. Then (17.1) takes the form

$$\frac{y_2(s) + y_2(t)}{y_1(t)y_3(s) + y_3(t)y_1(s)} = \frac{y_2(s + t) + y_2(0)}{y_1(s + t)y_3(0)}.$$

By Lemma 17.1, $y_3(0) \ne 0$. Since the denominators are nonzero, $y_1(2b) = 0$. Hence, putting $r = 2b - t$, we have

$$y_1(t)y_3(2b - t) + y_3(t)y_1(2b - t) = 0.$$

Equation (17.6) gives a relation of the form $y_3^2 = \alpha y_1^2 + \beta$. Then

$$y_1(t)^2(\alpha y_1(2b - t)^2 + \beta) = (\alpha y_1(t)^2 + \beta)y_1(2b - t)^2,$$

or $\beta(y_1(t)^2 - y_1(2b - t)^2) = 0$. Hence $\beta = 0$, since y_1 is nonconstant. But then $y_3(t) = 0$, and Lemma 17.1 forces y_1 constant; contradiction.

LEMMA 17.3

Suppose that $(y_1(t), y_2(t), y_3(t))$ is a nonconstant solution of (17.1) defined over $-\infty < t < \infty$. Then at least one of the components of this solution must vanish at least once on $-\infty < t < \infty$.

Proof. Suppose otherwise: Then the derivatives of the components must also be everywhere nonzero. Since I_1, I_2, and I_3 are nonequal, at most one of the right-hand sides of (17.4) through (17.6) can vanish. Let us suppose, then, that $I_2 c - m$ and $I_3 c - m$ are nonzero. Then

$$\frac{dy_1}{dt} = \pm\sqrt{(\alpha y_1^2 - \beta)(\gamma y_1^2 - \delta)}, \qquad \text{with} \quad \beta \ne 0, \quad \delta \ne 0.$$

At most transforming the system by equations of the type of (17.11), we can suppose that

$$y_1(0) > 0, \qquad \frac{dy_1}{dt}(0) < 0.$$

Thus $y_1(t) > 0$, and $(dy_1/dt)(t) < 0$ for $0 \leq t < \infty$; hence

$$\frac{dy_1}{dt} = -\sqrt{(\alpha y_1{}^2 - \beta)(\gamma y_1{}^2 - \delta)},$$

$$t = \int_{y_1(t)}^{y_1(0)} \frac{dx}{\sqrt{(\alpha x^2 - \beta)(\gamma x^2 - \delta)}} < \int_0^{y_1(0)} \frac{dx}{\sqrt{(\alpha x^2 - \beta)(\gamma x^2 - \delta)}}.$$

But this integral converges, since at each possible singularity the integrand has a singularity of order $-\frac{1}{2}$ (since $\beta \neq 0$, $\delta \neq 0$), which gives the contradiction.

Hence, in studying a nonconstant solution $(y_1(t), y_2(t), y_3(t))$, we can suppose (after making a time translation and a permutation) that

$$y_1(0) = 0. \tag{17.13}$$

(At this point a further transformation can be made by throwing the solution onto the one defining the Jacobian elliptic functions, but we shall not be particularly concerned with that here.) By Lemma 17.1, and (17.4) and (17.5), $I_2 c - m \neq 0$ and $I_3 c - m \neq 0$. Also, if (17.12) is satisfied,

$$y_1(-t) = -y_1(t); \qquad y_2(-t) = y_2(t); \qquad y_3(-t) = y_3(t). \tag{17.14}$$

To prove this, one can choose A, A_1, A_2, A_3 to make a change of variables such that

$$A_2 = A_3 = 1, \qquad A_1 = -1 = A.$$

By (17.11), $I_1 = I_1'$, $I_2 = I_2'$, $I_3 = I_3'$. Thus the new functions

$$z_1(t) = -y_1(-t), \qquad z_2(t) = y_2(-t), \qquad z_3(t) = y_3(-t)$$

satisfy the same system (17.1) as the old, with the same initial condition; whence, (17.14).

Clearly we can use a change of variable of the type of (17.12) to suppose in addition that

$$y_2(0) > 0, \qquad y_3(0) > 0. \tag{17.15}$$

So far we have been proceeding without assumptions of the signs of I_1, I_2, and I_3. Now the global behavior of the solutions is radically different, depending on whether or not all the signs are the same. The case of like signs is the one that occurs in the force-free rigid-body problem; the case of unlike signs will be left as an exercise. We can suppose without any essential loss in generality that

$$I_1 > 0, \qquad I_2 > 0, \qquad I_3 > 0. \tag{17.16}$$

We shall now show that we can suppose (at most permuting y_2 and y_3) that

$$\frac{dy_2}{dt}(t) < 0 \qquad \text{for sufficiently small } t > 0. \tag{17.17}$$

Suppose otherwise: Then,

$$I_2 \frac{dy_2}{dt} = (I_1 - I_3)y_1 y_3(t) > 0,$$

$$I_3 \frac{dy_3}{dt} = (I_2 - I_1)y_1 y_2(t) > 0 \qquad \text{for sufficiently small } t > 0.$$

Case 1 $(dy_1/dt)(0) > 0.$

Then $y_1(t) > 0$ for small $t > 0$, and $I_3 > I_2$. Then, also, $I_1 > I_3$ and $I_2 > I_1$, which is a contradiction.

Case 2 $(dy_1/dt)(0) < 0$

Then $I_3 < I_2$. Hence, also, $I_1 < I_3$, $I_2 < I_1$, which is again a contradiction.

Now, let $K > 0$ be the first positive real zero of y_2 or y_3. By the mean-value theorem,

$$y_1(t) \neq 0 \qquad \text{for} \quad 0 < t \leq K. \tag{17.18}$$

Further, if $(dy_3/dt)(t) > 0$ for $t > 0$ sufficiently small, then

$$y_2(K) = 0. \tag{17.19}$$

We can now show how to compute K. For example, suppose that

$$y_2(K) = 0. \tag{17.20}$$

Then $(dy_2/dt)(t) < 0$ for $0 < t \leq K$. We can solve (17.4) and (17.6) in the form

$$\frac{dy_2}{dt} = -\sqrt{(\alpha_2 y_2{}^2 - \beta_2)(\gamma_2 y_2{}^2 - \delta_2)} \qquad \text{for} \quad 0 \leq t \leq K.$$

Thus,

$$t = \int_{y_2(t)}^{y_2(0)} \frac{dx}{\sqrt{(\alpha_2 x^2 - \beta_2)(\gamma_2 x^2 - \delta_2)}} \qquad \text{for} \quad 0 \leq t \leq K.$$

Hence,

$$K = \int_0^{y_2(0)} \frac{dx}{\sqrt{(\alpha_2 x^2 - \beta_2)(\gamma_2 x^2 - \delta_2)}}. \tag{17.21}$$

In particular, notice that $K < \infty$.

Once we have found a K that is a zero of $y_2(t)$, what can be done with it? The addition formula (17.7) enables us to extract considerably more information, as described in the following theorem.

THEOREM 17.4

Let (y_1, y_2, y_3) be a nonconstant solution of (17.1) (with no assumptions on I_1, I_2, I_3 other than $I_1 \neq 0$, $I_2 \neq 0$, $I_3 \neq 0$); let $K \neq 0$ be such that $y_1(0) = 0 = y_2(K)$. Then

$$y_1(t + 2K) = -y_1(t), \qquad y_2(t + 2K) = -y_2(t), \qquad y_3(t + 2K) = y_3(t),$$

for all t for which these make sense. In particular, y_1 and y_2 are periodic with period $4K$, while y_3 is periodic with period $2K$.

Proof. Let us rewrite (17.7) in the form

$$(y_2(t) + y_2(s))(y_1(t + s)y_3(0)) = (y_2(t + s) + y_2(0))(y_1(t)y_3(s) + y_3(t)y(s_1)).$$

Put $t = K = s$. Now either

$$y_2(2K) + y_2(0) = 0 \qquad \text{or} \qquad y_1(t)y_3(2K - t) + y_1(2K - t)y_3(t) = 0.$$

$$(17.22)$$

We shall rule out this second identity. Now (17.5) can be solved in the form

$$y_3{}^2 = \frac{I_2 c - m - (I_2 I_1 - I_1{}^2)y_1{}^2}{(I_2 I_3 - I_3{}^2)}.$$

Substituting in this would give $I_2 c = m$. In particular, $y_3(0) = 0$, which would contradict the nonconstancy of the solution.

Now we can use (17.7) again, with a permutation of y_1, y_2, and y_3:

$$[y_1(t) + y_1(s)][y_2(t + s)y_3(0) + y_3(t + s)y_2(0)]$$
$$= [y_1(t + s) + y_1(0)][y_2(t)y_3(s) + y_3(t)y_2(s)].$$

Putting $t = s = K$ makes the right-hand side zero; hence

$$0 = y_2(2K)y_3(0) + y_3(2K)y_2(0),$$

whence, using (17.22), we have

$$y_3(2K) = y_3(0). \tag{17.23}$$

Similarly, playing with the other permutations proves that

$$y_1(2K) = 0. \tag{17.24}$$

Now put

$$z_1(t) = -y_1(t), \qquad z_2(t) = -y_2(t), \qquad z_3(t) = y_3(t).$$

Notice that $(z_1(t), z_2(t), z_3(t))$ is also a solution of (17.1), which has the same initial conditions at $t = 2K$ as does $(y_1(t), y_2(t), y_3(t))$ at $t = 0$. Thus

$$-y_1(t) = y_1(t + 2K),$$
$$-y_2(t) = y_2(t + 2K),$$
$$y_3(t) = y_3(t + 2K),$$

which proves the theorem.

Remark. Notice that Theorem 17.4 is purely formal and holds for the complex variable case as well. However, to consider this extension to complex variables would take us too far afield, and we must refer to Whittaker and Watson [1].

18 Accessibility Problems for Path Systems

General Remarks

From a higher point of view, the calculus of variations should be regarded as the "theory" of a real-valued function on an infinite dimensional space, namely, the space of curves on the underlying configuration space. One might think that it would be possible to eliminate the confusion and ambiguity that afflicts the subject by treating it consistently from this point of view. However, in searching for such a panacea, one must have respect for the fact that the calculus of variations has the longest history of any currently active branch of mathematics; in addition, this basic insight into the calculus of variations has been explicit since Volterra's pioneering work on "infinite dimensional manifolds" in the 1880's. In this chapter, we hope to demonstrate that this insight is useful for developing intuition into the mathematical structure of the subject. However, the foundations are still unsettled; there is no point in committing to print a full-scale exposition.

Let M be a manifold and let $P(M)$ denote the space of paths of M. (Recall that a *path* is a continuous map of an interval $[a, b]$ of real numbers into M that is piecewise C^∞.) By a *path system* on D we mean a subset (denoted, say, by π) of $P(M)$ having the property that if a path σ belongs to π, all paths obtain from σ by changing the parametrization of σ and by restricting σ to a subinterval of its domain of definition also belong to π.

Now, our basic intuition is that $P(M)$ is to be regarded as an "infinite dimensional manifold" and that we shall be considering path systems obtained by setting a set of real-value functions on $P(M)$ (usually uncountably infinite in number) equal to zero. Thus, in a sense, we are to regard a path system π as a "submanifold" of $P(M)$.

Let π be a given path system on M. Since paths can be freely parametrized, let us suppose they are defined over the interval $[0, 1]$, with the parameter denoted by t. For $p \in M$, let $\pi(p)$ be the set of all points of M that can be joined to p by a path in π. We can look at this in the following way: Consider the subspace of paths in π that begin at p, denoted say by π^p, and map $\pi^p \to M$ by sending a path into its end point. The "accessibility" problem, in full generality, is to describe $\pi(p)$ in terms of the differential geometric invariants of π.

We see the analogy with a problem for ordinary finite dimensional manifolds. Suppose A and B are two such spaces, and $\phi: A \to B$ is a map, with $\dim B \le \dim A$. We are interested in finding conditions that guarantee that ϕ is *onto* B. One such condition, of a local nature, is given by the implicit function theorem: For a point $\alpha \in A$, ϕ_* is a linear map $A_\alpha \to B_{\phi(\alpha)}$. If it is *onto*, ϕ covers a small neighborhood of $\phi(\alpha)$. If $\phi_*(A_\alpha) = B_{\phi(\alpha)}$ for all $\alpha \in A$, then it is easy to see that this local fact can be "expanded out" globally, provided there is some condition of uniformity for the norm of ϕ_* as α varies on A. Considered from the opposite point of view, the "critical points" for the discussion of onto-ness are the points $\alpha \in A$ such that $\phi_*(A_\alpha) \ne B_{\phi(\alpha)}$. Dually, such a critical point would be a point having the following property: There exists a function $f \in F(B)$ with $df \ne 0$ at $\phi(\alpha)$ but $d(\phi^*(f)) = 0$ at α. Now, a map may be onto, even though it has critical points. Consider the maps ϕ_1 and $\phi_2: R \to R$, defined by $\phi_1(x) = x^2$ and $\phi_2(x) = x^3$ for $x \in R$. Both have critical points at $x = 0$; the first is *not* onto; the second is. (As a side point, we may mention that the key fact is that the Jacobian $\phi_1'(x)$ of ϕ_1 changes sign, whereas the second does not.)

We shall not pursue the discussion of the type of singularities of mappings that are sufficient to guarantee that a map be onto. This would invoke a delicate and still largely unknown field. (See paper by Hartman and Nirenberg [1], for a beginning in this direction, at least for the case where A and B are of equal dimension.) However, this simple example does suggest one such invariant:

Suppose $f \in F(B)$ satisfies $df \ne 0$ at $\phi(\alpha)$, but $d\phi^*(f) = 0$ at α. Thus, $\phi^*(f)$ has a critical point in the ordinary sense; hence we can define its Hessian, which is a quadratic form on A_α. Suppose the Hessian is positive semidefinite. Then α has a neighborhood U in which

$$\phi^*(f)(\alpha') \ge \phi^*(f)(\alpha) \qquad \text{for all } \alpha' \in U,$$

that is, $f(\phi(\alpha')) - f(\phi(\alpha))$. But then $\phi(U)$ cannot cover a neighborhood of $\phi(\alpha)$, for otherwise f would have a critical point at $\phi(\alpha)$.

Another simple remark suggests itself: Consider the set of all functions $f \in F(B)$ such that $\phi^*(f) = $ constant. Obviously, a necessary condition that ϕ be onto is that any such function be constant on B. It is also *plausible* that in some cases (for example, if the image set $\phi(A)$ is not too wildly behaved) this condition will be sufficient.

Let us return to the case where we have the end-point mapping $\pi^p \to M$ of the space of a path from a given path system π on a manifold M beginning at the point p. Pursuing the analogy in the preceding paragraph, we can ask for functions on M that are constant when pulled back to π^p under the mapping. Such functions obviously have the geometric property of being *constant* along those paths in π beginning at p. As we shall see below, for common types of path systems defined by systems of ordinary differential equations, functions on M which are constant on paths of the system must satisfy certain systems of *partial* differential equations. Thus, if we can prove that these partial differential equations have no nonconstant solutions, we can hope to turn this around and actually *prove* that $\pi(p) = M$.

To make more explicit the program sketched in the last paragraph, let us make more definitions. Let U be an open subset of M. A function $f \in F(U)$ is said to be an *integral* of the path system π if

$$f(\sigma(t)) = f(\sigma(0)) \qquad \text{for } 0 \le t \le 1, \text{ every path}$$
$$\sigma: [0, 1] \to U \qquad \text{that belongs to } \pi.$$

The set of all such integrals will be denoted by $I(\pi, U)$. Since they can be multiplied and added, they form a ring of functions. We use these rings of functions to define a new path system, denoted by π^*, called the *completion* of π, in the following way:

A path $\sigma: [0, 1] \to M$ is in π^* if and only if for every open subset $U \subset M$, every $f \in I(\pi, U)$, $f(\sigma(t)) = $ constant for those values of t for which $\sigma(t) \in U$.

Clearly, $\pi \subset \pi^*$. (π^* is something like the dual of the dual of a vector space.) We say that the path system π satisfies the *duality principle* if

$$\pi^*(p) = \pi(p) \qquad \text{for all } p \in M. \tag{18.1}$$

Intuitively, we may summarize (18.1) by saying that all points are accessible from a point p along paths in π that are not "obviously inaccessible." For the existence of a nonconstant $f \in I(\pi, U)$ sets up a priori limitations on the accessible points, since all paths in π must lie on the hypersurfaces $f = $ constant. There are several other weaker versions of the duality principle that may be formulated, but the one we have just given should be sufficient to indicate the idea.

Now, there does not seem to be as yet any general theorem describing necessary and sufficient conditions that a path system satisfy the duality principle. This seems to be an important subject for further research. The closest thing to such a general theorem is a theorem due to Chow [1], which may be interpreted as proving the duality principle in the case where π consists of all the integral curves of a nonsingular vector-field system whose derived vector-field system is also nonsingular. In fact this is quite typical of the general situation, namely, that in order to prove the duality principle, certain local nonsingularity conditions must be imposed.

In turn, Chow's theorem is a generalization of a famous theorem due to Carathéodory [1] that gives a geometric condition that a Pfaffian equation admit an integrating factor. It is interesting that Carathéodory's theorem

arose from accessibility conditions. It asserts that the second law of thermodynamics, in its form postulating the nonexistence of a perpetual motion
machine of the "second kind," can be formulated as requiring that certain
points of the "phase space" of a physical system be nonaccessible along
adiabatic paths, that is, on integral paths of a Pfaffian form θ in phase space
representing "heat."

It is possible to prove the Lagrange multiplier rule for extremals of the
Lagrange variational problem, using accessibility idea. (This is due to Bliss
[1] and Radon [1].) We shall now explain this approach.

Suppose that D is a convex domain in R^n with coordinates $x_1, \ldots, x_n$. A
Lagrange variational problem in homogeneous form will be supposed given
on $T(D)$. Thus we are given functions $g_1(x, \dot{x}), \ldots, g_m(x, \dot{x})$ and $L(x, \dot{x})$ on
$T(D)$ that are homogeneous in x. Recall that a curve $x(t)$, $0 \le t \le 1$, in D is
an *extremal* of the Lagrange variational problem if

$$g_a\left(x(t), \frac{dx}{dt}\right) = 0 \qquad \text{for} \quad 0 \le t \le 1, 1 \le a \le m, \tag{18.2a}$$

$$\int_0^1 L\left(x(t), \frac{dx}{dt}\right) dt \le \int_0^1 L\left(\hat{x}(t), \frac{d\hat{x}}{dt}\right) dt \tag{18.2b}$$

for all paths $\hat{x}(t)$, $0 \le t \le 1$, such that

(i) $\hat{x}(0) = x(0)$, $\hat{x}(1) = x(1)$; that is, $\hat{x}(t)$ has the same end points as $x(t)$.
(ii) $g_a(\hat{x}(t), (d\hat{x}/dt)) = 0$ for $0 \le t \le 1$, $1 \le a \le m$, that is, the path $\hat{x}(t)$
satisfies the constraints given by (18.2a).

Bliss' idea is to convert this Lagrange variational problem into a *Mayer
variational problem*. Since we do not want to go into full detail here explaining
the Mayer problem,† we shall simply describe the situation explicitly without
attaching special labels to the construction.

Introduce another real variable, labeled y, to our variables $x_1, \ldots, x_n$.
Let D^* be the following convex set in R^{n+1}:

$$D^* = \{(x_1, \ldots, x_n, y) : (x_1, \ldots, x_n) \in D, \, -\infty < y < \infty\}.$$

Consider the following path system π in D^*: A path $(x(t), y(t))$, $0 \le t \le 1$, in
D^* lies in π if and only if

$$g_a\left(x(t), \frac{dx}{dt}\right) = 0 \qquad \text{and} \qquad \frac{dy}{dt} - L\left(x(t), \frac{dx}{dt}\right) = 0 \tag{18.3}$$

---

† The Mayer and Lagrange problems are equivalent in the sense that one can be transformed into the other, at least locally. We are concentrating on the Lagrange problem in this
book because we think it is more natural from a differential-geometric point of view, although
it seems that the Bliss school of the calculus of variations considered the Mayer problem to
be more basic.

for $1 \le a \le m$, $0 \le t \le 1$. Let $x(t)$, $0 \le t \le 1$, be an extremal curve of the Lagrange variational problem defined by $g_1, \ldots, g_m$ and L, that is, a curve satisfying (18.2). Construct $y(t)$ so that

$$\frac{dy}{dt} = L\left(x(t), \frac{dx}{dt}\right), \qquad y(0) = 0.$$

Then the curve $(x(t), y(t))$ in D^* belongs to π, that is, satisfies (18.3).

We now show that the fact that $x(t)$ is an extremal, that is, satisfies (18.2), *implies* that the point $(x(1), y(1) - \varepsilon)$ in D^* is inaccessible with respect to π from the point $(x(0), 0)$ in D^*, for any positive number ε. Suppose otherwise: that is, $(\hat{x}(t), \hat{y}(t))$, $0 \le t \le 1$, is a path in π joining these two points. Then, from (18.3), $g_a(\hat{x}(t), (d\hat{x}/dt)) = 0$; that is, $\hat{x}(t)$ satisfies the constraints, and $\hat{x}(0) = x(0)$, $\hat{x}(1) = x(1)$. Then

$$\frac{d\hat{y}}{dt} = L\left(\hat{x}(t), \frac{d\hat{x}}{dt}\right), \qquad \hat{y}(0) = 0;$$

hence,

$$\hat{y}(1) = \int_0^1 L\left(\hat{x}(t), \frac{d\hat{x}}{dt}\right) dt = y(1) - \varepsilon = \int_0^1 L\left(x(t), \frac{dx}{dt}\right) dt,$$

hence,

$$\int_0^1 L\left(\hat{x}(t), \frac{d\hat{x}}{dt}\right) dt < \int_0^1 L\left(x(t), \frac{dx}{dt}\right) dt,$$

contradicting that $x(t)$ is an extremal.

Apply the duality principle now. If π is sufficiently small, which we shall suppose is true, there is a function $f \in I(\pi, D^*)$, that is, a function $f(x, y)$ such that

$$\frac{d}{dt} f(x(t), y(t)) = 0 \qquad \text{for every curve } (x(t), y(t)) \text{ in } \pi;$$

hence,

$$\frac{\partial f}{\partial x_i}\frac{dx_i}{dt} + \frac{\partial f}{\partial y}\frac{dy}{dt} = 0 \qquad \text{or} \qquad \frac{\partial f}{\partial x_i}\frac{dx_i}{dt} + \frac{\partial f}{\partial y} L\left(x(t), \frac{dx}{dt}\right) = 0.$$

Now these conditions on f are *implied* by the following conditions:

$$\frac{\partial f}{\partial x_i}(x, y)\dot{x}_i + \frac{\partial f}{\partial y}(x, y)L(x, \dot{x}) = 0 \qquad (18.4)$$

for every $(x, \dot{x}, y)$ satisfying $g_a(x, \dot{x}) = 0$. These conditions are in turn *implied* by the following conditions: There exist functions $\lambda_a(x, y, \dot{x})$ such that

$$\frac{\partial f}{\partial x_i}(x, y)\dot{x}_i + \frac{\partial f}{\partial y}(x, y)L(x, \dot{x}) = \lambda_a(x, y. \dot{x})g_a(x, \dot{x}) \qquad (18.5)$$

identically in $(x, y, \dot{x})$. (We are using the summation convention, with the following range of indices: $1 \leq i, j, \ldots \leq n$; $1 \leq a, b, \ldots \leq m$.)

Now, conversely, (18.5) is implied by the preceding two conditions if suitable local regularity conditions are satisfied and if again D is sufficiently small. (This is just a matter of applying the implicit function theorem.) In this semi-intuitive account, we shall short-circuit the matter by assuming that (18.5) is true. Then, applying $\partial/\partial x_i$ to both sides of (18.5), we have

$$\frac{\partial f}{\partial x_i} + \frac{\partial f}{\partial y}\frac{\partial L}{\partial \dot{x}_i} = \frac{\partial \lambda_a}{\partial \dot{x}_i}g_a + \lambda_a\frac{\partial g_a}{\partial \dot{x}_i},$$

or multiplying by dx_i and summing, we have

$$df = \theta(\lambda_a)g_a + \lambda_a\theta(g_a) - \frac{\partial f}{\partial y}\theta(L),$$

where

$$\theta(\lambda_a) = \frac{\partial \lambda_a}{\partial \dot{x}_i}dx_i, \qquad \theta(g_a) = \frac{\partial g_a}{\partial \dot{x}_i}dx_i, \qquad \theta(L) = \frac{\partial L}{\partial \dot{x}_i}dx_i.$$

Thus $\theta(L)$ and $\theta(g_a)$ are the *Cartan 1-forms* associated with the Lagrangian functions. (Recall that L and g_a are assumed to be homogeneous in $\dot{x}$.) We can now eliminate df by applying d to both sides:

$$d(\theta(\lambda_a)g_a) = d(\lambda\theta(L) - \lambda_a\theta(g_a)), \qquad \text{where} \quad \lambda = \frac{\partial f}{\partial y}.$$

Now let $(x(t), y(t))$ be the curve in D^* satisfying (18.3), with $x(t)$ the given extremal of the Lagrange variational problem. Let $\sigma(t)$ be the curve $(x(t), y(t), (dx/dt))$ in $(x, y, \dot{x})$-space. Since $g_a(x, (dx/dt)) = 0$, we see that

$$\sigma \text{ is a characteristic curve of } d(\lambda\theta(L) - \lambda_a\theta(g_a)).$$

Working out the explicit conditions that this be so, we see that $x(t)$ satisfies the equation

$$\frac{d}{dt}\left(\lambda(t)\frac{\partial L}{\partial \dot{x}_i}\left(x(t), \frac{dx}{dt}\right) - \lambda_a(t)\frac{\partial g_a}{\partial \dot{x}_i}\right) = \lambda(t)\frac{\partial L}{\partial x_i}\left(x(t), \frac{dx}{dt}\right) - \lambda_a(t)\frac{\partial g_a}{\partial x_i}\left(x(t), \frac{dx}{dt}\right)$$

where $\lambda(t) = \lambda(x(t), y(t))$, $\lambda_a(t) = \lambda_a(x(t), y(t))$.

This says, however, that with this choice of the "Lagrange multipliers" $(\lambda(t), \lambda_a(t))$, the curve $x(t)$ in D is an extremal of the time-dependent, ordinary, unconstrained variational problem whose Lagrangian is: $\lambda(t)L + \lambda_a(t)g_a$. This, however, is just the "Lagrange multiplier rule" for finding the extremals of the Lagrange variational problem with which we started.

In summary, we may say that we have shown that the accessibility problem is really the basic one for the calculus of variations, underlying all the classical variational problems.

We now turn to a treatment of the accessibility problem for vector-field systems, and in particular, to the proof of Chow's theorem.

The Accessibility Problem for Vector-Field and Pfaffian Systems

Since the material in this section will be geometric and independent of coordinate systems, it will be convenient to work with a differentiable manifold M instead of a domain D in R^n. Recall the relevant notations: $F(M)$ denotes the ring of functions on M. (All functions, maps, vector fields, curves, etc., will be of differentiability class C^∞ unless mentioned otherwise.) $V(M)$ denotes the set of vector fields on M. Each $X \in V(M)$ is by definition a map $F(M) \to F(M)$ that defines a *derivation* of $F(M)$. For $f \in F(M)$, $X(f)$, the image of f under this map is the *Lie derivative* of f under X. (Alternatively, X can be thought of as a first-order partial differential operator on functions on M, and $X(f)$ is then the result of applying the operator symbolized by X to f.) Geometrically, if $\sigma(t)$, $a \le t \le b$, is an integral curve of X, then

$$\frac{d}{dt} f(\sigma(t)) = X(f)(\sigma(t)). \tag{18.6a}$$

For $p \in M$, M_p is the tangent space to M. Each $v \in M_p$ is by definition an R-linear map: $F(M) \to R$ such that

$$v(fg) = v(f)g(p) + f(p)v(g) \qquad \text{for all } f, g \in F(M).$$

Each $X \in V(M)$ determines a value $X(p) \in M_p$ at each $p \in M$.

$$X(p)(f) = X(f)(p) \qquad \text{for } f \in F(M).$$

If $\sigma(t)$, $a \le t \le b$, is a curve, $\sigma'(t)$, the tangent vector to σ at t may be defined as that element of $M_{\sigma(t)}$ such that

$$\frac{d}{d\lambda} f(\sigma(\lambda))|_{\lambda=t} = \sigma'(t)(f) \qquad \text{for all } f \in F(M).$$

Thus (18.6a) may also be expressed by the condition

$$\sigma'(t) = X(\sigma(t)) \qquad \text{for } a \le t \le b. \tag{18.6b}$$

Let $X \in V(M)$. From the existence theorem for systems of ordinary differential equations (when (18.6) is expressed in local coordinates, it is seen to be equivalent to such a system for the coordinates of $\sigma(t)$), we see that, given $p \in M$, there is a unique integral curve $\sigma(t; p)$ of X equal to p when $t = 0$, and defined for t sufficiently small, say $-\varepsilon \leq t \leq \varepsilon$. This ε can be chosen uniformly when p ranges over a compact set, and σ then depends in a C^∞ way on p and t. This local solution can be continued with, say, $\sigma(\varepsilon; p)$ replacing p. By uniqueness of the integral curves and the fact that $t \to \sigma(t + c)$, for constant c, is an integral curve of X whenever $t \to \sigma(t)$ is an integral curve, we see that for each $p \in M$, there are numbers $a(p)$ and $b(p)$, $a(p) < 0 < b(p)$, such that $\sigma(t; p)$ can be defined over $a(p) < t < b(p)$, but over no larger interval.

If $a(p) = -\infty$, $b(p) = +\infty$ for all $p \in M$, we say that X generates a *one-parameter group of diffeomorphisms* of M,† denoted by $\exp(tX)$. For $-\infty < t < \infty$, $\exp(tX)$ is the diffeomorphism of M such that $\exp(tX) \cdot p = \sigma(t, p)$, for $p \in M$. The group property

$$\exp(t_1 X) \cdot \exp(t_2 X) = \exp((t_1 + t_2)X)$$

follows from the fact mentioned above, that the integral curves of X are preserved under translation of t. Of course not every vector field generates such a one-parameter group. (For example, $M = R$, $X = x^2(\partial/\partial x)$.) However, we shall proceed as if this were so, since it may be easily checked by the reader that the proofs can be suitably modified.‡

Suppose now that X is a vector field on M and that $\phi: M \to M$ is a diffeomorphism. We have defined the transformed vector field $\phi_*(X)$ by any one of the following equivalent rules:

$$\phi_*(X(p)) = \phi_*(X)(\phi(p)) \qquad \text{for all } p \in M.$$

$$\phi^*(X(f)) = \phi_*^{-1}(X)(\phi^*(f)) \qquad \text{for all } f \in F(M).$$

ϕ maps integral curves of X into integral curves of $\phi(X)$.

Suppose now that Y is a vector field on M that generates a one-parameter group $t \to \phi_t = \exp(tY)$ of diffeomorphisms of M. Let $p \in M$. Then $s \to \exp(sX) \cdot p$ is the integral curve of X beginning at p. Thus $s \to$

---

† In the general case, X is said to generate a *one-parameter pseudogroup* of diffeomorphisms, but we shall not try to make the pseudogroup concept precise here.

‡ In addition, one can prove the following lemma, which shows that in arguments where the parametrization of integral curves does not matter, the possible noncompletability of integral curves does not matter: Let M be a manifold and let X be a vector field on X. Then there exists an everywhere positive function on an M such that (fX) generates a global one-parameter group of diffeomorphisms of M.

$\exp(tY)\exp(sX)\cdot p$ is an integral curve of $\phi_{t*}\text{-}(X)$; hence we have the basic formula

$$\exp(tY)\exp(sX)\cdot p = \exp(s(\exp tY)_*(X))\cdot \exp(tY). \qquad (18.7)$$

We know already that the one-parameter family $t \to (\exp tY)_*(X) = Z^t$ of vector fields is determined as the solution of the following system of partial differential equations:

$$\frac{\partial}{\partial t}Z^t = [Y, Z^t]. \qquad (18.8)$$

If everything is real-analytic, they can be "solved" by Lie series:

$$\exp(tY)_*(X) = \sum_{j=0}^{\infty} \frac{t^j \, Ad^j(Y)(X)}{j!} \qquad (18.9)$$

where $Ad\, Y(X) = [Y, X]$, $Ad^2\, Y(X) = [Y, [Y, X]]$, etc.
Now we can prove the Chow [1] accessibility theorem.

THEOREM 18.1

Let H be a real subspace of $V(M)$, the space of all vector fields on a manifold M. Let $\pi(H)$ be the following path system on M defined by H:

A path $\sigma(t)$, $0 \le t \le 1$, is in $\pi(H)$ if and only if $\sigma'(t) \in H_{\sigma(t)}$† for $0 \le t \le 1$.

Let $D(H)$ be the smallest completely integrable vector-field system on M containing H.‡ If $D(H) = V(M)$, then $\pi(p) = M$ for all $p \in M$.

Proof. If $[H, H] \subset H$, we are finished, since then $M_p = D(H)_p = H_p$ for all $p \in M$. Then there exists a pair $X, Y \in H$ with $[X, Y] \notin H$. For at least one value of t, say, $t = 1$, we must have, by (18.9), $(\exp tY)_*(X) \notin H$. Let H_1 be the vector-field system spanned by H and $\exp(Y)_*(X)$. By (18.7), every point that can be reached on an integral path of H_1 can be reached by an integral path of H. If $[H_1, H_1] \subset H_1$, we are finished, since then $H_1 = D(H) = V(M)$. If $[H_1, H_1] \not\subset H_1$, choose $X_1, Y_1 \in H_1$ so that $\exp(Y_1)_*(X_1) \notin H_1$; let H_2 be spanned by H_1 and $\exp(Y_1)_*(X_1)$, etc. This process must eventually come to an end, which proves the theorem.

† Recall that $H_p = \{X(p) : X \in H\}$ for $p \in M$, that is, H_p is the set of values of elements of H at p.
‡ $D(H)$ is called the derived system of H, since it is obviously generated by sums of iterated Jacobi brackets of elements of H with functions on M as coefficients.

Corollaries

(a) Suppose that $H \subset V(M)$ is a vector-field system on M, that $p \in M$, and that N is a submanifold of M that contains all integral paths of $D(H)$ starting at p, and satisfies: $N_q = D(H)_q$ for all $q \in N$. Then N is the set of points of M that can be reached from p along integral paths of H.

(b) Suppose that $D(H)$ is a nonsingular vector-field system; that is, $\dim D(H)_p = \text{constant}$ for $p \in M$. Let π be the path system consisting of the integral paths of H. Then π^*, as defined before, consists of the space of integral paths of $D(H)$; hence the "duality principle" for the accessibility problem is satisfied.

For the proof of (a), one should notice that both H and $D(H)$ are tangent to N; hence, restricting to N reduces to the situation stated in the theorem. For (b), notice that an $f \in F(M)$ is constant along integral paths of H if and only if

$$X(f) = 0 \qquad \text{for all } X \in H.$$

But then this is true when X is composed of iterated Jacobi brackets of elements of H; hence f is an integral of $D(H)$. Since $D(H)$ is nonsingular, the Frobenius integrability theorem assures us that locally the integral manifolds of $D(H)$ are obtained by setting all such functions equal to constants, which is precisely the "duality principle."

Some Examples

Example 1

The following problem arises in the theory of optimal control: Suppose $A_{ab}(t)$, $v_{au}(t)$ are given functions of t, $1 \leq a, b, \ldots \leq m$; $m + 1 \leq u, v, \ldots \leq n$. Consider the system of differential equations:

$$\frac{dx_a}{dt} = A_{ab}(t)x_b(t) + v_{au}(t)y_u(t), \qquad (18.10)$$

where the $x_a(t)$ are the unknown functions and the $y_a(t)$ are functions that can be chosen arbitrarily.†

THE PROBLEM

For given $x_a{}^0$ (for example, $x_a{}^0 = 0$), what are the set of points x_a that can be reached on solutions of (18.10) starting at $x_a{}^0$ for *all* choices of the

---

† Not necessarily even continuously. To make sure there are no difficulties with existence of solutions, suppose, for example, that the allowable $y_u(t)$ are piecewise differentiable.

functions $y_u(t)$? In physical problems, the x_a may be the position-velocity coordinates of a system, and y_u may be the forces. The problem posed is usually to get from initial point $x_a{}^0$ to final point x_a along a solution of (18.10), minimizing some performance criterion associated with the curve $(x_a(t), y_u(t))$. Clearly, an important preliminary problem, which we deal with here, is to know what points x_a can be reached from $x_a{}^0$ along any solution of (18.10) at all.

To convert the problem into one covered by Theorem 18.1, introduce t as a new variable and the 1-forms

$$w_a = dx_a - (A_{ab} x_b + v_{au} y_u)\, dt$$

on (x, y, t)-space. Let H be the dual vector-field system on this space: $X \in H \Leftrightarrow w_a(X) = 0$. Then, if a solution of (18.10) is regarded as a curve in (x, y, t)-space, it is an integral curve of H unless the $y_u(t)$ have discontinuities. To deal with this case also, notice that a curve along which $dt = dx_a = 0$ (that is, the x_a and t are constant while the $y_a(t)$ are arbitrary) is also an integral curve of H. Therefore solutions to (18.10) with simple jump discontinuities in the $y_a(t)$ give rise to continuous integral curves of H. For example, if $(x_a(t), y_u(t))$, $0 \le t \le 1$, is a solution of (18.10), with $\lim_{t \to 1/2 -} y_u(t) = y_u(\tfrac{1}{2}-) \ne y(\tfrac{1}{2}+)$, and $t = \tfrac{1}{2}$ is the only discontinuity of y, define

$$\hat{x}_a(s),\ \hat{y}_a(s),\ t(s), \qquad 0 \le s \le 2,$$

as follows:

$$\hat{x}_a(s) = x_a(s), \qquad 0 \le s \le \tfrac{1}{2}.$$
$$\hat{y}_a(s) = y_a(s), \qquad 0 \le s < \tfrac{1}{2}. \quad \hat{y}_a(\tfrac{1}{2}) = y_a(\tfrac{1}{2}-).$$
$$t(s) = s, \qquad 0 \le s \le \tfrac{1}{2}.$$
$$\hat{x}_a(s) = x_a(\tfrac{1}{2}), \qquad \tfrac{1}{2} \le s \le \tfrac{3}{2}.$$
$$\hat{y}_a(s) = 0, \qquad \tfrac{1}{2} \le s \le \tfrac{3}{2} \quad \text{is any curve such that } \hat{y}_a(\tfrac{3}{2}) = y_a(\tfrac{1}{2}+).$$
$$t(s) = \tfrac{1}{2}, \qquad \tfrac{1}{2} \le s \le \tfrac{3}{2}.$$
$$\hat{x}_a(s) = x_a(s - 1), \qquad \tfrac{3}{2} \le s \le 2.$$
$$\hat{y}(s) = y_a(s - 1), \qquad \tfrac{3}{2} \le s \le 2.$$
$$t(s) = s - 1, \qquad \tfrac{3}{2} \le s \le 2.$$

Conversely, an integral curve of H, that is, a curve $x(s), y(s), t(s), 0 \le s \le 1$, such that $w_a(x(s), y(s), t(s)) = 0$, gives rise to a solution of (18.10) with possibly discontinuous $y(s)$. For $0 \le s \le 1$ can be divided into intervals in which $dt = 0$ or $dt \ne 0$; that is, t changes or remains constant. In the former intervals, $(x(s), y(s), t(s))$ can be reparametrized by t so as to be a solution of (18.10). In the latter type of interval, t (hence x_a) remains constant, and the effect is for y_a to "jump" from one value to another while x_a and t remain constant.

We now turn to computing $D(H)$. Introduce the following vector fields in (x, y, t)-space:

$$Y_u = \frac{\partial}{\partial y_u}, \qquad X = \frac{\partial}{\partial t} + (A_{ab} x_b + v_{au} y_u) \frac{\partial}{\partial x_a}. \tag{18.11}$$

They span H, that is, satisfy $w_a(X_u) = 0 = w_a(Y)$.

Using (18.11), we have

$$[X, Y_u] = \left[\frac{\partial}{\partial t} + (A_{ab} x_b + v_{av} y_v) \frac{\partial}{\partial x_a}, \frac{\partial}{\partial y_u} \right] = -v_{au} \frac{\partial}{\partial x_a}.$$

Let $Z_u = -v_{au}(\partial/\partial x_a)$. Then $[Z_u, Z_v] = 0$.

Suppose now that Z is any vector field of the form $z_a(t)(\partial/\partial x_a)$. Then $\partial Z/\partial t$ will denote the field $[(\partial/\partial t), Z] = (d/dt)z_a(t)(\partial/\partial x_a)$. Then,

$$[Z, X] = -\frac{\partial Z}{\partial t} + (A_{ab} z_b) \frac{\partial}{\partial x_a} = \left[-\frac{d}{dt} z_a(t) + A_{ab} z_b \right] \frac{\partial}{\partial x_a}.$$

If $z = (z_a)$ denotes the $m \times 1$ vector function of t, $A = (A_{ab})$ the $m \times m$ matrix function of t, define ∇z as the $m \times 1$ vector function such that

$$(\nabla z)_a = A_{ab} v_b - \frac{d}{dt} v_b.$$

Then

$$[Z, X] = (\nabla z)_a \frac{\partial}{\partial x_a}.$$

$$[[Z, X], X] = (\nabla(\nabla z))_a \frac{\partial}{\partial x_a} = (\nabla^2 z)_a \frac{\partial}{\partial x_a}, \qquad \text{etc.}$$

Combining these calculations with Theorem 18.1, and our remarks above about the relation between solutions of (18.10) and integral curves of **H** we have proved:

THEOREM 18.2

For each u, define the $m \times 1$ vector function of t, $v_u = (v_{au})$. $D(H)$ is then spanned by the vector fields: X, Y_u (defined by (18.11)), and the fields

$$v_{au} \frac{\partial}{\partial x_a} = (v_u)_a \frac{\partial}{\partial x_a}, \qquad (\nabla v_u)_a \frac{\partial}{\partial x_a}, \qquad (\nabla^2 v_u)_a \frac{\partial}{\partial x_a}, \qquad \text{etc.}$$

Suppose that for each t, the dimension of the space of $m \times 1$ vectors spanned by $v_u(t)$, $\nabla v_u(t)$, $\nabla^2 v_u(t)$, etc., is m. Then, given points x^0, x and a real number $T > 0$, there is a solution $(x(t), y(t))$ of (18.10), $0 \leq t \leq T$, such that

$$x(0) = x^0, \qquad x(T) = x.$$

The $x(t)$ are continuous, piecewise smooth, but the $y(t)$ may possibly have simple jump discontinuities.

Example 2

We work now in a space of variables (x_i), $1 \leq i, j, \ldots \leq n$. Let $\omega = a_i \, dx_i$ be a 1-form. Let H be the vector-field system annihilating ω, that is, the set of vector fields $X = A_i \, dx_i$ satisfying $0 = \omega(X) = A_i a_i$. To avoid questions of singularities, we suppose that ω is everywhere nonzero. Then H is everywhere of dimension $n - 1$.

Let $F(H)$ be the set of all vector fields $X \in H$ such that $[X, H] \subset H$.

> $X \in F(H)$ if and only if $\omega(X) = 0$, and $X \lrcorner \, d\omega = f\omega$, for some function f. $F(H)$ is a completely integrable vector-field system, that is, $[F(H), F(H)] \subset F(H)$, and $fX \in F(H)$ for any function f, all $X \in F(H)$.

Proof. Suppose first that $\omega(X) = 0$ and $X \lrcorner \, d\omega = f\omega$. Then, for $Y \in H$,

$$\begin{aligned}
0 = X \lrcorner \, d\omega(Y) &= d\omega(X, Y) \\
&= X(\omega(Y)) - Y(\omega(X)) - \omega([X, Y]) \\
&= -\omega([X, Y]),
\end{aligned}$$

that is, $[X, Y] \in H$.

This reasoning can be reversed to prove the converse: If $X \in F(H)$, f is a function, $Y \in H$,

$$[fX, Y] = -Y(f)X \qquad f[X, Y] \in H,$$

that is, $fX \in F(H)$. If $X_1, X_2 \in F(H)$, $Y \in H$,

$$[[X_1, X_2], Y] = [X_1, [X_2, Y]] - [X_2, [X_1, Y]] \in \mathbf{H},$$

that is, $[X_1, X_2] \in F(H)$.†

Definition

The form ω is said to be *nonsingular* if $F(H)$ is a nonsingular vector-field system. A form ω is said to admit an *integrating factor* (that is, function) f if $d(f\omega) = 0$. Then $\omega = dg$, $X \in H$, that is, $\omega(X) = 0$ if and only if $X(g) = 0$.†

---

† Of course the "classical" assumption must always be made that f is nowhere zero.

In particular, $F(H) = H$. Suppose conversely that $F(H) = H$. We can then choose the coordinate system (x_i) so that $\omega(\partial/\partial x_i) = 0$ for $i > 1$. Hence, if $\omega = a_i \, dx_i$, then

$$a_i = 0 \quad \text{for } i > 1 \qquad \text{and} \qquad \omega = a_1 \, dx_1,$$

that is, ω admits an integrating factor. We say that the Pfaffian equation $\omega = 0$ is *completely integrable*. This, combined with Theorem 18.1, proves the following theorem of Carathéodory [1], historically the first "accessibility theorem."

THEOREM 18.3

If ω is a 1-form, with H the vector-field system defined by the Pfaffian equation $\omega = 0$, if $F(H)$ is nonsingular, ω admits an integrating factor if and only if the following geometric condition is satisfied: For each point x^0 of the space, there are points x arbitrarily close to x^0 that are inaccessible from x^0 along curves satisfying $\omega = 0$, that is, that are integral curves of H.

This theorem is the foundation for Carathéodory's "axiomatization"† of the second law of thermodynamics. (Recall that this is the law asserting the existence of entropy.) To see the connection, imagine that each point of space represents a state of a given physical system and that the form ω represents "heat," that is, the curves along which $\omega = 0$ represent changes of state in which no heat is added. Then, if all states could be reached from a given state *without* adding heat, clearly a "perpetual motion machine" could be constructed. For example, if our system were composed of a gas in a box, and if a state where all molecules with a velocity above a certain number were in one part and all molecules with velocity below that number were in the other part, and each part could be reached without adding heat, the faster (that is, hotter) molecules could be used to perform free work. Since nothing is free, there must be inaccessible points; hence, by Theorem 18.1, ω must admit an integrating factor; that is, ω can be written in the form $T \, dS$, where T is the "temperature" and S the "entropy." Of course T and S are not uniquely defined in this way. However, their other properties can be obtained by taking them as known for simple systems (for example, ideal gases) and postulating how they behave when systems are combined.

Example 3   Monge Systems

A *Monge system* is, classically, defined by a system of ordinary differential equations:

$$g_a(x, \dot{x}, t) = 0; \qquad \dot{x} = \frac{dx}{dt}; \qquad x = (x_1, \ldots, x_n) = (x_i).$$

† It would be better to call this a "geometrization" of thermodynamics.

(We adopt the range of indices $1 \le i, j, \ldots \le n; 1 \le a, b, \ldots \le m \le n$ and the summation convention.) A formulation in terms of manifolds would postulate: (a) a manifold M; (b) a subset $C \subset T(M) \times R$; (c) a curve $\sigma: [a, b] \to M$ satisfies the system if $(\sigma'(t), t) \in C$ for $a \le t \le b$. However, we shall work with the more explicit formulation in terms of coordinates. Let a point x^0 and an initial time, say, $t = 0$, be given. Our problem is to decide what is the set of pairs (x, T) such that there exists a solution, continuous and piecewise C^∞, of the system; say, $t \to x(t)$, with $0 \le t \le T$ and $x(T) = x'$?

We want to show that the "duality principle" for accessibility is satisfied here if appropriate regularity conditions are satisfied. The first such assumption is that the rank of the matrix $(\partial g_a / \partial \dot{x}_i)$ is maximal, that is, is equal to m.

By the implicit function theorem, the coordinate system can be chosen so that the system of differential equations defining the curves in the system takes the form

$$\frac{dx_a}{dt} = h_a\left(x(t), \frac{dx_{m+1}}{dt}, \ldots, \frac{dx_n}{dt}, t\right) \qquad \text{for} \quad a = 1, 2, \ldots, m.$$

Thus we can choose the functions $x_{m+1}(t), \ldots, x_n(t)$ at will, and determine the rest by solving these differential equations. However, consider the following Pfaffian system in the space of variables $(x_1, \ldots, x_n, \dot{x}_{m+1}, \ldots, \dot{x}_n, t)$:

$$dx_a - h_a \, dt = 0, \qquad dx_u - \dot{x}_u \, dt \qquad \text{for} \quad 1 \le a \le m; m + 1 \le u \le v.$$

Notice that a curve $t \to (x(t), \dot{x}_{m+1}(t), \ldots, \dot{x}_n(t), t)$ in these variables, that is, an integral curve of this Pfaffian system, gives a solution of the Monge system. In effect, we have "prolonged" the original Monge system to a Pfaffian system on the space of variables $(x, \dot{x}_u, t)$ having the property that the integral curves of the Pfaffian system and solution curves of the Monge system correspond under the projection. Consider the dual vector-field system H, that is, the space of vector fields X that satisfy

$$(dx_a - h_a \, dt)(X) = 0 = (dx_u - \dot{x}_u \, dt)(X).$$

A function $f(x, \dot{x}_u, t)$ is an integral of this vector-field system if df is a linear combination of the forms $(dx_a - h_a \, dt)$ and $(dx_u - \dot{x}_u \, dt)$. These forms do not contain $d\dot{x}_u$; hence $(\partial f / \partial \dot{x}_u)$ *must be zero*, that is, f is independent of $\dot{x}_u$. Such a function, then, must be an integral of the initial Monge system; thus the process of prolongation has not added any new integrals. Hence, if the duality principle holds for the prolonged Pfaffian system (which it will, by the Carathéodory–Chow theorem if the $D(H)$ is nonsingular), it will also hold for the original Monge system.

Returning to the connection established earlier between the accessibility problem for Monge systems and the validity of the Lagrange multiplier rule for the Lagrange variational problem, we see that these arguments prove the multiplier rule with an absolute minimum of technical apparatus, at the expense of making very strong assumptions about the local regularity of the data. There is another approach to these accessibility questions due to Bliss [1], which needs much less stringent regularity conditions. Bliss' approach has recently been revived by Pontryagin and his coworkers [1], and extended to treat the nonclassical variational problems with inequality constraints that are involved in the theory of optimal control. This work has been extended and clarified by Halkin [1] and Roxin [1]. Since the book by Pontryagin *et al.* [1] presents an excellent exposition of this approach, we shall limit ourselves to several qualitative comments.

Return to considering a general path system π on a manifold M, and let π^p again denote the set of all paths in the system that start at a point p of M. The type of accessibility provided by the Carathéodory–Chow approach is really "global" in nature. By this we mean that even though two points q and q' of M that are close together can both be joined to p by paths from π, we do not necessarily know that these paths are close together. To study this question, we must study the *local* properties of the end-point mapping of $\pi^p \to M$; that is, we must construct its "differential." First, of course, we must say what is meant by the "tangent space" to π^p at a "point," that is, a path σ.

Let us restrict ourselves to a simple case, namely: suppose that $\sigma: [0, 1] \to M$ is a curve, with $\sigma(0) = p$. A "curve" in π^p should be considered as a p one-parameter family $s \to \sigma_s$ of curves in M, each of which belongs to π^p. Thus, if $\sigma_s = \sigma$ for $s = 0$, we may think of this as a deformation of the curve σ. We can construct the "infinitesimal deformation" to this deformation as a vector field $v: t \to v(t) \in M_{\sigma(t)}$ along the curve σ as follows:

For $0 \le t \le 1$, $v(t)$ is the tangent vector to the curve $s \to \sigma_s(t)$ at $s = 0$. The condition that $\sigma_s(0) = p$ for all s obviously requires $v(0) = 0$. Thus it is reasonable to *define* the "tangent space" to π^p "at" a curve σ as the set of all vector fields $t \to v$ along σ that arise in this way as infinitesimal deformations corresponding to curves in π^p. (See Fig. 4.) Denote this space by $\pi_\sigma{}^p$.

Obviously, now, the "differential" of the end-point mapping $\pi^p \to M$ at a point $\sigma \in \pi^p$ is the mapping that assigns the end vector $v(1)$ to each such vector field $t \to v(t)$ along σ.

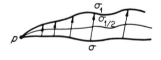

FIGURE 4

Suppose now that N is an ordinary finite dimensional manifold and that $\phi: N \to \pi^p$ is a mapping. Explicitly, then, to each point $\alpha \in N$, we are given a curve σ_α of π^p. We shall consider that this mapping is "smooth" if the mapping $(t, \alpha) \to \sigma_\alpha(t)$ from $N \times [0, 1] \to N$ is smooth (that is, C^∞) in the ordinary sense. This enables us to define a linear mapping from N_α to π_σ^p. Comparing this with the differential of the end-point mapping $\pi_\sigma^p \to M_{\sigma(1)}$ gives us a linear mapping $N_\alpha \to M_{\sigma_\alpha(1)}$, which is the differential of the mapping $N \to M$ that assigns $\sigma_\alpha(1)$ to σ_α. We conclude from the ordinary implicit function theorem for finite dimensional manifolds that if the mapping $N \to \pi^p$ can be chosen so that the linear mapping $N_\sigma \to M_{\sigma_\alpha(1)}$ is *onto*, then every point in a neighborhood of $\sigma_\alpha(1)$ can be reached by curves from π^p that are "close" to the initial curve σ. We shall not go further into this approach here. It is done quite simply and naturally in a classic paper by J. Radon [1]. Indeed, since this paper is one of the clearest and most elegant in the entire history of the calculus of variations, we prefer to suggest to the reader that he consult it directly, rather than attempt to reproduce its contents here. As a bonus, Radon also gives an exposition of the theory of the second variation, a subject we shall not touch on except in the context of Riemannian geometry, Part 3.

Part **3** GLOBAL RIEMANNIAN GEOMETRY

19 Affine Connections on Differential Manifolds

Introduction

Let M be a manifold. Recall that a *homogeneous, ordinary variational problem* on M is defined by giving a real-valued function $v \to L(v)$ on $T(M)$, called a *Lagrangian* on M, such that $L(\lambda v) = \lambda L(v)$ for $\lambda > 0$. Suppose that L satisfies the following condition:

$$L(u + v)^2 + L(u - v)^2 = 2L(u)^2 + 2L(v)^2 \qquad \text{for } u, v \in T(M).$$

We can then *define*, for $u, v \in T(M)$,

$$\langle u, v \rangle = \tfrac{1}{2}(L(u + v)^2 - L(u)^2 - L(v)^2),$$

and verify easily that on each tangent space M_x, $x \in M$, the mapping $(u, v) \to \langle u, v \rangle$ defines a symmetric, bilinear form such that

$$L(u) = \langle u, u \rangle^{1/2} \qquad \text{for all } u \in M_x.$$

We also write: $L(u) = \|u\|$. If, in addition, this bilinear form is positive definite, we say that L defines a *Riemannian metric* on M; the study of the geometric properties of the extremal curves of this Lagrangian (here called, in this special case, *geodesics*) constitutes *Riemannian geometry*.

Riemannian metric are the simplest general class of variational problems and have been studied more extensively than more general variational problems; therefore they appear naturally in a great many contexts in mathematics and physics. Although some of the basic general theorems of Riemannian geometry can be considered as special cases of theorems about general variational problems, there are many more special results, giving a deeper insight into the structure of the extremals. One general reason for this is that there is an additional element of structure, an *affine connection*, associated with a Riemannian metric, enabling one to study the differential equations for the extremals in a more detailed way, and leading to the concept of *curvature*.

There has recently been a resurgence of interest on the part of differential geometers in the study of global Riemannian geometry. We aim in this chapter to provide at least an introduction to this aspect of current research.

Definition

An affine connection on a manifold M is a map $V(M) \times V(M) \to V(M)$, denoted by $(X, Y) \to \nabla_X Y$ for $X, Y \in V(M)$, such that

$$\nabla_{(X_1 + X_2)}(Y_1 + Y_2) = \nabla_{X_1} Y_1 + \nabla_{X_2} Y_2 + \nabla_{X_1} Y_2 + \nabla_{X_2} Y_1 \qquad (19.1a)$$

for all $X_1, X_2, Y_1, Y_2 \in V(M)$. (Bilinearity.)

$$\nabla_{fX} Y = f \nabla_X Y \qquad (19.1b)$$
$$\qquad\qquad \text{for } f \in F(M); \ X, Y \in V(M).$$
$$\nabla_X(fY) = X(f)Y + f\nabla_X Y \qquad (19.1c)$$

Intuitively, an affine connection is a law of "covariant differentiation" ($\nabla_X Y$ is described as the covariant derivative of the vector field Y by the vector field X) of vector fields. The reader may protest at this point that we already have a method of "differentiating" Y by X, namely, the Jacobi bracket $[X, Y]$. Note, however, the difference in the formal properties of these two operations, particularly $[fX, Y] = -Y(f)X + f[X, Y]$.

To get a distinctive feeling for the difference, let us look at the situation in a typical manifold, namely, a convex domain D in R^n with coordinate functions x_i, $1 \le i, j, \ldots \le n$. The functions Γ_{ijk} in D such that

$$\nabla_{\partial/\partial x_i}\left(\frac{\partial}{\partial x_j}\right) = \Gamma_{ijk}\frac{\partial}{\partial x_k}$$

are called the *components* of the affine connection in the coordinate system (x_i). (In classical tensor analysis, they are more or less the Christoffel symbols.) On the one hand, they completely characterize the affine connection, since if

$$X = A_i \frac{\partial}{\partial x_i}, \qquad Y = B_j \frac{\partial}{\partial x_j},$$

we have, using the laws (19.1),

$$\nabla_X Y = A_i \nabla_{\partial/\partial x_i}\left(B_j \frac{\partial}{\partial x_j}\right)$$

$$= A_i \frac{\partial B_j}{\partial x_i}\frac{\partial}{\partial x_j} + A_i B_j \Gamma_{ijk}\frac{\partial}{\partial x_k}$$

$$= \left(A_i \frac{\partial B_k}{\partial x_i} + A_i B_j \Gamma_{ijk}\right)\frac{\partial}{\partial x_k}. \qquad (19.2)$$

On the other hand, it is readily verified that on changing to a different coordinate system, these components do not have a "tensorial" law of transformation. (The tipoff that this is so is that (19.1c) is postulated *instead* of the "tensorial" postulate $\nabla_X(fY) = f\nabla_X Y$.) This nontensorial character of an affine connection creates great difficulties in classical tensor analysis;

a triumph of the manifold point of view is that an affine connection can be described by the simple postulates (19.1). (They were first given by J. L. Koszul.) Equation (19.2) shows us in greater detail the difference between Jacobi bracket and covariant derivative. For example, in $\nabla_X Y$, only the components of Y are differentiated, and $\nabla_X Y(p) = 0$ if $X(p) = 0$.

An affine connection of M gives rise to a method of "parallel translation" of tangent vectors of M along any curve in M. First we shall describe in qualitative terms what we want to mean by this. Suppose that $\sigma : [a, b] \to M$ is a curve in M. (By a curve we mean C^∞ in the sense that there exists an $\varepsilon > 0$ such that σ can be extended as a C^∞ map to $(a - \varepsilon, b + \varepsilon)$.) The tangent spaces to two points of M are both n-dimensional real-vector spaces; hence they are isomorphic when considered as abstract vector spaces. However, there is no unique way of describing such an isomorphism. Of course, if M is Euclidian space itself, the tangent spaces are isomorphic with M (hence with each other), but we have been emphasizing that this must be ignored if one is interested in nonlinear phenomena. By "parallel translation" along σ we mean some method of setting up consistently and smoothly an isomorphism between $M_{\sigma(a)}$ and $M_{\sigma(b)}$ for $a \le t \le b$. It is to be expected, however, that the isomorphism one derives between $M_{\sigma(a)}$ and $M_{\sigma(b)}$ *will depend on the choice of curve joining $\sigma(a)$ to $\sigma(b)$.* We shall not worry here about the more general scheme for accomplishing this goal, but shall describe how an affine connection on M, that is, a covariant differentiation law ∇ satisfying (19.1), gives such a process.

Suppose the curve σ is an integral curve for a vector field X on M; that is, $\sigma'(t) = X(\sigma(t))$ for $a \le t \le b$. Of course not every curve can be so described, but those that can be are sufficiently plentiful for our purposes. Suppose that Y is another vector field on M. Consider the condition

$$\nabla_X Y(\sigma(t)) = 0 \qquad \text{for } a \le t \le b. \tag{19.3a}$$

If Y satisfies this condition, we say that its *covariant derivative along σ is zero.* Let us for the moment look at this condition in a domain $D \subset R^n$ with coordinates (x_i). Suppose that $\sigma(t) = (x_i(t)) = x(t)$. Using (19.2) and the relations

$$X = A_i \frac{\partial}{\partial x_i}, \qquad Y = B_j \frac{\partial}{\partial x_j}, \qquad \frac{dx_i}{dt} = A_i(x(t)),$$

we have

$$\nabla_X Y = \left(A_i(x(t)) \frac{\partial B_k}{\partial x_i}(x(t)) + A_i(x(t)) B_j(x(t)) \Gamma_{ijk}(x(t)) \right) \frac{\partial}{\partial x_k}(\sigma(t))$$

$$= \left[\frac{d}{dt}(B_k(x(t))) + \frac{dx_i}{dt} B_j(x(t)) \Gamma_{ijk}(x(t)) \right] \frac{\partial}{\partial x_k}(\sigma(t)).$$

Thus we see that (19.3a) is equivalent to the relations

$$\frac{d}{dt} B_k(x(t)) + \frac{dx_i}{dt} B_j(x(t))\Gamma_{ijk}(x(t)) = 0. \tag{19.3b}$$

As a first observation, notice that this condition on X and Y involves only the values of X and Y on the curve $\sigma(t)$. Thus, if $x(t) = (x_i(t))$, $a \leq t \leq b$, is an arbitrary curve in D, and if $v: [a, b] \to T(D)$ is a vector field along $x(t)$, that is, $v(t) \in D_{x(t)}$ for $a \leq t \leq b$, with components $v_i(t) = dx_i(v(t))$; that is, if

$$v(t) = v_i(t) \frac{\partial}{\partial x_i}(x(t)),$$

we may define another vector field, denoted by $\nabla v(t)$, along the curve $x(t)$ by the following formula and have reasonable expectations that the operator $v \to \nabla v$ on vector fields along the curve is of interest. (∇v is called the *covariant derivative* of v along the curve.)

$$\nabla v(t) = \left[\frac{d}{dt} v_k(t) + \frac{dx_i}{dt} v_j(t)\Gamma_{ijk}(x(t)) \right] \frac{\partial}{\partial x_k}(x(t)). \tag{19.4}$$

Note that $\nabla v(t) = 0$ if and only if

$$\frac{d}{dt} v_k(t) = -\frac{dx_i}{dt} v_j(t)\Gamma_{ijk}(x(t)). \tag{19.5}$$

As soon as $x(t)$ is given, (19.5) may be regarded as a system of first-order, linear, homogeneous differential equations for the components $v_k(t)$ of v. Thus we see that, given a $v^a \in D_{x(a)}$, there is a *unique* vector field $v(t)$ along the curve such that $\nabla v = 0$ and $v(a) = v^a$, and that if u^a is another element of $D_{x(a)}$, if the vector field $u(t)$ along $x(t)$ satisfies $\nabla u = 0$ and $u(a) = u^a$, then

$$\nabla(u(t) + v(t)) = 0 \quad \text{and} \quad u(a) + v(a) = a^a + v^a.$$

Thus the correspondence $v^a \to v(t)$ sets up an isomorphism between the vector spaces $D_{x(a)}$ and $D_{x(t)}$ for each $t \in [a, b]$. This is the desired "parallel translation" of tangent vectors along the curve.

We can sum up what we have proved for domains of R^n in terms of an arbitrary manifold, in the form of the following theorem. The proof for an arbitrary manifold can be done by referring pieces of the manifold back to R^n via charts, and will be left to the reader.

THEOREM 19.1

Let M be a manifold with an affine connection described by a covariant differentiation operation $(X, Y) \to \nabla_X Y$ satisfying (19.1). Let $\sigma: [a, b] \to M$

be a curve in M. A vector field on σ is a mapping, usually denoted by v, assigning a tangent vector $v(t) \in M_{\sigma(t)}$ to each $t \in [a, b]$.

Then there is an operation assigning a new vector field ∇v to each vector field v on σ, with the following properties:

(a) If $\alpha(t)$ is a real-valued function of t, $a \leq t \leq b$,

$$\nabla(\alpha(t)v(t)) = \frac{d\alpha}{dt}v(t) + \alpha(t)\nabla v(t).$$

(b) If u and v are vector fields along σ, then $\nabla u + \nabla v = \nabla(u + v)$.

(c) If X and Y are vector fields on M, with $\sigma'(t) = X(\sigma(t))$, $v(t) = Y(\sigma(t))$ for $a \leq t \leq b$, then $\nabla v(t) = \nabla_X Y(\sigma(t))$.

(d) If v_a is a given tangent vector in $M_{\sigma(a)}$, there is a unique vector field v along σ with $v(a) = v^a$ and $\nabla v = 0$. The correspondence $v^a \to v(t)$, for each $t \in [a, b]$, is linear, and sets up an isomorphism between $M_{\sigma(a)}$ and $M_{\sigma(t)}$, called the *parallel translation* of tangent vectors along σ. Any vector field v on σ such that $\nabla v = 0$ is said to be *self-parallel*.

If $M = R^n$, a special affine connection can be defined by requiring that $\nabla_{\partial/\partial x_i}(\partial/\partial x_j) = 0$; if $v(t) = v_i(t)(\partial/\partial x_i)(\sigma(t))$, the condition that $\nabla v = 0$ reduces to $(dv/dt)_i = 0$, that is, $v_i(t) = v_i(a)$. Thus the parallelism idea does not really depend on the curve, and the isomorphism between tangent spaces is that obtained by identifying the tangent space to Euclidean space at a point with Euclidean space itself. The *straight lines* in Euclidean space are those whose tangent vectors at different points are parallel, that is, curves $\sigma(t)$ satisfying

$$\nabla \sigma'(t) = 0. \tag{19.6a}$$

Thus we are justified in calling the curves satisfying (19.6a), in a space with a general affine connection, the *straight lines* or *self-parallel curves* of the space. Let us look at the conditions by referral via a chart back to a domain with coordinates (x_i) in R^n. If $\sigma(t) = (x_i(t))$, the components of the vector field $\sigma'(t)$ along σ are (dx_i/dt), and, using (19.5), (19.6a) becomes

$$\frac{d^2}{dt^2}x_i(t) = -\Gamma_{ijk}(x(t))\frac{dx_i}{dt}\frac{dx_j}{dt}. \tag{19.6b}$$

These differential equations are, of course, nonlinear and of second order. The most one can say is that there is a unique solution with $x(a)$ and $(dx/dt)(a)$; that is, with $\sigma(a)$ and $\sigma'(a)$ prescribed, that the solution to this initial value problem exists if b is sufficiently close to a, and that the obtained solution is a C^∞ function of the initial conditions $x(a)$ and $(dx/dt)(a)$. Of course we also have the following homogeneity condition:

If $t \to \sigma(t)$ is a solution of (19.6a), so is the
curve $t \to \sigma(\lambda t)$, where λ is a real constant. $\qquad$ (19.7)

Now we turn to the description of the *torsion* and *curvature tensor fields* associated with an affine connection on a manifold M given by a covariant differentiation operation satisfying (19.1). We shall mainly restrict ourselves to formal considerations, since our goal is to sketch the theory of affine connections in as efficient a manner as possible for use as a tool in Riemannian geometry. The torsion and curvature tensors are, respectively, maps T: $V(M) \times V(M) \to V(M)$ and $R: V(M) \times V(M) \times V(M) \to V(M)$, defined as follows for $X, Y, Z \in V(M)$:

$$T(X, Y) = \nabla_X Y - \nabla_Y X - [X, Y]. \tag{19.8a}$$

$$R(X, Y)(Z) = \nabla_X(\nabla_Y Z) - \nabla_Y(\nabla_X Z) - \nabla_{[X, Y]}Z. \tag{19.8b}$$

We write $R(X, Y)(Z)$ because we mean to suggest that R should be interpreted as a law assigning to each pair $(X, Y) \in V(M)$ a mapping $Z \to R(X, Y)(Z)$ of $V(M)$ into itself.

Certain algebraic properties of T and R should be evident. First, both T and R are skew-symmetric in X and Y. Second, both are obviously R-multilinear in their arguments. Less obviously, however (since ∇ is *not* $F(M)$-multilinear), they are both $F(M)$-multilinear with respect to multiplication of X, Y, or Z by functions from $F(M)$. For example, using (19.1), for $f \in F(M)$:

$$\begin{aligned} T(fX, Y) &= \nabla_{fX} Y - \nabla_Y(fX) - [fX, Y] \\ &= f\nabla_X Y - Y(f)X - f\nabla_Y X + Y(f)X - f[X, Y] \\ &= fT(X, Y). \end{aligned}$$

$$\begin{aligned} R(fX, Y)(Z) &= f\nabla_X\nabla_Y Z - \nabla_Y(f\nabla_X Z) - \nabla_{[fX, Y]}Z \\ &= f\nabla_X\nabla_Y Z - Y(f)\nabla_X Z - f\nabla_Y\nabla_X Z + Y(f)\nabla_X Z - f\nabla_{[X,Y]}Z \\ &= fR(X, Y)(Z). \end{aligned}$$

That f pulls through with no differentiations acting on it when the other arguments are multiplied by it is verified similarly. This property indicates the *tensorial character* of T and R. We can use this property to define the *values* of T and R at each point $p \in M$ in a way similar to that we used earlier to define the value of a differential form at a point.

The value of T at p, denoted by T_p, is to be a bilinear mapping $M_p \times M_p \to M_p$. For $u, v \in M_p$, choose vector fields $X, Y \in V(M)$ with $X(p) = u$, $Y(p) = v$, and define

$$T_p(u, v) = T(X, Y)(p).$$

The value of R at p, denoted by R_p, is to be a bilinear mapping $M_p \times M_p \times M_p \to M_p$ defined as follows: For $u_1, u_2, v \in M_p$, choose $X, Y, Z \in V(M)$ with $X(p) = u$, $Y(p) = u_2$, $Z(p) = v$, and

$$R_p(u_1, u_2)(v) = R(X, Y)(Z)(p).$$

Of course we must verify that these definitions make sense, that is, are independent of the vector fields chosen to extend the tangent vectors at p. One can show that it suffices to verify this for a neighborhood of each point p. Using charts, it suffices, then, to suppose that M is a convex domain of R^n, with coordinates (x_i). Thus, for example, if

$$u = u_i \frac{\partial}{\partial x_i}(p), \qquad v = v_i \frac{\partial}{\partial x_i}(p),$$

$$X = A_i \frac{\partial}{\partial x_i}, \qquad Y = B_i \frac{\partial}{\partial x_i}, \qquad \text{with} \quad A_i(p) = u_i, \quad B_i(M) = v_i,$$

and if

$$T\left(\frac{\partial}{\partial x_i}, \frac{\partial}{\partial x_j}\right) = T_{ijk} \frac{\partial}{\partial x_k},$$

(the T_{ijk} are the *components* of T with respect to the coordinate system (x_i)), then

$$T(X, Y)(p) = A_i B_j T\left(\frac{\partial}{\partial x_i}, \frac{\partial}{\partial x_j}\right)(p) = u_i v_i T_{ijk}(p) \frac{\partial}{\partial x_k}(p).$$

This shows quite explicitly that defining $T_p(u, v) = T(X, Y)(p)$ is legitimate, since it is independent of how u, v are extended to vector fields. Similar considerations hold also for the curvature tensor, of course.

Consider now a manifold M and a two-parameter family $\delta(s, t)$ in M, $a \le t \le b$, $0 \le s \le 1$; that is, δ is a map $[0, 1] \times [a, b] \to M$. The geometric interpretation of δ is mainly a matter of taste, of course, but the following picture will be most useful to us: For s held fixed, the curve $t \to \delta(s, t)$ is a curve in M, denoted by σ_s, say. Thus $s \to \sigma_s$ can be considered as a one-parameter family of curves, or as a curve in the space of curves of M. $\delta(s, t)$ can be thought of as a *homotopy* or *deformation* of the curve $t \to \sigma(t) = \sigma_s(t) = \delta(0, t)$. For notational convenience, we shall usually normalize the parametrization of t to be also the unit interval $[0, 1]$. A *vector field* on δ is a map denoted by, say, v, of $[0, 1] \times [0, 1] \to T(M)$, assigning to $s, t \in [0, 1]$ a tangent vector $v(s, t) \in M_{\delta(s, t)}$. The vector fields $\partial_s \delta$, $\partial_t \delta$ on δ are defined as follows:

> For $0 \le s, t \le 1$, $\partial_s \delta(s, t)$ and $\partial_t \delta(s, t)$ are, respectively, the tangent vectors to the curves $u \to \delta(u, t)$ and $u \to \delta(s, u)$ at $u = s$ and $u = t$. Thus $\partial_s \delta$ and $\partial_t \delta$ are the tangent vector fields to the curves obtained by holding, respectively, t and s constant and varying s and t.   (19.9)

Similarly, if $v: (s, t) \to v(s, t)$ is a vector field on δ, and if ∇ is a fixed affine connection on M, define $\nabla_s v$ and $\nabla_t v$ as vector fields on δ, the *covariant derivatives* of v in, respectively, the s and t-directions, as follows:

> For $0 \le s, t \le 1$, $\nabla_s v(s, t)$ and $\nabla_t v(s, t)$ are, respectively, the value of the covariant derivative vector fields at $u = s$ and $u = t$ of the vector fields $u \to v(u, t)$ and $u \to v(s, u)$ along the curves $u \to \delta(u, t)$ and $u \to \delta(s, u)$. $\hspace{2cm}$ (19.10)

The reader will find it easier to keep these definitions in mind by referring to a special case, namely: Suppose that X and Y are vector fields on M such that for each s, $t \to \delta(s, t)$ is an integral curve of X, and for each t, $s \to \delta(s, t)$ is an integral curve of Y. Then, from (19.9),

$$\partial_s \delta(s, t) = X(\delta(s, t)), \qquad \partial_t \delta(s, t) = Y(\delta(s, t)). \qquad (19.11)$$

Of course not all homotopies can be written in this form, but usually this type of homotopy is sufficiently general so that results proved for them extend to arbitrary homotopies.

If also there is a vector field Z on M so that $Z(\delta(s, t)) = v(s, t)$, (19.10) takes the form

$$\nabla_s v(s, t) = \nabla_Y Z(\delta(s, t)), \qquad (19.12a)$$

$$\nabla_t v(s, t) = \nabla_X Z(\delta(s, t)). \qquad (19.12b)$$

Note that if $X, Y \in V(M)$ satisfy (19.11), then

$$[X, Y](\delta(s, t)) = 0. \qquad (19.13)$$

Proof. It suffices to prove this in case δ is contained in a sufficiently small open set of M. We may as well suppose, then, that we are in a domain of R^n with coordinates (x_i). Suppose that

$$X = A_i \frac{\partial}{\partial x_i}, \qquad Y = B_i \frac{\partial}{\partial x_i},$$

and that

$$\delta(s, t) = (x_i(s, t)) = x(s, t).$$

Then (19.11) reduces to

$$\frac{\partial x_i}{\partial t} = A_i(x(s, t)), \qquad \frac{\partial x_i}{\partial s} = B_i(x(s, t)).$$

Thus,

$$0 = \frac{\partial^2 x_i}{\partial s \, \partial t} - \frac{\partial^2 x_i}{\partial t \, \partial x_i} = \frac{\partial A_i}{\partial x_j} \frac{\partial x_j}{\partial s} - \frac{\partial B_i}{\partial x_j} \frac{\partial x_j}{\partial t}$$

$$= \frac{\partial A_i}{\partial x_j}(x(s, t))B_j(x(s, t)) - \frac{\partial B_i}{\partial x_j}(x(s, t))A_j(x(s, t)),$$

whence (19.13).

Now we are prepared to state the fundamental formulas connecting this "covariant derivative along curves" concept with the curvature and torsion tensor fields:

> Suppose that $\delta(s, t)$, $0 \leq s, t \leq 1$, is a homotopy of curves in a manifold M with affine connection ∇, and that $v: (s, t) \to v(s, t) \in M_{\delta(s,t)}$. is a vector field on δ. Then,

$$\nabla_s \, \partial_t \, \delta(s, t) - \nabla_t \, \partial_s \, \delta(s, t) = T_{\delta(s,t)}(\partial_s \, \delta(s, t), \partial_t \, \delta(s, t)). \tag{19.14a}$$

$$\nabla_s \nabla_t v(s, t) - \nabla_t \nabla_s v(s, t) = R_{\delta(s,t)}(\partial_s \, \delta(s, t), \partial_t \, \delta(s, t))(v(s, t)), \tag{19.14b}$$

where, for each $p \in M$, T_p and R_p are respectively the values, as defined above, of the torsion and curvature tensors of the affine connection.

Proof. We shall give the proof only in the special case where there are vector fields X, Y on M related to δ via (19.11), and a vector field Z on M such that $v(s, t) = Z(\delta(s, t))$. The proof in complete generality must be done by a straightforward but tedious computation in local coordinates, which we leave to the reader as an exercise.

By (19.13),

$$[X, Y](\delta(s, t)) = 0.$$

$$\nabla_s \, \partial_t \, \delta(s, t) - \nabla_t \, \partial_s \, \delta(s, t) = \nabla_Y X(\delta(s, t)) - \nabla_X Y(\delta(s, t)) - [Y, X](\delta(s, t))$$

$$= T(Y, X)(\delta(s, t))$$

$$= T_{\delta(s,t)}(\partial_s \, \delta(s, t), \partial_t \, \delta(s, t)),$$

whence (19.14a).

By (19.12),

$$\nabla_t v(s, t) = \nabla_X Z(\delta(s, t)), \qquad \nabla_s v(s, t) = \nabla_Y Z(\delta(s, t)).$$

Then applying (19.12) again, we have

$$\nabla_s \nabla_t v(s, t) = \nabla_Y \nabla_X Z(\delta(s, t))$$

$$\nabla_t \nabla_s v(s, t) = \nabla_X \nabla_Y Z(\delta(s, t))$$

$$= [\nabla_Y \nabla_X Z + \nabla_{[X, Y]} Z + R(X, Y)(Z)](\delta(s, t)).$$

Now $R(X, Y)(Z)(\delta(s, t)) = R_{\delta(s,t)}(X(\delta(s, t)), Y(\delta(s, t)))(Z(\delta(s, t)))$, by definition of the "value" of R at a point. We have seen that $[X, Y](\delta(s, t)) = 0$ implies that $\nabla_{[X, Y]}(Z)(\delta(s, t)) = 0$. Subtraction now gives (19.14b).

As first application of (19.14), we have:

THEOREM 19.2

Suppose that M is a manifold with an affine connection. If, for any curve $\sigma: [a, b] \to M$, parallel translation of $M_{\sigma(a)}$ to $M_{\sigma(b)}$ along σ does not actually depend on the curve joining $\sigma(a)$ to $\sigma(b)$, then the curvature tensor of the affine connection is identically zero. Conversely, if the curvature tensor is identically zero and if M is simply connected, then parallel translation of tangent vectors along curves joining any two points of M really does not depend on the curve joining the two points.

Proof. Suppose that $\delta(s, t)$, $0 \le s, t \le 1$, is a homotopy of curves with fixed end points; that is,

$$\delta(s, 0) = \delta(0, 0), \qquad \delta(s, 1) = \delta(0, 1) \qquad \text{for } 0 \le s \le 1.$$

Let v^0 be an element of $M_{\delta(0, 0)}$, and define a vector field $v(s, t)$ on δ as follows: $v(s, 0) = v^0$, and the vector field $t \to v(s, t)$ on the curve $t \to \delta(s, t)$ is self-parallel. Analytically, this means that $\nabla_t v = 0$. Applying (19.14), we have

$$\nabla_s \nabla_t v = 0 = \nabla_t \nabla_s v + R(\partial_s \delta, \partial_t \delta)(v).$$

Now $v(s, 1) \in M_{\delta(s, 1)}$ is the parallel-translate of v^0 along the curve $t \to \delta(s, t)$. Thus, if parallel translation is independent of the curve, we must have

$$v(s, 1) = v(0, 1), \qquad \text{whence} \quad \nabla_s v(s, 1) = 0,$$

whence

$$R_{\delta(0, 1)}(\partial_s \delta(0, 1), \partial_t \delta(0, 1))(v(0, 1)) = 0.$$

Since v^0 and δ can be chosen completely arbitrarily, we must obviously have $R = 0$.

Conversely if $R = 0$, suppose $\sigma(t)$ and $\sigma_1(t)$, $0 \le t \le 1$, are two curves joining $\sigma(0)$ and $\sigma(1)$. If M is simply connected, we can find a fixed end-point homotopy $\delta(s, t)$ such that

$$\delta(0, t) = \sigma(t), \qquad \delta(1, t) = \sigma_1(t).$$

Let v be a vector field along δ such that $\nabla_t v = 0$ and $v(s, 0) = v^0$. Since $R = 0$, $\nabla_t \nabla_s v = \nabla_s \nabla_t v = 0$. Since $v(s, 0) = v^0$, also $\nabla_s v(s, 0) = 0$.

Hence, for fixed s, $\nabla_s v(s, t)$ is the parallel translate of $\nabla_s v(s, 0)$ along the curve $t \to \delta(s, t)$; hence $\nabla_s v(s, t)$ must also be zero. In particular, $\nabla_s v(s, 1) = 0$. Since $\delta(s, 1) = \delta(1, 1)$, this forces $v(s, 1) = v(0, 1)$ for all s; in particular $v(1, 1) = v(0, 1)$. But $v(1, 1)$ and $v(0, 1)$ are, respectively, the parallel translates of the vector v^0 along the curves σ and σ_1.   Q.E.D.

20 The Riemannian Affine
Connection and the First Variation Formula

Suppose that M is a manifold with a Riemannian Lagrangian $L \in F(T(M))$. As explained in the Introduction, this means that, for each $p \in M$, there is a positive definite symmetric bilinear form $(u, v) \to \langle u, v \rangle$ on each tangent space M_p such that

$$L(v) = \langle v, v \rangle^{1/2} = \|v\|.$$

If X, Y are vector fields on M, then *inner product* of X and Y, denoted by $\langle X, Y \rangle$, can be defined as

$$\langle X, Y \rangle(p) = \langle X(p), Y(p) \rangle.$$

This inner product has the properties:

$$\langle X, Y \rangle \in F(M) \qquad \text{for} \quad X, Y \in V(M). \tag{20.1a}$$

$$\langle X, Y \rangle = \langle Y, X \rangle. \tag{20.1b}$$

$$\langle f_1 X_1 + f_2 X_2, Y \rangle = f_1 \langle X_1, Y \rangle + f_2 \langle X_2, Y \rangle$$
$$\text{for} \quad f_1, f_2 \in F(M), \; X_1, X_2, Y \in V(M). \tag{20.1c}$$

$$\langle X, X \rangle \geq 0. \qquad \langle X, X \rangle(p) = 0 \quad \text{implies } X(p) = 0. \tag{20.1d}$$

Clearly, a Riemannian metric can be just as well defined by an inner product satisfying (20.1).

If (20.1d) is replaced by the weaker definiteness condition,

$$\langle X, Y \rangle = 0 \qquad \text{for all } Y \in V(M) \quad \text{implies } X = 0, \tag{20.1d'}$$

then the inner product is said to define a *pseudo-Riemannian* structure on M. Many of the elementary formal properties carry over from Riemannian to pseudo-Riemannian situations. However, since the deeper global properties of the geodesics do not carry over in a routine way, we shall restrict ourselves to the Riemannian case. Of course the pseudo-Riemannian case is very important for the theory of relativity, but we must refer for the moment to Lichnerowicz' book [1] for an account of this aspect.

THEOREM 20.1

Suppose that M is a manifold, with a Riemannian metric defined by an inner product for vector fields satisfying (20.1). Then there is a unique affine connection ∇ on M such that

(a) $\nabla_X Y = \nabla_Y X + [X, Y]$ for $X, Y \in V(M)$; that is, the torsion tensor is identically zero.

(b) $Z(\langle X, Y \rangle) = \langle \nabla_Z X, Y \rangle + \langle X, \nabla_Z Y \rangle$ for $Y, X, Z \in V(M)$.

This affine connection is called *the* Riemannian (or Levi-Civita) connection.

Proof. We prove uniqueness first. Rewrite (b) as

$$\langle \nabla_Z X, Y \rangle = Z \langle X, Y \rangle - \langle X, \nabla_Z Y \rangle$$

$$= (\text{using (a)}), Z \langle X, Y \rangle - \langle X, \nabla_Y Z \rangle - \langle X, [Z, Y] \rangle$$

$$= (\text{using (b) again}), Z \langle X, Y \rangle - \langle X, [Z, Y] \rangle$$
$$- Y \langle X, Z \rangle + \langle \nabla_Y X, Z \rangle$$

$$= (\text{using (a)}), Z \langle X, Y \rangle - \langle X, [Z, Y] \rangle$$
$$- Y \langle X, Z \rangle + \langle \nabla_X Y, Z \rangle + \langle [Y, X], Z \rangle$$

$$= (\text{using (b)}), Z \langle X, Y \rangle - \langle X, [Z, Y] \rangle - Y \langle X, Z \rangle$$
$$+ \langle [Y, X], Z \rangle - X \langle Y, Z \rangle - \langle Y, \nabla_X Z \rangle$$

$$= (\text{using (a)}), Z \langle X, Y \rangle - \langle X, [Z, Y] \rangle - Y \langle X, Z \rangle$$
$$+ \langle [Y, X], Z \rangle + X \langle Y, Z \rangle - \langle Y, \nabla_Z X \rangle - \langle Y, [X, Z] \rangle.$$

Finally, then, we have

$$\langle \nabla_Z X, Y \rangle = \tfrac{1}{2}(Z \langle X, Y \rangle - \langle X, [Z, Y] \rangle - Y \langle X, Z \rangle + \langle [Y, X], Z \rangle$$
$$+ X \langle Y, Z \rangle - \langle Y, [X, Z] \rangle). \qquad (20.2)$$

Since the right-hand side does not now involve ∇, uniqueness of ∇ is proved.

We can also use this formula to define $\nabla_Z X$ if it is verified (left to the reader) that when fZ or fY is substituted for Z or Y (for $f \in F(M)$), the function f pulls out to multiply everything on the right. Alternately, we work out ∇ in terms of a coordinate system (x_i).

Suppose

$$g_{ij} = \left\langle \frac{\partial}{\partial x_i}, \frac{\partial}{\partial x_j} \right\rangle.$$

The rules (20.1) imply that for each p, $(g_{ij}(p))$ is a positive definite, symmetric matrix. The g_{ij} are the *components* of the metric with respect to the co-ordinate system. The Lagrangian $L(v) = \|v\|$ can then be written as

$$L = (g_{ij}\dot{x}_i\dot{x}_j)^{1/2}. \tag{20.3}$$

$$\left\langle \nabla_{\partial/\partial x_i}\left(\frac{\partial}{\partial x_j}\right), \frac{\partial}{\partial x_k}\right\rangle = \Gamma_{ijh}g_{hk} = \frac{1}{2}\left(\frac{\partial g_{jk}}{\partial x_i} - \frac{\partial g_{ij}}{\partial x_k} + \frac{\partial g_{ik}}{\partial x_j}\right).$$

Let (g_{ij}^{-1}) be the inverse matrix to (g_{ij}). Finally, then,

$$\Gamma_{ijk} = \frac{1}{2}\left(\frac{\partial g_{jh}}{\partial x_i} - \frac{\partial g_{ij}}{\partial x_h} + \frac{\partial g_{ih}}{\partial x_j}\right)g_{hk}^{-1}. \tag{20.4}$$

This formula can serve to define ∇ in each coordinate patch. The proven uniqueness guarantees that the ∇ defined in each patch agrees in the overlap when two patches intersect; hence defines a ∇ operator globally on M.

We can use the Riemannian metric to define a length function for curves. If $\sigma: [a, b] \to M$, the *length* of σ is

$$\int_a^b \|\sigma'(t)\|\,dt = \int_a^b L(\sigma'(t))\,dt = \mathbf{L}(\sigma). \tag{20.5}$$

Of course the general theory of homogeneous, regular, ordinary variational problems developed in Chapter 14 applies in this special case, but it is instructive to go over the same ground, using the Riemannian affine connection, which is not available when discussing more general variational problems.

Certain normalizations of the parametrizations of curves are convenient. First we say that the curve σ is parametrized by arc length if $\langle \sigma'(t), \sigma'(t)\rangle = 1$ for $a \le t \le b$. In this case, $b - a$ is the length of the curve. We say that σ is parametrized *proportionally to arc length* if

$$b = 1, \quad a = 0, \quad \langle \sigma'(t), \sigma'(t)\rangle = \langle \sigma'(0), \sigma'(0)\rangle \quad \text{for } 0 \le t \le 1.$$

Then

$$\text{length } \sigma = \langle \sigma'(0), \sigma'(0)\rangle^{1/2}.$$

Consider a homotopy $\delta(s, t)$, $0 \le s, t \le 1$, with $\delta(0, t) = \sigma(t)$; that is, the homotopy defines a deformation of σ. For $0 \le s \le 1$, let σ_s be the curve $\sigma_s(t) = \delta(s, t)$. Let $\mathbf{L}(\sigma_s) = $ length of σ_s. We are interested in computing $(d/ds)\mathbf{L}(\sigma_s)$. For this purpose, we shall use freely the covariant differentiation of vector fields along curves and homotopies ideas developed in Chapter 19, always referring to the Riemannian connection given by Theorem 20.1.

We can suppose without any loss in generality that each of the curves $t \to \delta(s, t)$ is parametrized proportionally to arc length. Now

$$\mathbf{L}(\sigma_s) = \int_0^1 \langle \partial_t\,\delta(s, t), \partial_t\,\partial(s, t)\rangle^{1/2}\,dt.$$

Parametrization proportional to arc length implies

$$\langle \partial_t \, \delta(s, t), \, \partial_t \, \delta(s, t) \rangle = \mathbf{L}(\sigma_s)^2.$$

$$\frac{d}{ds} \mathbf{L}(\sigma_s) = \int_0^1 \frac{\partial}{\partial s} \langle \partial_t \, \delta(s, t), \, \partial_t \, \delta(s, t) \rangle^{1/2} \, dt$$

$$= \int_0^1 \frac{\langle \nabla_s \, \partial_t \, \delta(s, t), \, \partial_t \, \delta(s, t) \rangle \, dt}{\langle \partial_t \, \delta(s, t), \, \partial_t \, \delta(s, t) \rangle^{1/2}}$$

$$= \frac{1}{\mathbf{L}(\sigma_s)} \int_0^1 \langle \nabla_s \, \partial_t \, \delta(s, t), \, \partial_t \, \delta(s, t) \rangle \, dt$$

$$= \text{(using (19.14a); that is, the fact that the torsion tensor is zero),}$$

$$\frac{1}{\mathbf{L}(\sigma_s)} \int_0^1 \langle \nabla_t \, \partial_s \, \delta(s, t), \, \partial_t \, \delta(s, t) \rangle \, dt$$

$$= \text{(after integrating by parts),} \; \frac{1}{\mathbf{L}(\sigma_s)} \left(\langle \partial_s \, \delta(s, t), \, \partial_t \, \delta(s, t) \rangle \Big|_{t=0}^{t=1} \right.$$

$$\left. - \int_0^1 \langle \partial_s \, \delta(s, t), \, \nabla_t \, \partial_t \, \delta(s, t) \rangle \, dt \right).$$

Consider now the vector field $t \to v(t) = \partial_s \delta(0, t)$ along the initial curve $\sigma(t) = \delta(0, t)$. It may be thought of as the *infinitesimal deformation* corresponding to the deformation $s \to \sigma_s$ of σ. In terms of this vector field, the first variation formula is

$$\frac{1}{2} \frac{d}{ds} (\mathbf{L}(\sigma_s)^2) \Big|_{s=0} = \langle v(1,) \, \sigma'(1) \rangle - \langle v(0), \, \sigma'(0) \rangle - \int_0^1 \langle v(t), \, \nabla \sigma'(t) \rangle \, dt.$$

$$(20.6)$$

Now, if σ is to be considered as an extremal of the variational problem, it should be clear that it should satisfy

$$\nabla \sigma'(t) = 0; \qquad (20.7)$$

that is, the extremal or *geodesics* are the self-parallel curves or straight lines of the associated Riemannian affine connection. Of course it could be verified that (20.7) is just the Euler equation for the variational problem, but there is no real need to do this here explicitly. Having obtained the geodesics, we would expect next, following the general theory, to try and prove that, at least locally, they are minimizing by using extremal fields. However, again the general theory can be circumvented by use of the Riemannian connection (although the reader will notice that the "extremal field" idea appears in disguised form).

THEOREM 20.2

Let M be a Riemannian manifold and let p_0 be a point of M. For each $r > 0$, let $B(r)$ be the set of tangent vectors $v \in M_{p_0}$ whose length is less than r, that is, satisfying $\langle v, v \rangle < r^2$. (Thus, $B(r)$ is the open ball of radius r with center 0 in the vector space M_{p_0} considered as a Euclidean space with the inner product $\langle \ , \ \rangle$.) Then:

(a) If r is sufficiently small, there is a mapping denoted by $\exp: B(r) \to M$ such that, for $v \in B(r)$, $t \to \exp(tv)$, $0 \le t \le 1$, is the geodesic of M starting at p_0 and tangent there to v.

(b) The Jacobian of the map exp at the point $0 \in B(r)$ is nonzero.

(c) If r is sufficiently small, exp is a diffeomorphism of $B(r)$ with an open neighborhood $B(r, p_0)$ of p_0, called an open geodesic ball about p_0 of radius r.† As p_0 varies over any compact subset of M, the radius r of a geodesic ball can be chosen uniformly.

Proof. We have seen that, given $v \in M_{p_0}$, there is an $\varepsilon > 0$ and a geodesic $\sigma(t; v)$ defined for $0 \le t \le \varepsilon$, which is equal to p_0 for $t = 0$ and tangent at $t = 0$ to v. Since, in a coordinate system about p_0, σ is determined by a system of second-order ordinary differential equations, with p_0 and v determining the initial conditions, we see from the existence theorem on solutions of ordinary differential equations that σ also varies in a C^∞ way when p_0 and v vary over the tangent bundle to M. Further, ε can be chosen uniformly when p_0 and v vary over a compact subset of $T(M)$. We also have derived the homogeneity condition: For $\lambda > 0$, $t \to \sigma(\lambda t; v)$ is a geodesic beginning at p_0, defined for $0 \le t \le \varepsilon/\lambda$, tangent there to λv. By uniqueness, we have

$$\sigma(\lambda t; v) = \sigma(t; \lambda v).$$

Thus we can normalize $\varepsilon = 1$ at the expense of making v small; hence we can arrange that $\sigma(t; v)$ is defined for $0 \le t \le 1$, $\langle v, v \rangle < r^2$, when r is sufficiently small. This r will do for part (a), since we can then define

$$\exp(v) = \sigma(1; v) \qquad \text{when } v \in B(r).$$

To prove part (b), since M_{p_0} and M are the same dimension, it suffices to prove that $\exp_*$ maps the tangent space to M_{p_0} at 0 onto M_{p_0}. But, if $v \in M_{p_0}$, $t \to \exp(rt \cdot (v/r))$ is a curve in M beginning at p_0 and tangent there to v. Hence, $\exp_*$ maps the tangent vector to the curve $t \to rt \cdot (v/r)$ onto v.

Part (c) follows now from the implicit function theorem. Notice that an

---

† If $\phi: N \to N'$ is a (C^∞) map of manifolds, and if U is an open subset of N, we say that ϕ establishes a *diffeomorphism* of U with its image U if: (a) $\phi(U)$ is open in N', and (b) ϕ restricted to U has an inverse map $\phi(U) \to U$.

open geodesic ball of radius r can also be characterized as an open subset U of M containing p_0 such that:

(a) Each $p \in U$ can be joined to p_0 by a unique geodesic of length $<r$, and each geodesic of length less than r beginning at p_0 lies in U.

(b) The map $\exp^{-1} \colon U \to B(r)$ (defined because, by (a), exp restricted to $B(r)$ is 1-1 and onto U is C^∞).

Condition (b) is just a technical point; that is, (a) describes the intuitive geometric meaning of a geodesic ball, but seems to be necessary, since there are of course 1-1 onto C^∞ maps of manifolds that have no C^∞ inverses. For example, the map $x \to x^3$ of $R \to R$.

Another simple consequence of the first variation formula is: Suppose $\delta(s, t)$, $0 \le s, t \le 1$, is a deformation of curves such that

(a) the length of each curve $t \to \delta(s, t)$ is the same;
(b) $t \to \sigma(t) = \delta(0, t)$ is a geodesic;
(c) $t \to v(t) = \partial_s \delta(0, t)$ is the infinitesimal deformation.

Then, $\langle v(1), \sigma'(1) \rangle = \langle v(0), \sigma'(0) \rangle$. This result is known as *Gauss' lemma*.

THEOREM 20.3

Let M be a manifold with a Riemannian metric and let p_0 be a point of M. Suppose that $B(r, p_0)$ is an open geodesic ball about p_0 of radius r. Suppose that $p \in B(r, p_0)$ and that the length of the unique geodesic of length less than r joining p to p_0 is $W(p, p_0)$. Then the length of any path† joining p_0 to p is greater than $W(p, p_0)$ except if the path actually is the geodesic of length less than r joining p to p_0.

Proof. The function $p \to W(p, p_0)$ is a C^∞ function on $B(r, p_0) - p_0$, since it is just the carry over via $(\exp)^{-1}$ of the function $v \to \|v\|$ on $B(r) - (0)$, which is known to be C^∞.

Now, in general, given a function f defined in an open set U of a Riemannian manifold, we can define the *gradient vector field* in U, denoted by grad f, by either of the following equivalent conditions:

$$\langle \operatorname{grad} f, Y \rangle = df(Y) = Y(f) \qquad \text{for all } Y \in V(U). \tag{20.8a}$$

$$\langle \operatorname{grad} f(p), v \rangle = v(f) \qquad \text{for all } p \in U, \quad \text{all } v \in U_p. \tag{20.8b}$$

† Recall that a path is a continuous image of an interval of the real numbers, which is made up by putting a finite number of C^∞ curves end to end.

LEMMA 20.4

The function W defined in $U(r, p_0) - (p_0)$ satisfies the following condition:

$$\langle \text{grad } W, \text{grad } W \rangle = 1. \tag{20.9}$$

Further, any geodesic $\sigma(t)$, $0 \le t \le 1$, of length less than r, parametrized proportionally to arc length and beginning at p_0, satisfies the following condition:

$$\sigma'(t) = \frac{W(\sigma(t), p_0)}{t} \text{ grad } W(\sigma(t)). \tag{20.10}$$

In particular, σ is, after a change in parametrization, an integral curve of grad W for $0 < t \le 1$.

Proof. Let $\gamma(s)$, $0 \le s \le 1$, be a curve in $B(r, p_0) - (p_0)$, with $\gamma(0) = p$, $\gamma'(0) = v_1$. By definition of $B(r, p_0)$, there is a C^∞ homotopy $\delta(s, t)$, $0 \le s, t \le 1$, such that:

(a) $\delta(s, 1) = \gamma(s)$.
(b)   For each s, $t \to \delta(s, t)$ is the unique geodesic of length less than r joining p_0 to $\gamma(s)$, parametrized proportionally to arc length. Thus the length of this curve is equal to $W(\gamma(s), p_0)$.

Let $v(t) = \partial_s \delta(0, t)$ be the corresponding infinitesimal deformation. Since $\delta(s, 0) = p_0$, we have $v(0) = 0$. Also, $v(1) = v_1$. Thus the first variation formula (20.6) can be rephrased as follows:

$$\frac{1}{2} \frac{d}{ds} W(\gamma(s), p_0)^2 \bigg|_{s=0} = \langle v_1, \sigma'(1) \rangle.$$

But the left-hand side of this relation is

$$W(\gamma(0), p_0) \frac{d}{ds} W(\gamma(s), p_0) \bigg|_{s=0} = W(p, p_0)v_1(W) = W(p, p_0)\langle \text{grad } W(p), v_1 \rangle.$$

Since this must be true for all $v_1 \in M_p$, we have

$$W(p, p_0) \text{ grad } W(p) = \sigma'(1). \tag{20.11}$$

But, since the curve $t \to \sigma(t) = \delta(0, t)$ is parametrized proportionally to arc length, we have

$$\langle \sigma'(1), \sigma'(1) \rangle = (\text{length } \sigma)^2 = W(p, p_0)^2.$$

Also

$$\langle \sigma'(1), \sigma'(1) \rangle = W(p, p_0)^2 \langle \text{grad } W(p), \text{grad } W(p) \rangle.$$

Canceling, we have (20.8).

To prove (20.9), introduce for each $\lambda \in (0, 1]$, the geodesic

$$\sigma_\lambda(t) = \sigma(\lambda t), \qquad 0 \le t \le 1.$$

Then $\sigma_\lambda(1) = \sigma(\lambda)$. Substituting σ_λ for σ in (20.10) gives

$$\sigma_\lambda'(1) = W(\sigma(\lambda), p_0)(\text{grad } W)(\sigma(\lambda)).$$

But, $\sigma_\lambda'(1) = \lambda\sigma'(\lambda)$. Combining these two equations and changing λ back to t gives (20.9). Q.E.D.

LEMMA 20.5

Let U be an open subset of the Riemannian manifold M, and let F be a closed subset of U. Let W be a continuous nonnegative-valued function in U such that:

(a) $F = \{p \in U: W(p) = 0\}$.
(b) W is C^∞ in $U - F$, and there $\langle \text{grad } W, \text{grad } W \rangle = 1$.

Then any path in U joining a point $p_0 \in F$ to a point $p \in U - F$ must have length $\ge W(p)$, and equality can hold only if the path actually is a geodesic.

Proof. Let $\sigma(t)$ be a path joining p_0 to p, $0 \le t \le 1$. We can suppose without loss of generality that $\sigma(t) \in U - F$ for $0 < t \le 1$. Let ε be a number >0.

$$|W(\sigma(1)) - W(\varepsilon)| = \left| \int_\varepsilon^1 \frac{d}{dt} W(\sigma(\varepsilon)) \, dt \right|$$

$$= \left| \int_\varepsilon^1 dW(\sigma'(t)) \, dt \right|$$

$$= \left| \int_\varepsilon^1 \langle \text{grad } W(\sigma(t)), \sigma'(t) \rangle \, dt \right|$$

$$\le \int_\varepsilon^1 |\langle \text{grad } W(\sigma(t)), \sigma'(t) \rangle| \, dt$$

$$\le (\text{using the Schwarz inequality}\dagger \text{ and condition (b)},$$

$$\int_\varepsilon^1 \langle \sigma'(t), \sigma'(t) \rangle^{1/2} \, dt.$$

As $\varepsilon \to 0$, the left-hand side approaches, by continuity of W, $W(\sigma(1))$, while the right-hand side approaches the length of σ.

---

† The Schwarz inequality asserts that in a real-vector space V with a positive definite symmetric bilinear form $\langle \, , \, \rangle$, for all $u, v \in V$: $|\langle u, v \rangle| \le \langle u, u \rangle^{1/2} \langle v, v \rangle^{1/2}$. Equality can hold only if u and v are proportional.

Suppose that

$$W(\sigma(1)) = \int_0^1 \langle \sigma'(t), \sigma'(t) \rangle^{1/2} \, dt.$$

Choose ε sufficiently small that $W(\varepsilon) < W(\sigma(1))$. Then

$$\int_0^1 \langle \sigma'(t), \sigma'(t) \rangle^{1/2} \, dt \leq \int_\varepsilon^1 |\langle \text{grad } W(\sigma(t)), \sigma'(t) \rangle| \, dt + W(\varepsilon).$$

Now, $\int_0^\varepsilon \langle \sigma'(t), \sigma'(t) \rangle \, dt \geq W(\varepsilon)$; hence

$$\int_0^1 \langle \sigma'(t), \sigma'(t) \rangle^{1/2} \, dt \leq \int_\varepsilon^1 |\langle \text{grad } W(\sigma(t)), \sigma'(t) \rangle| \, dt + \int_0^\varepsilon \langle \sigma'(t), \sigma'(t) \rangle^{1/2} \, dt.$$

Hence,

$$\int_\varepsilon^1 \langle \sigma'(t), \sigma'(t) \rangle^{1/2} \, dt \leq \int_\varepsilon^1 |\langle \text{grad } W(\sigma(t)), \sigma'(t) \rangle| \, dt$$

or

$$0 \leq \int_\varepsilon^1 (|\langle \text{grad } W(\sigma(t)), \sigma'(t) \rangle|$$
$$- \langle \sigma'(t), \sigma'(t) \rangle^{1/2} \langle \text{grad } W(\sigma(t)), \text{grad } W(\sigma(t)) \rangle) \, dt.$$

By the Schwarz inequality, this is possible only if the integrand is zero, forcing $\sigma'(t)$ and grad $W(\sigma(t))$ to be proportional; that is, σ is, perhaps after a change in parametrization, an integral curve of grad W. The proof of Lemma 20.5 will be completed after proving the following lemma.

LEMMA 20.6

Let W be a C^∞ function in an open set U of a Riemannian manifold such that $\langle \text{grad } W, \text{grad } W \rangle = 1$. Then any integral curve of W is a geodesic.

Proof. For $X \in V(U)$, we have

$$0 = X \langle \text{grad } W, \text{grad } W \rangle = 2 \langle \nabla_X \text{grad } W, \text{grad } W \rangle$$
$$= 2 \langle \nabla_{\text{grad } W} X, \text{grad } W \rangle + 2 \langle [X, \text{grad } W], \text{grad } W \rangle$$
$$= 2 \text{ grad } W(\langle X, \text{grad } W \rangle) - 2 \langle X, \nabla_{\text{grad } W} \text{grad } W \rangle$$
$$+ 2 \langle [X, \text{grad } W], \text{grad } W \rangle.$$

Now suppose that $0 = \langle \text{grad } W, X \rangle = X(W)$. Then

$$\langle [X, \text{grad } W], \text{grad } W \rangle = [X, \text{grad } W](W) = X \text{ grad } W(W) - \text{grad } W X(W)$$
$$= X(\langle \text{grad } W, \text{grad } W \rangle) - 0 = 0.$$

Thus we have

$$\langle X, \nabla_{\text{grad } W} \text{ grad } W \rangle = 0.$$

Since X can be an arbitrary vector field perpendicular to grad W, for each $p \in U$, $\nabla_{\text{grad } W} \text{ grad } W(p)$ must be a scalar multiple of grad $W(p)$. On the other hand,

$$0 = \text{grad } W(\langle \text{grad } W, \text{grad } W \rangle) = \langle \nabla_{\text{grad } W} \text{ grad } W, \text{grad } W \rangle.$$

Hence this scalar multiple must be zero. Thus we have finally

$$\nabla_{\text{grad } W} \text{ grad } W = 0.$$

Suppose that $\sigma(t)$, $0 \leq t \leq 1$, is an integral curve of grad W; that is,

$$\sigma'(t) = \text{grad } W(\sigma(t)).$$

By the very definition of the covariant derivative of a vector field along a curve, we have

$$\nabla \sigma'(t) = \nabla_{\text{grad } W} \text{ grad } W(\sigma(t)) = 0;$$

hence σ is a geodesic.

Return to the proof of Theorem 20.2. The lemmas prove that for $p \in B(r, p_0)$, $W(p, p_0)$ is greater than the length of any curve in $B(r, p_0)$ joining p to p_0 other than the geodesic of length $W(p, p_0)$ joining p to p_0. The only other possibility is a path $\sigma(t)$, $0 \leq t \leq 1$, joining p to p_0 that does not completely lie in $B(r, p_0)$. Since $M - B(r, p_0)$ is closed in M, there must be a first instant $t_0 \in (0, 1)$ at which $\sigma(t_0) \notin B(r, p_0)$. We must then have: length $\sigma \geq r > W(p, p_0)$. For otherwise the length of the curve is, say, $r - \varepsilon$. Suppose, for example, that $\sigma(t) = \exp(v(t))$ for $0 \leq t < t_0$, where $t \to v(t)$ is a curve in $B(r)$. But as we have seen, $v(t)$ must then lie in $B(r - \varepsilon)$; hence there is a sequence (t_α) of real numbers, $1 \leq \alpha < \infty$, converging to t_0 with $v(t_\alpha) \to v_0 \in B(r)$ as $\alpha \to \infty$. Then, by continuity of the exp mapping and σ, $\exp(v(t_\alpha))$ converges to both $\text{Exp}(v)$ and $\sigma(t_0)$ as $\alpha \to \infty$; hence, $\sigma(t_0) \in B(r)$, a contradiction. This finishes the proof of Theorem 20.3.

COROLLARY 1

Let M be a Riemannian manifold and define a real-valued function $d: M \times M \to R$ as follows: For $p, q \in M$, $d(p, q)$ is the greatest lower bound of the length of all paths joining p to q.

Then d satisfies all the axioms necessary to define a "distance function" on M, that is, to define a metric on M in the sense of point-set topology.

The topology on M defined by this metric agrees with that already given by the manifold structure.

If $B(r, p_0)$ is an open geodesic ball defined about p_0, if $p \in B(r, p_0)$, if $W(p, p_0)$ is the function defined above, then

$$d(p, p_0) = W(p, p_0). \qquad (20.12)$$

Further, if $\sigma(t)$, $0 \le t \le 1$, is a path in M such that $d(\sigma(0), \sigma(1)) = \text{length } \sigma$, then σ (after possible reparametrization) is an unbroken geodesic curve joining $\sigma(0)$ to $\sigma(1)$.

Proof. To show that d is a bona fide distance function in the sense of point-set topology, we must show that

(a) $d(p, q) = d(q, p)$ (symmetry).
(b) $d(p, q) \le d(p, p_0) + d(p_0, q)$ (triangle inequality).
(c) $d(p, q) = 0$ implies $p = q$.

(a) and (b) follow immediately from the definition of d. To prove (c), note first that (20.11) follows from the theorem. Hence, if r is the radius of a geodesic ball about p, and if $d(p, q) < r$, then q must lie in this geodesic ball. Then, further, if $d(p, q) = 0$, also $W(p, q) = 0$, and we see that $p = q$. That the topologies agree is merely a fancy way of saying that a sequence (p_α), $1 \le \alpha < \infty$, of points of M converges to p as $\alpha \to \infty$ if and only if $d(p, p_\alpha) \to 0$ as $\alpha \to 0$. This follows similarly by circling p with a geodesic ball.

To prove the last remark, notice that the additivity of the length, when paths are placed end to end, forces $d(\sigma(a), \sigma(b)) = \text{length } \sigma$ for $a \le t \le b$, whenever $a, b \in [0, 1]$ if it is true for $a = 0$, $b = 1$.

Let r be a uniform radius of geodesic balls about all points of σ. We can suppose without loss of generality that $d(\sigma(0), \sigma(1)) = 1 = \text{length } \sigma$, and that σ is parametrized by arc length; that is, length of σ, $0 \le t \le t_0$, is t_0. Thus

$$\sigma(t_0 \pm \varepsilon) \in B(\sigma(t_0), r) \qquad \text{if } 0 \le \varepsilon < r.$$

By the theorem, $\sigma(t)$ must be an unbroken geodesic for $t_0 \le t \le t_0 + \varepsilon$ and $t_0 - \varepsilon \le t \le t_0$. There is an a priori possibility of the two geodesic segments meeting in a corner at $t = t_0$, but the fact that t_0 can be any element of $[0, 1]$ rules this out also. Progressing by "continuous induction"† on t, $0 \le t \le 1$, proves that $\sigma(t)$ is an unbroken geodesic for $0 \le t \le 1$.

† Ordinary induction proves statements about functions $k \to f(k)$, whose domain is the set of all integers, by proving the statement for $k = 0$, then by showing that its truth for k implies its truth for $k + 1$. Continuous induction, very useful in differential geometry, proves statements about maps $t \to f(t)$ defined over an interval, say, $0 \le t \le 1$, by proving it for $t = 0$, then by showing that its truth for $t_0 \in [0, 1]$ implies its truth for $t_0 + \delta$, where δ is some small number independent of t_0. Its basis is, of course, the fact that any interval of real numbers is connected, and the remark that verifying this condition verifies that the set of all t for which the statement is true is open and closed. When, as above, we think it is routine to carry out this process, we shall leave it to the reader as an exercise.

COROLLARY 2

Suppose that N is a submanifold of a Riemannian manifold M, that $\sigma: [0, 1] \to M$ is a geodesic in M such that

(a) $\sigma(1) \in N$.

(b) $d(p, \sigma(0)) \geq$ length σ for all $p \in N$; that is, σ realizes the shortest distance from $\sigma(0)$ to any point of N. Then

$$\langle \sigma'(1), v \rangle = 0 \qquad \text{for all } v \in N_{\sigma(1)};$$

that is, σ is perpendicular to N at its point of contact.

Proof. The first variation formula tells us that if $s \to \sigma_s$ is any deformation of σ with $v: t \to v(t)$ the infinitesimal deformation vector field along σ, then

$$\mathbf{L}(\sigma) \frac{d}{ds} \mathbf{L}(\sigma_s) \bigg|_{s=0} = \langle v(1), \sigma'(1) \rangle - \langle v(0), \sigma'(0) \rangle.$$

If such a deformation has its end point fixed at $t = 0$, and if $s \to \sigma_s(1)$ lies in N, then the left-hand side must be zero, $v(0) = 0$, which forces

$$\langle v(1), \sigma'(1) \rangle = 0.$$

Of course $v(1)$ must then be in $N_{\sigma(1)}$, but we do not know a priori that any $v \in N_{\sigma(1)}$ can be exhibited as $v(1)$ of such a deformation. However, it is clear that this is so if $\sigma(0)$ is in a sufficiently small neighborhood of $\sigma(1)$. Now use the fact that $\sigma(t)$, $t_0 \leq t \leq 1$, must be a minimizing curve from $\sigma(t_0)$ to $\sigma(1)$ for each $t_0 \in [0, 1)$, to finish the job.

21 The Hopf–Rinow Theorem
Applications to the Theory of Covering Spaces

The results in Chapter 20 are basically local in nature, but we shall see in this chapter that they can be put together to prove interesting and nontrivial results concerning the global properties of the geodesics of a Riemannian manifold. While the main difference between "modern" and "classical" differential geometry is this concern with global results, this is also a good illustration of the maxim that there is often in practice not a great deal of difference between the two sorts of problems.

THEOREM 21.1 (HOPF–RINOW)

Let M be a Riemannian manifold and let p_0 be a point of M such that all geodesics beginning at p_0 can be indefinitely extended. Then:

(a) Any point of M can be joined to p_0 be a geodesic whose length is the distance between it and p_0.

(b) As a metric space in the sense of topology, M is complete in the sense that any Cauchy sequence of points has a limit. Further, every bounded closed subset of M is compact.

Conversely, if (b) is true, then a geodesic beginning at any point of M can be indefinitely extended. In particular, any two points of M can be joined by at least one geodesic realizing the distance.

Proof. Let $B(r, p_0)$ and $S(r, p_0)$ be the set of all points $p \in M$ such that, respectively,

$$d(p, p_0) < r \qquad \text{and} \qquad d(p, p_0) = r.$$

Let exp: $M_{p_0} \to M$ be the map that assigns to each $v \in M_{p_0}$ the point $\exp(v) = \sigma(1, v)$, where $t \to \sigma(t, v)$ is the geodesic beginning at $t = 0$, tangent there to v. (Since geodesics can be parametrized over $(-\infty, \infty)$, there is no necessity of assuming that v is small in length.)

We shall prove by continuous induction on r that all points in $B(r, p_0)$ can be joined to p_0 by a geodesic realizing the distance. Now, if r is sufficiently small, this is so by Theorem 20.3. Suppose that r_0 is the least upper bound of numbers having this property. If we suppose that $r_0 < \infty$, we shall derive a contradiction.

Clearly, r_0 itself has the property. First we show that all elements $S(r_0, p_0)$ can be joined to p_0 by a geodesic of length r_0. For if $p \in S(r, p_0)$, there is at least one sequence (p_α), $1 \leq \alpha < \infty$, in $B(r_0, p_0)$, converging to p as $\alpha \to \infty$. Then there is a sequence $v_\alpha \in M_{p_0}$ with $\|v_\alpha\| \leq r_0$ and $p_\alpha = \exp(v_\alpha)$. By at most taking subsequences, we can suppose that v_α itself converges to v, say, as $\alpha \to \infty$. We must then have: $\|v\| \leq r_0$, $\exp(v_\alpha) \to \exp(v)$ as $\alpha \to \infty$ by the continuity of the exp mapping; hence $p = \exp v$. If $\|v\| < r_0$, we would have $p \in B(r_0, p_0)$, which is not so; hence $t \to \exp tv$, $0 \leq t \leq 1$, is a geodesic of length r_0 joining p_0 to p. Note further that $S(r_0, p_0)$ is the image under exp of a compact set; hence it is compact.

Second, the definition of r_0 as a least upper bound implies that there is a sequence (r_α) of real numbers, all $> r_0$, converging to r_0 as $\alpha \to \infty$, and a new sequence of points $p_\alpha \in S(r_\alpha, p_0)$, each of which cannot be joined to p_0 by a geodesic of length r_α. Let q_α be a point of $S(r_0, p_0)$ such that

$$d(p_\alpha, q_\alpha) \leq d(p_\alpha, q) \qquad \text{for all } q \in S(r_0, p_0).$$

(Such a point exists, since $S(r_0, p_0)$ is compact.) Again, since $S(r_0, p_0)$ is compact, we can suppose, after possibly taking subsequences, that $q_\alpha \to q_0 \in S(r_0, p_0)$, as $\alpha \to \infty$. Then, using the triangle inequality, we see that $p_\alpha \to q_0$ as $\alpha \to \infty$. In particular, if α is sufficiently large, p_α lies in a geodesic ball about q_α. The geodesics realizing the distance from p_α to q_α and from p_0 to q_α cannot meet with a corner at q_α: For otherwise the corner could be "cut across" to define a path joining p_α to p_0 of length less than $r_0 + d(p_\alpha, q_\alpha)$, which would provide a curve joining p_α to $S(r_0, p_0)$ of length less than $d(p_\alpha, q_\alpha)$. (See Fig. 5.)

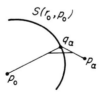

$S(r_0, p_0)$

q_α

p_α

p_0

FIGURE 5

For similar reasons, $r_0 + d(p_\alpha, q_\alpha) = d(p_\alpha, r_0)$. But, the geodesics meeting without a corner at q_α define an unbroken geodesic of length $r_0 + d(p_\alpha, q_\alpha) = d(p_\alpha, r_0)$ joining p_0 to p_α, which is the desired contradiction.

To prove that all bounded closed sets are compact, note that any such set is contained as a closed set in $B(r, p_0) \cup S(r, p_0)$ for r sufficiently large, which we know is compact. Completeness as a metric space follows.

To prove the converse, we shall show, assuming that M as a metric space is complete, that any geodesic $\sigma(t)$ defined for $0 \leq t < 1$ can be extended to be defined over $0 \le t \le 1 + \varepsilon$, for some $\varepsilon > 0$. That any geodesic segment can be extended over $(-\infty, \infty)$ is then proved by continuous induction on t.

Geodesics are parametrized proportionally to arc length. Thus, if $0 \le s$, $t < 1$,

$$d(\sigma(s), \sigma(t)) \le \text{(constant)} \times |s - t|.$$

By the completeness of the metric space,

$$\lim_{t \to 1} \sigma(t) \text{ exists and equals, say, } p_1.$$

But then the union of the set of points of σ with p_1 is compact. Applying the fundamental existence theorem for geodesics, there exists an $\varepsilon > 0$ such that *uniformly* in $t_0 \in [0, 1)$ there exists a geodesic starting at each t_0, tangent there to $\sigma'(t_0)$ and defined over $0 \le t \le \varepsilon$. Except for a translation of parameter, this constructed geodesic segment must agree with σ; hence σ can be extended beyond 1 by taking t_0 sufficiently close to 1.

This finishes the proof of the Hopf–Rinow theorem, one basic theorem in global Riemannian geometry. We shall now discuss some useful applications of this theorem to the theory of covering spaces.

Definition

Let M and N be connected topological spaces; $\phi \colon M \to N$ a continuous map of M onto N. ϕ is called a *covering map* if each point $p \in N$ has an open neighborhood U such that each component of $\phi^{-1}(U)$ is homeomorphic to U under ϕ.

This purely topological definition is most useful when combined with differentiability assumptions. We shall limit ourselves to proving here the following sufficient condition that a differentiable map be a covering map. It will have useful applications later on.

THEOREM 21.2

Let M and N be manifolds, $\phi \colon M \to N$ a (C^∞) map with everywhere nonzero Jacobian. Then ϕ is a covering map of M onto N if and only if the following condition is satisfied:

> There is a pair (p_0, q_0) of points, $p \in M$, $q \in N$, with $\phi(p_0) = q_0$, such that, for every curve $\sigma \colon [0, 1] \to N$ with $\sigma(0) = q_0$, there is a lifted curve $\gamma \colon [0, 1] \to M$, with $\gamma(0) = p_0$ and $\phi(\gamma(t)) = \sigma(t)$ for $0 \le t \le 1$.   (21.1)

The proof will consist in a series of lemmas.

LEMMA 21.3

Let M and N be a Riemannian manifold, $\phi: M \to N$ a map that is a local isometry; that is, it satisfies

$$\langle \phi_*(u), \phi_*(v) \rangle = \langle u, v \rangle \qquad \text{for all } p \in M, \quad \text{all } u, v \in M_p.$$

Suppose in addition that M is complete† as a Riemannian manifold. Then ϕ is a covering map.

Proof. It is easily seen that ϕ carries geodesics of M into geodesics of N. Let $q \in N$, and let $B(r, q)$ be an open geodesic ball about q. We shall show that every component of $\phi^{-1}(B(r,q))$ is mapped diffeomorphically by ϕ onto $B(r, q)$.

Of course it follows from the local isometry condition that ϕ has nonzero Jacobian; hence, by the implicit function theorem, it maps open sets into open sets. Let $p \in \phi^{-1}(q)$. A point of M whose distance from p is less than r can be joined to p by a geodesic whose length is that distance, whose projection under ϕ lies then in $B(r, q)$. Thus, if $B(r, p)$ is the set of points of M whose distance from p is less than r, then $\phi(B(r, p)) = B(r, q)$. (It is onto $B(r, q)$, since if $\sigma(t)$, $0 \le t \le 1$, is a geodesic of N starting at q of length less than r, if $\sigma_1(t)$, $0 \le t \le 1$, is the geodesic of M such that $\sigma_1(0) = p$, $\sigma_1'(0) = \phi_*^{-1}(\sigma'(0))$, then $\phi(\sigma_1(t)) = \sigma(t)$, by uniqueness of geodesics in N.)

To prove: ϕ restricted to $B(r, p)$ is 1-1.

Suppose that $p_1, p_2 \in B(r, p)$, with $\phi(p_1) = \phi(p_2)$. p_1 and p_2 are endpoints of geodesics of M beginning at p of length less than r. Their projections lie in $B(r, q)$ and meet at beginning and at end points; hence they coincide. Then p_1 must equal p_2; otherwise, ϕ_* could not be 1-1. Thus, ϕ, as 1-1, onto nonzero Jacobian map: $B(r, p) \to B(r, q)$ must be a diffeomorphism.

We now show that $B(r, p)$ is a connected component of $\phi^{-1}(B(r, q))$. Suppose that $\gamma(s)$, $0 \le s \le 1$, is a curve in $\phi^{-1}(B(r, q))$, with $\gamma(0) = p$. We must show that the distance of $\gamma(s)$ to p is less than r for $0 \le s \le 1$, that is, that $\gamma(s) \in B(r, p)$. Now N is also a complete Riemannian manifold, for a small geodesic segment of N can be lifted via ϕ to M, extended to $(-\infty, \infty)$, using completeness of M, and the projection down to N must by uniqueness be the extension to $(-\infty, \infty)$ of the small geodesic segment with which we started. Thus the exp map of N can be extended over all of N_q.

---

† A Riemannian manifold is said to be complete if conditions of the Hopf–Rinow theorem are satisfied for example, the condition that all geodesics can be indefinitely extended. In this case, map exp can be defined over the whole tangent space at each point.

By the definition of $B(r, q)$ as a geodesic ball, there is a curve $v(s) \in N_q$ with

$$\langle v(s), v(s) \rangle < r^2.$$

$$\exp(v(s)) = \phi(\gamma(s)) \qquad \text{for } 0 \leq s \leq 1;$$

$$v(0) = 0.$$

Let $u(s)$ be the curve in M_p with $\phi_*(u(s)) = v(s)$ for $0 \leq s \leq 1$. Clearly, then, $\phi \exp(u(s)) = \phi(\gamma(s))$. Since both curves $s \to \exp(u(s))$ and $\gamma(s)$ have the same image under ϕ and coincide for $s = 0$, they must coincide for all s (otherwise ϕ_* could not be 1-1). In particular, the distance of $\gamma(s)$ to p is majorized by $\|u(s)\|$, that is, by r; hence $\gamma(s) \in B(r, p)$, which is what we had to prove.

Finally, it should be clear that the collection of $B(r, p)$, where p runs through $\phi^{-1}(q)$, exhausts the connected components of $\phi^{-1}(B(r, q))$. Since q is arbitrary in N, this proves that ϕ is a covering map.

LEMMA 21.4 (NOMIZU–OZEKI)

Let M be a manifold with a Riemannian metric. Then M has a new Riemannian metric conformal to the old, which is in addition complete.

Proof. Two Riemannian metrics $(u, v) \to \langle u, v \rangle$ and $(u, v) \to \langle u, v \rangle'$ are said to be *conformal* if there is a positive valued C^∞ function of an M such that

$$\langle u, v \rangle' = f(p)^2 \langle u, v \rangle \qquad \text{whenever } u,v \in M_p.$$

For $p, q \in M$, let $d(p, q)$ and $d'(p, q)$ be, respectively, the distance between p and q with respect to the old and new metrics. For $r > 0$, let $B(r, p)$ and $B'(r, p)$ be the set of $q \in M$ such that, respectively, $d(p, q) < r$ and $d'(p, q) < r$.

Let $c(p)$ be the least upper bound of the set of numbers r such that the closure of $B(r, p)$ is compact. Then the closure of $B(c(p), p)$ must be noncompact. Now, if $c(p_0) = \infty$ for some p_0, we would be finished, for bounded closed subsets in the old metric would be compact. Then we can suppose that $0 < c(p) < \infty$.

We now prove

$$|c(p) - c(q)| \leq d(p, q) \qquad \text{for all } p,q \in M. \tag{21.2}$$

By symmetry, it suffices to prove that

$$c(q) \geq c(p) - d(p, q).$$

Suppose, then, that (p_α), $1 \leq \alpha < \infty$, is a sequence of points of M such that $d(q, p_\alpha) \leq r < c(p) - d(p, q)$. Then $d(p, p_\alpha) \leq d(p, q) + d(q, p_\alpha) \leq d(p, q) + r < d(p, q) + c(p) - d(p, q) = c(p)$. Thus a subsequence of the (p_α) converges, since the closure of $B(d(p, q) + r, p)$ is compact. Also, then, $B(r, q)$ is compact; hence $c(q) \geq c(p) - d(p, q)$.

Expression 21.2 shows that c is a continuous function of p; hence, so is $1/c$. Let the function f used to define the new metric be any C^∞ function f such that

$$f(p) > \frac{1}{c(p)} \qquad \text{for all } p \in M.$$

$$B'\left(\frac{1}{3}, p\right) \subset B\left(\frac{c(p)}{2}, p\right) \qquad \text{for all } p \in M. \qquad (21.3)$$

In particular, the closure of $B'(\frac{1}{3}, p)$ in M is compact.

For the proof, let $\sigma(t)$, $0 \leq t \leq 1$, be any path in M starting at p whose length in the new metric is less than $1/3$. Suppose that σ is parametrized proportionally to arc length in the old metric, and that the length of σ in the old metric is L. Then

$$\int_0^1 f(\sigma(t))\langle \sigma'(t), \sigma'(t)\rangle^{1/2} \, dt = \text{length of } \sigma \text{ in new metric} < \tfrac{1}{3}$$

$$= L \int_0^1 f(\sigma(t)) \, dt$$

$$\geq L \int_0^1 \frac{1}{c(\sigma(t))} \, dt.$$

By (21.2),

$$c(\sigma(t)) \leq c(\sigma(0)) + d(\sigma(0), \sigma(t)) \leq c(p) + L.$$

Combining these inequalities, we have

$$L < \tfrac{1}{3}(L + c(p)), \qquad \text{or} \qquad \tfrac{2}{3}L < \tfrac{1}{3}c(p), \qquad \text{or} \qquad L < \frac{c(p)}{2}.$$

This proves that $\sigma(1) \in B((c(p)/2), p)$; hence it proves (21.3).

To prove that M is complete in the new metric is now a consequence of the Hopf–Rinow theorem, since the "uniform radius" for compact sets makes it easy to show that geodesics can be indefinitely extended.

We can now prove Theorem 21.2. That (21.1) is satisfied if ϕ is a covering map is easy to see, and will be left to the reader as an exercise. Conversely, make N into a complete Riemannian manifold, using Lemma 21.4. One can make M into a Riemannian manifold so that ϕ is a local isometry by setting

$$\langle u, v \rangle = \langle \phi_*(u), \phi_*(v) \rangle \qquad \text{for } u,v \in M_p, \, p \in M.$$

(We refer to this as *pulling back* the metric on N via ϕ.)

To infer that ϕ is a covering map, it suffices, in view of Lemma 21.3, to show that this metric on M is complete. By the Hopf–Rinow theorem (Theorem 21.1), it suffices to show that geodesics of M starting at p_0 can be indefinitely extended. Then let $\sigma(t)$, $0 \leq t \leq \varepsilon$, be a small geodesic segment of M starting at p_0. Let a be the least upper bound of the numbers t_0 such that the geodesic σ can be extended over $0 \leq t \leq t_0$. Thus σ can be extended over $0 \leq t < a$, but no farther. However, $\phi(\sigma(t))$ is a geodesic of N, for $0 \leq t \leq a$. If $a < \infty$, this geodesic can be extended over $0 \leq t \leq a + \varepsilon$, by completeness of N. By (21.1), it can be lifted to a curve of M starting at p_0, which clearly must be a geodesic of M. Since ϕ has nonzero Jacobian, this lifting must agree with σ for $0 \leq t < a$; hence, also, $0 \leq t \leq a + \varepsilon$. This is a contradiction; hence $a = \infty$ and σ can be indefinitely extended.

COROLLARY

Let M be a complete Riemannian manifold, p_0 a point of M. Suppose that the map exp: $M_{p_0} \to M$ has an everywhere nonzero Jacobian. (In terms of a later definition, this condition means that p_0 has no conjugate points.) Then this map is a covering map. In particular, if M is simply connected, the map exp is a diffeomorphism.

Proof. Lemma 21.3 applies, since the pullback of the metric on M via exp; has the straight lines $t \to tv$ as the geodesic through the origin; hence it is complete by the Hopf–Rinow theorem. That ϕ is a diffeomorphism if M is simply connected is a standard fact about covering maps. (The proofs are left to the reader as an exercise.)

22 The Second Variation
Formula and Jacobi Vector Fields

Suppose that $\delta(s, t)$, $0 \leq s, t \leq 1$, is a homotopy in the Riemannian manifold M. For fixed s, let σ_s be the curve $t \to \delta(s, t)$, assumed to be parametrized proportionally to arc length. Let $\sigma = \sigma_0$, and let $v(t) = \partial_s \delta(s, t)$ be the vector field on σ defining the corresponding infinitesimal deformation. Suppose that σ is a geodesic. If $L(\sigma_s)$ is the length of the curve σ_s, we have, from the first variation formula (20.6),

$$L(\sigma_s) \frac{d}{ds} L(\sigma_s) = \langle \partial_s \delta(s, 1), \partial_t \delta(s, 1) \rangle - \langle \partial_s \delta(s, 0), \partial_t \delta(s, 0) \rangle$$

$$- \int_0^1 \langle \partial_s \delta(s, t), \nabla_t \partial_t \delta(s, t) \rangle \, dt.$$

Now, using (19.14), we have

$$\nabla_s \nabla_t \partial_t \delta(s, t) = \nabla_t \nabla_s \partial_t \delta(s, t) + R_{\delta(s, t)}(\partial_s \delta(s, t), \partial_t \delta(s, t))(\partial_t \delta(s, t))$$
$$= \nabla_t \nabla_t \partial_s \delta(s, t) + R_{\delta(s, t)}(\partial_s \delta, \partial_t \delta)(\partial_t \delta)(\delta(s, t)). \qquad (22.1)$$

Thus,

$$L(\sigma) \frac{d^2}{ds^2} L(\sigma_s) \bigg|_{s=0} = \frac{\partial}{\partial s} \left(\langle \partial_s \delta(s, 1), \partial_t \delta(s, 1) \rangle - \langle \partial_s \delta(s, 0), \partial_t \delta(s, 0) \rangle \right) \bigg|_{s=0}$$

$$- \int_0^1 \langle v(t), \nabla \nabla v(t) + R_{\sigma(t)}(v(t), \sigma'(t))(\sigma'(t)) \rangle \bigg) dt. \qquad (22.2)$$

This is the *second variation formula of arc length*. We shall be mainly interested in the case where the homotopy δ has fixed end points; that is, $\delta(s, 0) = \sigma(0)$, $\delta(s, 1) = \sigma(1)$. In this case the first two terms on the right-hand side of (22.2) vanish. Since, in addition, $v(0) = 0 = v(1)$, the first term in the integrand can be integrated by parts, to give in this case,

$$L(\sigma) \frac{d^2}{ds^2} L(\sigma_s) \bigg|_{s=0} = \int_0^1 \langle \nabla v(t), \nabla v(t) \rangle - \langle v(t), R_{\sigma(t)}(v(t), \sigma'(t))(\sigma'(t)) \rangle \, dt.$$

$$(22.3)$$

This is the most useful form of the second variation formula. For example, if $L(\sigma) =$ distance from $\sigma(0)$ to $\sigma(1)$ (in this case we say that σ is a minimizing geodesic), the left-hand side of (22.3) must be ≥ 0. It is clear, qualitatively at least, that this will involve nontrivial conditions on the quantities (in particular, the curvature tensor R) on the right-hand side. Our goal is to work out these conditions in detail.

Note for future reference that the second variation formula applies also to homotopies $\delta(s, t)$ such that $t \to \delta(s, t)$ is, for each s, merely a path, but where, for each t, $s \to \delta(s, t)$ is a C^∞ curve. Conversely, given a vector field $v(t)$, $0 \leq t \leq 1$, along a geodesic $\sigma(t)$ whose length $\|v(t)\|$ is sufficiently small (if M is complete, this condition is unnecessary) and whose components in local coordinate systems are continuous, piecewise C^∞ functions of t, we can define such a deformation $\delta(s, t)$ with $\partial_s \delta(0, t) = v(t)$ by the formula

$$\delta(s, t) = \exp(sv(t)); \qquad (22.4)$$

that is, for each t, $s \to \delta(s, t)$ is the geodesic starting at $\sigma(t)$ and tangent there to $v(t)$. If $L(s)$ is the length of the path $t \to \exp \delta(s, t)$, $0 \leq t \leq 1$, it should be clear that the first and second variation formulas hold. For example, if $v(0) = 0 = v(1)$, then $\delta(s, 0) = \sigma(0)$, $\delta(s, 1) = \sigma(1)$,

$$\frac{d}{ds} L(0) = 0,$$

$$L(0) \frac{d^2}{ds^2} L(0) = \int_0^1 \langle \nabla v(t), \nabla v(t) \rangle - \langle v(t), R_{\sigma(t)}(v(t), \sigma'(t))(\sigma'(t)) \rangle \, dt.$$

In particular, if the integral is <0 or >0, each of the paths $t \to \delta(s, t)$ is respectively, for sufficiently small s, shorter or longer than σ.

THEOREM 22.1

If $\sigma(t)$, $0 \leq t \leq 1$, is a geodesic of a Riemannian manifold M, if $v: t \to v(t) \in M_{\sigma(t)}$ is a vector field along σ that is the infinitesimal deformation corresponding to a deformation $s \to \sigma_s$ of σ, with each σ_s a geodesic of M (called a geodesic deformation of σ), then $v(t)$ satisfies the following Jacobi differential equation

$$\nabla\nabla v(t) + R_{\sigma(t)}(v(t), \sigma'(t))(\sigma'(t)) = 0. \qquad (22.5)$$

Any vector field satisfying these (linear, second order, homogeneous ordinary) differential equations is called a *Jacobi field* along σ. If, further, σ_s is a geodesic deformation with fixed end points, then length (σ_s) is constant in s.

Proof. Equation (22.5) follows from (22.1), on remarking that the explicit condition that $\sigma_s(t) = \delta(s, t)$ define a geodesic deformation is: $\nabla_t \, \partial_t \, \delta(s, t) = 0$.

Definition

Let $\sigma(t)$, $0 \leq t \leq 1$, be a geodesic of M. The point $\sigma(1)$ is said to be *conjugate* to $\sigma(0)$ with respect to σ if there is a nonzero Jacobi vector field v along σ such that $\sigma(0) = 0 = \sigma(1)$.

THEOREM 22.2

Let M be a complete Riemannian manifold and let p be a point of M. Let exp: $M_p \to M$ be the usual exponential map that assigns to each $v \in M_p$ the end point of the geodesic starting to p and tangent to v. Let $\sigma(t)$, $0 \leq t \leq 1$, be a geodesic of M with $\sigma(0) = p$. Then $\sigma(1)$ is conjugate to $\sigma(0)$ with respect to σ if and only if the map exp has a zero Jacobian at the point $\sigma'(0) \in M_p$.

Proof. Suppose first that exp has a nonzero Jacobian at $\sigma'(0)$. Let $\gamma(s)$, $0 \leq s \leq 1$, be a curve in M_p such that (a) $\gamma(0) = \sigma'(0)$; (b) $\exp_*(\gamma'(0)) = 0$, but $\gamma'(0) \neq 0$.

Let δ be the homotopy

$$\delta(s, t) = \exp(t\gamma(s)), \qquad 0 \leq s, t \leq 1.$$

If $v(t) = \partial_s \delta(s, t)$, then $v(0) = 0$, since δ has the $t = 0$ end point fixed. But $\partial_s \delta(0, 1) =$ tangent vector to curve $s \to \exp(\gamma(s))$ at $s = 0 = \exp_*(\gamma'(0)) = 0$. Now

$$\nabla_t \, \partial_s \, \delta(0, 0) = \nabla_s \, \partial_t \, \delta(0, 0).$$

Since $\partial_t \delta(s, 0) = \gamma(s)$,

$$\nabla v(0) = \nabla_s \, \partial_t \, \delta(0, 0) = \left. \frac{d\gamma(s)}{ds} \right|_{s=0} \neq 0;$$

hence $v(t)$ cannot be identically zero.

The converse will follow from the following more general result.

LEMMA 22.3

Let $v(t)$ be any Jacobi vector field on σ, let $\gamma(s)$, $0 \leq s \leq 1$, be any curve in M with $\gamma(0) = p$, $\gamma'(0) = v(0)$. Let $u(s)$ be any vector field along γ such that $\nabla u(0) = \nabla v(0)$,† $u(0) = \sigma'(0)$. Let $\delta(s, t) = \exp(tu(s))$. Then δ is a geodesic deformation of σ whose infinitesimal deformation vector field is precisely v.

Proof. $D_s \delta(0, 0) = v(0)$, since $\gamma(s) = \exp(0 \cdot u(s))$.

$$\nabla_t \, \partial_s \, \delta(0, 0) = \nabla_s \, \partial_t \, \delta(0, 0).$$

† Of course ∇u is the covariant derivative of $t \to u(s)$ along $s \to \gamma(s)$, while ∇v is the covariant derivative of $t \to v(t)$ along $t \to \sigma(t)$.

Now $\partial_t \delta(s, 0) = u(s)$; hence $\nabla_t \partial_s \delta(0, 0) = \nabla u(0) = \nabla v(0)$. Thus $t \to \partial_s \delta(0, t)$ $= v_1(t)$ and $t \to v(t)$ are two Jacobi vector fields along σ such that $v_1(0) = v(0)$, $\nabla v_1(0) = \nabla v(0)$. By the uniqueness of solution of the Jacobi differential equations (22.3), $v(t) = v_1(t) = \partial_s \delta(0, t)$ for all t, which proves the lemma.

Return to the theorem. Suppose that $t \to v(t)$ is a Jacobi vector field along σ such that $v(0) = 0 = v(1)$. Apply the lemma with $\gamma(s) = \sigma(0)$ and $u(s) = s\nabla v(0) + \sigma'(0)$ for $0 \le s \le 1$. Then $0 = v(1) = \partial_s \delta(0, 1)$, where

$$\delta(s, t) = \exp(t(\sigma'(0) + s \nabla v(0))).$$

Thus the image under $\exp_*$ of the tangent vector to the curve $s \to \sigma'(0)$ $+ s \nabla v(0)$ at $s = 0$ is zero; that is, $\exp_*$ is not 1-1 on the tangent space to M_p at $\sigma'(0)$.   Q.E.D.

We now turn to the main theorem, due to Jacobi, concerning the significance of conjugate points in the calculus of variations.

THEOREM 22.4

Let M be a Riemannian manifold and let $\sigma(t)$, $0 \le t \le 1$, be a geodesic of M. Suppose that for some $t_0 \in (0, 1)$, $\sigma(t_0)$ is a conjugate point of $\sigma(0)$ along σ for $0 \le t \le t_0$. Then σ is not a minimizing geodesic between $\sigma(0)$ and $\sigma(1)$, since there exists a continuous, piecewise C^∞ vector field v^* vanishing at the end points of σ with $H(v^*) < 0$. Also, of course, one deduces that if $H(v^*) \ge 0$ for all piecewise C^∞ vector fields vanishing at the end points of σ, then $\sigma(t)$ cannot be a conjugate point of $\sigma(0)$ for $0 \le t < 1$.

LEMMA 22.5

Let M be a Riemannian manifold, let $\sigma: [0, 1] \to M$ be a geodesic such that $\sigma(1)$ is not a conjugate point of $\sigma(0)$ with respect to σ. Then, given an element $v_1 \in M_{\sigma(1)}$, there is a unique Jacobi vector field $v(t)$, $0 \le t \le 1$, along σ such that $v(0) = 0$, $v(1) = v_1$.

Proof. We see from the Jacobi differential equations that a Jacobi vector field v is determined uniquely by its values $v(0)$ and $\nabla v(0)$. Thus, if $v(0) = 0$, a v exists, given an arbitrary $\nabla v(0)$; that is, the space of all such Jacobi fields is a vector space of the same dimension as M. The map $v \to v(1)$ must then be an isomorphism of vector spaces, since it has kernel zero.

LEMMA 22.6

Let M be a Riemannian manifold; $\sigma: [0, 1] \to M$ a geodesic. Let v^s be a continuous one-parameter family of Jacobi fields along σ such that

$$\lim_{s \to 0} v^s(t) = 0 \qquad \text{for } 0 \le t \le 1.$$

Then

$$\lim_{s \to 0} \nabla v^s(t) = 0 \qquad \text{for } 0 \le t \le 1.$$

Proof. As we remarked above, the linear space of all Jacobi vector fields has $2 \times \dim M$ as its dimension. Suppose v_i, $1 \le i \le 2n$, forms a basis for this vector space. Thus

$$v^s = a_i(s)v_i.$$

We must show that $\lim_{s \to 0} v^s(t)$ for all t implies that $\lim_{s \to 0} a_i(s) = 0$. This will finish the proof, since then $\nabla v^s = a_i(s) \nabla v_i$.

We can suppose the v_i chosen so that $v_i(0) = 0$ for $1 \le i \le n$, but $(v_i(0))$ for $n + 1 \le 1 \le 2n$ forms a basis of $M_{\sigma(0)}$. Then

$$\lim_{s \to 0} v^s(0) = \lim_{s \to 0} \left(\sum_{j \ge n+1} a_i(s)v_i(0) \right) = 0,$$

forcing $\lim_{s \to 0} a_i(s) = 0$ for $\sigma = n + 1 \le i \le 2n$. Now, an interval of σ, say, $0 \le t \le \varepsilon$, is free of conjugate points. Then

$$\lim_{s \to 0} v^s(\varepsilon) = \lim_{s \to 0} \left(\sum_{j \ge n+1} a_i(s)v_i(\varepsilon) + \sum_{j \le n} a_i(s)v_i(\varepsilon) \right) = 0.$$

Since $\sigma(\varepsilon)$ is not a conjugate point, the $(v_i(\varepsilon))$ are linearly independent elements of $M_{\sigma(\varepsilon)}$. This forces

$$\lim_{s \to 0} \left(\sum_{j \le n} a_i(s)v_i(\varepsilon) \right) = 0;$$

hence $\lim_{s \to 0} a_i(s) = 0$ for all i.

If $\sigma(t)$ is a geodesic in M and v is a continuous, piecewise C^∞ vector field on σ, define

$$H(v) = \int_0^1 [\langle \nabla v(t), \nabla v(t) \rangle - \langle R_{\sigma(t)}(v(t), \sigma'(t))(\sigma'(t), v(t)) \rangle] \, dt; \quad (22.6)$$

that is, $H(v)$ is an abbreviation for the second variation formula in the fixed end-point case. Thus, if $H(v) < 0$ for some such vector field vanishing at $t = 0$ and $t = 1$, σ is not a minimizing geodesic joining $\sigma(0)$ to $\sigma(1)$. Further, if v is a Jacobi vector field, we see, after integrating by parts the first term of the integrand of (22.6), that

$$H(v) = \langle \nabla v(1), v(1) \rangle - \langle \nabla v(0), v(0) \rangle. \quad (22.7)$$

Return to the proof of the Jacobi theorem. Let $v(t)$, $0 \le t \le 1$, be a nonzero Jacobi vector field on the geodesic $\sigma(t)$, $0 \le t \le 1$, such that $v(0) = 0 = v(t_0)$ for some $t_0 \in (0, 1)$. To prove t is not minimizing, there is no loss in generality in supposing that for $0 < s < t_0$ and $t_0 - s$ sufficiently small, no conjugate points of $\sigma(s)$ are along $\sigma(t)$, $s \leq t \leq 1$. For each such s, let $u^s(t)$ be a Jacobi field such that

$$u^s(1) = 0, \qquad u^s(s) = v(s).$$

Since $\lim_{s \to t_0} v(s) = 0$, we see, by an argument similar to that used in Lemma 22.6, that $\lim_{s \to t_0} u^s(t) = 0$ for $0 \leq t \leq 1$; thus, by Lemma 22.6 itself,

$$\lim_{s \to t_0} (\nabla u^s)(t) = 0 \qquad \text{for } 0 \leq t \leq 1. \tag{22.8}$$

Let $v^s(t)$ be the continuous, piecewise C^∞ vector field on σ such that

$$v^s(t) = v(t) \quad \text{for } 0 \leq t \leq s, \qquad v^s(t) = u^s(t) \quad \text{for } s \leq t \leq 1.$$

Using (22.7) and the fact that $u^s(1) = 0$, we have

$$H(v^s) = \langle \nabla v(s), v(s) \rangle - \langle \nabla u^s(s), u^s(s) \rangle$$
$$= \langle \nabla v(s) - \nabla u^s(s), v(s) \rangle.$$

Now $H(v^s) \to 0$ as $s \to t_0$. We then try to find the first derivative of $s \to H(v^s)$ at $s = t_0$:

$$\frac{H(v^s)}{s - t_0} = \left\langle \nabla v(s) - \nabla u^s(s), \frac{v(s)}{s - t_0} \right\rangle.$$

But $\lim_{s \to t_0} v(s)/(s - t_0) = \nabla v(t_0)$, and $\lim_{s \to t_0} \nabla u^s(s) = 0$, by (22.8). Thus

$$\lim_{s \to t_0} \frac{H(v^s)}{s - t_0} = \langle \nabla v(t_0), \nabla v(t_0) \rangle > 0.$$

Hence $H(v^s) < 0$ for $s < t_0$ and $(t_0 - s)$ sufficiently small, which proves that there is a shorter path than σ joining $\sigma(0)$ to $\sigma(1)$.   Q.E.D.

Having shown that geodesics are not minimizing beyond the first conjugate point, we may ask: What if it has no conjugate points? (The case where the end point $\sigma(1)$ is the first conjugate point is the borderline case that can go either way.) It is unreasonable to expect that the absence of conjugate points, without any further assumptions, would imply that the geodesic was minimizing, since a geodesic's being minimizing is a global property, whereas the absence of conjugate points is a local condition. Thus the reasonable expectation is that the absence of conjugate points will imply that the length of the geodesic will be less than that of "nearby" paths joining the same end points. One way of making this precise is by requiring that $H(v) > 0$ for all nonzero, continuous, piecewise differentiable vector fields on the geodesic vanishing at the end points. We shall now show that this (and more) is true.

THEOREM 22.7

Let $\sigma(t), 0 \leq t \leq 1$, be a geodesic of a Riemannian manifold M. Suppose that $\sigma(t)$ is not a conjugate point of $\sigma(0)$ with respect to σ for $0 \leq t \leq 1$. (We shall say in this case that σ contains no conjugate points.)

Let v be a Jacobi vector field on σ such that $v(0) = 0$. If u is any other continuous, piecewise differentiable vector field along σ with $u(0) = 0$, $u(1) = v(1)$, then $H(u) \geq H(v)$. Equality holds only if $u = v$.

Proof. Suppose dim $M = n$. Let v_i, $1 \leq i, j, \ldots \leq n$, be Jacobi vector fields on σ such that $v_i(0) = 0$ and so that the vectors $\nabla v_i(0)$ form a basis of $M_{\sigma(0)}$. By Lemma 22.5, $v_i(t)$ forms a basis for $M_{\sigma(t)}$ for $0 < t \leq 1$. Suppose that $u(t) = a_i(t)v_i(t)$ for $0 < t \leq 1$:

$$H(u) = \lim_{\varepsilon \to 0} \int_{\varepsilon}^{1} [\langle \nabla u(t), \nabla u(t) \rangle - \langle u(t), R_{\sigma(t)}(u(t), \sigma'(t))(\sigma'(t)) \rangle] \, dt$$

$$= \lim_{\varepsilon \to 0} H_\varepsilon(u),$$

where $H_\varepsilon(u)$ is the integral.

We now evaluate $H_\varepsilon(u)$:

$$\nabla u = \frac{da_i}{dt} v_i + a_i \nabla v_i.$$

Substituting,

$$H_\varepsilon(u) = \int_{\varepsilon}^{1} \left[\left\langle \frac{da_i}{dt} v_i, \frac{da_j}{dt} v_j \right\rangle + 2a_i \frac{da_j}{dt} \langle \nabla v_i, v_j \rangle \right.$$

$$\left. + a_i a_j \langle \nabla v_i, \nabla v_j \rangle - \langle v_i, R(v_j, \sigma')(\sigma') \rangle \right] dt.$$

We now prove that

$$\frac{d}{dt} (\langle \nabla v_i(t), v_j(t) \rangle - \langle \nabla v_j(t), v_i(t) \rangle) = 0. \tag{22.9}$$

(This holds for any pair of Jacobi vector fields, independently of the initial conditions.)

The left-hand side of (22.9) is

$$\langle \nabla \nabla v_i, v_j \rangle + \langle \nabla v_i, \nabla v_j \rangle - \langle \nabla \nabla v_j, v_i \rangle - \langle \nabla v_j, \nabla v_i \rangle = - \langle R(v_i, \sigma')(\sigma'), v_j \rangle$$

$$+ \langle R(v_j, \sigma')(\sigma'), v_i \rangle$$

$$= 0,$$

using the identities for the curvature tensor to be provided in Chapter 23.

In our case, where $v_i(0) = v_j(0)$, note that (22.9) implies that

$$\langle \nabla v_i, v_j \rangle = \langle \nabla v_j, v_i \rangle. \tag{22.10}$$

Returning to $H_\varepsilon(u)$, using (22.10), integrating by parts the third term, and applying Jacobi equations, we have

$$H_\varepsilon(u) = \int_\varepsilon^1 \left\langle \frac{da_i(t)}{dt} v_i(t), \frac{da_j(t)}{dt} v_j(t) \right\rangle dt + a_i(t)a_j(t)\langle \nabla v_i(t), v_j(t) \rangle \Big|_{t=\varepsilon}^{t=1}.$$

Now $v(1) = u(1)$ implies that

$$v(t) = a_i(1)v_i(t).$$

Thus,

$$H(v) = a_i(1)a_j(1)\langle \nabla v_i(1), v_j(1) \rangle;$$

hence,

$$H_\varepsilon(u) = H(v) + \int_\varepsilon^1 \left\langle \frac{da_i}{dt} v_i, \frac{da_j}{dt} v_j \right\rangle dt - \langle a_i(\varepsilon) \nabla v_i(\varepsilon), u(\varepsilon) \rangle.$$

Now

$$a_i \nabla v_i = \nabla u - \frac{da_i}{dt} v_i.$$

Define a vector field $t \to w(t)$ along σ for $0 < t \leq 1$ by

$$w(t) = \frac{da_i(t)}{dt} v_i.$$

Then u is a Jacobi field if and only if $w(t) = 0$ for $0 \leq t \leq 1$. Substituting in $H_\varepsilon(u)$, we have

$$H_\varepsilon(u) = H(v) + \int_\varepsilon^1 \langle w(t), w(t) \rangle \, dt - \langle \nabla u(\varepsilon), u(\varepsilon) \rangle + \langle w(\varepsilon), u(\varepsilon) \rangle.$$

We suppose that $w(t)$ is not identically zero. To finish the proof of the theorem, we must show that $H(u) - H(v) > 0$. Suppose otherwise: Since $u(\varepsilon) \to 0$ as $\varepsilon \to 0$, we must clearly have

$$\lim_{\varepsilon \to 0} \langle w(\varepsilon), w(\varepsilon) \rangle = \infty;$$

hence, also

$$\lim_{\varepsilon \to 0} \langle w(\varepsilon), u(\varepsilon) \rangle = -\infty.$$

Now we can choose numbers ε arbitrarily close to zero for which

$$\langle w(\varepsilon), w(\varepsilon) \rangle = \max_{\varepsilon \leq t \leq 1} \langle w(t), w(t) \rangle.$$

If ε is so chosen, with $\varepsilon < \frac{1}{2}$,

$$\int_{\varepsilon}^{1} \langle w(t), w(t) \rangle \, dt \geq \langle w(\varepsilon), w(\varepsilon) \rangle (1 - \varepsilon) \geq \frac{1}{2} \langle w(\varepsilon), w(\varepsilon) \rangle$$

$$= \frac{1}{2} \frac{\|w(\varepsilon)\|}{\|u(\varepsilon)\|} \|w(\varepsilon)\| \|u(\varepsilon)\|$$

$$\geq \text{(using the Schwarz inequality)}, \frac{1}{2} \frac{\|w(\varepsilon)\|}{\|u(\varepsilon)\|} |\langle w(\varepsilon), u(\varepsilon) \rangle|$$

$$= \frac{1}{2} \frac{\langle w(\varepsilon), w(\varepsilon) \rangle^{1/2}}{\langle u(\varepsilon), u(\varepsilon) \rangle^{1/2}} |\langle w(\varepsilon), u(\varepsilon) \rangle|.$$

Hence, as $\varepsilon \to 0$ through these specially chosen values, $\int_{\varepsilon}^{1} \langle w(t), w(t) \rangle \, dt$ grows much faster than $|\langle w(\varepsilon), u(\varepsilon) \rangle|$; hence the inequality

$$\lim_{\varepsilon \to 0} H_{\varepsilon}(u) - H(v) \leq 0$$

is impossible.   Q.E.D.

The proof of Theorem 22.7 is due to Ambrose [1], and has the great advantage of being direct and explicit. The theorem was actually originally proved (Morse [1]) by exploiting the basic "extremal field" idea of the calculus of variations. For example, when one tries to find vector fields along σ with end points at $t = 0$ and $t = 1$ fixed, which minimize H (which, from (22.6), is merely an ordinary, nonhomogeneous variational problem), it is seen that a vector field v that does minimize H must satisfy the Jacobi equations; that is, the Jacobi equations are the Euler equations of the second variation formula!

We now turn to the simplest important geometric application of these "second variation" ideas, the theorem of S. Myers.

THEOREM 22.8

Let M be a complete Riemannian manifold of dimension n. Suppose α is a positive number such that the Ricci curvature of all tangent vectors of M (see below for the definition) is $\geq \alpha > 0$. Then M is compact. Further, every geodesic of M of length $\geq \sqrt{n/\alpha} \, \pi$ must contain at least one conjugate point, and M has diameter $\leq \sqrt{n/\alpha} \, \pi$.

Proof. Let $\sigma(t)$, $0 \leq t \leq 1$, be a geodesic of M that is free of conjugate points. Let $n = \dim M$, and let v_i, $1 \leq i, j, \ldots \leq n$, be self-parallel vector fields (that is, $\nabla v_i = 0$) along σ whose values at each $\sigma(t)$ form a basis of $M_{\sigma(t)}$, and with $\langle v_i(t), v_j(t) \rangle = \delta_{ij}$.

If $v(t) = a_i(t)v_i(t)$, with $a_i(0) = a_i(1)$, we must have, by Theorem 22.7, $H(v) \geq 0$. But

$$H(v) = \int_0^1 [\langle \nabla v, \nabla v \rangle - \langle v, R(v, \sigma')(\sigma') \rangle] \, dt$$

$= $ (after integrating by parts the first term and using $v(0) = v(1) = 0$),

$$- \int_0^1 [\langle \nabla\nabla v, v \rangle + \langle v, R(v, \sigma')(\sigma') \rangle] \, dt.$$

Suppose we try to find such a v satisfying

$$\nabla\nabla v = -\lambda^2 v \qquad \text{for some constant } \lambda > 0.$$

Working out the conditions v would have to solve, we see that the simplest vector fields of this type would be

$$u_i(t) = \sin(\pi t)v_i(t).$$

Then

$$H(u_i) = \pi^2 \int_0^1 \sin^2(\pi t) \, dt - \int_0^1 \sin^2(\pi t) \langle v_i(t), R_{\sigma(t)}(v_i(t), \sigma'(t))(\sigma'(t)) \rangle \, dt$$

$$\geq 0.$$

Definition

Let p be a point of a Riemannian manifold M. Let v be a unit tangent vector of p. The *Ricci curvature* of v, denoted by $R(v)$, is the trace of the linear transformation $u \to R_p(u, v)(v)$ of M_p. If v is any nonzero tangent vector, define

$$R(v) = R\left(\frac{v}{\|v\|}\right).$$

Thus we have

$$R(\sigma'(t)) = R\left(\frac{\sigma'}{|\sigma'(t)|}\right)$$

$$= \sum_{i=1}^{n} \frac{\langle v_i(t), R_{\sigma(t)}(v_i(t), \sigma'(t))(\sigma'(t)) \rangle}{\|\sigma'(t)\|^2},$$

since these are the diagonal elements in the matrix of the linear transform

$$v \to R_{\sigma(t)}\left(v, \frac{\sigma'(t)}{\|\sigma'(t)\|}\right)\left(\frac{\sigma'(t)}{\|\sigma'(t)\|}\right)$$

with respect to the basis $(v_i(t))$ of $M_{\sigma(t)}$. Finally, then,

$$0 < \sum_{i=1}^{n} H(u_i) = n\pi^2 \int_0^1 \sin^2(\pi t)\, dt - \int_0^t \sin^2(\pi t) R(\sigma'(t))\, dt \cdot (\text{length } \sigma)^2$$

$$\le \int_0^1 \sin^2(\pi t)\, dt \left(n\pi^2 - \min_{0 \le t \le 1} R(\sigma'(t)) \cdot (\text{length } \sigma)^2 \right).$$

Thus,

if $\min_{0 \le t \le 1} R(\sigma'(t)) \ge \alpha > 0$, and if $\sigma(t)$, $0 \le t \le 1$,
contains no conjugate points, then length $\sigma < \sqrt{(n/\alpha)}\pi$.   (22.11)

To finish the proof of the theorem, suppose that p, q are arbitrary points of M. Since the metric is complete, there is a geodesic $\sigma(t)$, $0 \le t \le 1$, joining p to q, with $d(p, q) = \sigma$. By the Jacobi theorem (Theorem 22.6), $\sigma(t)$ is not a conjugate point of $\sigma(0)$ for $0 \le t < 1$ (else σ could not be minimizing for $0 \le t \le 1$), whence length $\sigma \le \sqrt{n/\alpha}\,\pi$, by (22.10). Thus $d(p, q) \le \sqrt{n/\alpha}\,\pi$ and the diameter of M is

$$\sup_{p,\, q \in M} d(p, q) \le \sqrt{\frac{n}{\alpha}}\,\pi.$$

By the Hopf–Rinow theorem, M is also compact.

23 Sectional Curvature and the Elementary Comparison Theorems

Definition

Let M be a Riemannian manifold, with $R(\ ,\ )(\ )$ its curvature tensor. If $p \in M$ and $u, v \in M$ are orthogonal tangent vectors of unit length, and if Γ is the two-dimensional subspace of M_p spanned by u and v (a *tangent plane*), then

$$K(\Gamma) = \langle u, R_p(u, v)(v) \rangle$$

is called the *sectional curvature* of the plane Γ.

We shall now collect the algebraic formulas concerning the curvature tensor and sectional curvature that will be needed. As the definition, recall that for $X, Y, Z \in V(M)$,

$$R(X, Y)(Z) = \nabla_X \nabla_Y Z - \nabla_Y \nabla_X Z - \nabla_{[X, Y]} Z. \qquad (23.1)$$

This is called the *Ricci identity*, and expresses the noncommutativity of iterated covariant derivatives.

Suppose we assume that X, Y, and Z commute; that is, $[X, Y] = 0 = [Y, Z] = [X, Z]$. We get an identity for the curvature tensor when we apply ∇_Y to the torsion-free identity, namely,

$$
\begin{aligned}
\nabla_Y(\nabla_X Z) &= \nabla_Y \nabla_Z X = \nabla_Z \nabla_Y X + R(Y, Z)(X) = \nabla_Z \nabla_X Y + R(Y, Z)(X) \\
&= \nabla_X \nabla_Z Y + R(Z, X)(Y) + R(Y, Z)(X) \\
&= \nabla_X \nabla_Y Z + R(Z, X)(Y) + R(Y, Z)(X) \\
&= \nabla_Y \nabla_X Z + R(X, Y)(Z) + R(Z, X)(Y) + R(Y, Z)(X);
\end{aligned}
$$

hence,

$$R(X, Y)(Z) + R(Z, X)(Y) + R(Y, Z)(X) = 0. \qquad (23.2)$$

This is called the *permutation identity* for the curvature tensor. Because of the tensorial character of R, it holds for arbitrary $X, Y, Z \in V(M)$. We remember it in the following way: Consider the function $(X, Y, Z) \to$ (the sum of the six permutations of $R(X, Y)(Z)$, each permutation multiplied by its signature). Equation (23.2) expresses the fact that this function is identically zero. (Since $R(X, Y) = -R(Y, X)$, the six terms collapse to three.)

Now suppose that $X, Y, Z, W \in V(M)$ commute:

$$\langle R(X, Y)(Z), W \rangle$$
$$= \langle \nabla_X \nabla_Y Z - \nabla_Y \nabla_X Z, W \rangle$$
$$= X(\langle \nabla_Y Z, W \rangle) - \langle \nabla_Y Z, \nabla_X W \rangle - Y(\langle \nabla_X Z, W \rangle) + \langle \nabla_X Z, \nabla_Y W \rangle$$
$$= XY(\langle Z, W \rangle) - X(\langle Z, \nabla_Y W \rangle) - Y(\langle Z, \nabla_X W \rangle) + \langle Z, \nabla_Y \nabla_X W \rangle$$
$$\quad - YX(\langle Z, W \rangle) + Y(\langle Z, \nabla_X W \rangle) + X(\langle Z, \nabla_Y W \rangle) - \langle Z, \nabla_X \nabla_Y W \rangle$$
$$= \langle Z, \nabla_Y \nabla_X W - \nabla_X \nabla_Y W \rangle.$$

Hence,

$$\langle R(X, Y)(Z), W \rangle = -\langle Z, R(X, Y)(W) \rangle. \tag{23.3}$$

Again, because of the tensorial nature of R, this identity holds for arbitrary X, Y, Z, W; hence, also for the value of R on tangent vectors. It expresses the *skew-symmetry* of the linear transformation $R(X, Y)$ with respect to the form $\langle \ , \ \rangle$.

Finally an identity can be proved by combining (23.2) and (23.3) in a rather complicated way, following the proof given by Helgason [1, p. 69]. First write (23.2) in the form

$$\langle R(X, Y)(Z), W \rangle + \langle R(Z, X)(Y), W \rangle + \langle R(Y, Z)(X), W \rangle = 0.$$

Permute W with X, Y, and Z in turn to obtain these more similar identities:

$$\langle R(W, Y)(Z), X \rangle + \langle R(Z, W)(Y), X \rangle + \langle R(Y, Z)(W), X \rangle = 0$$
$$\langle R(X, W)(Z), Y \rangle + \langle R(Z, X)(W), Y \rangle + \langle R(W, Z)(X), Y \rangle = 0$$
$$\langle R(X, Y)(W), Z \rangle + \langle R(W, X)(Y), Z \rangle + \langle R(Y, W)(X), Z \rangle = 0.$$

Now add these four identities, noting that many terms cancel by (23.3), and identity $R(X, Y) = -R(Y, X)$, giving

$$2\langle R(X, W)(Z), Y \rangle + 2\langle R(W, Y)(Z), X \rangle + 2\langle R(Z, W)(Y), X \rangle = 0$$

or, using (23.3),

$$\langle R(X, W)(Z) + R(W, Z)(X), Y \rangle + \langle R(W, Y)(Z), X \rangle = 0$$
$$= (using\ (23.2)\ again),$$
$$= -\langle R(Z, X)(W), Y \rangle + \langle R(W, Y)(Z), X \rangle.$$

This leads to our third basic identity for the curvature tensor, which we write in the more easily remembered form

$$\langle R(X, Y)(Z), W \rangle = \langle R(Z, W)(X), Y \rangle. \tag{23.4}$$

Now we can show that $K(\Gamma)$ really does not depend on the choice of orthonormal vectors generating Γ. Suppose that

$$u' = \cos\theta u + \sin\theta v, \qquad v' = -\sin\theta u + \cos\theta v.$$

$$R(u', v') = (\cos^2\theta + \sin^2\theta)R(u, v) = R(u, v)$$

by skew-symmetry of $(u, v) \to R(u, v)$.

$$\begin{aligned}
\langle u', R(u', v')(v') \rangle &= \langle u', R(u, v)(v') \rangle \\
&= \langle \cos\theta u + \sin\theta v, R(u, v)(-\sin\theta u + \cos\theta v) \rangle \\
&= (\cos^2\theta + \sin^2\theta)\langle u, R(u, v)(v) \rangle = K(\Gamma),
\end{aligned}$$

by (23.3).

We can easily derive the formulas for $K(\Gamma)$ in case vectors u, v span Γ, but are not orthonormal. Put

$$u' = \frac{u}{\|u\|}, \qquad v' = \frac{v - \dfrac{\langle v, u\rangle u}{\|u\|^2}}{\left\|v - \dfrac{\langle v, u\rangle u}{\|u\|^2}\right\|}.$$

(u', v') are orthonormal generators of Γ (the Gram–Schmidt orthonormalization process).

$$R(u', v') = \frac{R(u, v)}{\|u\| \left\|v - \dfrac{\langle v, u\rangle u}{\|u\|^2}\right\|}$$

and by (23.3),

$$\langle u', R(u, v)(v') \rangle = \frac{\langle u, R(u, v)(v) \rangle}{\|u\| \left\|v - \dfrac{\langle v, u\rangle u}{\|u\|^2}\right\|}.$$

Now

$$\begin{aligned}
\left\|v - \frac{\langle v, u\rangle u}{\|u\|^2}\right\|^2 \|u\|^2 &= \left(\|v\|^2 - \frac{\langle u, v\rangle^2}{\|u\|^2}\right)\|u\|^2 \\
&= \|u\|^2\|v\|^2 - \|u\|^2\|v\|^2\cos^2\theta \\
&= \|u\|^2\|v\|^2\sin^2\theta,
\end{aligned}$$

where θ is the angle between u and v. Thus

$$K(\Gamma) = \frac{\langle u, R(u, v)(v) \rangle}{\|u\|^2\|v\|^2\sin^2\theta}. \tag{23.5}$$

Geometrically, of course, the denominator is just the square of the area of the parallelogram determined by u and v.

It will be recognized at once from the preceding definition that essentially it is the sectional curvature of the plane Γ, that is, $K(\Gamma) = \langle u, R_p(u, v)(v) \rangle$, that appears in the second term of the second variation formula (22.3). As a first observation, the sign of the curvature plays a crucial role. For example, if the sectional curvature is always ≤ 0, if $\sigma(t)$, $0 \leq t \leq 1$, is any geodesic, if v is any continuous piecewise C^{∞} vector field on σ, then $H(v) > 0$ unless $v = 0$ identically. By Theorem 22.4, σ can have no conjugate points. We deduce from the corollary to Lemma 21.4:

THEOREM 23.1 (HADAMARD AND CARTAN)

Suppose that M is a complete Riemannian manifold whose sectional curvature is always nonpositive. Let $p \in M$. Then, exp: $M_p \to M$ is a covering map.

As a second observation notice from the definition the following property of the Ricci curvature of a unit tangent vector $v \in M_p$: With respect to any orthonormal basis (v_i), $1 \leq i \leq n$, of M_p chosen so that, say, $v = v_1$, the Ricci curvature is the sum of the sectional curvatures in the planes spanned by v and v_i, $2 \leq i \leq n$.

Thus, if the sectional curvatures of M are bounded from below by a positive number, so are the Ricci curvatures; hence, by Theorem 22.8, if M is complete it is also compact, and its diameter is bounded from above, depending only on this positive number. The ultimate purpose of the Rauch type of comparison theorem is to refine this result by giving more information about the topology of such a Riemannian manifold, but in this chapter we shall restrict ourselves to developing fundamental analytical tools. First, however, we discuss the more classical geometric interpretations of the sectional curvature.

THEOREM 23.2

Let p be a point of a Riemannian manifold and Γ a plane in M_p, $K(\Gamma)$ the sectional curvature of that tangent plane. For each $r > 0$, let γ_r be the circle in Γ about the origin of radius r. Let $L(r)$ be the length of the curve $\exp(\gamma_r)$ in M (assuming that r is sufficiently small so that the exp mapping is defined in some convex ball of M_p about 0 containing γ_r). Then

$$\frac{dL}{dr}(0) = 2\pi, \qquad \frac{d^2L}{dr^2}(0) = 0, \qquad \frac{d^3L}{dr^3}(0) = -6\pi K(\Gamma).$$

Thus, taking the Taylor expansion of $L(r)$, we have a new geometric definition of $K(\Gamma)$.

$$K(\Gamma) = \lim_{r \to 0} \frac{\text{length } \gamma_r - \text{length } \exp(\gamma_r)}{\pi r^3}, \qquad (23.6)$$

Proof. Since this is purely a local result about p, we can (and will), for simplicity of notation only, suppose that M is complete. Then, let $\delta(s, t,)$ $0 \le s, t \le 1$, be a homotopy such that:

(a) $\delta(s, 0) = p$.
(b) $s \to \partial_t \delta(s, 0)$ is the circle of unit length in Γ, that is, γ_1, in its arc-length–proportional parametrization.
(c) $\delta(s, t) = \exp(t \, \partial_s \delta(s, 0))$, that is, $t \to \delta(s, t)$ is the geodesic starting from p tangent there to $\gamma_1(s)$.

Then,

$$L(t) = \int_0^1 \langle \partial_s \delta(s, t), \partial_s \delta(s, t) \rangle^{1/2} \, ds,$$

$$\frac{dL}{dt} = \int_0^1 \frac{\langle \nabla_s \partial_t \delta(s, t), \partial_s \delta(s, t) \rangle}{\| \partial_s \delta(s, t) \|} \, ds.$$

LEMMA 23.3

Let $\delta(s, t), 0 \le s, t \le 1$ be a homotopy with $\delta(s, 0) = \delta(0, 0)$, but $\nabla_t \, \partial_s \delta(s, 0) \ne 0$. Then

$$\lim_{t \to 0} \frac{\partial_s \delta(s, t)}{\| \partial_s \delta(s, t) \|} = \frac{\nabla_t \, \partial_s \delta(s, 0)}{\| \nabla_t \, \partial_s \delta(s, 0) \|}.$$

Proof.

$$\lim_{t \to 0} \frac{\| \partial_s \delta(s, t) \|}{t^2} = \text{by L'Hôpital's rule (since } \| \partial_s \delta(s, 0) \| = 0).$$

$$\lim_{t \to 0} \frac{\langle \nabla_t \partial_s \delta(s, t), \partial_s \delta(s, t) \rangle}{t} = \| \nabla_t \, \partial_s \delta(s, 0) \|.$$

$$\lim_{t \to 0} \frac{\partial_s \delta(s, t)}{t} = \nabla_t \, \partial_s \delta(0, t).$$

$$\lim_{t \to 0} \frac{\partial_s \delta(s, t)}{\| \partial_s \delta(s, t) \|} = \lim_{t \to 0} \frac{\partial_s \delta(s, t)}{t} \cdot \frac{t}{\| \partial_s \delta(s, t) \|}$$

$$= \frac{\nabla_t \, \partial_s \delta(s, 0)}{\| \nabla_t \, \partial_s \delta(s, 0) \|}. \qquad \text{Q.E.D.}$$

Applying Lemma 23.3,

$$\frac{dL}{dt}(0) = \int_0^1 \lim_{t \to 0} \left\langle \nabla_s \partial_t \delta(s, t), \frac{\partial_s \delta(s, t)}{\|\partial_s \delta(s, t)\|} \right\rangle dt$$

$$= \int_0^1 \|\nabla_s \partial_t \delta(s, 0)\| \, dt$$

$$= \text{length } \gamma_1 = 2\pi.$$

$$\frac{d^2 L}{dt^2} = \int_0^1 \left[\frac{\langle \nabla_t \nabla_s \partial_t \delta, \partial_s \delta \rangle + \|\nabla_s \partial_t \delta\|^2 \rangle}{\|\partial_s \delta\|} \right.$$

$$\left. - \frac{\langle \nabla_t \partial_s \delta, \partial_s \delta \rangle^2}{\|\partial_s \partial\|^3} \right] ds.$$

Now $\nabla_t \nabla_s \partial_t \delta = \nabla_s \nabla_t \partial_t \delta + R(\partial_t \delta, \partial_s \delta)(\partial_t \delta)$, and $t \to \delta(t, s)$ is a geodesic; hence $\nabla_t \partial_t = 0$. Then

$$\frac{d^2 L}{dt^2} = \int_0^1 \left[\frac{\langle R(\partial_t \delta, \partial_s \delta)(\partial_t \delta), \partial_s \delta \rangle}{\|\partial_s \delta\|} + \frac{\|\nabla_s \partial_t \delta\|^2 - \langle \nabla_t \partial_s \delta, (\partial_s \delta/\|\partial_s \delta\|) \rangle^2}{\|\partial_s \delta\|} \right] ds.$$

First, note by Gauss' lemma that $\langle \partial_t \delta, \partial_s \delta \rangle = 0$. Let $\Gamma(s, t)$ be the plane in $M_{\delta(s,t)}$ spanned by $\partial_t \delta(s, t)$ and $\partial_s \delta(s, t)$. Since

$$\frac{\partial_s \delta(s, t)}{t} \to \nabla_s \partial_t \delta(s, 0) \qquad \text{as } t \to 0,$$

and $\partial_t \delta(s, 0)$, $\nabla_s \partial_t \delta(s, 0) \in \Gamma$, we see that $K(\Gamma(s, t)) \to K(\Gamma)$ as $t \to 0$.

$$K(\Gamma(s, t)) = - \left\langle R_{\delta(s, t)}\left(\partial_t \delta, \frac{\partial_s \delta}{\|\partial_s \delta\|}\right)\left(\partial_t \delta, \frac{\partial_s \delta}{\|\partial_s \delta\|}\right)\right\rangle$$

$$= - \frac{\langle R(\partial_t \delta, \partial_s \delta)(\partial_t \delta), \partial_s \delta \rangle}{\|\partial_s \delta\|^2}.$$

$$\frac{\langle R(\partial_t \delta, \partial_s \delta)(\partial_t \delta), \partial_s \delta \rangle}{\|\partial_s \delta\|} = - K(\Gamma(s, t)) \|\partial_s \delta\|.$$

$$\frac{1}{\|\partial_s \delta\|} \frac{d}{dt} (\|\nabla_s \partial_t \delta\|^2) = 2 \langle \nabla_t \nabla_s \partial_t \delta, \nabla_s \partial_t \delta \rangle \cdot \frac{1}{\|\partial_s \delta\|}$$

$$= 2 \left\langle R\left(\partial_t \delta, \frac{\partial_s \delta}{\|\partial_s \delta\|}\right)(\partial_t \delta), \nabla_s \partial_t \delta \right\rangle \to$$

$$- 2K(\Gamma) \|\nabla_s \partial_t \delta(s, 0)\| \qquad \text{as } t \to 0.$$

$$\left\langle \nabla_t \partial_s \delta, \frac{\partial_s \delta}{\|\partial_s \delta\|} \right\rangle^2 \to \left\langle \nabla_t \partial_s \delta, \frac{\nabla_t \partial_s \delta}{\|\nabla_t \partial_s \delta\|} \right\rangle^2 \qquad \text{as } t \to 0 = \|\nabla_s \partial_t \delta(s, 0)\|.$$

Putting the calculations together, we see that

$$\frac{d^2 L}{dt^2}(0) = 0,$$

$$\frac{d^3 L}{dt^3}(0) = \lim_{t \to 0} \frac{d^2 L/dt^2}{t} = \lim_{t \to 0} \frac{d^2 L/dt^2}{\|\partial_s \delta\|} \cdot \|\nabla_t \partial_s \delta\|$$

$$= -3K(\Gamma) \int_0^1 \|\nabla_t \partial_s \delta\| \, ds = -6\pi K(\Gamma). \qquad \text{Q.E.D.}$$

COROLLARY 1

Let M and N be Riemannian manifolds, $\phi: N \to M$ a map such that

$$\|\phi_*(v)\| = \|v\| \qquad \text{for all } v \in T(N),$$

(that is, ϕ is an isometric immersion of N in M). Let $p_0 \in N$ and let Γ be a plane in N_{p_0} such that, for all $v \in \Gamma$, $t \to \phi(\exp(tv))$ is a geodesic of M. Then $K_N(\Gamma) = K_M(\phi_*(\Gamma))$, where K_N and K_M are the sectional curvatures with respect to the metrics on N and M.

Proof. Let γ_r be the circle of radius r in Γ. Since ϕ is isometric, the length of $\phi(\exp(\gamma_r))$ and $\exp(\gamma_r)$ are the same. But, $\phi(\exp(\gamma_r)) = \exp(\phi_*(\gamma_r))$. $\phi_*(\gamma_r)$ is the circle of radius r in $\phi_*(\Gamma)$. The result follows from (23.6), applied to Γ and $\phi_*(\Gamma)$.

This corollary leads to another geometric interpretation of the sectional curvature of a Riemannian manifold M. Suppose first that $\dim M = 2$. Since $\dim M_p = 2$, there is only one sectional curvature associated with each point. The function thus defined over M is called the *Gaussian curvature* of M. Now suppose that $\dim M > 2$; let $p \in M$, and let Γ be a two-dimensional subspace of M. The union of all geodesics of M starting at p and tangent there to Γ, at least locally about p, determines a two-dimensional submanifold $N(\Gamma)$ about p. Now any submanifold of a Riemannian manifold has on it an induced Riemannian metric obtained by restricting the inner product to the tangent spaces to the submanifold. (The resulting metric on the submanifold is such that the inclusion map of the submanifold into the big manifold is an isometric immersion.) If we apply this to $N(\Gamma)$, we see from Corollary 1 that the Gaussian curvature of $N(\Gamma)$ at p is precisely the sectional curvature of Γ. Of course this fact can also be taken as a geometric definition of sectional curvature.

Another remark resulting from Corollary 1 is that if $\dim M = \dim N$ (that is, if ϕ is a local isometry of M on N), ϕ preserves the sectional curvature.

This remark is also, of course, implicit in the fact that the Riemann curvature tensor is invariantly attached to the metric.

We shall present another useful corollary after a preliminary definition.

Definition

Let M and N be Riemannian manifolds and let $\phi: M \to N$ be a map such that $\phi_*(M_p) = N_{\phi(p)}$ for all $p \in M$. (ϕ is then called a *maximal rank* mapping of M into N. It follows from the implicit function theorem that ϕ is then an open mapping.) For $p \in M$, let $F_p = \{v \in M_p : \phi_*(v) = 0\}$. F_p is called the space of *vertical vectors* with respect to ϕ. Let $F_p^{\perp} = \{v \in M_p : v \text{ is perpendicular to } F_p; \text{ that is, } \langle v, u \rangle = 0 \text{ for all } u \in F_p\}$. ϕ is said to be a *compatible* mapping between the Riemannian structures on M and N if

$$\|\phi_*(v)\| = \|v\| \qquad \text{for all } v \in F_p^{\perp}, \quad \text{all } p \in M. \tag{23.7}$$

COROLLARY 2

Let $\phi: M \to N$ be a compatible, maximal rank mapping between Riemannian manifolds. Let $p \in M$ and let Γ be a two-dimensional subspace of $F_p^{\perp}$. Then,

$$K_N(\phi_*(\Gamma)) \geq K_M(\Gamma). \tag{23.8}$$

Proof. One can show that if $v \in F_p^{\perp}$, if $\sigma(t)$, $0 \leq t \leq 1$, is a geodesic starting at p and tangent there to v, that (a) $\sigma'(t) \in F_{\sigma(t)}^{\perp}$, for all $t \in [0, 1]$; and (b) $t \to \phi(\sigma(t))$ is a geodesic of M. If v is an arbitrary vector of M_p, $v = v_1 + v_2$, with $v_1 \in F_p$, $v_2 \in F_p^{\perp}$, $\langle v_1, v_2 \rangle = 0$. Thus $\|v\|^2 = \|v_1\|^2 + \|v_2\|^2$. But $\|v_2\| = \|\phi_*(v_2)\| = \|\phi_*(v)\|$. Hence $\|v\| \geq \|\phi(v)\|$. In particular, if γ is any curve of M, length $\gamma \geq$ length $\phi(\gamma)$.

Let γ_r be the circle of radius r about 0 in Γ.

$$\text{length exp}(\gamma_r) \geq \text{length } \phi \text{ exp}(\gamma_r).$$

But

$$\phi \text{ exp}(\gamma_r) = \text{exp}(\phi_*(\gamma_r)).$$

Using (23.5), we now get (23.8). Corollary 2 is very useful in proving that certain spaces have nonnegative curvature.

The sectional curvature also has a geometric interpretation in terms of the comparative size of geodesic triangles in the Riemannian and Euclidean spaces. The following theorem is representative of this type of result.

THEOREM 23.4

Let M be a Riemannian manifold, $p \in M$, $v_0, v_1 \in M_p$. For $t \in [0, 1]$, let $D(t) =$ distance from $\operatorname{Exp}(tv_0)$ to $\operatorname{Exp}(tv_1)$, $\theta =$ angle between v_0 and v_1. Then $D(t)^2$ has a Taylor expansion of the form

$$D(t)^2 = \|v_1 - v_0\| t^2 + K(\Gamma)\|v_0\|^2 \|v_1\|^2 \sin^2 \theta t^4 + \cdots. \tag{23.9}$$

Proof. It is most convenient at this point to use Taylor's formula for covariant derivatives.

LEMMA 23.5

Let $\sigma: [0, 1] \to M$ be a curve in an affinely connected manifold M. Let $v(t)$, $0 \leq t \leq 1$, be a vector field along σ. Then v admits a Taylor expansion:

$$v(t) = v(0) + \nabla v(0)t + \frac{\nabla^2 v(0)}{2!} t^2 + \cdots + \frac{\nabla^N v(0)}{N!} t^N + u(t)t^{N+1}. \tag{23.10}$$

(Literally, (23.10) makes no sense, since $v(t) \in M_{\sigma(t)}$, while the vector on the right-hand side belongs to $M_{\sigma(0)}$, However, we mean implicitly that they are compared by parallel-translating the left-hand side along σ from $\sigma(t)$ to $\sigma(0)$.)

Proof. Of course, if $\sigma(t)$ is constant, $v(t)$ is just an ordinary vector-valued function in $M_{\sigma(0)}$; hence this is just the usual Taylor's formula. We can reduce to this case, however, by the following trick: For $t \in [0, 1]$, let $w(t)$ be the vector in $M_{\sigma(0)}$ which parallel-translates along σ to give $v(t)$. It is easily seen that $(dw/dt)(t)$ parallel-translates along σ to give $\nabla v(t)$. Thus the classical Taylor expansion for $w(t)$ parallel-translates along σ to give (23.10).

Return to Theorem 23.6. Let $\delta(s, t)$, $0 \leq s \leq 1$, $0 \leq t \leq t_0$, be a homotopy in M such that:

(a) $\delta(s, 0) = p$.
(b) $\delta(0, t) = \exp(v_0 t)$, $\delta(1, t) = \exp(v_1 t)$ for $0 \leq t \leq t_0$.
(c) For each t, $s \to \delta(s, t)$ is a geodesic parametrized proportionally to arc length.

(If t_0 is sufficiently small, obviously such a homotopy can be constructed.) For notational convenience we shall assume that $t_0 = 1$. Note that

$$D(t)^2 = \int_0^1 \|\partial_s \delta(s, t)\|^2 \, ds.$$

Condition (c) implies that $s \to \partial_t \delta(s, t)$ is a Jacobi vector field along the geodesic $s \to \delta(s, t)$. From (a), the Jacobi equations reduce at $t = 0$ to

$$\nabla_s \nabla_s \partial_t \delta(s, 0) = 0.$$

Thus, in view of the conditions $\partial_t \delta(0, 0) = v_0$, $\partial_t \delta(1, 0) = v_1$ derived from (b), we have

$$\partial_t \delta(s, 0) = (1 - s)v_0 + sv_1.$$
$$\nabla_t \partial_s \delta(s, 0) = \nabla_s \partial_t \delta(s, 0) = v_1 - v_0.$$

Thus the Taylor expansion of $\partial_s \delta(s, t)$ about $t = 0$ is

$$\partial_s \delta(s, t) = (v_1 - v_0)t + \cdots + (\text{higher-order terms in } t).$$
$$\nabla_t \nabla_t \partial_s \delta(s, t) = \nabla_t \nabla_s \partial_t \delta(s, t) = \nabla_s \nabla_t \partial_t \delta + R(\partial_t \delta, \partial_s \delta)(\partial_t \delta).$$

Hence,

$$D(t)^2 = \int_0^1 \| (v_1 - v_0)t + \tfrac{1}{2}(\nabla_s \nabla_t \partial_t \delta(s, t)$$
$$+ R(\partial_t \delta(s, t), \partial_s \delta(s, t))(\partial_t \delta(s, t)))t^2 + \cdots \|^2 \, ds.$$

Now

$$\int_0^1 \langle (v_1 - v_0)t, \nabla_s \nabla_t \partial_t \delta(s, t) \rangle \, ds = \int_0^1 \left[\frac{\partial}{\partial_s} \langle (v_1 - v_0)t, \nabla_t \partial_t \delta(s, t) \rangle \right] ds$$
$$= \langle (v_1 - v_0)t, \nabla_t \partial_t \delta(1, t) \rangle$$
$$- \langle (v_1 - v_0)t, \nabla_t \partial_t \delta(0, t) \rangle$$
$$= 0 \text{ (by condition (b))}.$$

We now prove

$$\int_0^1 \langle \nabla_s \nabla_t \partial_t \delta(s, 0), \nabla_s \nabla_t \partial_t \delta(s, 0) \rangle \, ds = 0. \tag{23.11}$$

Integrating by parts and taking into account condition (b), we have

$$(\text{left-hand side } (23.11)) = \int_0^1 - \langle \nabla_s \nabla_s \nabla_t \partial_t \delta(s, 0), \nabla_t \partial_t \delta(s, 0) \rangle \, ds.$$
$$\nabla_s \nabla_s \nabla_t \partial_t \delta = \nabla_s(\nabla_t \nabla_s \partial_t \delta + R(\partial_s \delta, \partial_t \delta)(\partial_t \delta))$$
$$= \nabla_t \nabla_s \nabla_t \partial_s \delta + R(\partial_s \delta, \partial_t \delta)(\nabla_s \partial_t \delta)$$
$$+ (\nabla_s R)(\partial_s \delta, \partial_t \delta)(\partial_t \delta)$$
$$+ R(\nabla_s \partial_s \delta, \partial_t \delta)(\partial_t \delta) + R(\partial_s \delta, \nabla_s \partial_t \delta)(\partial_s \delta)$$
$$+ R(\partial_s \delta, \partial_t \delta)(\nabla_t \partial_s \delta).$$

Now $\nabla_s \partial_s \delta = 0$, by condition (c). Hence

$$\nabla_t \nabla_s \nabla_t \partial_s \delta = \nabla_t (R(\partial_s \delta, \partial_t \delta)(\partial_s \delta))$$
$$= (\nabla_t R)(\partial_s \delta, \partial_t \delta)(\partial_s \delta) + R(\nabla_t \partial_s \delta, \partial_t \delta)(\partial_s \delta)$$
$$+ R(\partial_s \delta, \nabla_t \partial_t \delta)(\partial_s \delta) + R(\partial_s \delta, \partial_t \delta)(\nabla_t \partial_s \delta).$$

Finally we see that $\nabla_s \nabla_s \nabla_t \partial_t \delta(s, 0) = 0$. This proves (23.11).
Now

$$\int_0^1 \left\langle (v_1 - v_0), \frac{R(\partial_t \delta, \partial_s \delta)(\partial_t \delta)}{t} \right\rangle (s, 0) \, ds$$

$$= \int_0^1 \langle (v_1 - v_0), R((1 - s)v_0 + sv_1, v_1 - v_0)((1 - s)v_0 + sv_1) \rangle \, ds$$

$$= \int_0^1 \langle v_1 - v_0, R(v_0, v_1 - v_0)(v_0)(1 - s)^2 + R(v_1, v_1 - v_0)(v_0)s(1 - s)$$

$$+ R(v_1, v_1 - v_0)(v_1)s^2 + R(v_0, v_1 - v_0)(v_1)(1 - s)s \rangle \, ds$$

$$= \tfrac{1}{3}\langle v_1, R(v_0, v_1)(v_0) \rangle + \tfrac{1}{6}\langle v_1, R(v_1, -v_0)(v_0) \rangle$$

$$+ \tfrac{1}{3}\langle -v_0, R(v_1, -v_0)(v_1) \rangle + \tfrac{1}{6}\langle -v_0, R(v_0, v_1)(v_1) \rangle$$

$$= \langle v_1, R(v_0, v_1)(v_0) \rangle = K(\Gamma) \|v_0\|^2 \|v_1\|^2 \sin^2 \theta,$$

where θ is the angle between v_0 and v_1, and Γ is the plane of M_p spanned by v_0 and v_1; whence (23.9).

Note that the first term on the right-hand side of (23.9) gives the "law of cosines," or basically, the Pythagorean theorem, for triangles in Euclidean geometry. Note also that $\tfrac{1}{2}\|v_0\| \|v_1\| |\sin \theta| t^2$ is the Euclidean area of the triangle. Thus (23.8) shows that the sectional curvature gives the deviation of the law of cosines for small triangles. Many other formulas of trigonometry on Riemannian spaces can also be derived, using (23.9) as a replacement for the law of consines, or independently in a similar way.

So far, we have been comparing to a certain infinitesimal order the geometric entities in a Riemannian space with the corresponding entitites in a Euclidean space. These are very classical results (mostly due to Riemann); only recently have results of this type been proved that are global and that enable one to compare goemetric entities in two, possibly both, non-Euclidean, Riemannian spaces. The following comparison theorem, due to Rauch, is the foundation of much of the work.

THEOREM 23.6

Let M be a manifold, with two Riemannian metrics defined on it. For $p \in M$, $u, v \in M_p$, let $\langle u, v \rangle$ and $\langle u, v \rangle^*$ be the inner product in the two metrics. Let R and R^* be the Riemann curvature tensors of the unstarred and starred metrics. For $u, v \in M_p$, let $K(u, v)$ and $K^*(u, v)$ be the sectional curvature on the unstarred and starred metrics of the plane spanned by u and v.

Let p_0 be a point of M such that the inner products on M_p agree. Let $\sigma: [0, 1] \to M$ be a curve beginning at p_0, which is a geodesic in both metrics, which has the same length in both metrics, and such that for $0 < t \leq 1$, $\sigma(t)$ is not a conjugate point of $\sigma(1)$ (with respect to σ) in the unstarred metric.

Let $v(t)$ be a vector field along σ which vanishes at $t = 0$, which is a Jacobi field with respect to both metrics, and such that

$$\langle v(t), \sigma'(t) \rangle = 0 = \langle v(t), \sigma'(t) \rangle^* \qquad \text{for } 0 \leq t \leq 1.$$

For $t \in [0, 1]$, let $u(t) \in M_{\sigma(t)}$ be defined as follows:

Parallel-translate $v(t)$ to $\sigma(1)$ along σ, using the starred affine connection; then parallel-translate this vector at $\sigma(1)$ back to $\sigma(t)$ along σ, using the unstarred affine connection. The result is $u(t)$. Then

$$\frac{1}{2(\text{length } \sigma)^2} \frac{d}{dt} (\langle v(t), v(t) \rangle - \langle v(t), v(t) \rangle^*)$$

$$\leq \int_0^t [K^*(v(\lambda), \sigma'(\lambda)) - K(u(\lambda), \sigma'(\lambda))] \langle v(\lambda), v(\lambda) \rangle^* \, d\lambda. \qquad (23.12)$$

Equality holds if and only if $v(\lambda) = u(\lambda)$ for $0 \leq \lambda \leq t$.

Proof. It suffices to prove (23.12) in case $t = 1$ and to suppose that length $\sigma = 1$. Let $\dim M = n$. Choose the following indices and summation convention: $1 \leq i, j, \ldots \leq n$.

Let $(w_i(t)), (z_i(t))$ be vector fields along σ such that:

(a) $w_i(1) = z_i(1)$.
(b) $\langle w_i(t), w_j(t) \rangle = \delta_{ij}$; $\langle z_i(t), z_j(t) \rangle^* = \delta_{ij}$.
(c) $\nabla w_i = 0 = \nabla^* z_i$.

(∇ and ∇^* denote covariant differentiation with respect to the unstarred and starred affine connection, respectively.) Suppose that $v(t) = a_i(t)w_i(t) = b_i(t)z_i(t)$. Writing out the Jacboi equations for v for both metrics, using (b) and (c), we have

$$\frac{d^2 b_i(t)}{dt^2} + b_j \langle z_i(t), R^*(z_j(t), \sigma'(t))(\sigma'(t)) \rangle^* = 0. \qquad (23.13)$$

From (a), $a_i(1) = b_i(1)$. Hence $u(t) = b_i(t)w_i(t)$. Since $u(0) = v(0) = 0$, $u(1) = v(1)$, we have, by Theorem 22.7,

$$\langle v(1), \nabla v(1)\rangle = \int_0^1 [\langle \nabla v(t), \nabla v(t)\rangle - \langle v(t), R(v(t), \sigma'(t))(\sigma'(t))\rangle]$$

$$\leq \int_0^1 [\langle \nabla u(t), \nabla u(t)\rangle - \langle u(t), R(u(t), \sigma'(t))(\sigma'(t))\rangle]\, dt$$

$$= \int_0^1 \left[\frac{db_i}{dt}\frac{db_j}{dt} - b_i b_j\langle w_i, R(w_j, \sigma'(t))(\sigma'(t))\rangle\right] dt$$

$$= \text{(after integrating by parts and using (23.13))}\ b_i(1)\frac{db_i}{dt}(1)$$

$$+ \int_0^1 [b_j\langle z_i, R^*(z_j, \sigma')(\sigma')\rangle^* b_i - \langle u, R(u, \sigma')(\sigma')\rangle]\, dt$$

$$= \langle v(1), \nabla v(1)\rangle^* + \int_0^1 [\langle v, R'(v, \sigma')(\sigma')\rangle^*$$

$$- \langle u, R(u, \sigma')(\sigma')\rangle]\, dt.$$

Since $\|v\|^2 = \|u\|^2 = b_i b_i$,

$$K(u, \sigma') = \left\langle \frac{u}{\|u\|}, R\left(\frac{u}{\|u\|}, \sigma'\right)(\sigma')\right\rangle, \quad K^*(v, \sigma') = \left\langle \frac{v}{\|v\|^*}, R^*\left(\frac{v}{\|v\|^*}, \sigma'\right)(\sigma')\right\rangle,$$

we have

$$\frac{1}{2}\frac{d}{dt}(\langle v(t), v(t)\rangle - \langle v(t), v(t)\rangle^*)\Big|_{t=1} = \langle \nabla v(1), v(1)\rangle - \langle \nabla v(1), v(1)\rangle^*$$

$$\leq \int_0^1 [K^*(v(t), \sigma'(t))$$

$$- K(u(t), \sigma'(t))]\langle v(t), v(t)\rangle^*\, dt,$$

which proves the theorem.

COROLLARY 3

Suppose that M is a Riemannian manifold with two Riemannian metrics $\langle\ ,\ \rangle$ and $\langle\ ,\ \rangle^*$. Let $p_0 \in M$ satisfy the following conditions:

(a) The geodesics beginning at p_0 in the two metrics coincide and have the same length.

(b) If $\sigma\colon [0, 1] \to M$ is any geodesic beginning at p_0, having no conjugate points of p_0, then

$$K^*(u, \sigma'(t)) \leq K(v, \sigma'(t)) \qquad \text{for all } t \in [0, 1],\ \text{all } u, v \in M_{0(t)}.$$

Let p be any point of M lying on a geodesic from p_0 having no conjugate points of p_0. Then

$$\langle u, u \rangle \leq \langle u, u \rangle^* \qquad \text{for all } u \in M_p.$$

Intuitively, inside the "conjugate locus" of p_0 the starred metric is bigger than the unstarred one.

Proof. In view of the relation between Jacobi vector fields and geodesic deformations, the Jacobi fields of both metrics that are zero at p_0 must coincide. Thus (b) implies that

$$\frac{d}{dt}\left(\langle v(t), v(t) \rangle - \langle v(t), v(t) \rangle^*\right) \leq 0$$

for each Jacobi field that is zero at p_0; hence

$$\langle v(t), v(t) \rangle \leq \langle v(t), v(t) \rangle^*.$$

If $\sigma(1)$ is not a conjugate point of $\sigma(0) = p_0$, the values at $t = 1$ of all Jacobi vector fields that are zero at p_0 spans $M_{\sigma(1)}$. The corollary then follows.

The following more qualitiative comparison theorem is due to Morse and Schoenberg. Both comparison theorems may be considered as generalizations of the classical Sturm comparison theorem.

THEOREM 23.7

Let M be a Riemannian manifold, and let $\sigma: [0, 1] \to M$ be a geodesic of M such that $\sigma(1)$ is the first conjugate point of $\sigma(0)$ along σ. Suppose that c_1 and c_2 are positive real numbers such that

$$c_1 \leq K(v, \sigma'(t)), \qquad (23.14a)$$

$$K(v, \sigma'(t))| \leq |c_2, \qquad (23.14b)$$

for all $t \in [0, 1]$, all $v \in M_{\sigma(t)}$. Then

(a) length $\sigma \leq \pi/\sqrt{c_1}$,   (b) $\pi/\sqrt{c_2} \leq$ length σ.   (23.15)

Proof. Suppose for the moment that $\sigma(1)$ is an arbitrary geodesic of M. Let $u_i(t)$, $0 \leq t \leq 1$, $2 \leq i \leq n$ (summation convention), be vector fields along σ such that $\nabla u_i(t) = 0$, $\langle u_i(t), u_j(t) \rangle = \delta_{ij}$, $\langle u(t), \sigma'(t) \rangle = 0$. Suppose that v is a vector field along σ of the form $v(t) = a_i \sin(k\pi t)u_i(t)$. Thus

$$\|v(t)\|^2 = \sin^2(k\pi t) \cdot a_i a_i, \qquad \nabla v = k\pi a_i \cos(k\pi t)u_i(t).$$

$$H(v) = \int_0^1 [\langle \nabla v, \nabla v \rangle - \langle v, R(v, \sigma')(\sigma') \rangle] \, dt$$

$$= a_i a_i \int_0^1 [k^2\pi^2 \cos^2(k\pi t) - \sin^2(k\pi t) \cdot \|\sigma'(t)\|^2 K(\sigma'(t), v(t))] \, dt,$$

where $K(\sigma'(t), v(t))$ is the sectional curvature in the plane spanned by $\sigma'(t)$ and $v(t)$. By (23.14), the integrand is no greater than

$$k^2\pi^2 \cos^2(k\pi t) - c_1 \sin^2(k\pi t)\|\sigma'(t)\|^2.$$

But

$$\|\sigma'(t)\| = \text{length } \sigma.$$

Take $k = 1$. Note that $\int_0^1 \cos^2(\pi t)\, dt = \int_0^1 \sin^2(\pi t)\, dt$ and $v(0) = 0 = v(1)$. If there are no conjugate points on σ, we must have $H(v) \geq 0$. This forces length $\sigma \leq \pi/\sqrt{c_1}$, and hence proves (23.15a), since the same inequality obviously holds if $\sigma(1)$ is the first conjugate point of $\sigma(0)$.

We turn to proving (23.15b). Let $v(t)$, $0 \leq t \leq 1$, be a continuous, piecewise C^∞ vector field along σ, with $v(0) = 0 = v(1)$, and $\langle \sigma'(1), v(1)\rangle = 0$. Using a Fourier series expansion of the components of v, we can write

$$v(t) = \sum_{k=1}^{\infty} a_{ik} \sin(k\pi t)u_i(t).$$

Since v is piecewise C^∞, the Fourier series for ∇v also converges and is,

$$\nabla v(t) = \sum_{k=1}^{\infty} a_{ik} k\pi \cos(k\pi t)u_i(t).$$

Suppose that $\sigma(1)$ is a conjugate point of $\sigma(0)$. We can then choose the vector field v so that $H(v) = 0$. Then

$$0 = H(v) = \int_0^1 [\|\nabla v(t)\|^2 - \|v(t)\|^2\|\sigma'(t)\|^2 K(\sigma'(t), v(t))]\, dt$$

$$\geq \int_0^1 [\|\nabla v(t)\|^2 - \|v(t)\|^2\|\sigma'(t)\|^2 c_2]\, dt.$$

Now

$$\|\nabla v(t)\|^2 = \sum_{k,l=1}^{\infty} a_{ik} a_{il} kl\pi^2 \cos(k\pi t) \cos(l\pi t),$$

$$\|v(t)\|^2 = \sum_{k,l=1}^{\infty} a_{ik} a_{il} \sin(k\pi t) \sin(l\pi t).$$

$$\int_0^1 \cos(k\pi t) \cos(l\pi t)\, dt = \int_0^1 \cos(k + l)\pi t\, dt + \int_0^1 \sin(k\pi t) \sin(l\pi t)\, dt$$

$$= \frac{\sin(k + l)\pi t}{k + l}\bigg|_0^1 + \int_0^1 \sin(k\pi t) \sin(l\pi t)\, dt$$

$$= 0 + \int_0^1 \sin(k\pi t) \sin(l\pi t)\, dt.$$

Thus,

$$z \geq \sum_{k,\,l=1}^{\infty} a_{ik}\, a_{il}(\pi^2 kl - (\text{length } \sigma)^2 c_2) \int_0^1 \sin(k\pi t) \sin(l\pi t)\, dt.$$

Suppose now that (23.15b) is not true; that is,

$$(\text{length } \sigma)^2 c_2{}^2 < \pi^2 \leq \pi^2 kl \qquad \text{for } k, l \geq 1.$$

But

$$\sum_{k,\,l=1}^{\infty} a_{ik}\, a_{il} \int_0^1 \sin(k\pi t) \sin(l\pi t)\, dt = \sum_{i=2}^{n} \left(\sum_{k=1}^{\infty} a_{ik} \int_0^1 \sin(k\pi t)\, dt \right)^2 \geq 0.$$

These inequalities are thus contradictory, whence (23.15), and the theorem is proved.

This theorem can also be proved by using the Rauch comparison theorem, that is, Theorem 23.6.

24 Submanifolds of Riemannian Manifolds

Throughout this chapter, let M be a Riemannian manifold. Thus, each $p \in M$ has a positive definite inner product $\langle \ , \ \rangle$ defined by the metric. M carries the Riemannian affine connection $(X, Y) \to \nabla_X Y$. Now recall that technically a *submanifold* must be considered as a pair (N, ϕ) consisting of another manifold N and a mapping $\phi \colon N \to M$ such that:

(a) For $p \in N$, $\phi_* \colon N_p \to M_{\phi(p)}$ is 1-1.
(b) ϕ itself is 1-1.

If (a) is satisfied, but not necessarily (b), the pair is called an *immersed submanifold*: By the implicit function theorem, every point of N has a neighborhood so that ϕ restricted to this neighborhood is a submanifold. Intuitively, an immersed submanifold is locally a submanifold, but may have "self-intersections." However, many differential geometric facts proved about submanifolds carry over with little difficulty to immersed submanifolds, so we shall restrict attention here to submanifolds.

If (N, ϕ) is a submanifold, it is customary to suppress explicit reference to ϕ, to identify N with the subset $\phi(N)$ of M and each N_p with the subspace $\phi_*(N_p)$ of $M_{\phi(p)}$. When there is little possibility of confusion, we shall do so.

Let N be a submanifold of M. Since each N_p is identified with a subspace of M_p, the given inner product $\langle \ , \ \rangle$ on M_p can be restricted to N_p to define a positive definite inner product there also: Thus N inherits a Riemannian metric from its embedding, called the *induced metric*. Our first job is to compute the affine connection and the curvature for the induced metric. For $p \in N$, let $N_p^\perp$ be the orthogonal complement of N_p in M_p with respect to the form $\langle \ , \ \rangle$. An element $v \in N_p^\perp$ (satisfying $\langle v, w \rangle = 0$ for all $w \in N_p$) is called a *normal vector* to N. Define

$$N^\perp = \bigcup_{p \in N} N_p^\perp,$$

the *normal vector bundle* to N. It is readily verified that $N^\perp$ is a submanifold of $T(M)$, the tangent bundle to M, whose dimension is equal to that of M. A vector field $X \in V(M)$ is said to be *tangent* or *nomal* to N if, respectively, $X(p) \in N_p$ or $X(p) \in N_p^\perp$ for all $p \in N$. Suppose that X and Y are tangent to

N, while Z is normal. Note that, for $f \in F(M)$:

$$\langle \nabla_X(fY), Z \rangle(p) = \langle f\nabla_X Y, Z \rangle(p) + \langle X(f)Y, Z \rangle$$
$$= f(p)\langle \nabla_X Y, Z \rangle(p),$$

since $\langle Y, Z \rangle(p) = 0$.

$$\langle \nabla_{(fX)} Y, Z \rangle(p) = f(p)\langle \nabla_X Y, Z \rangle(p) = \langle \nabla_X Y, fZ \rangle(p).$$

These identities are the tipoff that the mapping of vector fields into functions: $(X, Y, Z) \rightarrow \langle \nabla_X Y, Z \rangle$ possesses a " value " at each $p \in N$; that is, if $u \in N_p^\perp$, $v, w \in N_p$, choose $X, Y, Z \in V(M)$ such that X and Y are tangent to N, Z normal to N, so that $X(p) = v$, $Y(p) = w$, $Z(p) = u$, and *define*

$$S_u(v, w) = \langle \nabla_X Y, Z \rangle(p) = \langle \nabla_X Y(p), Z(p) \rangle. \tag{24.1}$$

Considered as a function in the indicated subset of $T(M) \times T(M) \times T(M)$, S is called the *second fundamental form* of N. (This is the classical terminology; the first fundamental form is just the inner product $\langle \, , \, \rangle$ on $T(M)$ restricted to $T(N)$.) The symmetric bilinear form $(v, w) \rightarrow S_u(v, w)$ defined on $T(N)$ is called the *value* of the second fundamental form on u. It must be verified that this is independent of the extension of u, v, w to vector fields, but we shall do this in a moment after computing in terms of a local basis of vector fields.

As algebraic properties, note from (24.1) that $S_u(v, w)$ varies linearly when u, v, or w are varied separately; that is, S as a function of $N_p^\perp \times N_p \times N_p \rightarrow R$ is multilinear. A less automatic property is *symmetry*, namely,

$$S_u(v, w) = S_u(w, v). \tag{24.2}$$

Proof. First note that if X and $Y \in V(M)$ are tangent to N, so is $[X, Y]$. To prove this, let $p \in N$. Revert to explicit mention of the map $\phi: N \rightarrow M$ defining the submanifold. For $v \in N_p$, $f \in F(M)$, $\phi_*(v)(f) = v(\phi^*(f))$. Hence $\phi_*(v)(f) = 0$, provided $\phi^*(f) = 0$. Thus, eliminating ϕ again from the notation,

$$N_p \subset \{v \in M_p : v(f) = 0 \quad \text{for all } f \in F(M) \text{ that vanish on } M\}.$$

Conversely, it is seen (using the implicit function theorem, which is left as exercise) that the set on the right-hand side has the same dimension (as a vector space) as N_p; hence equality holds.

Now suppose that $f \in F(M)$ vanishes on N and that $X, Y \in V(M)$ are tangent to N. Thus

$$0 = X(p)(f) = X(f)(p) = Y(p)(f) = Y(f)(p) \quad \text{for all } p \in N.$$
$$[X, Y](p)(f) = [X, Y](f)(p) = X(Y(f)) - Y(X(f))(p) = 0,$$

since $Y(f)$ and $X(f)$ are functions vanishing on N. Thus $[X, Y](p) \in N_p$ for all $p \in N$.

Returning to (24.2), suppose that $X, Y \in V(M)$ are tangent to N, and $Z \in V(M)$ is normal to N. If $u = Z(p)$, $v = X(p)$, $w = Y(p)$,

$$S_u(v, w) = \langle \nabla_X Y, Z \rangle(p) = \langle \nabla_Y X, Z + [X, Y], Z \rangle(p)$$
$$= \langle \nabla_Y X, Z \rangle(p) + \langle [X, Y](p), Z(p) \rangle = S_u(w, v),$$

since $[X, Y](p) \in N_p$, $Z(p) \in N_p^\perp$. This proves (24.2).

We must learn how to compute the second fundamental form in terms of a local basis for vector fields.

LEMMA 24.1

Let p be a point of N, let (v_i), $1 \le i, j, \ldots \le m \dim M$, be an orthonormal basis of M_p such that:

(a) (v_i), for $1 \le i \le n = \dim N$, is a basis for N_p.
(b) (v_i), $n + 1 \le i = m$, is a basis for $N_p^\perp$.

Then there is an open set U of M containing p and a basis (X_i) of vector fields in U such that

$$\langle X_i, X_j \rangle = \delta_{ij} \qquad \text{for } 1 \le i, j \le m.$$

(Any basis of vector fields satisfying this condition is called an *orthonormal basis*.) Now

X_i, for $1 \le i \le n$, is tangent to $N \cap U$,
$X_i(p) = v_i$ for $1 \le i \le m$,
$[X_i, X_j]$, for $1 \le i, j, \ldots \le n$, is expressible, in $N \cap U$,
in terms of $X_1, \ldots, X_n$.

Proof. Since N is a submanifold of M, U can first be chosen so that it carries a coordinate system of functions (x_i) so that: $U \cap N = \{q \in U: x_{n+1}(q) = 0 = \cdots = x_m(q)\}$ (exercise in the implicit function theorem). From $(\partial/\partial x_i)(x_j) = 0$ for $1 \le i \le n$, $n + 1 \le j \le m$, it follows that the vector fields $(\partial/\partial x_1), \ldots, (\partial/\partial x_n)$ are tangent to N. Recall the Gram–Schmidt orthogonalization linear algebra process of constructing an orthonormal basis from a given basis. Thus

$$X_1' = \frac{\partial/\partial x_1}{\|\partial/\partial x_1\|}, \qquad X_2' = \frac{(\partial/\partial x_2) - \langle (\partial/\partial x_2), X_1 \rangle X_1'}{\|(\partial/\partial x_2) - \langle (\partial/\partial x_2), X_1' \rangle X_1'\|}, \qquad \text{etc.}$$

The construction is such that the vector fields X_1' obtained form an orthonormal basis of vector fields so that the $X_1', \ldots, X_n'$ are also tangent to N, while the $X'_{n+1}, \ldots, X_m'$ are therefore normal to N. Thus we have expressions of the form

$$v_i = \sum_{j=1}^{n} c_{ij} X_j'(p) \qquad \text{for } 1 \le i \le n,$$

$$v_i = \sum_{j=n+1}^{m} c_{ij} X_j'(p) \qquad \text{for } n+1 \le i \le m.$$

Each of the matrices occurring in these relations is an orthogonal matrix. If now we define

$$X_i = \sum_{j=1}^{n} c_{ij} X_j', \qquad 1 \le i \le n,$$

$$X_i = \sum_{j=n+1}^{m} c_{ij} X_j', \qquad \text{for } n+1 \le i \le m,$$

the vector fields $(X_1, \ldots, X_m)$ will do the required job. Q.E.D.

Let us say that a basis of vector fields having the same properties as the bases $X_1, \ldots, X_n$ constructed in Lemma 24.1 is a *local moving frame*† for the submanifold geometry of N. Lemma 24.1 can then be interpreted as asserting the existence of a plentiful supply of local moving frames. Suppose now that we work with *any* such local moving frame $X_1, \ldots, X_n$ defined in U. Since the indices $1 \le i, j, \ldots \le n$ must systematically be split into two parts to account for N_p and $N_p^{\perp}$, it is convenient to introduce the following further ranges of indices, with the corresponding summation conventions in force:

$$1 \le i, j, \ldots \le n; \qquad 1 \le a, b, \ldots \le n; \qquad n+1 \le \alpha, \beta, \ldots \le m. \quad (24.3)$$

Suppose that $\nabla_{X_i} X_j = \Gamma_{ijk} X_k$ (that is, the Γ_{ijk}) are the components of the Riemannian affine connection with respect to the basis (X_i). The $\Gamma_{ab\alpha}$ determine the second fundamental form, since

$$\Gamma_{ab\alpha} = \langle \nabla_{X_a} X_b, X_\alpha \rangle = -\langle X_b, \nabla_{X_a} X_\alpha \rangle = -\Gamma_{a\alpha b} \qquad (24.4a)$$

$$-\Gamma_{a\alpha b}(p) = \Gamma_{ab\alpha}(p) = S_{X_\alpha(p)}(X_a(p), X_b(p)) \qquad \text{for } p \in U \cap N. \quad (24.4b)$$

Note that $0 = X_i(\langle X_j, X_k \rangle) = \langle \nabla_{X_i} X_j, X_k \rangle + \langle X_j, \nabla_{X_i} X_k \rangle$; hence

$$0 = \Gamma_{ijk} + \Gamma_{ikj}. \qquad (24.5a)$$

$$0 = \nabla_{X_i} X_j - \nabla_{X_j} X_i - [X_i, X_j] \qquad \text{(torsion zero condition).} \quad (24.5b)$$

---

† This, translated into our language, is what E. Cartan meant (specialized to this geometric situation) by a "répère mobile."

Hence,

$$0 = \Gamma_{ijk} X_k - \Gamma_{jik} X_k - [X_i, X_j]. \tag{24.5c}$$

Conversely, the Γ_{ijk} are uniquely determined by these conditions, since obviously another set of Γ satisfying (24.5a) and (24.5c) would determine the Riemannian affine connection, which we know is unique.

LEMMA 24.2

Consider the X_a as vector fields X_a^* in $N \cap U$ by restriction; that is, $X_a^*(p) = X_a(p) \in N_p$ for $p \in U \cap N$. Let ∇^* be the Riemannian affine connection associated with induced Riemannian metric on N. Then

$$\nabla_{X_a^*}^* X_b^* = \Gamma_{abc}^* X_c^* \tag{24.6}$$

where the Γ_{abc}^* are the Γ_{abc} restricted to $N \cap U$.

Proof. From (24.5a), we have $\Gamma_{abc}^* + \Gamma_{bac}^* = 0$. Also, the fact that $[X_a, X_b]$ is tangent to N forces, using (24.5b), $\Gamma_{ab\alpha} - \Gamma_{ba\alpha} = 0$. (In view of (24.4), this is just the symmetry of the second fundamental form.) Hence, from (24.5b) again,

$$\Gamma_{abc}^* X_c^* - \Gamma_{bac}^* X_c^* - [X_a^*, X_b^*] = 0.$$

By the preceding remarks leading to (24.5) (repeated for the metric on N) *defining* ∇^* by (24.6) gives an affine connection on $U \cap N$, which satisfies the two conditions needed to prove its identity with *the* Riemannian connection.

Q.E.D.

Another way of stating (24.6) is

$$\nabla_{X_a} X_b(p) - \nabla_{X_a}^* X_b(p) = S_{X_a(p)}(X_a(p), X_b(p)) X_a(p). \tag{24.7}$$

To find the relation between the curvature of the metrics on M and N and the second fundamental form, it is necessary to apply covariant derivatives of both sides of (24.7) and use the various identities we have developed. However, there is a much neater way of doing this, developed by E. Cartan, using a dual differential form point of view. It will repay our investment to detour a moment to develop this approach.

LEMMA 24.3

Let U be an open set of a Riemannian manifold M of dimension n ($1 \le i, j, \ldots \le n$) which has an orthonormal basis (X_i) of vector fields; that is, $\langle X_i, X_j \rangle = \delta_{ij}$. Let ω_i be the dual basis of differential forms; that is,

$$\omega_i(X_j) = \delta_{ij}.$$

Let Γ_{ijk} be the functions in U such that

$$\nabla_{X_i} X_j = \Gamma_{ijk} X_k,$$

and let ω_{ij} be the 1-forms defined by

$$\omega_{ij} = \Gamma_{kij}\omega_k. \tag{24.8}$$

Then

$$\text{(a)} \quad \omega_{ij} + \omega_{ji} = 0, \qquad \text{(b)} \quad d\omega_i = \omega_{ij} \wedge \omega_k. \tag{24.9}$$

Conversely, any set of forms ω_{ij} satisfying (24.9a) and (24.9b) is uniquely determined and given by (24.8).

Let the 2-forms Ω_{ij} be defined by

$$\Omega_{ij} = d\omega_{ij} - \omega_{ik} \wedge \omega_{kj}. \tag{24.10}$$

Then the curvature tensor is determined as follows:

$$\langle R(X, Y)(X_i), X_j\rangle = \Omega_{ij}(X, Y) \qquad \text{for } X, Y \in V(U). \tag{24.11}$$

Proof. Equation (24.9a) is equivalent to (24.5a). We show that (24.9b) is equivalent to (24.5b):

$$
\begin{aligned}
(d\omega_i - \omega_{ij} \wedge \omega_j)(X_k, X_l) &= X_k(\omega_i(X_l)) - X_l(\omega_i(X_k)) - \omega_i([X_k, X_l]) \\
&\quad - \omega_{ij}(X_k)\omega_j(X_l) - \omega_{ij}(X_l)\omega_j(X_k) \\
&= -\omega_i([X_k, X_l]) - \Gamma_{kij}\delta_{jl} + \Gamma_{lij}\delta_{jk} \\
&= -\omega_i([X_k, X_l]) + \Gamma_{kli} - \Gamma_{lki}.
\end{aligned}
$$

This shows that (24.9b) is equivalent to (24.5b); hence, also that the ω_{ij} are uniquely determined by (24.9), since they determine the unique Riemannian connection. Note, for example, that for $X, Y \in V(U)$,

$$\nabla_X Y = [X(\omega_k(Y)) + \omega_j(Y)\omega_{jk}(X)]X_k. \tag{24.12}$$

In particular,

$$\nabla_{X_i} X_j = \omega_{jk}(X_i)X_k \qquad \text{and} \qquad \omega_k(\nabla_X X_j) = \omega_{jk}(X).$$

From (24.10),

$$
\begin{aligned}
d\omega_{ij}(X, Y) &= X(\omega_{ij}(Y)) - Y(\omega_{ij}(X)) - \omega_{ij}([X, Y]) \\
&= X(\langle X_j, \nabla_Y X_i\rangle) - Y(\langle X_j, \nabla_X X_i\rangle) - \langle X_j, \nabla_{[X, Y]} X_i\rangle \\
&= \langle \nabla_X X_j, \nabla_Y X_i\rangle - \langle \nabla_Y X_j, \nabla_X X_i\rangle + \langle X_j, R(X, Y)(X_i)\rangle \\
&= \omega_k(\nabla_X X_j)\omega_k(\nabla_Y X_i) - \omega_k(\nabla_Y X_j)\omega_k(\nabla_X X_i) + \langle X_j, R(X, Y)(X_i)\rangle \\
&= \omega_{jik}(X)\omega_{ik}(Y) - \omega_{kj}(Y)\omega_{ki}(X) + \langle X_j, R(X, Y)(X_i)\rangle,
\end{aligned}
$$

whence (24.11), using (24.10).

This finishes the proof of Lemma 24.3. The forms ω_{ij} satisfying (24.9) are called the *connection forms* of the Riemannian affine connection with respect to the orthonormal basis (X_i). The 2-forms Ω_{ij} are called the *curvature forms*. Suppose now that we return to the case where X_a, $1 \leq a, b, \ldots \leq n$, are tangent to $U \cap N$. Then, since $\omega_\alpha(X_a) = 0$ for $n + 1 \leq \alpha, \beta, \ldots \leq m$, the 1-forms ω_α, when restricted to $U \cap N$, are zero. If ω is a differential form on $U \cap N$, let ω^* denote that form restricted to $U \cap N$ (that is, is pulled back via the map $U \cap N \to U$ defining the submanifold structure of $U \cap N$). Thus the forms $(\omega_a{}^*)$ are a basis of forms on $U \cap N$ dual to the orthonormal basis $(X_a{}^*)$ of vector fields on $U \cap N$. But

$$d\omega_a{}^* = (\omega_{ai} \wedge \omega_i)^* = \omega_{ab}^* \wedge \omega_b{}^*.$$

Since clearly $\omega_{ab}^* + \omega_{ba}^* = 0$, the forms ω_{ab}^* are the corresponding connection forms on $U \cap N$. (This is the dual statement t o(24.6).) The corresponding curvature forms Ω_{ab}^* can be easily computed:

$$\Omega_{ab}^* = d\omega_{ab}^* - \omega_{ac}^* \wedge \omega_{cb}^* = (\Omega_{ab})^* + (\omega_{a\alpha})^* \wedge (\omega_{\alpha b})^*$$

$$= (\Omega_{ab})^* - \Gamma_{a\alpha c} \omega_c{}^* \wedge \Gamma_{b\alpha c_1} \omega_{c_1}^*.$$

Now using the relations (24.11) and (24.4) between the curvature forms, Christoffel symbols and the curvature, we have Theorem 24.4.

THEOREM 24.4

Let N be a submanifold of a Riemannian manifold M. Let $p \in N$, u, v, w, $w_1 \in N_p$, and let (v_α), $n = \dim N < \alpha \leq m = \dim M$, be any orthonormal basis for $N_p^\perp$. Then

$$\langle w, R_N(u, v)(w_1) \rangle - \langle w, R(u, v)(w_1) \rangle = \sum_{\alpha = n+1}^{m} S_{v_\alpha}(w_1, v) S_{v_\alpha}(w, u)$$

$$- S_{v_\alpha}(w_1, u) S_{v_\alpha}(w, v), \qquad (24.13)$$

where $R(,)( )$ and $R_N(,)( )$ are respectively the curvature tensors of M and N, and where $S_{(\ )}(,)$ is the second fundamental form of N. In particular, if u, v are unit orthonormal vectors of N_p, then

$$K_N(u, v) - K(u, v) = \sum_{\alpha = n+1}^{n} S_{v_\alpha}(v, v) S_{v_\alpha}(u, u) - S_{v_\alpha}(u, v)^2, \qquad (24.14)$$

where $K(u, v)$ and $K_N(u, v)$ are respectively the sectional curvatures of M and N in the plane spanned by u and v.

COROLLARY

Suppose that N is a hypersurface in M; that is, $\dim M = \dim N + 1$. Let v_n be a generating vector of $N_p^{\perp}$. Then, for $u, v \in N_p$,

$$K_N(u, v) - K(u, v) = \text{the product of the eigenvalues of the quadratic form } S_{v_n}(\ , \ ) \text{ restricted to the plane spanned by } u \text{ and } v.$$

(These eigenvalues are called the *principal curvatures* of the plane.)

To prove the corollary, recall the following facts from linear algebra:

(i)   A vector $v \in N_p$ is an eigenvector with eigenvalue λ of $S_{v_n}(\ , \ )$ if

$$S_{v_n}(v, u) = \lambda \langle v, u \rangle \qquad \text{for all } u \in N_p.$$

(ii)   The set of all eigenvectors corresponding to a given eigenvalue is a linear subspace of N_p.

(iii)   Eigenvectors corresponding to different eigenvalues are perpendicular with respect to $\langle \ , \ \rangle$.

Hence, to compute (for $u, v \in N_p$) the sectional curvature of the plane spanned by u and v, we can choose u and v so that they are eigenvectors for eigenvalues λ_1 and λ_2 of $S_{v_n}(\ , \ )$ restricted to the plane, and satisfy

$$\langle u, v \rangle = 0, \qquad \langle u, u \rangle = 1, \qquad \langle v, v \rangle = 1.$$
$$S_{v_n}(u, v) = \lambda_1 \langle u, v \rangle = 0,$$
$$S_{v_n}(u, u) = \lambda_1 \langle u, u \rangle = \lambda_1,$$
$$S_{v_n}(v, v) = \lambda_2 \langle v, v \rangle = \lambda_2,$$

whence, from (24.14),

$$K_N(u, v) - K(u, v) = \lambda_1 \lambda_2. \qquad \text{Q.E.D.}$$

Now we turn to the second variation formula in a more general form than that considered in Chapter 22, namely, when we consider homotopies whose end points are not necessarily fixed, but which lie on two submanifolds of M. Explicitly, suppose that:

(a) $\delta(s, t)$, $0 \le s, t \le 1$, is a homotopy in N, with each curve $t \to \delta(s, t)$ parametrized proportionally to arc length. N and N' are submanifolds of M: $\delta(s, 0) \in N$ and $\delta(s, 1) \in N'$ for $0 \le s \le 1$; that is, the end points of the homotopy lie on N and N'. Further, $\sigma(t) = \delta(s, 0)$; $v(t) = \partial_s \delta(0, t) \in M_{\sigma(t)}$. Hence, $t \to v(t)$ is the vector field on σ representing the infinitesimal deformation of σ.

(b) $R(,)( )$ is the curvature tensor of M; $S_{( )}(,)$ and $S_{( )}(,)$ are the second fundamental forms of N and N', respectively. $L(s) =$ length of curve $t \to \delta(s, t)$, $0 \le t \le 1$.

From (20.6) we have

$$L(0) \frac{d}{ds} L(s) \bigg|_{s=0} = \langle v(t), \sigma'(t) \rangle \bigg|_{t=0}^{t=1} - \int_0^1 \langle v(t), \nabla \sigma'(t) \rangle \, dt.$$

This is the first variation formula. It vanishes if

$v(0) \in N_{\sigma(0)}$, $v(1) \in N'_{\sigma(1)}$, that is, $v(0)$ and $v(1)$ are tangent to, respectively, N and N'.   (24.15a)

$\sigma'(0) \in N^{\perp}_{\sigma(0)}$, $\sigma'(1) \in N'^{\perp}_{\sigma(1)}$, that is, σ is perpendicular and N' at, respectively, $t = 0$ and $t = 1$.   (24.15b)

$\sigma(t)$ is a geodesic, that is, $\nabla \sigma'(t) = 0$.   (24.15c)

Formula (24.15a) is, of course, implied by our assumptions that $\delta(s, 0) \in N$ and $\delta(s, 1) \in N'$. Let us suppose further that the remaining conditions are satisfied. We can now carry out the differentiation in the first term of the right-hand side of (22.2), with the result that

$$L(0) \frac{d^2 L}{ds^2} \bigg|_{s=0} = [\langle \nabla_s \partial_s \delta(s, t), \sigma'(t) \rangle \bigg|_{s=0} + \langle v(t), \nabla v(t) \rangle] \bigg|_{t=0}^{t=1}$$

$$- \int_0^1 \langle v(t), \nabla \nabla v(t) + R(v(t), \sigma'(t))(\sigma'(t)) \rangle \, dt.$$

Let us examine the term of the form, say, $\langle \nabla_s \partial_s \delta(s, 0), \sigma'(0) \rangle$, which at first sight does not have a familiar form. However, we shall as usual assume that $\delta(s, t)$ is of a special form, namely, that there exists a vector field $X \in V(M)$ that is tangent to N such that

$$\partial_s \delta(s, t) = X(\delta(s, t)).$$

Then

$$\langle \nabla_s \partial_s \delta(s, 0), \sigma'(0) \rangle = \langle \nabla_X X(\delta(s, 0)), \sigma'(0) \rangle$$

$$= S_{\sigma'(0)}(v(0), v(0)) \qquad \text{for } s = 0.$$

Since this formula is independent of the X chosen, we can be reasonably confident that it holds in general. (Explicit verification is left to reader!) Finally, then, we can write the *second variation formula* in several forms:

$$L(0) \frac{d^2}{ds^2} L(s)\bigg|_{s=0} = S_{\sigma'(t)}(v(t), v(t)) + \langle \nabla v(t), v(t) \rangle \bigg|_{t=0}^{1}$$

$$- \int_0^1 \langle v(t), \nabla\nabla v(t) + R(v(t), \sigma'(t))(\sigma'(t)) \rangle \, dt$$

$$= S_{\sigma'(t)}(v(t), v(t))\bigg|_{t=0}^{1}$$

$$+ \int_0^1 \langle \nabla v(t), \nabla v(t) \rangle - \langle v(t), R(v(t), \sigma'(t))(\sigma'(t)) \rangle \, dt$$

$$= S_{\sigma'(t)}(v(t), v(t))\bigg|_{t=0}^{t=1}$$

$$+ \int_0^1 [\|\nabla v(t)\|^2 - K(v(t), \sigma'(t))\|v(t)\|^2 L(0)^2 \sin^2 \theta(t)] \, dt.$$

$$(24.16)$$

The second form is obtained from the first by integrating by parts the first term in the integrand. The third is obtained from the second by applying the Gram–Schmidt process to the vectors $v(t)$, $\sigma'(t)$; ($\theta(t)$ is the angle between $v(t)$ and $\sigma'(t)$; $L(0)$, the length of the curve $t \to \delta(0, t) = \sigma(t)$, is equal to $\|\sigma'(t)\|$, since σ is parametrized proportionally to arc length).

There is an obvious interest in the first two terms on the right-hand side of (24.16), particularly in knowing geometric conditions that they be zero. The following theorem will give us such conditions.

THEOREM 24.5

Let M be a complete Riemannian manifold, let N be a submanifold of M, let $\delta(s, t)$, $0 \le s, t \le 1$, be a homotopy in N such that $\delta(s, 0) \in N$. Let $\sigma(t) = \delta(0, t)$, and $v(t) = \partial_s \delta(0, t)$. Conclusion: If, for each s, the curve $t \to \delta(s, t)$ is perpendicular to N at $t = 0$, then

$$\langle \nabla v(0), u \rangle = -S_{\sigma'(0)}(v(0), u) \qquad \text{for all } u \in N_{\sigma(0)}. \qquad (24.17)$$

Conversely, if $\sigma(t)$, $0 \le t \le 1$, is a curve in M, with $\sigma(0) \in N$, $\sigma'(0) \in N_{\sigma(0)}^\perp$, and if u_0 and $u_1 \in N_{\sigma(0)}$ satisfy $u_0 \in M_{\sigma(0)}$,

$$\langle u_1, u \rangle = -S_{\sigma'(0)}(u_0, u) \qquad \text{for all } u \in N_{\sigma(0)},$$

then there is at least one homotopy $\delta(s, t)$, $0 \le s, t \le 1$, such that

$$\delta(s, 0) \in N, \qquad \partial_t \delta(s, 0) \in N_{\partial(s, 0)}^\perp. \qquad (24.18)$$

For each s, $t \to \delta(s, t)$ is a geodesic $\delta(s, t) = \sigma(t)$. If $v(t) = \partial_s \delta(0, t)$, then

$t \to v(t)$ is a Jacobi vector field along σ satisfying $v(0) = u_0$, $\nabla v(0) = u_1$. In particular, v satisfies the initial conditions (24.17).

Proof. It suffices to prove this theorem locally, that is, to suppose that N is contained in an open set U that has defined on it a basis of vector fields $X_1, \ldots, X_n \in V(U)$ such that

$$\langle X_i, X_j \rangle = \delta_{ij} \qquad \text{for } 1 \le i, j \le n = \dim M$$
$$\text{(summation convention in force)}$$

so $X_1, \ldots, X_n$ are tangent to N.

Then let $A_i(s, t)$, $B_i(s, t)$ be the functions such that

$$\partial_t \delta(s, t) = A_i(s, t)X_i(s, t), \qquad \partial_s \delta(s, t) = B_i(s, t)X_i(s, t).$$

Our assumptions about δ are equivalent to the conditions

$$A_i(s, 0) = 0 \qquad \text{for } 1 \le i \le n; \qquad B_i(s, 0) = 0 \qquad \text{for } n + 1 \le i \le m.$$

Now

$$\nabla_v(0) = \nabla_t \partial_s \delta(0, 0) = \nabla_s \partial_t \delta(0, 0) = \nabla_s \left(\sum_{n+1 \le i \le m} A_i X_i \right).$$

Hence

$$\langle \nabla_v(0), X_j(\sigma(0)) \rangle = \sum_{\substack{n+1 \le i \le m \\ 1 \le k \le m}} A_i(0, 0)B_k(0, 0) \langle \nabla_{X_k} X_i, X_j \rangle(\sigma(0)) \qquad \text{for } 1 \le j \le n,$$

$$= -\langle \sigma'(0), \nabla_{v(0)} X_j \rangle$$

$$= -S_{\sigma'(0)}(v(0), X_j(\sigma(0))),$$

which proves (24.17).

Now we deal with the converse. Let $\gamma(s)$, $0 \le s \le 1$, be any curve in N with $\gamma'(0) = u_0$. We show that there exists a vector field $s \to w(s) \in N_{\gamma(s)}$ along γ such that

$$w(s) \in N_{\gamma(s)}^\perp, \qquad \text{for } 0 \le s \le 1, \quad \nabla w(0) = u_1, \quad w(0) = \sigma'(0).$$

To do this (again it suffices to work locally), we can choose again the orthonormal bases X_i for vector fields such that X_i, $1 \le i \le n$, is tangent to N. Suppose that

$$\sigma'(t) = \sum_{n+1 \le i \le m} A_i(t)X_i(\sigma(t)), \qquad \gamma'(s) = \sum_{1 \le i \le n} B_i(s)X_i(\gamma(s)).$$

Let us *look* for $w(s)$ of the form

$$w(s) = \sum_{n+1 \le j \le m} \alpha_j(s)X_j(\gamma(s)).$$

Then

$$\nabla w(s) = \sum_{n+1 \le j \le m} \frac{d\alpha_j}{ds} X_j(\gamma(s)) + \sum_{\substack{n+1 \le j \le m \\ 1 \le i \le n}} B_i(s)\alpha_j(s)\nabla_{X_i} X_j(\gamma(s)).$$

This *suggests* that we choose the $\alpha_j(s)$, hence $w(s)$, so that

$$\alpha_j(s) = \langle X_j, \sigma'(0)\rangle \qquad \text{for } n+1 \le j \le m,$$

$$\frac{d\alpha_k}{ds}(0) = \langle u_1, X_k\rangle - \sum_{\substack{n+1 \le j \le m \\ 1 \le i \le n}} B_i(0)\alpha_j(0)\langle \nabla_{X_i} X_j, X_k\rangle(\sigma(0))$$

$$\text{for } n+1 \le k \le m.$$

To show that $w(s)$ so defined satisfies the required conditions, it remains only to check that

$$\langle \nabla w(0), X_k\rangle = \langle u_1, X_k\rangle \qquad \text{for } 1 \le k \le n.$$

But, for $1 \le k \le n$,

$$\langle \nabla w(0), X_k\rangle = \sum_{\substack{n+1 \le j \le m \\ 1 \le i \le n}} B_i(0)\alpha_j(0)\langle X_k, \nabla_{X_i} X_j\rangle(\sigma(0))$$

$$= -\sum B_i(0)\alpha_j(0)\langle \nabla_{X_i} X_k, X_j\rangle(\sigma(0))$$

$$= -\langle \nabla_{\sigma'(0)} X_k, \sigma'(0)\rangle$$

$$= -S_{\sigma'(0)}(u_0, X_k(\sigma(0)))$$

$$= \langle u_1, X_k\rangle, \qquad \text{as required.}$$

Now that we have verified the existence of a vector field $s \to w(s)$ along the curve $s \to \gamma(s)$, we can proceed to the proof of the converse. Choose the homotopy $\delta(s, t)$ so that

$$\delta(s, t) = \exp(tw(s)) \qquad \text{for } 0 \le s, t \le 1.$$

It should be clear that δ satisfies all conditions of (24.18) except possibly the initial conditions, which we now verify:

$$\partial_t \delta(s, 0) = w(s) \qquad \text{and} \qquad \partial_s \delta(s, 0) = \gamma(s),$$

by the definition of the exponential map. Thus

$$v(0) = \partial_s \delta(0, 0) = \gamma'(0) = u_0,$$

$$\nabla v(0) = \nabla_t \partial_s \delta(0, 0) = \nabla_s \partial_t \delta(0, 0) = \nabla w(0) = u_1,$$

which completes the proof.

This theorem suggests several definitions. First, if $\sigma(t)$, $0 \leq t \leq 1$, is a geodesic that is perpendicular to N at $t = 0$, we say that a Jacobi field $t \to v(t)$ along σ is *transversal* to N if it satisfies

$$v(0) \in N_{\sigma(0)} \qquad (24.19a)$$

$$\langle \nabla v(0), u \rangle = -S_{\sigma'(0)}(v(0), u) \qquad \text{for all } u \in N_{\sigma(0)}. \qquad (24.19b)$$

The second part of the theorem asserts that such a vector field arises as the infinitesimal deformation of at least one geodesic deformation of σ such that each geodesic of the deformation is initially perpendicular to N. Let us say that a point $\sigma(t_0)$ of σ, $0 < t_0 \leq 1$, is a *focal point* of N with respect to σ if a nonzero transversal Jacobi field exists which is zero at t_0. The dimension of all such Jacobi fields (notice that $v(t_0) = 0$ and (24.19) are linear homogeneous conditions) is called the *index* of the focal point: Let $N^{\perp} = \bigcup_{p \in N} N_p^{\perp}$ be the normal bundle to N, and let exp: $N^{\perp} \to M$ be the map such that, for $v \in N_p^{\perp}$, $t \to \exp(tv)$ is the geodesic starting at p which is tangent there to v. We then have:

COROLLARY TO THEOREM 24.5

If $u \in N^{\perp}$, $p = \exp(u)$, then p is a focal point of N with respect to the geodesic $t \to \exp(tu)$ if and only if $\exp_*: (N^{\perp})_u \to M_p$ is not 1-1; that is, if and only if exp has a zero Jacobian at u.

Proof. Suppose first that $\exp_*$ is not 1-1. Let $\gamma(s)$, $0 \leq s \leq 1$, be a curve in N, $w(s) \in N_{\gamma(s)}^{\perp}$, be a vector field on γ such that $s \to \exp(w(s))$ has a zero tangent vector at $s = 0$, $w(0) = u$. If $\delta(s, t) = \exp(tw(s))$, $v(t) = \partial_s \delta(0, t)$, then $v(t)$ is a Jacobi vector field along $t \to \exp(tu)$ that is transversal to N and vanishes at $t = 1$; that is, $p = \exp(u)$ is a focal point with respect to the geodesic $t \to \exp(tu)$, according to the above definition.

Conversely, if $t \to v(t)$ is a Jacobi vector field along the geodesic $t \to \exp(tu)$ that vanishes at $t = 1$ and that is transversal to N, by Theorem 24.5 we can construct a geodesic deformation $\delta(s, t)$ satisfying (24.18), such that $\partial_s \delta(0, 0) = v(0)$, $\nabla_t \partial_s \delta(0, 0) = \nabla v(0)$. Then $t \to \partial_s \delta(0, t)$ would be a Jacobi field along $t \to \exp(tu)$ satisfying the same initial conditions at $t = 0$ as $v(t)$; hence, must coincide with $v(t)$. But then

$$\delta(s, 1) = \exp(\partial_s \delta(s, 0));$$

hence, $s \to \delta(s, 1)$ is a curve starting at $\exp(u)$, which is the image under exp of a curve in $N^{\perp}$, and which has a zero tangent vector at $s = 0$. Hence, $\exp_*$ is not 1-1 at u, as required to finish the proof of the corollary.

The corollary provides us with important qualitative information about the distribution of focal points. For example, if $u \in N^{\perp}$, and if $\exp(u)$ is not a focal point (with respect to $t \rightarrow \exp(tu)$), then $\exp(u')$ is not a focal point with respect to $t \rightarrow \exp(tu')$ for all $u' \in N^{\perp}$ that are sufficiently close to u. Further, by Sard's theorem, the set of points $p \in M$ that are focal points with respect to *some* geodesic joining p to N and perpendicular to N is of measure zero. Note further that in case N is a point, say $p_0 \in N$, $N^{\perp} = M_{p_0}$, and the focal points are just conjugate points in the sense defined in Chapter 22. Many of the results proved in Chapters 22 and 23 concerning conjugate points can be generalized to apply to focal points. The Jacobi theorem (Theorem 22.4) is the prime example, and takes the following form:

THEOREM 24.6

Let N be a submanifold of a complete Riemannian manifold M, let $u \in N^{\perp}$ be such that $\exp(u)$ is a focal point of N with respect to the geodesic $t \rightarrow \exp(tu)$. Then, for $a > 1$, $t \rightarrow \exp(tu)$ is not the geodesic of minimal length joining $\exp(au)$ to N.

The proof is similar to the proof of Theorem 22.4, and is left as an exercise.

Now we turn to various elementary geometric applications of these concepts. The first one we have in mind is concerned with the following situation: N is a submanifold of a Riemannian manifold M, p_0 is a point of M, q_0 is a point of N. We ask: What are *sufficient* conditions that guarantee that the real-valued function $q \rightarrow d(p_0, q)$, for $q \in N$, cannot have a relative maximum at $q = q_0$? It will turn out that this is a question that unifies many isolated geometric questions concerning Riemannian spaces, and whose answer falls out in a natural way from the second variation formula. The basic theorem is:

THEOREM 24.7

Let N be a submanifold of a complete Riemannian manifold M. Let p_0 be a point of M, $u \in N_{p_0}$ such that $\exp(u) \underset{\text{def}}{\equiv} p \in N$, and such that the geodesic $t \rightarrow \exp(tu) = \sigma(t)$ is perpendicular to N at $t = 1$. Suppose further that σ satisfies the following condition: For every Jacobi vector field $t \rightarrow v(t)$ along σ such that $v(0) = 0$,

$$\langle \nabla v(t), v(t) \rangle > 0 \qquad \text{for } 0 \leq t \leq 1. \tag{24.20}$$

Suppose in addition that N satisfies any one of the following conditions:

$$N \text{ is a minimal submanifold of } M \tag{24.21}$$

or

$$\dim M \leq 2(\dim N) - 1,$$

and

$$K_N(u_1, u_2) \leq K(u_1, u_2) \qquad \text{for all } u_1, u_2 \in T(N). \tag{24.22}$$

Then there is at least one geodesic deformation $\delta(s, t)$, $0 \le s, t \le 1$, with $\delta(0, t) = \sigma(t)$, $\delta(s, 0) = p$, $\delta(s, 1) \in N$, and with

> length of $t \to \delta(s, t)$ $0 \le t \le 1$, actually greater than the length of σ, if s is sufficiently small, but not zero.

Intuitively, p cannot be a relative maximum of the function $q \to d(p_0, q)$ on N, although this is not strictly true (unless N has within a geodesic ball about p_0 and σ is a minimizing geodesic), so we have stated the theorem in this complicated and more precise form.

A word of definition is needed for the terms used in the statement of the theorem. First, a submanifold N of a Riemannian manifold M, in general, is said to be a *minimal* submanifold of M if for all $p \in N$, all $w \in N^{\perp}$,

$$\lambda_1(w) + \cdots + \lambda_n(w) = 0, \qquad (24.23)$$

where $\lambda_1(w), \ldots, \lambda_n(w)$ are the eigenvalues (counted according to multiplicity) of the symmetric bilinear form $S_u(\ ,\ )$ on N_p ($n = \dim N$).

The geometric interpretation in terms of N minimizing " surface area " will be explained in a second volume. (In case $M = R^3$, with the Euclidean metric, $\dim N = 2$, this definition gives the classical one, that is, soap bubbles.)

The proof consists of a series of lemmas.

LEMMA 24.8

σ contains no conjugate points of $\sigma(0)$ with respect to σ.

The proof is almost obvious:

$$\frac{d}{dt}(v(t), v(t)) = 2\langle \nabla v(t), v(t) \rangle > 0;$$

hence $v(t)$ cannot vanish because $v(0) = 0$; hence, no conjugate points.

LEMMA 24.9

If $v_1 \in N_p$ is such that $S_{\sigma'(1)}(v_1, v_1) = 0$, then there is a geodesic homotopy $\delta(s, t)$ such that

$$\delta(s, 0) = p_0, \qquad \delta(s, 1) \in N, \qquad \delta(0, t) = \sigma(t), \qquad \partial_s \delta(0, 1) = v_1,$$

and $t \to \delta(s, t)$ is of greater length than $t \to \sigma(t)$ if s is > 0, but sufficiently small.

Proof. The fact that $\sigma(1)$ is not a conjugate point of $\sigma(0) = p_0$ with respect to σ implies, we know, that $\exp_*$ is 1-1 in the neighborhood of $(M_{p_0})_u$, where $u \in M_{p_0}$ is such that $\sigma(t) = \exp(tu)$.

Thus there exists a curve $\gamma(s)$ in M starting at p_0, such that $s \to \exp(\gamma(s))$ is any curve in N, in particular, chosen to be tangent to v_1 at $s = 0$. Now define

$$\delta(s, t) = \exp(t\gamma(s)), \qquad L(s) = \text{length of } t \to \delta(s, t).$$

If $v(t) = \partial_s \delta(0, t)$, we see from the second variation formula (24.16) that

$$L(0)\frac{d^2 L}{ds^2}(0) = S_{\sigma'(1)}(v(1), v(1)) + \langle \nabla v(1), v(1) \rangle$$

$$- \int_0^1 \langle v(t), \nabla \nabla v(t) + R(v(t), \sigma'(t))(\sigma'(t)) \rangle \, dt$$

$$= \langle \nabla v(1), v(1) \rangle,$$

since $v(t)$ is a Jacobi vector field, and $v(1) = v_1$. By (24.20), this is greater than zero; whence, the lemma.

Now, in case N is a minimal submanifold of M according to the definition (24.23), $S_{\sigma'(1)}(\ ,\ )$ must have at least one nonpositive and one nonnegative eigenvector; hence it must have at least one $v_1 \in N_{\sigma'(1)}$ that annihilates $S_{\sigma'(1)}$. This suffices to prove the theorem in case condition (24.21) is satisfied. Condition (24.22) is more difficult to handle. The tool is the following lemma, conjectured by Chern and Kuiper [1], but proved by Otsuki [1].

LEMMA 24.10

Let W be a vector space over the real numbers of dimension d. Let $Q_1(\ ,\ ), \ldots, Q_{d-1}(\ ,\ )$ be symmetric, bilinear forms over V such that

$$\sum_{i=1}^{d-1} Q_i(w_1, w_1)Q_i(w_2, w_2) - Q_i(w_1, w_2)^2 \leq 0 \qquad (24.24)$$

for all choice of vectors $w_1, w_2 \in W$. Then there is at least one nonzero vector $w \in W$ such that

$$Q_1(w, w) = 0 = \cdots = Q_{d-1}(w, w).$$

For the proof, we must refer to Otsuki's paper [1].

To apply this to the theorem, we choose $W = N_p$, $Q_1 = S_{\sigma'(1)/\|\sigma'(1)\|}$, and $Q_2, \ldots, Q_{d-1}$ are the second fundamental forms $S_{u_2}(\ ,\ ), \ldots, S_{u_{d-2}}(\ ,\ )$, where $(\sigma'(1)/\|\sigma'(1)\|, u_2, \ldots, u_{d-1})$ is an orthonormal basis of $N_p^\perp$. That (24.24) is satisfied is a consequence of the assumptions made in (24.22), namely, that $K_N(\ ,\ ) \leq K(\ ,\ )$, and the fundamental formula (24.14) relating $K_N(\ ,\ ) - K(\ ,\ )$ and the second fundamental forms. Now, to have

Lemma 24.10 apply to give the vector $v_1 \in N_p$ needed to satisfy $S_{\sigma'(1)}(v_1, v_1)$, we must have

$$\dim M - \dim N = d - 1 \qquad \text{and} \qquad d \le \dim N,$$

whence

$$\dim M \le 2(\dim N) - 1,$$

which is precisely the condition postulated in (24.22).   Q.E.D.

For $p_0 \in M$, $r > 0$, recall that

$$B(p_0, r) = \{p \in M : d(p_0, p) < r\},$$

that is, $B(p_0, r)$ is the ball of radius r about p_0.

COROLLARY TO THEOREM 24.7

Suppose $r > 0$ is such that, for all $u \in M_{p_0}$ and $\|u\| < r$, the geodesic $t \to \exp(tu)$ satisfies (24.20) for $0 \le t \le 1$, and such that $d(\exp(u), p_0) = \|u\|$. Then $B(p_0, (r/2))$ is geodesically convex in the sense that, for $p, q \in B(p_0, (r/4))$, any geodesic of shortest length joining p to q must be completely in $B(p_0, (r/2))$. In particular, there is a geodesically convex ball about each point of M.

Proof. By the triangle inequality for the distance function $d(,)$ we have $d(p, q) \le d(p, p_0) + d(p, q) < r$. Let $\gamma(s)$, $0 \le s \le 1$, be a geodesic of length $d(p, q)$ joining p to q. Then $d(p_0, \gamma(s)) < r$ for $0 \le s \le 1$; hence $\gamma(s) \in B(p_0, r)$ for $0 \le s \le 1$. But, by Theorem 24.7, the function $s \to d(p_0, \gamma(s))$ cannot have a maximum for $0 < s < 1$, since $s \to \gamma(s)$ is a geodesic of M hence $d(p_0, \gamma(s)) \le d(p_0, p) < r/2$. That is, $\gamma(s) \in B(p_0, (r/2))$ for $0 \le s \le 1$.

To show that each point p_0 has a convex ball, it remains only to show that such a positive real number r exists. Suppose, then, that $\sigma(t)$, $0 \le t \le 1$, is a geodesic of M, with $\sigma(0) = p_0$, and that $t \to v(t)$ is a Jacobi vector field along σ that vanishes at $t = 0$. Then

$$\frac{d}{dt} \langle \nabla v(t), v(t) \rangle = \langle \nabla \nabla v(t), v(t) \rangle + \langle \nabla v(t), \nabla v(t) \rangle$$

$$= -\langle R(v(t), \sigma'(t))(\sigma'(t)), v(t) \rangle + \langle \nabla v(t), \nabla v(t) \rangle,$$

which is obviously greater than zero, provided $\|\sigma'(0)\|$ is sufficiently small, and $\|\nabla v(0)\|$ is bounded, say, $\|\nabla v(0)\| \le 1$ and $\|\sigma'(0)\| \le r$. But if this holds for all such $v(t)$ with $\|\nabla v(0)\| \le 1$, clearly $\langle \nabla v(t), v(t) \rangle > 0$. Now this r might vary as $\|\sigma'(0)\|$ varies. But again the infimum of such r is positive as $\sigma'(0)$ varies in direction about p_0.   Q.E.D.

Note an additional fact that follows from this argument: $(d/dt)\langle \nabla v(t), v(t)\rangle$ is always > 0 if

$$\langle v(t), R(v(t), \sigma'(t))(\sigma'(t))\rangle \leq 0.$$

This condition is automatically implied by the condition: The sectional curvature of M is nonpositive. This condition, together with the condition that M be simply connected, implies (Theorem 23.1) that exp: $M_{p_0} \to M$ is a diffeomorphism. With these conditions we conclude that:

> The geodesic balls $B(p_0, r)$, for any $r > 0$, are geo-
> desically convex, if the curvature is nonpositive and
> if M is simply connected. $\qquad$ (24.25)

Another result of this type is:

> If $u \in M_{p_0}$, $\|u\| = r$, if (24.20) is satisfied along the
> geodesic $t \to \exp(tu) = \sigma(t)$, then
>
> $$\exp(\{w \in M_{p_0} \|w\| = r\})$$
>
> is a submanifold about $\exp(u)$, and its second
> fundamental form $S_{-\sigma'(1)}(\ ,\ )$ is positive definite there. $\qquad$ (24.26)

Proof. That it is a submanifold follows from the implicit function theorem, since $\exp(u)$ is not a conjugate point of p_0 (Lemma 24.9). If $v_1 \in M_{\exp(u)}$ is tangent to the submanifold, there is a Jacobi field $t \to v(t)$ with $v(0) = 0$, $v(1) = v_1$, and a geodesic deformation $t \to \delta(s, t)$ with $v(t) = \partial_s \delta(0, t)$, $\|\partial_t \delta(s, 0)\| = r$, $\delta(s, 0) = p_0$. From the second variation formula, we have

$$S_{\sigma'(1)}(v_1, v_1) + \langle \nabla v(1), v(1)\rangle = 0;$$

whence (24.26). Reversing the arguments, the converse of (24.26) is also true, and gives a geometric interpretation of (24.20), namely:

> If $\sigma(t)$, $0 \leq t \leq 1$, is a geodesic of M with $\sigma(0) = p_0$,
> containing no conjugate points of p_0, if, for $0 < r \leq$
> $\|\sigma'(0)\|$, the second fundamental form of $\exp\{w \in M_{p_0}:$
> $\|w\| = r\}$ in the direction $-\sigma'(r/\|\sigma'(0)\|)$ is positive
> definite, then σ satisfies condition (24.20). $\qquad$ (24.27)

Calculation of the Second Fundamental Form of Hypersurfaces

Let f be a real-valued function on a Riemannian manifold M. We want to see how the second fundamental form, hence also the curvature, of the hypersurface $f = $ constant can be computed in terms of f. Construct the gradient (vector) field of f; an element of $V(M)$, denoted by grad f and defined by

$$\langle \text{grad } f, X \rangle = X(f) \qquad \text{for all } X \in V(M).$$

Thus if $p \in M$ is not a critical point for f, that is, if $df \neq 0$ at p, then

$$f - f(p) = 0$$

defines a hypersurface† in a neighborhood of p, and grad $f(p)$ is perpendicular to this hypersurface. Hence $(\text{grad } f / \|\text{grad } f\|)(p)$ is the unit normal to the hypersurface, and the second fundamental form is

$$(X, Y) \rightarrow \left\langle \frac{\text{grad } f}{\|\text{grad } f\|}, \nabla_X Y \right\rangle,$$

for X, Y tangent to the hypersurface, that is, satisfying

$$X(f) = 0 = Y(f).$$

Since $\langle X, \text{grad } f \rangle = 0 = \langle Y, \text{grad } f \rangle$, this can be rewritten as

$$-\frac{\langle \nabla_X \text{grad } f, Y \rangle}{\|\text{grad } f\|}.$$

Let us compute this in terms of an orthonormal moving frame. Let U be an open set of M containing p, with a basis (ω_i) of 1-differential forms that is dual to an orthonormal basis X_i of vector fields in U.

$$(1 \leq i, j, \ldots \leq m = \dim M; \text{ summation convention in force.})$$

Suppose that

$$df = f_i \omega_i, \qquad df_i = f_{ij} \omega_j.$$

Then we see that

$$\text{grad } f = f_i X_i, \qquad \|\text{grad } f\|^2 = f_i f_i.$$

Let (ω_{ij}) be the connection forms corresponding to the given orthonormal basis. Then, for $X \in V(M)$, by (24.12),

$$\nabla_X \text{grad } f = [X(f_i) + f_j \omega_{ji}(X)] X_i.$$

Hence

$$\langle \nabla_X \text{grad } f, Y \rangle = (X(f_i) + f_j \omega_{ji}(X)) \omega_i(Y).$$

---

† A *hypersurface* of a manifold is a submanifold of one lower dimension (that is, of codimension 1).

Thus the eigenvalues of the (normalized) second fundamental form are precisely those of the quadratic form (in i, k):

$$(\lambda_i) = \lambda_i \rightarrow \frac{1}{2}\left(f_{ik} + f_{ki} + f_j(\omega_{ji}(X_k) + \frac{\omega_{jk}(X_i))\lambda_i\lambda_k}{\|\operatorname{grad} f\|}\right), \qquad (24.28)$$

restricted by the condition $f_i\lambda_i = 0$.

Example

$M = $ Euclidean space, with the flat Euclidean metric $f = \frac{1}{2}a_{ij}x_ix_j$, where $(x_1, \ldots, x_n)$ are the Euclidean coordinate system, (a_{ij}) is a symmetric constant matrix. Put the $\omega_i = dx_i$. $df = a_{ij}x_j\,dx_i$, hence

$$f_i = a_{ij}x_j, \qquad f_{ij} = a_{ij}.$$

Since $\omega_{ij} = 0$, the above quadratic form reduces to

$$\frac{a_{ij}\lambda_i\lambda_j}{\|\operatorname{grad} f\|}.$$

These formulas plainly indicate how the second fundamental form is to be computed in principle in terms of the algebraic properties of the matrix (a_{ij}).

Let us carry this out explicitly for the simplest case, namely: Suppose $a_{ij} = \delta_{ij}, f = \frac{1}{2}x_ix_i$; hence $f = r^2$ determines a sphere of radius $r\sqrt{2}$. Suppose, then, that $f(x) = r^2$.

$$f_i = x_i, \qquad f_if_i = x_ix_i = 2f = 2r^2.$$

Hence,

$$\|\operatorname{grad} f\| = \sqrt{2}\,r.$$

The quadratic form is then $\lambda_i\lambda_j/\sqrt{2}\,r$, whence:

> The (normalized) second fundamental form of a sphere of radius r has all eigenvalues equal to $1/\sqrt{r}$. Thus, it has constant sectional curvature equal to $1/r$.

Totally Geodesic Submanifolds

Definition

A submanifold N of a Riemannian manifold M is said to be *geodesic at a point* $p \in N$ if each sufficiently small geodesic of M beginning at p and tangent there to N lies in N completely. N is said to be *totally geodesic* if it is geodesic at each of its points.

Of course this is the geometric definition of a totally geodesic submanifold, designed to generalize the concept of "plane" in Euclidean geometry. We now want to show that this definition is equivalent to several others and that this equivalence is reasonably nontrivial and useful.

THEOREM 24.11

A submanifold N of a Riemannian manifold M is totally geodesic if and only if its second fundamental form of N is identically zero.

Proof. Let $p \in N$, and suppose that N is geodesic at p. Let $\sigma(t)$, $0 \leq t \leq 1$, be a curve in N, beginning at p, which is also a geodesic of M. Set $v = \sigma'(0) \in N_p$. Pick a $u \in N_p^\perp$. Then, almost by definition,

$$S_u(v, v) = \langle u, \nabla v(0) \rangle = \langle u, \nabla \sigma'(0) \rangle = 0.$$

Hence,

if N is geodesic at p, $S_u(\ , \ )$ is identically zero for all $u \in N_p^\perp$.

This proves one part of Theorem 24.11. Turn to the converse; suppose that $S_{(\ )}(\ , \ )$ is identically zero. By (24.7), we see that

$$\nabla_X Y = \nabla_X^* Y,$$

for any pair X, Y of vector fields of M that are tangent to N. (∇^* denotes covariant differentiation in the induced metric on N.) In particular, we have proved:

LEMMA 24.12

If the second fundamental form of N is identically zero, then every curve on N that is a geodesic in the induced metric on N is a geodesic of M also.

But this property of N clearly implies that it is geodesic at each point, by the uniqueness of geodesics.   Q.E.D.

Another useful geometric characterization of total geodesity is Theorem 24.13.

THEOREM 24.13

A submanifold N of a Riemannian manifold M is totally geodesic in M if and only if the following condition is satisfied:

Each sufficiently small geodesic of M whose end points lie on N must lie completely in N.   (24.29)

Proof. Suppose N is totally geodesic. Let $\sigma(t)$, $0 \leq t \leq 1$, be a geodesic of M with $\sigma(0)$ and $\sigma(1) \in N$. If length σ is sufficiently small, $\sigma(1)$ lies in a geodesic ball about $\sigma(0)$, and $\sigma(1)$ can be joined to $\sigma(0)$ by a geodesic nth induced metric on N: By Lemma 24.12 and the uniqueness of geodesics, these must coincide.

Conversely, suppose that (24.29) is satisfied. Let $\sigma(t)$, $0 \leq t \leq 1$, be a geodesic of N in the induced metric. If length σ is sufficiently small, $\sigma(1)$ can be joined to $\sigma(0)$ by a geodesic of M. By (24.29), this geodesic must also lie in N; hence, by the length-minimizing property† of geodesics, it must also be a geodesic of N, which by uniqueness of geodesics on N must equal σ. Thus every geodesic of N is a geodesic of M; hence N is totally geodesic in M. Q.E.D.

This completes our study of the more or less superficial properties of totally geodesic submanifolds. We now go a little deeper and investigate the relation between the properties of totally geodesic submanifolds of M and its curvature tensor.

THEOREM 24.14

Let N be a totally geodesic submanifold of a Riemannian manifold M. Then, for $p \in N$,

$$R(N_p, N_p)(N_p) \subset N_p, \qquad R(N_p; N_p, N_p)(N_p) \subset N_p, \qquad \text{etc.,}$$

where $R(\ ;\ ,\ )$, $R(\ ;\ ;\ ,\ )(\ )$, etc., denote the successive covariant derivatives of the curvature tensor.

Proof. First we must define the *covariant derivative* of the curvature tensor. It is to be an $F(M)$-multilinear mapping $V(M) \times V(M) \times V(M) \times V(M) \to V(M)$, denoted by

$$X, Y, Z, W \to R(X; Y, Z)(W),$$

and defined by

$$R(X; Y, Z)(W) = \nabla_X(R(Y, Z)(W)) - R(\nabla_X Y, Z)(W)$$
$$- R(Y, \nabla_X Z)(W) - R(Y, Z, \nabla_X W). \qquad (24.30)$$

It is easily verified that this formula does actually define an $F(M)$-multilinear mapping; hence it forms what is classically known as a "tensor-field" on M. Our earlier discussion of how to define the values at a point of such tensor fields as differential forms and vector fields can be extended to

† Notice that up to this point we have been using only the self-parallel property of geodesics.

show that all these covariant derivatives of the curvature tensor possess "values" at points of M. For example, the value at p is a multilinear map $M_p \times M_p \times M_p \times M_p \to M_p$, denoted by

$$(v, v_1, v_2, v_3) \to R(v; v_1, v_2)(v_3).$$

For $X, Y, Z, W \in V(M)$, $R(X; Y, Z)(W)(p) = R(X(p); Y(p), Z(p))(W(p))$. This definition can be iterated to define the higher covariant derivatives of the curvature tensor.

Now we know that N totally geodesic is equivalent to $\nabla_X Y$ tangent to N, for any $X, Y \in V(M)$ tangent to N. Hence $\nabla_Z \nabla_X Y$ and $\nabla_X \nabla_Z Y$ are tangent to N, for X, Y, Z tangent to N. By the Ricci identity connecting iterated covariant derivatives, we see that $R(X, Z)(Y)$ is tangent to N. This leads to the statement:

$$R(N_p, N_p)(N_p) \subset N_p.$$

Further covariant derivation leads to the analogous statement for the covariant derivatives.   Q.E.D.

Theorem 24.14 tells us that the tangent spaces to totally geodesic submanifolds cannot be arbitrary. The following theorem tells us what Riemannian manifolds have a maximal number of totally geodesic submanifolds. One feels intuitively that a "generic" Riemannian manifold can have very few totally geodesic submanifolds, but research in this direction is not very advanced.

THEOREM 24.15

Let M be a Riemannian manifold of dimension ≥ 3 such that each two- and three-dimensional tangent subspace is tangent to, respectively, a two- and three-dimensional totally geodesic submanifold. Then M has constant sectional curvature.

Proof. Let $p \in M$, and let N_p be any two-dimensional subspace of M_p. Then $R(N_p, N_p)(N_p) \subset N_p$. Let $v \in M_p \cap N_p^\perp$. Now

$$R(N_p, N_p)(N_p^\perp) \subset N_p^\perp,$$

since each linear transformation $R(u_1, u_2)$ is skew-symmetric. $R(N_p, N_p)(v)$ must belong to $N + (v)$, since $N_p + (v)$ is tangent to a three-dimensional totally geodesic submanifold. By skew-symmetry of $R(,)$, these two relations are compatible only if $R(N_p, N_p)(v) = 0$. Since v is arbitrary in $N_p^\perp$,

$$R(N_p, N_p)(N_p^\perp) = 0. \qquad (24.31)$$

Let v_1, v_2 be orthonormal vectors in N_p. Then, since N_p is an arbitrary two-dimensional subspace, there are relations of the form

$$R(v_1, v_2)(v_1) = -av_2, \qquad R(v_1, v_2)(v_2) = av_2,$$

$$R(v_1, v)(v) = bv_1, \qquad R(v_1, v)(v_2) = 0, \qquad R(v_1, v_2)(v) = 0.$$

We want to prove that $a = b$. Let v_1, v_2 be orthonormal vectors in N_p. Since (24.31) holds for arbitrary two-dimensional subspaces,

$$R(v_1, v + v_2)(v - v_2) = 0.$$

But also $R(v_1, v + v_2)(v - v_2) = R(v_1, v)(v) - R(v_1, v_2)(v_2) = (b - a)v_1$, which implies $a = b$.

This implies that the sectional curvatures of all two-dimensional subspaces of M_p are the same. We now show that they remain constant when p varies over M. Let X_i $(1 \leq i, j, \ldots \leq m = \dim M$; summation convention) be an orthonormal basis for vector fields on an open subset of M, let ω_i be a dual basis of 1-forms, and let $\Omega_{ij} = R_{ijkl}\omega_k \wedge \omega_l$ be the corresponding curvature forms. Let $p - K$ be the function on M whose value at each point p is the common value of the sectional curvatures at this point. Then, by (24.31),

$$R_{ijkl}X_l(p) = R(X_i, X_j)(X_k)(p) = \begin{cases} 0 & \text{if } k \neq i \text{ or } j \\ K(p)X_i(p) & \text{if } k = j, i - j. \end{cases}$$

This implies that

$$\Omega_{ij} = K\omega_i \wedge \omega_j. \tag{24.32}$$

The Bianchi identities for the curvature tensor are

$$d\Omega_{ij} = \omega_{ik} \wedge \Omega_{kj} - \Omega_{ik} \wedge \omega_{kj},$$

where (ω_{ij}) are the connection forms.

From (24.32),

$$d\Omega_{ij} = K\omega_{ik}\omega_k \wedge \omega_j - K\omega_i \wedge \omega_k \wedge \omega_{kj}.$$

But also

$$d\Omega_{ij} = dK \wedge \omega_i \wedge \omega_j + K\omega_{ik} \wedge \omega_k \wedge \omega_j - K\omega_i \wedge \omega_{jk} \wedge \omega_k.$$

Combining these two different ways of computing $d\Omega_{ij}$, we have

$$dK \wedge \omega_i \wedge \omega_j = 0.$$

Here is where we use the fact that $m \geq 3$. The 1-form dK can have zero inner product with all 2-forms only if it is zero; that is, $K = $ constant.   Q.E.D.

25 Groups of Isometries

One theme pervading mathematics for at least a hundred years is the emphasis on the reciprocity between a geometric structure and its group of automorphisms. This attitude pervades physics: For example, we may say that the whole point of the Theory of Special Relativity is to replace the automorphism group of Newtonian mechanics (the Galilean group) by the Lorentz group.

Thus our study of Riemannian manifolds must take into account the group of its automorphisms. Since a complete development would involve us in the technicalities of Lie group theory, we shall limit our treatment to several topics that will give the flavor of what may be called "group-theoretical geometry," trying to get along with a minimum of Lie group theory. As usual in mathematics, the subject is rich and attractive precisely because it involves the interaction of two seemingly different disciplines, but this creates difficulties in exposition.

Let M be a Riemannian manifold, supposed, for simplicity, to be complete. A diffeomorphism $\phi: M \to M$ is said to be an *isometry* of M if

$$\|\phi_*(u)\| = \|u\| \qquad \text{for all } u \in T(M),$$

where $u \to \|u\| = \langle u, u \rangle^{1/2}$ is the length function defined by the metric. Then ϕ preserves the length of curves; hence it also preserves distances between points. (It is an interesting fact that, conversely, a distance preserving homeomorphism is an isometry.) Since obviously the product of two isometries is an isometry, as is the inverse, the set of all isometries forms a *group*†. Now, the first general result of interest is that the group of all isometries forms a *Lie group*.

Let $I(M)$ be the group of isometries of M. As a start, we shall take over the following theorem without proof, which can be found in Helgason's book [1].

THEOREM 25.1

Let M be a Riemannian manifold. $I(M)$ can be made into a Lie group so that:

---

† It is assumed that the reader is familiar with the definition and elementary algebraic properties of groups, as well as certain standard notations.

(a) The map $I(M) \times M \to$ which assigns $\phi(p)$ to each pair $(\phi, p) \in I(M) \times M$ is differentiable.

(b) If $p \in M$, and $\phi_1, \phi_2, \ldots$ is a sequence in $I(M)$ so that $\lim_{j \to \infty} \phi_j(p)$ exists, then at least one subsequence of all ϕ converges to an element of $I(M)$.

The first topic to be studied concerns the relation between the orbits and isotropy groups of a closed subgroup G of $I(M)$. It is known that G itself is a Lie group that acts, in the manner by which it is defined, as a differentiable transformation group on M. For $p \in M$, the *isotropy subgroup*, denoted by G^p, of G at p, is defined by

$$G^p = \{g \in G : gp = p\}.$$

By (b) of Theorem 25.1, G^p is compact. The *orbit* of G at p, denoted by Gp, is defined by

$$Gp = \{gp : g \in G\}.$$

(It is convenient to simplify the notation $g(p)$, that is, the transform of p by the diffeomorphism of M which is g, to gp when no confusion is likely.) Assertion (b) of Theorem 25.1 implies that each orbit is a closed subset of M. Further, each orbit is a submanifold. For the coset space G/G^p is a manifold and the map $G/G^p \to M$ obtained by passing to the quotient from the map $g \to g \cdot p$ if $G \to M$ is a submanifold map. It is even a regularly embedded submanifold, since part (b) of Theorem 25.1 implies that a convergent sequence in Gp must also converge when considered as a sequence in G/G^p.

Now we can state the main general result concerning the structure of the orbits and isotropy subgroups of a closed group of isometries.

THEOREM 25.2

Let G be a closed group of isometries of a complete Riemannian manifold M. Let $p \in M$, and let $N = Gp$, the orbit of G at p. Then there is an open set U of M containing N such that:

(a) $GU = U$, that is, U is the union of orbits of G.
(b) Every $q \in U$ can be joined to N by exactly one geodesic whose length is $d(q, N)$.
(c) For $q \in U$, G^q is conjugate within G to a subgroup of G^p.
(d) U is dense in M.

The main part of the proof is in the following lemma.

LEMMA 25.3

Let N be a closed, regularly embedded submanifold of a Riemannian manifold M. Let $N^{\perp}$ be the normal tangent vector bundle to N. Consider N

as a submanifold of $N^\perp$, via the zero cross section.† Define:

$V = \{v \in N^\perp$: There are no focal points of N along the geodesic $t \to \exp(tv)$, $0 \le t \le 1$, and this geodesic is the only geodesic of length $\le \|v\|$ joining $\exp(v)$ to $N\}$.

Then V is an open subset of $N^\perp$ which contains N. exp restricted to V is a diffeomorphism of $\exp(V)$ with V.

Proof. Suppose that $v_0 \in V$ and that any neighborhood of v_0 in $N^\perp$ contains points of $N^\perp$ not lying in V. Now, since v_0 is not a focal point, that is, the Jacobian of exp: $N^\perp \to M$ is nonsingular at v_0, a neighborhood of v_0 in $N^\perp$ contains no focal points. Thus there are two sequences $v_1, v_2, \ldots$; $u_1, u_2, \ldots$ of elements of $N^\perp$ with

(a) $\lim_{j \to \infty} v_j = v_0$.
(b) $\exp(u_j) = \exp(v_j)$ for $1 \le j < \infty$, but $u_j \ne v_j$.
(c) $\|u_j\| \le \|v_j\|$ for $1 \le j < \infty$.
(d) The geodesics $t \to \exp(tu_j)$ and $t \to \exp(tv_j)$ contain no focal points.

Suppose that $u_j \in N^\perp_{p_j}$. We see that all points p_j lie at a bounded distance from p, where p is the point such that $v_0 \in N_p^\perp$. Since the metric on M is complete and N is a closed regularly embedded submanifold of M, we can assume without loss of generality that

$$\lim_{j \to \infty} p_j = q \in N, \qquad \lim_{j \to \infty} u_j = u \in N_q^\perp.$$

Then $\exp(u) = \exp(v_0)$, $\|u\| \le \|v\|$, which implies that $u = v_0$ by the definition of V. This, however, contradicts the fact that there is a neighborhood of v_0 in $N^\perp$ on which exp is 1-1 when restricted.

This shows that V is open in $N^\perp$. Now, by its definition, exp is 1-1 when restricted to V. Since it also has nonzero Jacobian at each point of V, exp is a diffeomorphism of V with $\exp(V)$.

Return to the case where N is the orbit $G \cdot p$ of a closed subgroup G of $I(M)$. If $V \subset N^\perp$ is as described in Lemma 25.3, it should be clear that‡

$$g_* v \in V \qquad \text{for all } v \in V.$$

Hence,

$$g(\exp V) = \exp V;$$

† That is, $p \in N$ is identified with the zero element of $N_p^\perp$.
‡ If g denotes by the element of G and the diffeomorphism of M derived from $G \subset I(M)$, g_* denotes the linear extension of g to tangent vectors. $g \to g_*$ defines an action of G on $N^\perp$. Since g sends a geodesic of M into a geodesic, the actions of G on M and $N^\perp$ commute with the map $\exp N^\perp \to M$.

hence the $U \subset M$ required for the theorem can be chosen as $\exp(V)$. This will, at any rate, satisfy (a) and (b). To prove (c), let $q \in U$, and let $\sigma(t)$, $0 \le t \le 1$, be the geodesic of minimal length joining q to N. We have

$$G^q \subset G^{\sigma(0)}.$$

For otherwise there is a $g \in G^q$ such that $g \notin G^{\sigma(0)}$; that is, $g\sigma(0) \neq \sigma(0)$, but $gq = q$. Then σ and $g\sigma$ would be distinct geodesics of minimal length joining q to N, contradicting that $q \in U$.

But $\sigma(0) \in N = Gp$; hence $\sigma(0) = gp$ for some $g \in G$. Then one checks easily that

$$G^{\sigma(0)} = G^{gp} = gG^p g^{-1} = \mathrm{Ad}\ g(G^p).$$

That is,

$$\mathrm{Ad}\ g^{-1}(G^q) \subset G^p.$$

To show that U is dense in M, suppose $q \in M$ and $\sigma(t)$, $0 \le t \le 1$, is a geodesic of length $d(q, N)$ joining q to N. Then $\sigma(t) \in U$ for $0 \le t < 1$. For otherwise there would be another geodesic γ joining $\sigma(t_0)$ to N, γ perpendicular to N at $\gamma(1)$. The corner between σ and γ at $\sigma(t_0)$ could be cut across to give a curve of shorter length than σ joining q to N; contradiction.

This finishes the proof of Theorem 25.2.

Remarks

(A)   Theorem 25.2 may be regarded as providing a local structure theorem for a group of isometries, asserting that in the neighborhood of an orbit the action of a closed isometry group is, in a sense, built up from the action of a transitive isometry group, namely, G on Gp, and a linear action of the isotropy subgroup, namely, G^p on $N_p{}^\perp$.

(B)   Let us say that a point $p \in M$ is a *maximal point* for the action of G on M if

$$\dim G^p \le \dim G^q \qquad \text{for all } q \in M,$$

or, equivalently,

$$\dim Gp \ge \dim Gq \qquad \text{for all } q \in M.$$

Let us say that a point $p \in M$ is a *principal point* for the action of G on M if p is a maximal point, and if the number of connected components† of G^p is no greater than the number of connected components of G^q, for any other

---

† Recall that G^p is a compact topological group; hence, as a topological space, it has only a finite number of connected components. As in any topological group, the component containing the identity element is an invariant subgroup of G^p.

maximal point $q \in M$. Thus Theorem 25.2 guarantees that if p is a principal point or maximal point for the action of G, so are all points of U. In particular, the set of all principal and maximal points are both open and dense in M.

In general, if $p \in M$, $g \in G^p$, g_* maps $N_p{}^\perp$ into $N_p{}^\perp$. This defines a homomorphism of G into the group of linear transformations on $N_p{}^\perp$. (This is the linear action referred to in (A) above.) Notice that:

> If p is a principal point for the action of G on M, for each $g \in G^p$, $g_*: N_p{}^\perp \to N_p{}^\perp$ is the identity map.

To prove this remark, suppose $u \in N_p{}^\perp$. We may suppose that $\|u\|$ is sufficiently small so that $\exp(tu) \in U$ for $0 \le t \le 1$. Thus $G^{\exp(u)} \subset G^p$. Since p is a principal point, $G^{\exp(u)} = G^p$; hence $g \exp(u) = \exp(u)$. But $g \exp(u) = \exp(g_*(u))$; hence $\exp(u) = \exp(g_*(u))$, forcing $u = g_*(u)$.

Hence the action of G in a neighborhood of a principal orbit is "trivial" in the sense that a neighborhood is the product of the orbit by a cell of Euclidean space, and the group action on the Euclidean cell is trivial, that is, every element of the group acts as the identity. Another way of putting this is to say that, at the principal points, the structure of isometry groups is just that determined by the extreme types, namely, the transitive groups and the trivial groups. Now we would like to get some idea of the structure of the action of G at points that are not principal orbits. Let us say that two points $p, q \in M$ lie in the *same orbit class* if the isotropy subgroups G^p and G^q are conjugate within G.

THEOREM 25.4

Let G be a closed group of isometries of a complete Riemannian manifold M. Let C be a compact subset of M. Then there are only a finite number of orbit classes among the points of C.

Proof. Proceed by induction on M. If it is zero dimensional, G must be a finite group; hence the statement is obvious. Suppose it is not true for M, but is true for all manifolds of lower dimension. Let (p_j), $1 \le j < \infty$, be a sequence of points of C such that the isotropy subgroups G^{p_j} are all non-conjugate within G. Since C is compact, we can suppose that $\lim_{j \to \infty} p_j = p$.

Let $N = Gp$, the orbit of G at p, and let $N^\perp$ be the normal tangent vector bundle to N. Define

$$S = \{v \in N^\perp : \|v\| = 1\}.$$

S is a manifold of one less dimension than M. G acts on S: For a given $g \in G$ gives, by definition, a diffeomorphism of M. Its differential g_* is a diffeomorphism of $T(M)$, and the correspondence $g \to g_*$ defines an action of G on $T(M)$. (Exercise: Prove this.) S is a submanifold of $T(M)$ and clearly each g_* maps S into itself; hence it defines an action of G on S as a transformation group. We want to apply our induction hypothesis to this action. To do this we must know that S admits a Riemannian metric having the property that G acts as a group of isometries. This will follow from a lemma.

LEMMA 25.5

Let M be a Riemannian manifold. Then $T(M)$ admits a Riemannian metric having the property that the group of isometries of M, when extended to an action on $T(M)$, acts as an isometry group on $T(M)$.

We leave the proof of this lemma as an exercise.

At any rate, we suppose that there are only a finite number of orbit classes of the action of G on S. Suppose that q is a point of M that is close to p, that is, so that $q = \exp v$, for some $v \in V$, where V is the subset of $N^\perp$ that is described in Lemma 25.3. Note that

$$G^q = G^{v/\|v\|},$$

where the right-hand side is the isotropy group of the action of G on S. For if $g_*(v) = v$, then

$$gq = g \exp(v) = \exp(g_*(v)) = \exp(v) = q.$$

That is, $G^{v/\|v\|} \subset G^q$.

If $gq = q$, then $g_*(v) = v$, for otherwise $\exp(v) = \exp(g_*(v))$, contradicting the definition of V, whence $G^q \subset G^{v/\|v\|}$.

Hence there are only a finite number of orbit classes among the orbits of points near p, which contradict the fact that $\lim_{j \to \infty} p_j = p$, and that the orbit classes among the (p_j) are distinct.

In studying the distribution of the various orbits of G, it is convenient to consider the set of orbits as itself forming a space.

Definition

Let G be a closed group of isometries of a Riemannian space M. The *orbit space* of the action of G on M is a space, denoted by $G\backslash M$, abstractly constructed as follows: A point of $G\backslash M$ is an orbit of the action of G on M. $G\backslash M$ is made into a metric space as follows:

For $p, q \in M$, the "distance" between the orbits Gp and Gq is just the minimal distance $d(Gp, Gq)$ between the subsets, defined as usual by using the given Riemannian metric on M.

Define the projection mapping $\phi: M \to G\backslash M$ by assigning $\phi(p) = Gp$ to each $p \in M$.

THEOREM 25.6

The orbit space $G\backslash M$ with the distance function defined as above is a well-defined metric space. The projection mapping $\phi: M \to G\backslash M$ defined above is an open, continuous mapping.

Let M^0 be the set of $p \in M$ such that Gp is a principal orbit of G, and let $(G\backslash M)^0$ be the set of principal orbits, that is, the image under ϕ of M^0. Then $(G\backslash M)^0$ can be made into a manifold so that $\phi: M^0 \to (G\backslash M)^0$ is a maximal rank mapping, in fact a principal fiber bundle with structure group G.

Proof. Given $p \in M$, one can choose a point q on any given orbit of G so that

$$d(p, q) = d(Gp, Gq),$$

(since M is complete and the orbits of G are all closed in M). This fact suffices to show that the metric space axioms are satisfied for $G\backslash M$.

$$d(Gp, Gq) = 0 \Rightarrow d(p, q) = 0 \Rightarrow p = q \Rightarrow Gp = Gq.$$

$$d(Gp, Gq) = d(p, q) = d(q, p) = d(Gq, Gp).$$

To show transitivity, that is,

$$d(Gp, Gr) \le d(Gp, Gq) + d(Gq, Gr),$$

choose q and r on their respective orbits so that

$$d(Gp, Gq) = d(p, q), \qquad d(Gq, Gr) = d(q, r).$$

Then $d(Gp, Gr) \le d(p, r) \le d(p, q) + d(q, r)$, whence transitivity.

Continuity of ϕ also follows easily from this property of the orbits. Suppose that U is an open subset of M, that $p \in U$, and that $d(Gq, Gp)$ is sufficiently small. As remarked above, we can choose q so that $d(Gq, Gp) = d(p, q)$. Hence $q \in U$ if $d(Gq, Gp)$ is sufficiently small, and $\phi(U)$ is open in $G\backslash M$.

There is another way of stating this result:

$$\phi^{-1}(\phi(U)) \text{ is open.}$$

But $\phi^{-1}(\phi(U))$ is the *saturation* of U with respect to G, that is, the union of all orbits of G that touch U.

Turn to the last statement of the theorem. We have seen that M^0 is open in M (Theorem 25.2). Let $p \in M^0$ and $N = Gp$. If V is the subset of $N^\perp$ defined in Theorem 25.2, we have seen that $\exp(V)$ is an open subset of M^0, and that $\exp(V \cap Mp)$ intersects each orbit of G only once. Thus $V \cap Mp \to \phi \exp(V \cap Mp)$ provides a homeomorphism of an open subset of Gp with an open subset of a Euclidean space. It is readily verified that these homeomorphisms combine in the right way to provide a manifold structure for $G\backslash M^0$, which has almost by definition the property that ϕ is a maximal rank mapping.

The fact that $\phi\colon M^0 \to \phi(M^0)$ is a principal fiber bundle mapping follows now at once from the definition of principal fiber bundle, which goes as follows:

Definition

Let E and B be topological spaces, let $\phi\colon E \to B$ be a continuous mapping, and let G be a topological group that acts on E. This setup is said to define a *principal fiber bundle with structure group G and projection map ϕ*, denoted by (E, B, ϕ, G), if each point $b \in B$ has a neighborhood $U \subset B$ and a mapping $\phi\colon U \times G \to E$, such that:

(a) $\phi(U \times G)$ is an open subset of E, and ϕ is a homeomorphism with this subset.

(b) For $b' \in U$, $g, g' \in G$,

$$g\phi(b, g') = \phi(b, gg').$$

Roughly, we may say that a principal fiber bundle is determined by the action of a topological group G on a space E so that (i) G acts simply on E, that is, $g \in G$, $e \in E$, $ge = e$ implies $g = $ identity; (ii) each point of E has a neighborhood invariant under G which is isomorphic to the simplest type of action of G, namely, G acting on a product $U \times G$ by leaving each element of U fixed and acting on G by left translations.

Return to the case where G is a closed group of isometries acting on a complete Riemannian manifold M. Now the principal orbits of G are dense in $G\backslash M$ and hence have a manifold structure. This fact, together with some computations of orbit classes in special cases, suggests that an orbit space be regarded as a sort of "generalized manifold," with the distance function on it that we have used above to define a "generalized Riemannian structure."

We proceed then with a geometric study of the orbit space $G\backslash M$, based on the fact that it is a metric space in the natural way described above.

Lemma 25.7

Let G be a Lie group of isometries of a Riemannian manifold M. Let $\sigma\colon [0, 1] \to M$ be a geodesic of M that is perpendicular to one orbit of G, say, to $G\sigma(0)$. Then $\sigma(t)$ is perpendicular to $G\sigma(t)$ for $0 \le t \le 1$.

Proof. Let $g(s)$, $0 \le s \le 1$, be a curve in G, with $g(0) = $ the identity element. Let $\delta(s, t) = g(s)\sigma(t)$, $0 \le s, t \le 1$. δ is a homotopy in M having the property that, for fixed s, the curve $t \to \delta(s, t)$ is a geodesic whose length is equal to the length of σ (since each transformation $g(s)$ is an isometry of M and hence maps geodesics of M into geodesics). Let $v(t) = \partial_s \delta(0, t)$; that is, $t \to v(t)$ is the vector field on γ representing the infinitesimal deformation. The *first variation formula* implies that

$$\langle v(t), \gamma'(t) \rangle = \langle v(a), \gamma'(a) \rangle \qquad \text{for } 0 \le t \le 1.$$

Now $v(a) \in (G\gamma(a))_{\gamma(a)}$; hence $\langle v(0), \gamma'(0) \rangle = 0$, implying that $\langle v(t), \gamma'(t) \rangle = 0$. But, as γ varies over all such curves in G, $v(t)$ fills up the tangent space to the orbit of G at $\gamma(t)$; hence $\gamma'(t)$ is perpendicular to the orbit as required.

Say that a geodesic of M is *transversal* to the action of G if it is perpendicular to each orbit of G that it touches. Lemma 25.7 then asserts that there is a plentiful supply of such transversal geodesics. Let $\sigma(t)$, $0 \le t \le 1$, be one of them. We say that a Jacobi vector field $t \to v(t)$ along σ is *transversal* to the action of G if there is a geodesic deformation $\delta(s, t)$ of σ whose infinitesimal deformation vector field is v, that is, so that $v(t) = \partial_s \delta(0, t)$. A curve of $G\backslash M$ is a *geodesic* of $G\backslash M$ if it is equal to the projection under the projection map $M \to G\backslash M$ of a geodesic of M that is transversal to the action of G. (The justification for this simplification is that it can be shown that these are precisely the curves that locally minimize arc length, as arc length is defined in the general theory of metric spaces.)

THEOREM 25.8

Let G be a closed group of isometries of a complete Riemannian manifold M. Let L be a closed subgroup of G, and put

$$M(L) = \{p \in M : G^p \text{ is conjugate within } G \text{ to } L\}.$$

Then $M(L)$ and $G\backslash M(L)$ are manifolds and the projection map $M(L) \to G\backslash M(L)$ is a fiber space map. Further, $G\backslash M(L)$ is a totally geodesic subset of $G\backslash M$.

Proof. Obviously, if two points of M lie on the same orbit of G, then the isotropy subgroups of these two point are conjugate in G. Hence $M(L)$ contains the entire orbit of any point it touches: By $G\backslash M(L)$ we mean the subset of the orbit space consisting of those orbits that lie in $M(L)$.

Let $p \in M$, let N be the orbit of G at p, and let U be the neighborhood of N having the properties listed in Theorem 25.2. We have seen that, for any $q \in U$, G^q is conjugate to a subgroup of G^p. Suppose that $G^p = L$, that is, $p \in M(L)$. Any $q \in U$ can then be transformed by an element of G so that $G^q \subset G^p$, and so that the unique geodesic of shortest length joining q to N ends at p. Suppose $t \to \exp(tv)$, $0 \le t \le 1$, $v \in N_p^\perp$, is this geodesic. Then $q \in M(L)$ if and only if $G^q = G^p$. This fact and the geometric properties of U force the following conclusion: $G^p = G^p$ if and only if $g_*(v) = v$ for all $g \in G^p$.

This suggests the following way to parametrize points of $M(L)$ close to p. Define

$$N_p^\perp(L) = \{v \in N_p^\perp : g_*(v) = v \text{ for all } g \in L\}.$$

There is a map $G/L \times N_p^\perp(L) \to M$ defined as follows: For $g \in G, v \in N_p^\perp(U)$, map (g, v) into $\exp(g_*(v))$. Since $\exp((ge)_* v) = \exp(g_* e_*(v)) = \exp(g_*(v))$, this map passes to the quotient to define the desired map of $G/L \times N_p^\perp(L)$. (G/L denotes the space of left cosets of L in G, considered, of course, as a homogeneous space of G.) If we restrict to the product of G/L with a sufficiently small neighborhood of 0 in $N_p^\perp(L)$, by our above remarks this map is a homeomorphism with a neighborhood of p in $M(L)$. Similarly, mapping this neighborhood of zero in $N_p^\perp(L)$ onto $M(L)$, then projecting on $G\backslash M(L)$, defines a homeomorphism with a neighborhood of the orbit Gp. If we use these homeomorphisms to define manifold structures for $M(L)$ and $G\backslash M(L)$ (it is left to the reader to check that the manifold axioms are fulfilled), that the map $M(L) \to G\backslash M(L)$ is a fiber space map follows more or less by definition.

Turn to the totally geodesic statement. We must make precise what is meant by "totally geodesic" in $G\backslash M$, since it is not quite a Riemannian manifold. Now, of all the equivalent defining properties of a totally geodesic submanifold of a Riemannian manifold, one is adapted to generalize to a metric space: We say that a subset A of a metric space Q is *totally geodesic* if, given $q \in A$, there is a neighborhood U of q in Q such that every geodesic curve of Q starting at q, which lies in U and ends on A, must lie completely in A. In the case $Q = G\backslash M$, with the fact that geodesics in Q are projections of G-transversal geodesics in M, we see that the neighborhood constructed above of the orbit whose isotropy group is L has precisely this property; hence $G\backslash M(L)$ is totally geodesic in $G\backslash M$.   Q.E.D.

The next question is: Given a subgroup $L \subset G$, does the metric space structure on $G\backslash M$, restricted to $G\backslash M(L)$, arise from a Riemannian metric on $G\backslash M(L)$, and how can this Riemannian metric be computed in terms of the given Riemannian metric on M?

THEOREM 25.9

Let M be a complete Riemannian manifold, and let L be a group of isometries of M. Let $F(L)$ be the fixed point set of L; that is,

$$F(L) = \{p \in M : gp = p \text{ for all } g \in L\}.$$

Then $F(L)$ is a closed, regularly embedded totally geodesic submanifold of M. In addition, for $p \in F(L)$, the tangent space to $F(L)$ at p, namely $F(L)_p$, is precisely

$$\{v \in Mp : g_*(v) = v \text{ for all } g \in L\}.$$

Proof. Let $p, q \in F(L)$. Let $\sigma(t)$, $0 \le t \le 1$, be the geodesic joining p to q, and let $g \in L$. If p and q are sufficiently close together (for example, if q lies on a convex ball about p), then $g\sigma(t) = \sigma(t)$ for $0 \le t \le 1$. (Otherwise there would be two small geodesics joining p to q.) If $v = \sigma'(0)$, then $g_*(v) = v$ and $q = \exp(v)$.

This shows that the intersection of $F(L)$ and a sufficiently small neighborhood of p is contained in

$$\exp(\{v \in Mp\colon g_*(v) = v \text{ for all } g \in L\}).$$

This provides coordinate systems to make $F(L)$ into a manifold. The argument also shows that it is a totally geodesic submanifold, since a sufficiently small geodesic of M whose end points lie on $F(L)$ must then lie completely in $F(L)$.

THEOREM 25.10

Let G be a closed group of isometries of a complete Riemannian manifold M. Let L be a compact subgroup of G, and let $N(L, G)$ be the normalizer of L in G; that is,

$$N(L, G) = \{g \in G\colon gLg^{-1} \subset L\}.$$

Let $F^0(L) = \{p \in M\colon G^p = L\}$. Then $F^0(L)$ is an open submanifold of $F(L)$, which is left invariant by the action of $N(L, G)$, and

$$N(L, G)\backslash F^0(L) \text{ is isomorphic to } G\backslash M(L).$$

All orbits of $N(L, G)$ on $F^0(L)$ are principal.

Proof. To show that $F^0(L)$ is open in $F(L)$, suppose $p \in F^0(L)$ and that $q \in F(L)$ is sufficiently close to p. Then $G^p = L \subset G^q$. We have seen that G^q is conjugate to a subgroup of G^p. This, however, is possible (since they are compact) if and only if $G^q = L$, that is, $q \in F^0(L)$.

Suppose now that $p \in F^0(L)$, $g \in G$, and $gp \in F^0(L)$. Then $G^p = L = G^{gp}$. But

$$G^{gp} = gG^pg^{-1} = gLg^{-1}.$$

(*Proof.* Let $h \in G^{gp}$. Then $hgp = gp$, or $g^{-1}hgp = p$, or $g^{-1}hp \in G^p$, or $h \in gG^pg^{-1}$.) Thus g must belong to $N(L, G)$.

Let $p \in F^0(L)$. The orbit of p under $N(L, G)$ must be contained in $M(L)$. Thus we obtain a map of $N(L, G)\backslash F^0(L) \to G\backslash M(L)$, which is obviously onto. Let us show that it is 1-1: Suppose, then, that points $p, q \in F^0(L)$ lie on the same orbit of G. The argument in the last paragraph shows that p and q must lie on the same orbit of $N(L, G)$.

The isotropy subgroup of $N(L, G)$ at each point of $F^0(L)$ is obviously $N(L, G) \cap L$; hence all orbits are principal and the orbit space $N(L, G) \backslash F^0(L)$ is a manifold. That the mapping

$$N(L, G) \backslash F^0(L) \to G \backslash M(L)$$

is differentiable is seen by referring back to the way in which the manifold structures were defined. (Details are left to the reader.)

To complete the proof, we shall show that this map is an isometry of Riemannian manifolds. Let p and q be points of $F^0(L)$ that are close together, and let $\sigma(t)$, $0 \le t \le 1$, be a geodesic of minimal length joining Gp to Gq. After translating by G, we can suppose that $\sigma(0) = p$. Now length $\sigma \le d(p, q)$. Hence, if $d(p, q)$ is sufficiently small, we have

$$G^{\sigma(1)} \subset G^p = L.$$

But $\sigma(1) = gq$, for some $g \in G$; hence $G^{\sigma(1)} = L$, hence $\sigma(1) \in F^0(L)$, and $g \in N(L, G)$. Thus

$$d(Gp, Gq) \ge d(N(L, G)p, N(L, G)q).$$

The reverse inequality is obvious. Q.E.D.

We change direction now to treat the infinitesimal properties of groups of isometries. First we must describe the *Lie algebra* of a Lie group.

Definition

Let G be a Lie group. Its *Lie algebra*, usually denoted by **G**, is defined as follows:

(a) An element of **G** is a one-parameter subgroup of G, that is, a mapping $g: R \to G$ such that

$$g(t + s) = g(t) \cdot g(s) \qquad \text{for } -\infty < t, s < \infty.$$

(b) **G** is defined as a real Lie algebra (in the abstract sense) as follows: If g_1 and g_2 are one-parameter subgroups, that is, elements of **G**, then $g_1 + g_2$ is the one-parameter subgroup g_3:

$$g_3(t) = \lim_{n \to \infty} \left(g_1\left(\frac{t}{n}\right) g_2\left(\frac{t}{n}\right) \right)^n.$$

The Jacobi bracket, $[g_1, g_2]$, is the one-parameter sugbroup g_4:

$$g_4(t) = \lim_{n \to \infty} \left(g_1\left(-\frac{t}{n}\right) g_2\left(-\frac{t}{n}\right) g_1\left(\frac{t}{n}\right) g_2\left(\frac{t}{n}\right) \right)^{n^2}.$$

It is shown in treatises in the theory of Lie groups that these limits exist, define one-parameter subgroups, and that these operations satisfy the algebraic conditions necessary to show that **G** is well defined as a Lie algebra.

For our purposes, it is most important to see what the Lie algebra means in terms of transformation groups. Suppose, then, that G acts as a transformation group (in a C^∞ way) on a manifold M. Each one-parameter subgroup $t \to g(t)$ in G then acts on M. We have seen that it has a unique vector field X as an infinitesimal generator; that is, each orbit $t \to g(t)p$ of g is an integral curve of X. It is most important to realize that this mapping $\mathbf{G} \to V(M)$ is a Lie algebra homomorphism; that is, that the sum and bracket of two one-parameter subgroups have as infinitesimal generators the sum and Jacobi bracket of this infinitesimal generator. (Again we assume this as a basic fact in the theory of Lie groups.) This homomorphism $\mathbf{G} \to V(M)$ may be described as the *infinitesimal version* of the action of G on M.

Return to the case of a Riemannian manifold.

THEOREM 25.11

Let X be the infinitesimal generator of a one-parameter group of transformations of a Riemannian manifold M. Then this is a one-parameter group of isometries if and only if

$$\langle \nabla_Y X, Z \rangle + \langle \nabla_Z X, Y \rangle = 0 \qquad \text{for all } Y, Z \in V(M). \qquad (25.1)$$

These conditions amount to a system of differential equations for the vector field X. These equations are called the *Killing equations*, and the solutions are called *Killing vector fields*.

Proof. Let $t \to g(t)$ be the one-parameter transformation group generated by X. If Y is a vector field, let p be the vector field: $p \to g(t)_*(Y(g(-t)p))$. The following relation is easily derived:

$$\left. \frac{\partial}{\partial t} g(t)_*(Y) \right|_{t=0} = [Y, X].$$

Expressing the fact that g_t is a group of isometries, we have

$$
\begin{aligned}
g(t)^*(\langle Y, Z \rangle)(p) &= \langle Y(g(t)p), Z(g(t)p) \rangle \\
&= \langle g(-t)_*(Y(g(t)p)), g(-t)_*(Z(g(t)p)) \rangle \\
&= \langle g(-t)_*(Y), g(-t)_*(Z) \rangle(p).
\end{aligned}
$$

Taking $\partial/\partial t$ and setting $t = 0$, we have

$$X(\langle Y, Z \rangle) = \langle [X, Y], Z \rangle + \langle Y, [X, Z] \rangle \qquad \text{for all } Y, Z \in V(M). \quad (25.2)$$

(Although we shall not pursue the point, the equations are those guaranteeing that the *Lie derivative* by X of the metric tensor is zero.) But

$$X(\langle Y, Z\rangle) = \langle \nabla_X Y, Z\rangle + \langle Y, \nabla_X Z\rangle,$$

using one of the characteristic properties of the Riemannian affine connection. Since the connection has zero torsion, $[X, Y] = \nabla_X Y - \nabla_Y X$. Combining these three equations gives the Killing equations, (25.1).

Conversely, if X is a Killing vector field, (25.2) is verified. To show that $t \to g_t$ is a group of isometries, it is most convenient to use a local coordinate system, $x_1, \ldots, x_n$ ($1 \le i, j, \ldots \le n = \dim M$; summation convention). Then $g_{ij} = \langle (\partial/\partial x_i), (\partial/\partial x_j)\rangle$ are the components of the metric tensor in this coordinate system, and the length of a curve $x_i(s)$ is

$$g_{ij} \frac{dx_i}{ds} \frac{dx_j}{ds}.$$

First suppose that the coordinate system may be chosen so that $X = \partial/\partial x_1$. Then, using (25.2),

$$X(g_{ij}) = \left\langle \left[X, \frac{\partial}{\partial x_i}\right], \frac{\partial}{\partial x_j}\right\rangle + \left\langle \frac{\partial}{\partial x_i}, \left[X, \frac{\partial}{\partial x_j}\right]\right\rangle = 0,$$

and the length of a curve is

$$g_{ij}(x_2(s), \ldots, x_n(s)) \frac{dx_i}{ds} \frac{dx_j}{ds}.$$

But the integral curves of X, that is, the orbits of $g(t)$, are then

$$t \to x_2(x_1(0) + t, x_2(0), \ldots, x_n(0)),$$

and we see quite explicitly that these transformations preserve length.

In case X cannot be put (locally) in this canonical form, proceed as follows: Introduce $M' = M \times (-\infty, \infty)$, with t the additional coordinate, $X' = X + (\partial/\partial t)$, and the metric on M' that is the product of that on M and the Euclidean metric on $(-\infty, \infty)$. It is readily verified that X' is a Killing vector field for this product metric and that the one-parameter group it generates is a group of isometries if and only if $t \to g_t$ is composed of isometries. But the above argument can be applied to X', since it is everywhere nonzero.

Q.E.D.

Remark. As a bonus from this proof, we see that a metric admits a Killing vector field that is nonzero in a neighborhood of a point if and only if the point admits a coordinate system in which the components g_{ij} of the metric are functions of $x_2, \ldots, x_n$ alone.

The following geometric fact is useful as an illustration of what can be done with the Killing equations.

THEOREM 25.12

Let X be a Killing vector field on a Riemannian manifold M, and let $f = \langle X, X \rangle$ be the length function of X on M. Then a point $p \in M$ is a critical point for f if and only if the integral curve of X beginning at p is a geodesic of M.

Proof. Let $Y \in V(M)$.

$$Y(\langle X, X \rangle) = 2\langle \nabla_Y X, X \rangle = -2\langle \nabla_X X, Y \rangle.$$

Hence p is a critical point for $\langle X, X \rangle$ if and only if $\nabla_X X(p) = 0$. If $X(p) = 0$, we are finished, since we count a constant integral curve of X as a geodesic, even if a degenerate one. Suppose $X(p) \neq 0$. Let $\sigma(s)$, $0 \le t \le 1$, be the geodesic of M, with $\sigma(0) = p$, $\sigma'(0) = X(p)$. Let $v(s) = X(\sigma(s))$, that is, v is X restricted to σ. A general property is: v is a *Jacobi vector field* on σ. This is easiest to see if X generates a global one-parameter group of isometries: $t \to \phi_t$. Then $s \to \phi(\sigma_t(s))$ is also a geodesic; hence $\delta(s, t) = \phi_t(\sigma(s))$ is a geodesic deformation of σ whose infinitesimal deformation field is precisely v. That v is Jacobi follows from our earlier work. In the case where X does not generate a global isometry group, a slight variant of this argument may be used: $\delta(s, t)$ may still be defined, for t sufficiently small, so that for each s, $t \to \delta(s, t)$ is an integral curve of X. Again we must prove that $s \to \delta(s, t)$ is geodesic. This can be done, for example, by reducing X to canonical form, as in the proof of Theorem 6.3. But

$$\nabla v(0) = \nabla_{\sigma'(0)} X = \nabla_X X(p).$$

Thus p is a critical point if $\nabla v(0) = 0$, that is, if and only if (by the uniqueness of Jacobi fields)

$$X(\sigma(s)) = v(s) = \sigma'(s) \qquad \text{for } 0 \le s \le 1.$$

This is precisely the desired conclusion.

A detailed study of the Killing equations as differential equations is not possible here, but we shall do a few items of this nature as illustrations.

LEMMA 25.13

Let X be a Killing vector field on M; p a point such that $X(p) = 0 = \nabla_v X$, for all $v \in M_p$. Then X is identically zero on M.

Proof. Let $\sigma(s)$, $0 \le s \le 1$, be a geodesic of M beginning at p. We have seen that X restricted to σ is a Jacobi vector field. The initial value of this Jacobi field and its first covariant derivative must vanish; hence X restricted to σ must vanish identically, hence X is zero in a neighborhood of p. Thus the set of all points where X is zero is both open and closed; hence, equals M, since M is connected.   Q.E.D.

THEOREM 25.14

Let M be a Riemannian manifold, and let $\mathbf{I}(M)$ denote the set of Killing vector fields on M. Then:

(a) $\mathbf{I}(M)$ is a Lie subalgebra of $V(M)$.
(b) If $n = \dim M$, then $\dim \mathbf{I}(M) \le n(n + 1)/2$.
(c) If $X \in \mathbf{I}(M)$, $Y, Z \in V(M)$, then

$$\nabla_Y \nabla_Z X = R(Y, X)(Z) + \tfrac{1}{2}\nabla_{[Y, Z]} X.$$

(d) For $X, Y \in \mathbf{I}(M)$, $Z \in V(M)$,

$$R(X, Y)(Z) = \nabla_{[X, Y]} Z - \tfrac{1}{2}\nabla_{[Z, X]} Y + \tfrac{1}{2}\nabla_{[Z, Y]} X + [Z, [X, Y]].$$

Proof. The straightforward computation needed to prove (a) is left to the reader.

We now prove (b):

For $p \in M$, let $\mathbf{I}(M)^p = \{X \in \mathbf{I}(M): X(p) = 0\}$. Since $\mathbf{I}(M)^p$ is the kernel of the restriction map $X \to X(p)$, it suffices to show that

$$\dim \mathbf{I}(M)^p \le \frac{n(n + 1)}{2} - n = \frac{n(n - 1)}{2}.$$

Now each $X \in \mathbf{I}(M)^p$ has, by definition, a singular point at p. We can then define the *linear approximation* to X at p, l_X, as a linear transformation: $Mp \to Mp$ as follows: $l_X(v) = [Y, X](p)$, where $Y \in V(M)$ is such that $Y(p) = v$. For $w \in Mp$,

$$\langle l_X(v), w \rangle = \langle [Y, X], w \rangle = \langle \nabla_X Y, w \rangle - \langle \nabla_Y X, w \rangle$$
$$= \langle \nabla_{X(p)} Y, w \rangle - \langle \nabla_Y X, w \rangle$$
$$= -\langle \nabla_v X, w \rangle,$$

since $X(p) = 0$. We conclude:

$$l_X(v) = -\nabla_v X \qquad \text{for } v \in Mp.$$

X is identically zero if and only if $l_X = 0$ (using Lemma 25.13).

l_X is a skew-symmetric (with respect to the form $\langle \, , \, \rangle$) linear transformation of Mp.

Thus $\dim \mathbf{I}(M)^p \le$ dimension of space of skew-symmetric $n \times n$ real matrices $= n(n - 1)/2$.

Turn to the proof of (c). If σ is a geodesic of M, we see that X restricted to σ is a Jacobi vector field. Then, writing out the Jacobi equations,

$$\nabla_{\sigma'(s)} \nabla_{\sigma'(s)} X = R(\sigma'(s), X)(\sigma'(s)).$$

Since σ is arbitrary,

$$\nabla_Y \nabla_Y X = R(Y, X)(Y) \qquad \text{for all } Y \in V(M).$$

We want to "polarize" this identity:

$$\nabla_{(Y+Z)} \nabla_{(Y+Z)} X = \nabla_Y \nabla_Y X + \nabla_Z \nabla_Z X + \nabla_Z \nabla_Y X + \nabla_Y \nabla_Z X$$
$$= R(Y + Z, X)(Y + Z)$$
$$= R(Y, X)(Y) + R(Z, X)(Z) + R(Y, X)(Z) + R(Z, X)(Y).$$

Hence,

$$\nabla_Z \nabla_Y X + \nabla_Y \nabla_Z X = R(Z, X)(Y) + R(Y, X)(Z).$$
$$\nabla_Z \nabla_Y X + \nabla_Y \nabla_Z X = 2\nabla_Y \nabla_Z X + R(Z, Y)(X) + \nabla_{[Z, Y]} X$$

(using the Ricci identity for iterated covariant derivatives).

Use the "cyclic permutation identity" for the curvature tensor:

$$R(Z, X)(Y) - R(Z, Y)(X) - R(Y, X)(Z) = 0.$$

Putting these together gives (c).

Proof of (d):

$$[[X, Y], Z] = \nabla_{[X, Y]} Z - \nabla_Z [X, Y] = \nabla_{[X, Y]} Z - \nabla_Z \nabla_X Y + \nabla_Z \nabla_Y X$$
$$= (\text{using (c)}), \nabla_{[X, Y]} Z - R(Z, Y)(X) - \tfrac{1}{2}\nabla_{[Z, X]} Y$$
$$+ R(Z, X)(Y) + \tfrac{1}{2}\nabla_{[Z, Y]} X.$$

Use the cyclic identity for R:

$$R(Z, X)(Y) - R(Z, Y)(X) - R(Y, X)(Z) = 0,$$

and we get (d).   Q.E.D.

In favorable cases, formula (d) may be applied to compute the curvature tensor of M in terms of the Lie-algebra structure of $\mathbf{I}(M)$. The most favorable situation is when M is a symmetric homogeneous space.

Definition

Suppose that a manifold M is acted on transitively by a Lie group G, with K the isotropy subgroup of G at a fixed point $p \in M$ (so that M is the coset space G/K). Let $\mathbf{G}$ be the Lie algebra of G, $\mathbf{K}$ the subalgebra corresponding to K. M is then said to be a *symmetric homogeneous space* (relative to the action of G) if there is an automorphism α of $\mathbf{G}$ such that

$$\mathbf{K} = \{X \in \mathbf{M} : \alpha(X) = X\}; \qquad \alpha^2 = \text{the identity}.$$

This condition can be rephrased as follows: Put

$$\mathbf{P} = \{X \in \mathbf{G} : \alpha(X) = -X\}.$$

Then,

(a) **G** is the direct sum of **K** and **P**;
(b) $[\mathbf{K}, \mathbf{P}] \subset \mathbf{P}$;
(c) $[\mathbf{P}, \mathbf{P}] \subset \mathbf{K}$.

Conversely, if a subspace **P** of **G** exists satisfying these three conditions, α can be defined as the identity on **K**, and minus the identity on **P**, so that the *symmetric* condition is equivalent to the existence of such a **P**. We also say that a **K** satisfying this condition is a *symmetric subalgebra*.

The symmetric spaces are very important for differential geometry, since on the one hand they include most of the interesting "classical" spaces, such as spaces of constant curvature, projective spaces, and Grassman varieties, and on the other hand their geometric properties can be treated with general methods that do not work so well for more complicated sorts of spaces. They form a "max-min" class of spaces, that is, they seem to be the largest class of spaces that can be treated with certain unified techniques. Of course this definition is not the most geometric one possible, but we must refer to Helgason's book [1] for details. We shall present two general theorems about them as illustrations.

THEOREM 25.15

Suppose $M = G/K$ is a symmetric homogeneous space, and that M is a Riemannian manifold on which G acts as a group of isometries. Let P be the subspace of **G** satisfying (a), (b), and (c) of the definition.

(a) For $X, Y, Z \in \mathbf{P}$,

$$R(X(p), Y(p))(Z(p)) = [Z, [X, Y]](p),$$

where p is the point of M at which K is the isotropy subgroup of G. Qualitatively, the curvature tensor of M is determined completely by the algebraic properties of **G**.

(b) The covariant derivative of the curvature tensor of M is zero; that is, the curvature tensor is invariant under parallel translation.

Proof. The infinitesimal action of G on M defines **G** as a Lie algebra of Killing vector fields on M. The basic conditions we need are: The restriction map $X \to X(p)$ defines an isomorphism of **P** with Mp.

For $X, Y \in \mathbf{P}$, $[X, Y](p) = 0$. Theorem 25.14 gives

$$R(X, Y)(Z) = \nabla_{[X, Y]}Z - \tfrac{1}{2}\nabla_{[Z, X]}Y$$
$$+ \tfrac{1}{2}\nabla_{[Z, Y]}X + [Z, [X, Y]] \qquad \text{for } X, Y, Z \in \mathbf{G}. \qquad (25.3)$$

If we take $X, Y, Z \in \mathbf{P}$, and restrict to p, we have part (a).

We now prove

$$\nabla_X Y(p) = 0 \qquad \text{for } X, Y \in \mathbf{P}. \qquad (25.4)$$

First $\nabla_X Y(p) = (\nabla_Y X + [X, Y])(p) = \nabla_Y X(p)$. Take $Z \in \mathbf{P}$:

$$\begin{aligned}
\langle \nabla_X Y, Z \rangle(p) &= -\langle \nabla_Z Y, X \rangle(p) = -\langle \nabla_Y Z, X \rangle(p) \\
&= \langle \nabla_X Z, Y \rangle(p) = \langle \nabla_Z X, Y \rangle(p) \\
&= -\langle \nabla_Y X, Z \rangle(p) = -\langle \nabla_X Y, Z \rangle(p),
\end{aligned}$$

or

$$\langle \nabla_X Y, Z \rangle(p) = 0; \qquad \text{hence } \langle \nabla_X Y(p), Mp \rangle = 0,$$

forcing $\nabla_X Y(p) = 0$.

The *covariant derivative* of the curvature tensor is an $F(M)$-multilinear mapping of

$$V(M) \times V(M) \times V(M) \times V(M) \to V(M),$$

denoted by $R(\ ;\ ,\ ,\ )(\ )$, and defined by the identity

$$\nabla_W(R(X, Y)(Z)) = R(W; X, Y)(Z) + R(\nabla_W X, Y)(Z) + R(X, \nabla_W Y)(Z)$$
$$+ R(X, Y)(\nabla_W Z) \qquad \text{for } X, Y, Z, W \in V(M). \qquad (25.5)$$

(This identity can be turned around actually to define the covariant derivative of R, or any tensor field, for that matter. One simply puts $R(W; X, Y)(Z)$ on the left-hand side, everything else on the right-hand side, uses the resulting formula to define $R(W; X, Y)(Z)$ in terms of R and ∇, and then verifies that the formula is $F(M)$-multilinear.)

We now demonstrate how this can be used to show that the vanishing of $R(W; X, Y)(Z)$ identically is necessary and sufficient for the invariance of R (or any tensor field, for that matter) under parallel translation. Let $\sigma(t)$, $0 \le t \le 1$, be a regular curve of M, and let $v_1(t), v_2(t), v_3(t)$ be self-parallel vector fields on σ; that is,

$$\nabla v_1 = 0 = \nabla v_2 = \nabla v_3.$$

Invariance under parallel translation of R means, then, that

$$\nabla(R(v_1, v_2)(v_3)) = 0.$$

It is sufficient to verify this in a special case, namely, suppose X, Y, Z, W are vector fields such that

$$\sigma'(t) = W(\sigma(t)), \qquad 0 \le t \le 1,$$

$$X(\sigma(t)) = v_1(t), \qquad Y(\sigma(t)) = v_2(t), \qquad Z(\sigma(t)) = v_3(t).$$

Then

$$\nabla v_1(t) = \text{(by definition)}, \nabla_W X(\sigma(t)),$$

$$\nabla v_2(t) = \nabla_W Y(\sigma(t)), \qquad \text{etc.}$$

$$\nabla(R(v_1, v_2)(v_3)) = \nabla_W(R(X, Y)(Z))(\sigma(t)) = 0,$$

if $R(\; ; \, , \,)(\,)$ vanishes identically. The converse follows by just inverting the argument.

After this excursion into tensor analysis, we return to proving part (b). Since G acts transitively on M and any isometry preserves R and all its covariant derivatives (the proof is left to the reader), it suffices to prove that the covariant derivative of R vanishes at p. Using (25.4) and (25.5), it suffices to prove that

$$\nabla_W(R(X, Y)(Z))(p) = 0 \qquad \text{for } X, Y, Z, W \in \mathbf{P}.$$

By (25.4), $\nabla_W([Z, [X, Y]])(p) = 0$. Thus, when we apply ∇_W to both sides of (25.3), it suffices to deal with a term of the form

$$\nabla_W \nabla_{[X, Y]} Z = \text{(using Theorem 25.14)}, R(W, Z)([X, Y]) + \tfrac{1}{2}\nabla_{[W, [X, Y]]} Z.$$

But $[X, Y] \in \mathbf{K}$; hence $[W, [X, Y]] \in \mathbf{P}$, and we see that both terms vanish at p, which finishes the proof.

26 Deformation of Submanifolds in Riemannian Spaces

Let M and N be Riemannian manifolds with, say, dim $N <$ dim M. The *embedding* and *deformation* problems can be described as follows:

(A) Does there exist an isometric embedding of N in M, that is, a mapping $\phi: N \to M$ that is 1-1 and satisfies

$$\|\phi_*(v)\| = \|v\| \qquad \text{for } v \in T(N)?$$

(B) Given two isometric embeddings $\phi_1, \phi_2: N \to M$, does there exist an isometry $\alpha: M \to M$ such that

$$\phi_1 = \alpha\phi_2?$$

If not, how can the family of all isometric embeddings be described? These may be described as the two main problems of Riemannian geometry. Both involve the theory of nonlinear partial differential equations (mostly of the yet-to-be-created kind); hence we cannot present much more than a series of incomplete comments, which at most will serve to introduce the reader to the problems. In addition in this chapter we mean to introduce the more general ideas that will appear in the second volume of this book.

The Generalization of Developable Surfaces

Classically, a *developable surface* is a surface in Euclidean 3-space satisfying the condition: *Each point of the surface is contained in a curve having the property that the tangent plane to the surface is self-parallel along the curve.* One of the main theorems of elementary surface theory is that the Gaussian curvature of the developable surface is zero and that, conversely, if the Gaussian curvature is zero and if certain local regularity conditions are satisfied, then the surface is developable. (Actually, the classical theory of surfaces is imprecise on this point.)

This definition makes sense for an arbitrary submanifold of a Riemannian manifold if, of course, one replaces "parallel" by the parallel translation of Riemannian geometry. Let us make this precise. Suppose N is a submanifold of the Riemannian manifold M, ∇ is the covariant derivative operation

362

associated with the Riemannian structure on M, and $\langle \ , \ \rangle$ is the inner product. Let Q be a submanifold of N such that:

> For each curve $\sigma(t)$, $0 \leq t \leq 1$, in Q, the field $t \to N_{\sigma(t)}$
> is self-parallel under parallel translation along σ.

The condition for this is that $t \to \nabla v(t)$ be tangent to N for any vector field $t \to v(t)$ along σ that is tangent to N. This implies the following condition:

> $\nabla_X Y$ is tangent to N, for each X, $Y \in V(M)$ such that
> X is tangent to Q, Y is tangent to N. $\qquad$ (26.1)

Let $S_{(\ )}(\ ,\ )$ be the second fundamental form of N; that is,

> $S_u(X, Y) = \langle \nabla_X Y, u \rangle$ for each X, Y tangent to N,
> each $u \in N^{\perp}$. $\qquad$ (26.2)

Then (26.1) is equivalent to

$$S_{N_p{}^{\perp}}(Q_p, N_p) = 0 \qquad \text{for all } p \in Q. \qquad (26.3)$$

Equation (26.1) can now be iterated: $\nabla_{X_1} \nabla_X Y$ is tangent to N, for each X, X_1 tangent to Q, each Y tangent to N. But

$$\nabla_{X_1} \nabla_X Y = \nabla_X \nabla_{X_1} Y + R(X, X_1)(Y);$$

hence,

$$R(Q_p, Q_p)(N_p) \subset N_p \qquad \text{for all } p \in Q. \qquad (26.4)$$

We can iterate by covariantly differentiating (26.4), giving the conditions

$$R(Q_p; \ldots; Q_p; Q_p, Q_p)(N_p) \subset N_p \qquad \text{for all } p \in S. \qquad (26.5)$$

$(R(\ ; \ldots; \ , \ )(\ )$ denotes all successive covariant derivatives of the curvature tensor, as defined in Chapter 23.)

THEOREM 26.1

Let N be a submanifold of a Riemannian manifold M, Q a submanifold of N. Conditions (26.3) through (26.5) are necessary and sufficient that the tangent spaces to N be self-parallel along Q.

That these conditions are sufficient is easily seen by reversing these steps. We now search for the conditions for the existence of such a Q. Condition (26.2) suggests the following definition.

Definition

Let N be a submanifold of M. A vector $v \in N_p$ is a *characteristic vector* (of the second fundamental form) if

$$S_u(v, N_p) = 0 \qquad \text{for all } u \in N_p{}^{\perp}. \qquad (26.6)$$

C_p denotes the set of characteristic vectors ($C_p(N)$ if ambiguity is possible). Let C_p' be the following subspace of C_p:

$$C_p' = \{v \in C_p \colon R(v, N_p)(N_p) \subset N_p, \qquad (26.7a)$$

and

$$R(v; N_p; \dots; N_p; N_p, N_p)(N_p) \subset N_p \text{ for all } p \in S\}. \qquad (26.7b)$$

THEOREM 26.2

Let N be a submanifold of M, with C_p' defined for $p \in M$ by (26.7). Suppose that

$$\dim C_p' = \text{constant for } p \in N. \qquad (26.8)$$

Then, through each $p \in N$, there is a unique maximal connected submanifold Q such that

$$Q_q = C_q' \qquad \text{for each } q \in Q. \qquad (26.9)$$

Further, Q is a totally geodesic submanifold of M (hence also of N) such that the tangent spaces to N are self-parallel along Q.

Proof. Let $\mathbf{C}' = \{X \in V(M) \colon X(p) \in C_p' \text{ for each } p \in N\}$. Condition (26.8) implies that $\mathbf{C}'(p) = C_p'$ for all $p \in N$. Thus $\mathbf{C}'$ forms a nonsingular vector-field system on N. We want to show that

$$\nabla_X Y \in \mathbf{C}' \qquad \text{for } X, Y \in \mathbf{C}'. \qquad (26.10)$$

This will also show that $[X, Y] \in \mathbf{C}'$; hence, that $\mathbf{C}'$ is completely integrable.

The global form of the Frobenius complete integrability theorem will imply the existence of Q. Formula (26.10) will also imply that Q is a totally geodesic submanifold of M.

Now we prove (26.10):

$\nabla_X Y(p) \in C_p$ for all $p \in N$ if and only if $\nabla_{(\nabla_X Y)} Z$ is tangent to N, for Z tangent to N. $\qquad (26.11)$

But

$$
\begin{aligned}
\nabla_{(\nabla_X Y)}(Z) &= \nabla_Z \nabla_X Y + [\nabla_X Y, Z] \\
&= \nabla_X \nabla_Z Y + R(Z, X)(Y) + [\nabla_X Y, Z] \\
&= \nabla_X \nabla_Y Z + \nabla_X([Z, Y]) + R(Z, X)(Y) + [\nabla_X Y, Z],
\end{aligned}
$$

which is plainly tangent to N, which proves (26.11).

Now, for Z, W tangent to N,

$$R(\nabla_X Y, Z)(W) = \nabla_X(R(Y, Z)(W)) - R(Y, \nabla_X Z)(W) - R(Y, Z)(\nabla_X W),$$

which we see is tangent to N.

The further conditions necessary to prove (26.10) follow in a similar way, using the definition of iterated covariant derivatives of R. Q.E.D.

So far, we have been working with an arbitrary M. In case M is special, for example, of constant curvature, results even closer to the classical theory of developable surfaces can be obtained. For example:

THEOREM 26.3

Suppose that N is a submanifold of M, that

$$C = \{X \in V(M): X(p) \in C_p \text{ for all } p \in N\},$$

and dim C_p is constant for $p \in N$, and that

$$R(C_p, C_p)(N_p) \subset N_p \qquad \text{for all } p \in N. \tag{26.12}$$

Then the vector field system C is completely integrable, and if Q is one of its integral submanifolds, then the tangent spaces to N are self-parallel along Q. If, further,

$$R(C_p, N_p)(N_p) \subset N_p \tag{26.13}$$

then Q is a totally geodesic submanifold of M.

We leave it as an exercise to the reader to show that (26.13) is automatically satisfied if M has constant curvature.

Proof. We prove that C is completely integrable, that is, $[C, C] \subset C$. For $X, Y \in C$, Z tangent of N,

$$\nabla_{[X, Y]} Z = \nabla_X \nabla_Y Z - \nabla_Y \nabla_X Z - R(X, Y)(Z),$$

which is tangent to N. The rest of the theorem follows routinely from our work in proving Theorems 26.1 and 26.2.

In summary, we may say that this work develops a generalization of the classical theory of developable surfaces to reasonably general Riemannian situations. The classical theory completely ignores the possibility of singularities in the developable structure, and only recently (Massey [1] and Hartman-Nirenberg [1]) has work begun on the singularities. A developable surface in 3-space with singularities may be described as a surface $Q \subset R^3$ such that each point $p \in S$ satisfies either (a) or (b):

(a) p is contained in a line segment lying in S along which the tangent plane is self-parallel.

(b) The principal curvatures are zero at p, that is, the second fundamental form is zero at p.

(The necessary and sufficient condition for this is that S be of zero Gaussian curvature.) In this form the conditions may be generalized to higher dimensional and Riemannian situations, but this goes beyond the scope of this book.

Deformation Problems for Riemannian Submanifolds

In this section we shall compare different isometric embedding of the same Riemannian manifold N into a Riemannian manifold M. Hence, for the sake of clarity, we explicitly label submanifold mappings, supposing that ϕ and ϕ' are two isometric embeddings of N into M. In addition to being isometries, we shall suppose that ϕ and ϕ' satisfy the following condition, which will simplify the discussion considerably. (Note that it is automatically satisfied if M is of constant curvature, which is the classical situation.)

> If $p \in N$, $u, v \in N_p$, then the sectional curvature of the
> planes spanned by $\phi_*(u)$, $\phi_*(v)$ and $\phi_*'(u)$, $\phi_*'(v)$
> are the same.   (26.14)

We shall not repeat this fixed assumption throughout this section. Let ϕ and ϕ' be two isometric embeddings of a Riemannian manifold N in a Riemannian manifold M. Let $\phi(N)^{\perp}$ and $\phi'(N)^{\perp}$ be the normal vector bundles to the submanifolds determined by ϕ and ϕ'. Then ϕ and ϕ' are *rigidly related* if there is a map $\psi: \phi(N)^{\perp} \to \phi'(N)^{\perp}$ such that:

> For $p \in N$, ψ maps the normal tangent vectors to
> $\phi(N)$ at $\phi(p)$ linearly onto the normal tangent vectors
> to $\phi'(N)$ at $\phi'(p)$, preserving the inner product on
> these normal vectors that is inherited from M.   (26.15a)

For $p \in N$, $u \in \phi(N)^{\perp}_{\phi(p)}$, $v, w \in N_p$,

$$S_u(\phi_*(v), \phi_*(w)) = S'_{\psi(u)}(\phi_*'(v), \phi_*'(w)),$$ (26.15b)

where $S_{()}(\ ,\ )$ and $S'_{()}(\ ,\ )$ are, respectively, the second fundamental forms of N and N'.

Condition (26.15a) can be summarized in the language of fiber bundles by saying that ψ is a bundle isomorphism of the two normal vector bundles defined on N by the isometric embeddings. It is easy to see that such isomorphisms exist locally: Whether they exist globally is a purely topological question, toward which much current research in differential topology is applicable. For a geometer, (26.15b) is the key condition. However, we must defer a further explanation of its geometric meaning. Suffice it to say that in case M is a space of constant curvature (which is the classical situation), it suffices to guarantee that ϕ_1 and ϕ_2 are related by an isometry α of M; that is, $\phi_1 = \alpha\phi_2$.

In favorable cases it can be proved that two isometric embeddings are rigidly related for purely algebraic reasons. The following theorem offers at least a qualitative explanation of this.

THEOREM 26.4

Let ϕ be an isometric embedding of N in M. Suppose that $m = \dim M$, $n = \dim N$. Choose the following range of indices and summation conventions:

$$1 \le i, j, \ldots \le n; \qquad 1 \le a, b, \ldots \le m - n.$$

For each $p \in N$, choose a fixed orthonormal basis (v_i) of N_p and (u_a) of $\phi(N)_{\phi(p)}^{\perp}$. Consider the second fundamental forms $(S_{u_a}(\ , \ ))$ as symmetric bilinear forms on N_p, and let θ_{ia} be the 1-covectors, that is, 1-forms, on N_p, defined by

$$\theta_{ia}(v) = S_{u_a}(v, v_i) \qquad \text{for } v \in N_p.$$

Suppose that:

(a)   Any other set θ'_{ia} of 1-forms on N_p related to the θ_{ia} as

$$\theta'_{ia} \wedge \theta'_{ja} = \theta_{ia} \wedge \theta_{ja}, \qquad \theta'_{ia}(v_j) = \theta'_{ja}(v_i) \tag{26.16}$$

must be deducible from the θ_{ia} by relations of the form

$$\theta'_{ia} = M_{ab}\theta_{ib}, \tag{26.17}$$

where (M_{ab}) is an orthogonal matrix, that is, satisfies $M_{ab}M_{cb} = \delta_{ac}$. (In other words, relations (26.16) must imply (26.17), from some choice of M_{ab}.)

(b)   The forms $S_{u_a}(\ , \ )$ are linearly independent. Then any other isometric embedding of N in M (satisfying (26.14) as always) is rigidly related to ϕ.

Proof. Let $\phi': N \to M$ be another isometric embedding. For $p \in N$, let (u_a') be an orthonormal basis for $\phi'(N)_{\phi'(p)}^{\perp}$, let $S'_{u'_a}(\ , \ )$ be the corresponding second fundamental forms, and let θ_{ia} be 1-forms defined by $\theta_{ia}(v) = S'_{u'_a}(v, v_i)$. That (26.16) is satisfied is implied by the fundamental relation between second fundamental forms and curvature, and the fact that (26.14) is satisfied. Let M_{ab} be the orthogonal matrix satisfying (26.17). Define a linear mapping $\psi_p: \phi(N)_{\phi(p)}^{\perp} \to \phi'(N)_{\phi'(p)}^{\perp}$ by the condition

$$\psi_p(u_a) = M_{ba}u_b'.$$

Now it is readily verified that ψ_p is independent of the bases we have used to define it; hence we may consider it as defining a global map $\psi: \phi(N)^{\perp} \to \phi'(N)^{\perp}$, satisfying (26.15a). Further, condition (26.15b) follows trivially from (26.17).   Q.E.D.

Remarks. The condition that $S_{u_1}(\ ,\ ), \ldots, S_{u_{m-n}}(\ ,\ )$ be linearly independent forms forces a condition between n and m, namely,

$$m - n \le \frac{n(n + 1)}{2} \qquad \text{or} \qquad m \le \frac{(n + 1)(n + 2)}{2}.$$

(Since $(n(n + 2)/2)$ is the maximal number of linearly independent quadratic forms on a vector space of dimension n, this corresponds to the intuitive fact that when m is too big in relation to n, there is just too much freedom in the perpendicular direction to hope to get rigidity.)

Finding effective sufficient conditions for reasonably general cases that (26.17) be satisfied is a difficult algebraic problem which is beyond the scope of this book. In case dim M − dim $N = 1$, that is, N is a hypersurface in M, the answer is quite simple, and was found by E. Cartan [3]. We shall follow his proof.

THEOREM 26.5

Let $\phi: N \to M$ be an isometric embedding of N as a hypersurface in M such that the following condition is satisfied:

> For $p \in M$, the dimension of the space of characteristic vectors of the second fundamental form of N at $\phi(p)$ is no greater than $n - 3$. Then ϕ is rigidly related to any other isometric embedding of N in M. (26.18)

Proof. Let $S(\ ,\ ) = S_{u_n}(\ ,\ ), \theta_i = \theta_{in}, \theta_i' = \theta_{in}$, in the notation of Theorem 26.4

Let C_p be the set of characteristic vectors of S; that is,

$$C_p = \{v \in N_p : S(v, w) = 0 \text{ for all } w \in N_p\}.$$

Notice also that

$$C_p = \{v \in N_p : \theta_i(v) = 0 \text{ for } 1 \le i \le n\}.$$

Equation (26.16) takes the form

$$\theta_i \wedge \theta_j = \theta_i' \wedge \theta_j'.$$

At most relabeling things, we can suppose that $\theta_1, \ldots, \theta_\alpha$ are a maximal linearly independent set from among the θ_i ($\alpha = n - $ dim C_p, since $\theta_1 = 0 = \cdots = \theta_\alpha$ defines C_p). Thus the 2-covectors $\theta_i \wedge \theta_j$, $1 \le i, j \le \alpha$, are linearly independent; hence so are the $\theta_i' \wedge \theta_j'$ for $1 \le i, j \le \alpha$. This implies that the $\theta_1', \ldots, \theta_\alpha'$ are linearly independent. Turning the argument around, we see that $\theta_1', \ldots, \theta_\alpha'$ are a maximal set of linearly independent forms from the θ_a'.

Now $\alpha \geq 3$. For $v \in C_p$, $1 \leq i, j \leq \alpha$,

$$0 = v \lrcorner (\theta_i' \wedge \theta_j') = \theta_i'(v)\theta_j' - \theta_j'(v)\theta_i'.$$

Since i can be chosen different from j (requiring only $\alpha \geq 2$, as a matter of fact), $\theta_i'(v) = 0$. By symmetry, we see that

$$C_p = \{v \in N_p : \theta_i'(v) = 0\} = \{v \in N_p : S'(v, w) = 0 \text{ for all } w \in N_p\},$$

where S' is the symmetric (by assumption (26.16)) form defined by

$$S'(v, v_i) = \theta_i'(v) \qquad \text{for } v \in N_p.$$

Notice that we must prove that

$$S(\ ,\ ) = \pm S'(\ ,\ ),$$

since a one-dimensional orthogonal matrix must be ± 1. Since the characteristic vectors of S and S' are the same, it suffices to prove this relation on $C_p^\perp$ or, what amounts to the same thing, to suppose the special case $C_p = 0$ or $\alpha = n$. Now

$$0 = \theta_1 \wedge \theta_1 \wedge \theta_2 = \theta_1 \wedge \theta_1' \wedge \theta_2'.$$

Thus θ_1, θ_1', and θ_2' must be linearly dependent, or since θ_1' and θ_2' are independent, θ_1 is dependent on θ_1' and θ_2'. Similarly, θ_1 is dependent on θ_1' and θ_3'. However, since θ_1', θ_2', θ_3' are independent (here we use $\alpha \geq 3$), θ_1 must be dependent on θ_1' alone, say $\theta_1' = a_1\theta_1$. But, 1 has played no privileged role; hence

$$\theta_i' = a_i \theta_i \qquad \text{for } 1 \leq i \leq \alpha \qquad \text{(no summation)}.$$

But then

$$\theta_i' \wedge \theta_j' = a_i a_j \theta_i \wedge \theta_j \qquad \text{(no summation)}.$$

Hence,

$$a_i a_j = 1 \qquad\qquad \text{for } 1 \leq i < j < \alpha.$$

$$a_1 a_2 = a_1 a_3; \qquad \text{hence } a_2 = a_3.$$

By symmetry, $a_i = a_1$ for $1 \leq j \leq \alpha$; hence $a_1^2 = 1$, which is what is required to finish the proof.

Part **4** DIFFERENTIAL GEOMETRY
AND THE CALCULUS OF VARIATIONS:
ADDITIONAL TOPICS
IN DIFFERENTIAL GEOMETRY

27 First-Order Invariants of Submanifolds and Convexity for Affinely Connected Manifolds

As in Euclidean geometry, many of the geometric properties of submanifolds of Riemannian manifolds really involve only the underlying affine connection. It is worth our while to change the point of view from that of the calculus of variations and attempt to describe the geometric invariants of submanifolds more systematically, using mainly the underlying affine connection. As a bonus, of course, the results will hold also for pseudo-Riemannian manifolds, which is of interest for applications to physics (for example, the Theory of General Relativity).

In this chapter, M will be a manifold with a given affine connection, denoted by ∇, and N will be a submanifold. We shall assume that ∇ has zero torsion tensor. Recall that ∇ is defined by a bilinear mapping of $V(M) \times V(M) \to V(M)$, say, $(X, Y) \to \nabla_X Y$, satisfying

$$\nabla_X(fY) = X(f)Y + f\nabla_X Y \tag{27.1}$$

$$\nabla_{fX} Y = f\nabla_X Y \qquad \text{for } X, Y \in V(M), \quad f \in F(M). \tag{27.2}$$

Recall the significance of these laws. Equation (27.2) implies that the connection depends "tensorially" on X, but (27.1) implies that this is not so in Y. However, it may be possible to consider quotient relations that kill off the first term on the right-hand side of (27.1), and hence convert the covariant derivative operation into a genuine "tensor field." We can now apply this remark.

Definition

For each point $p \in N$, define a bilinear mapping, $S: N_p \times N_p \to M_p/N_p$ as follows: For u, v tangent vectors to N at p, choose vector fields X and Y *that are tangent* to N, that satisfy $X(p) = u$, $Y(p) = v$, and set

$S(u, v) =$ image of $\nabla_X Y(p)$ under the quotient projection map $M_p \to M_p/N_p$.

To verify that $S(\ ,\ )$ is well defined, notice that the map $(X, Y) \to \nabla_X Y(p) \to M_p/N_p$ is bilinear also when X and Y that are tangent to N are multiplied by functions. $S(\ ,\ )$ is called the *second fundamental form* of N.

To get a real-valued bilinear form from S, choose any 1-covector ω at p that is *zero* on N_p and so passes to the quotient to define a linear form on M_p/N_p. Define:

$$S_\omega(u, v) = \omega(S(u, v)) = \omega(\nabla_X Y), \text{ if } X \text{ and } Y \text{ are vector}$$
fields tangent to N with $X(p) = u$, $Y(p) = v$.

We now present in the formal lemmas some of the main geometric properties of this form.

LEMMA 27.1

$S(\ , \ )$ is a symmetric bilinear form.

Proof. The torsion tensor $T(\ , \ )$ is

$$T(X, Y) = \nabla_X Y - \nabla_Y X - [X, Y].$$

If X and Y are tangent to N, then so is $[X, Y]$. Thus $T(X, Y) = 0$ implies $\nabla_X Y - \nabla_Y X(p) \equiv 0 \pmod{N_p}$, which shows that $S(X(p), Y(p)) = S(Y(p), X(p))$.
                                                                                                Q.E.D.

LEMMA 27.2

Let $u \in N_p$ be a tangent vector to N that is tangent to a geodesic of the affine connection on M that lies on N. Then $S(u, u) = 0$. In particular, if N is geodesic at p, $S(\ , \ )$ is identically zero at p.

Proof. Let X be a vector-field tangent to N such that $X(p) = u$ and the integral curve of X beginning at p is a geodesic. By the definition of geodesic, $\nabla_X X = 0$ along the geodesic, in particular at p, whence $S(u, u) = 0$.

N is said to be *geodesic* at p if all geodesics beginning at p and tangent there to N remain tangent. That $S(\ , \ )$ identically zero at p is a necessary condition should now be evident.

LEMMA 27.3

Let $p \to H_p \subset M_p$ be a field of tangent subspaces of N defined for $p \in N$ such that

$$M_p = N_p \oplus H_p.$$

Such a field defines an induced affine connection on N, denoted by ∇^N, in the following way:

> For X^*, $Y^* \in V(N)$, choose $X, Y \in V(M)$ which reduce to X^* and Y^* on N. For $p \in N$, put $\nabla^N_{X*} Y^*(p) =$ projection of $\nabla_X Y(p)$ on N_p.

Proof. The main point is to show that the projection of $\nabla_X Y(p)$ on N_p is zero if X or Y are zero on N. But this should be rather evident.

If H_p is identified with M_p/N_p, note that this definition of ∇^N can be rewritten as

$$\nabla_X^N Y - \nabla_X Y = S(X, Y) \qquad \text{for } X, Y \in V(M), \text{ tangent to } N.$$

LEMMA 27.4

If $S(\ ,\ )$ is identically zero for all points $p \in N$, then N is totally geodesic; that is, N is geodesic at each of its points.

Proof. Since this is a purely local problem, we can suppose that there is at least one such field $p \to H_p$ of tangent subspaces enabling us to define an induced affine connection on N. Notice that $S(\ ,\ ) = 0$ implies that this connection really does not depend on H (hence there is an induced connection globally defined on N). Also, $\nabla_X Y = \nabla_X^N Y$ for X, Y tangent to N. In particular, a geodesic of N in the induced connection is a geodesic for the given connection on M. By the uniqueness of geodesics having given tangent vector, this proves that N is geodesic at each point. Q.E.D.

Convex Hypersurfaces and Functions

Now we turn to the following question: Let f be a real-valued function on M, and let p be a point of N that is a critical point for f restricted to N. Then df restricted to N is zero at p; that is,

$$df(v) = v(f) = 0 \qquad \text{for all } v \in N_p. \tag{27.3}$$

We now ask how to compute the Hessian of f, restricted to N, at the critical point p. Now, in general, the Hessian is a quadratic form, denoted by $v \to h_f(v)$, on N_p. It can be defined as follows: For $v \in N_p$, pick a vector field X that is tangent to N, satisfies $X(p) = N$, and put

$$h_f(v) = X(X(f))(p). \tag{27.4}$$

We want to express (27.4) more precisely in terms of the geometry of N and f. Suppose that f itself does not have a critical point at p. Then (27.3) expresses the geometric fact that N and the level surface $f^{-1}(f(p))$ are tangent at p. Let $S_{df}^f(\ ,\ )$ be the second fundamental form. A basic formula is

$$h_f(v) = S_{df}(v, v) - S_{df}^f(v, v). \tag{27.5}$$

To prove (27.5), start from (27.4):

$$X(X(f)) = X(df(X)) = \nabla_X(df)(X) + df(\nabla_X X).$$

Now $df(\nabla_X X)(p) = S_{df}(v, v)$, by definition.

$\nabla_X(df)(X)(p)$ depends only on the value of X at p; hence we can choose a vector field Y satisfying $Y(f) = 0$, $Y(p) = X(p)$. Then

$$\nabla_X(df)(X)(p) = \nabla_Y(df)(Y)(p) = Y(df(Y)) - df(\nabla_Y Y)(p)$$
$$= -S^f_{df}(Y(p), Y(p)),$$

which proves (27.5).

To realize the significance of this formula, let us compute $S^f_{df}(\ ,\ )$ in case M is Euclidean space, with coordinates (x_i), $1 \leq i \leq n$, and the flat affine connection (that is, $\nabla_{\partial/\partial x_i}(\partial/\partial x_j) = 0$):

$$df = \frac{\partial f}{\partial x_i}\, dx_i.$$

Suppose $Y = A_i(\partial/\partial x_i)$ satisfies $df(Y) = 0$; that is, $A_i(\partial f/\partial x_i) = 0$.

$$S^f_{df}(Y, Y) = df(\nabla_Y Y) = df\left(A_i \frac{\partial A_1}{\partial x_i}\frac{\partial}{\partial x_j}\right) = A_i \frac{\partial A_j}{\partial x_i}\frac{\partial f}{\partial x_j} = -A_i A_j \frac{\partial^2 f}{\partial x_i\, \partial x_j}.$$

Recall that the function f is said to be convex if its Hessian matrix $(\partial^2 f/(\partial x_i\, \partial x_j))$ is positive semidefinite. This then implies that:

$$\text{The form } v \to S^f_{df}(v, v) \text{ is nonpositive.} \qquad (27.6)$$

Such a condition, verified at all noncritical points of f, is then the appropriate generalization of "convex function" to an affinely connected manifold. Similarly, we can say that a hypersurface N of M is *convex* if, for each $p \in N$, each form λ on M_p with $\lambda(N_p) = 0$, the following condition is satisfied:

$$\text{The form } v \to S_\lambda(v, v) \text{ on } N_p \text{ does not change sign.}$$

Now we turn to the question of proving "geometric convexity" of regions bounded by convex hypersurfaces.

THEOREM 27.5

Suppose that f is a function on N such that $f(p) = 0$, $f^{-1}(0)$ is a hypersurface that is geodesic at p and is tangent to the hypersurface N at p. Suppose that $S_{df}(v, v) \leq 0$ for all $v \in N_p$. Then p has a neighborhood U such that

$$f(q) \leq 0 \qquad \text{for all } q \in N \cap U;$$

that is, N lies, in a neighborhood of p, completely on "one side" of the hypersurface $f^{-1}(0)$.

Notice the analogy with the statement in Euclidean geometry that a convex hypersurface lies completely on one side of its tangent plane.

Proof. Using (27.5), we see that the function $q \to f(q)$, for $q \in N$, has a relative maximum at $q = p$. Q.E.D.

THEOREM 27.6

Suppose that f is a real-valued function on M such that:

For $t \in [0, 1]$, the hypersurface $f^{-1}(t)$ is strictly convex in the sense that $S^f_{df}(v, v) < 0$ for all $v \in M_p$, satisfying $v(f) = 0$, $0 \le f(p) \le 1$.

Then the set of all points $p \in M$ such that $0 \le f(p) \le 1$ is geodesically convex in the sense that a geodesic whose end points lie on the set lies completely on the set.

Proof. Suppose $\sigma(t)$, $0 \le t \le 1$, is a geodesic with $0 \le f(\sigma(0))$ and $f(\sigma(t)) \le 1$. If $f(\sigma(t))$, for $0 \le t \le 1$, does not lie on the interval $[0, 1]$, there is a point $t_0 \in (0, 1)$ that is a relative maximum for $t \rightarrow f(\sigma(t))$. Thus we can apply (27.5), with N taken as the geodesic σ. The first term of (27.5), $S_{df}(v, v)$, is zero, since it is the second fundamental form of σ, which is zero, since σ is a geodesic. Our hypotheses then assert that the Hessian of f restricted to σ must be positive at t_0, which is a contradiction.   Q.E.D.

These simple results suffice to give the idea of the geometric meaning of formula (27.5). Many more sophisticated applications are possible.

28 Affine Groups of Automorphisms. Induced Connections on Submanifolds. Projective Changes of Connection

Let M continue to be a manifold with a torsion-free affine connection ∇. Suppose that ∇' is another affine connection. We shall show that the "difference," $D(\ ,\ )$ of ∇ and ∇' is a *tensor field*.

For $X, Y \in V(M)$, put $D(X, Y) = \nabla_X Y - \nabla_X' Y$. For $f \in F(M)$, note that $D(fX, Y) = fD(X, Y)$,

$$D(X, fY) = fD(X, Y) + X(f)Y - X(f)Y = fD(X, X). \qquad (28.1)$$

Then $D(\ ,\ )$ is $F(M)$-multilinear; hence, defines a tensor field on M. Clearly it is also *symmetric* in X and Y.

Suppose now that ϕ is a diffeomorphism of M and that ∇' is the "transformed" affine connection; that is,

$$\phi_*(\nabla_X Y) = \nabla'_{\phi_*(X)} \phi_*(Y) = D(\phi_*(X, \phi_*(Y))) + \nabla_{\phi_*(X)} \phi_*(Y). \qquad (28.2)$$

Suppose further that $t \to \phi_t$ is a one-parameter group of diffeomorphisms whose infinitesimal generator is the vector field Z. We know then that

$$\frac{\partial}{\partial t} \phi_t{}^*(X)\bigg|_{t=0} = \lim_{t \to 0} \frac{\phi_t{}^*(X) - X}{t} = [Z, X].$$

Substituting ϕ_t for ϕ in (28.2), differentiating with respect to t, we have

$$[Z, \nabla_X Y] = D'(X, Y) + \nabla_{[Z, X]} Y + \nabla_X[Z, Y], \qquad (28.3)$$

where D' is some tensor field. (If one uses this relation as the definition of D', it can be easily verified independently that it is a tensor field.)

Now, if ϕ preserves the affine connection, that is, is an *automorphism* $\nabla' = \nabla$, then if Z generates a one-parameter group of connection automorphisms, we have

$$[Z, \nabla_X Y] = \nabla_{[Z, X]} Y + \nabla_X[Z, Y] \qquad \text{for all } X, Y \in V(M). \qquad (28.4)$$

This reasoning can be readily reversed (exercise!) to show that (28.4) is also sufficient that the vector field Z generate a one-parameter group of connection automorphisms.

LEMMA 28.1

Suppose that $\phi: M \to M$ is a connection automorphism, that M is connected and that p is a point of M such that

$$\phi(p) = p; \qquad \phi_*: M_p \to M_p \quad \text{is the identity.}$$

Then ϕ acts as the identity on M.

Proof. The set of all points of M that are fixed under ϕ is obviously closed in M. We shall show that it is also open in M, which will prove that it is all of M.

ϕ maps geodesics of the connection into geodesics. Since it leaves p fixed and leaves fixed all tangent vectors starting at p, it leaves fixed all geodesics starting at p, hence leaves fixed each point of a neighborhood of p; that is, the set of all fixed points of ϕ is open in M.   Q.E.D.

Now, if Z is a vector field in M, the condition that the one-parameter group generated by Z leave p fixed is obviously $Z(p) = 0$; that is, p is a singular point of Z. If this condition is satisfied, we can define a linear transformation $\phi_Z: M_p \to M_p$ in the following way:
For $v \in M_p$, pick any vector field Y such that $Y(p) = v$, and set

$$l_Z(v) = [Y, Z](p). \tag{28.5}$$

(The reader can readily verify, following a pattern we have used many times before (for example, in the definition of the second fundamental form) that the vanishing of Z at p guarantees that this does not depend on how v is extended to a vector field.) The linear transformation l_Z is called the *linear part* of Z at p. To justify this name, we can look at it in local coordinates, say $(x_1, \ldots, x_n)$, with $x_i(p) = 0$.

$$Z = A_i \frac{\partial}{\partial x_i} \qquad \text{with} \quad A_i(0) = 0.$$

Then

$$\left[\frac{\partial}{\partial x_j}, Z\right] = \frac{\partial A_i}{\partial x_j}(0) \frac{\partial}{\partial x_i} \qquad \text{so that} \qquad l_Z\!\left(\frac{\partial}{\partial x_j}\right) = \frac{\partial A_i}{\partial x_j}(0) \frac{\partial}{\partial x_i};$$

that is, $((\partial A_i/\partial x_j)(0))$ is the matrix of the linear transformation l_Z. The $((\partial A_i/\partial x_j)(0))$ are, of course, just the first terms in the Taylor series of $A_i(x)$ about $x = 0$.

LEMMA 28.2

Let Z be a vector field, with $Z(p) = 0$. Then $l_Z = 0$ on M_p if and only if the one-parameter group generated by Z acts as the identity on tangent vectors at p.

We leave the proof to the reader.

From Lemmas 28.1 and 28.2, we have immediately Lemma 28.3.

LEMMA 28.3

If Z generates a group of connection automorphisms, if $Z(p) = 0 = l_z$, then Z is zero at every point of M.

Now we turn to the following question: Suppose that Z is a vector field that generates a one-parameter group of connection automorphisms, that is, satisfies (28.4). Suppose that N is a submanifold of M and that Z is tangent to N; that is, $Z(p) \in N_p$ for all $p \in N$ so that Z restricted to N defines a vector field on N.

Definition

Let Z be a vector field on a manifold N. We say that Z *vanishes* to the kth *order at a point* $p \in N$ if

$$Z(p) = 0 \quad \text{and} \quad [X_1, [\cdots [X_k, Z] \cdots]](p) = 0 \qquad (28.6)$$

for all choices of k-tuples of vector fields $(X_1, \ldots, X_k)$ on N. (Notice that X vanishes to the first order if $Z(p) = 0$ and $l_Z = 0$.)

Return to the case where N is a submanifold of M, Z is tangent to N, and Z satisfies (28.4). We ask: Is it possible that Z *restricted* to N vanishes to the kth order at a point of N without vanishing everywhere on M? This is clearly possible for some choices of N. For example, if N is a plane in Euclidean space M, there is clearly a nontrivial one-parameter group of affine transformations of M leaving every point of the plane fixed. However, we can find conditions on N that prevent this.

Let X and Y be vector fields tangent to N. Then, by (28.4),

$$[Z, \nabla_X Y] = \nabla_{[Z, X]} Y + \nabla_X [Z, Y] = \nabla_{[Z, X]} Y + \nabla_{[Z, Y]} X + [X, [Z, Y]].$$

Thus, if Z restricted to N vanishes to the second order at p, then

$$[Z, \nabla_X Y](p) = 0.$$

If every tangent vector at p can be written as a combination of N_p and vectors of the form $\nabla_X Y(p)$, for X, Y tangent to N, then we see that $l_Z = 0$; hence, by Lemma 28.3, Z is identically zero on M. In general, let us call the space of vectors spanned by N_p and $\{\nabla_X Y(p): X, Y$ vector fields tangent to $N\}$ the *first osculating space* to N. Then we have the following rather trivial theorem, which is important for the qualitative picture given us of the relation of the "induced geometry" on N to the group of affine connection automorphisms.

THEOREM 28.4

Let N be a submanifold of the affinely connected space M, let Z be a vector field that is tangent to N and generates a one-parameter group of connection automorphisms. Suppose that the first osculating space to N at p fills up N_p. Then if Z restricted vanishes to the second order at p, it must vanish everywhere on M.

This analysis can be carried further to get criteria for nonvanishing of the order, higher than 2, by considering the higher osculating spaces to N. (The second osculating space to N at p would be that spanned by N_p, the set of $\nabla_X Y(p)$ and $\nabla_X, \nabla_{X_1} Y(p)$, for vector fields X, X_1, Y tangent to N, and so on for the higher osculating spaces. We leave this to the reader, since it involves a simple iteration of the basic argument, that is, applying (28.4) to $[Z, \nabla_X \nabla_{X_1} Y]$.

Theorem 28.4 is not the best possible answer. There are clearly submanifolds having the property that a vector field satisfying (28.4), vanishing to the first order when restricted to N, vanishes identically. For example, this is so if N admits an "induced affine connection," that is, one that is left invariant by an affine automorphism of M which maps N into itself. (For example, we have seen that if N is totally geodesic, it admits such an "induced connection.") We shall now turn to this more basic question of induced affine connections on submanifolds, using Cartan's "method of the moving frame." (Indeed, this problem gives a good introduction to Cartan's theory.)

The most complete work on this subject is by Klingenberg [1]. We shall be working with a particularly simple case, namely, that where N is a hypersurface in M.

Of course this question is a purely local one, so that we are free to choose "moving frames," that is, a basis $(\omega_1, \ldots, \omega_n)$ for 1-forms on M. (Choose the following range of indices and summation convention: $1 \leq i, j, \ldots \leq n = \dim M$; $1 \leq a, b, \ldots \leq n - 1$.) Let (ω_{ij}) be the *connection forms* associated with this basis, and the affine connection. As definition,

$$\omega_{ij}(X) = -\omega_i(\nabla_X X_j) \qquad \text{for } X \in V(M). \tag{28.7}$$

Then the following relations hold:

$$d\omega_i = \omega_{ij} \wedge \omega_j \tag{28.8}$$

(expressing the fact that the torsion tensor is zero).

$$d\omega_{ij} = \omega_{ik} \wedge \omega_{kj} + \Omega_{ij}, \qquad \Omega_{ij} = R_{ijkl} \omega_k \wedge \omega_l. \tag{28.9}$$

(The R_{ijkl} are the components of the curvature tensor $R(\ ,\ )(\ )$, just as defined earlier for Riemannian geometry.)

Now we can arrange the moving frame so that $\omega_n = 0$ on N. By (28.8),

$$d\omega_n = \omega_{nj} \wedge \omega_j, \qquad \text{whence } \omega_{na} \wedge \omega_a = 0 \quad \text{restricted to } N.$$

Suppose that (ω_i') is another such moving frame. They are related to the (ω_i) by relations of the form $\omega_i = M_{ij}\omega_j'$, where (M_{ij}) is a matrix-valued function on M, whose determinant is not zero. Let (ω_{ij}') be the connection forms (defined by (28.7)) in the primed system. The transformation law between the (ω_{ij}) and (ω_{ij}') is readily calculated from (28.7), and is found to be

$$\omega_{ij} = M_{ik}\omega_{kl}'M_{lj}^{-1} + dM_{ik}M_{kj}^{-1}, \qquad (28.10)$$

and (M_{ij}^{-1}) is the inverse matrix to (M_{ij}). Suppose that the primed frame also satisfies $\omega_n' = 0$; that is, $M_{na} = 0$ restricted to N. Our goal is to use this freedom to change frames to satisfy more conditions. From (28.10), we then have

$$\omega_{na} = M_{nn}\omega_{na}'M_{ab}^{-1}, \text{ restricted to } N, \text{ hence } \omega_{na} \cdot \omega_a = M_{nn}\omega_{na}' \cdot \omega_a'. \quad (28.11)$$

(The dot ($\cdot$) indicates the *symmetric* product of 1-forms; that is, if θ_1, θ_2 are 1-forms, $\theta_1 \cdot \theta_2(X,\ Y) = \frac{1}{2}(\theta_1(X)\theta_2(Y) + \theta_1(Y)\theta_2(X))$.) It can be readily seen that the form

$$u,v \rightarrow \omega_{na} \cdot \omega_a(u,\ v)$$

is the second fundamental form of N, $(u,\ v) \rightarrow S_{\omega_n}(u,\ v)$. We shall suppose that this form is definite, that is, that

$$S_{\omega_n}(u,\ v) = 0 \qquad \text{for all } u \text{ tangent to } N \text{ implies } v = 0.$$

For simplicity, we suppose that the form is positive definite—the cases of other signatures of the quadratic form $u \rightarrow S_{\omega_n}(u,\ u)$ can be handled similarly. The law of transformation (28.11) then assures us that a moving frame (ω_i) can be chosen so that $\omega_{na} \cdot \omega_a = \omega_a \cdot \omega_a$; that is, so that

$$\omega_{na} = \omega_a \quad \text{restricted to } N. \qquad (28.12)$$

Suppose that (ω_i') is another choice of moving frame satisfying (28.12). Then the transition functions (M_{ij}) must satisfy

$$M_{ac}M_{ab} = \delta_{cb}M_{nn} \qquad \text{and} \qquad M_{na} = 0 \quad \text{restricted to } N. \qquad (28.13)$$

Differentiate (28.13):

$$dM_{ac}M_{ab} + M_{ac}dM_{ab} = \delta_{ab}dM_{nn}$$

or

$$dM_{ac}M_{ba}^{-1} + M_{ca}^{-1}dM_{ab} = \delta_{ab}dM_{nn}M_{nn}^{-1}.$$

Hence,

$$dM_{ab}M_{ba}^{-1} + M_{ba}^{-1}dM_{ab} = (n-1)\,dM_{nn}M_{nn}^{-1},$$

or

$$dM_{ab}M_{ba}^{-1} = \left(\frac{n-1}{2}\right)dM_{nn}M_{nn}^{-1}.$$

Let

$$\theta = \omega_{aa} - \left(\frac{n-1}{2}\right)\omega_{nn}',\qquad \theta' = \omega_{aa}' - \left(\frac{n-1}{2}\right)\omega_{nn}'.$$

Computing the relation between θ and θ', we have

$$\theta = M_{an}\omega_b' M_{ba}^{-1} + \theta' - \left(\frac{n-1}{2}\right)M_{nn}\omega_a' M_{an}^{-1}. \tag{28.14}$$

Now, given the primed moving frame, we can arrange the unprimed moving frame by a change of frame for which the transition functions (M_{ij}) satisfy (28.11), that is, leave the relation (28.12) invariant, and such that

$$\theta = 0. \tag{28.15}$$

In fact we can accomplish this by a choice of (M_{ij}) satisfying $M_{nn} = 1$; $M_{ab} = \delta_{ab}$; $M_{an}^{-1} = -M_{an}$; for with these choices, (28.14) set equal to zero can be regarded as a set of equations for M_{an}.

Now, with conditions (28.13) imposed, let us see how the possible changes of frame are restricted. Using (28.14) again and the relation $\theta = \theta' = 0$, we have

$$0 = M_{an}\omega_c' M_{ca}^{-1} - \left(\frac{n-1}{2}\right)M_{nn}\omega_c' M_{cn}^{-1}.$$

Hence,

$$M_{nn}M_{ca}^{-1} = \left(\frac{n-1}{2}\right)M_{nn}M_{cn}^{-1},\qquad M_{bc}M_{an}M_{ca}^{-1} = \left(\frac{n-1}{2}\right)M_{bc}M_{cn}^{-1}M_{nn};$$

hence,

$$M_{bn} = -\left(\frac{n-1}{2}\right)M_{bc}M_{ca}^{-1}M_{an} = -\left(\frac{n-1}{2}\right)M_{bn},$$

forcing

$$M_{bn} = 0. \tag{28.16}$$

But this relation tells us that the set of vectors v satisfying $\omega_a(v) = 0$ are left invariant when the moving frames are chosen; that is, for $p \in N$, there is a subspace H_p of M_p such that $M_p = N_p \oplus H_p$. Further, the reader can convince himself by working through the above argument that a connection auto-morphism of M that maps N onto itself will preserve the splitting of the tan-gent space of M at points of N. (For example, notice that the transformation applied to a moving frame satisfying (28.13) and (28.15) will again satisfy (28.13) and (28.15).) Hence, if we use this field $p \rightarrow H_p$ of subspaces to define an induced affine connection on N (as explained in the beginning of this chapter), an affine transformation of M leaving N invariant will be an auto-morphism of the induced connection on N. Summing up, we have proved Theorem 28.5

THEOREM 28.5

Let N be a hypersurface in an affinely connected space M whose second fundamental form is definite. Then there is an "induced" affine connection on N which is preserved by every connection automorphism of M which leaves N invariant.

The procedure we have followed is typical of Cartan's method of the moving frame. In terms of the jargon, what we have done is to reduce the structure group of the tangent bundle of M restricted to N in a "natural" way to a subgroup that is small enough to enable one to define an induced affine connection on N. Many examples of this reduction process can be found in Cartan's book on the method of the moving frame [3], although the general-ities are not very clear there. A general (although sketchy) treatment of these matters can be found in a paper by Hermann [9].

Projective Change of Connections

If two affine connections, ∇ and ∇', are given on a manifold M, we have seen that their "difference" $D(\, , \,)$ is a tensor field. Recall that

$$D(X, Y) = \nabla_X Y - \nabla_X' Y \qquad \text{for } X, Y \in V(M).$$

We may ask: When are ∇ and ∇' related in such a way that the second funda-mental forms of a submanifold with respect to the connection are the same? The answer is Theorem 28.6.

THEOREM 28.6

Suppose that θ is a 1-form on M such that

$$\nabla_X Y - \nabla_X' Y = \tfrac{1}{2}(\theta(X)Y + \theta(Y)X) \qquad (28.17)$$

for each pair $(X, \ Y \in V(M))$. Then a submanifold N of M has the same second fundamental form with respect to ∇' as it does with respect to ∇. Conversely, if this property is valid for every submanifold of M, then ∇ and ∇' are related by (28.17).

Further, (28.17) is satisfied if and only if ∇ and ∇' are projectively related in the classical sense, that is, their geodesics differ only by a change in parametrization.

Proof. Suppose (28.17) is satisfied. Let N be a submanifold of M. Let ω be a 1-form on M such that $\omega(N_p) = 0$ for all $p \in N$. Then, for X, Y vector fields that are tangent to N, we have

$$S_\omega(X, Y) = \omega(\nabla_X Y) = \omega(\nabla_X' Y) = S_\omega'(X, Y),$$

in view of (28.17). The converse is obvious.

Suppose now that the geodesics of ∇ and ∇' differ only by a change in parametrization. Let X be a vector field whose integral curves are geodesics of ∇; that is, $\nabla_X X = 0$. Then the integral curves must, after a change in parametrization, be geodesics of ∇'; that is,

$$\nabla_X' X = fX \qquad \text{for some} \quad f \in F(M).$$

Let $D(X, Y) = \nabla_X Y - \nabla_X' Y$. Then

$$\nabla(X, X) = -fX.$$

Since D is a *tensor field*, this must hold for an arbitrary vector field on M. Polarization of this identity (that is, substitution of $X + Y$ in place of X) shows that (28.17) is satisfied. The converse is readily obtained by reversing these steps and observing that, at least locally, each geodesic can be exhibited as the integral curve of a vector field X satisfying $\nabla_X X = 0$. Q.E.D.

29 The Laplace–Beltrami Operator

Let M be a manifold, with a pseudo-Riemannian metric on M defined by a definite inner product $\langle \ , \ \rangle$ on tangent vectors. Associated with the metric we can define a linear differential operator Δ that acts on functions on M. By specializing the metric, many of the differential operators that are important in mathematical physics may be obtained. For example, the ordinary Laplace operator

$$\frac{\partial^2}{\partial x^2} + \frac{\partial^2}{\partial y^2} + \frac{\partial^2}{\partial z^2}$$

is associated with the flat Euclidean metric on Euclidean space; the d'Alembertian, or wave, operator

$$\Box = \frac{1}{c^2} \frac{\partial^2}{\partial t^2} - \frac{\partial^2}{\partial x^2} - \frac{\partial^2}{\partial y^2} - \frac{\partial^2}{\partial z^2}$$

is associated with the Lorentz metric on space-time. Our aim in this chapter is to illustrate the power of the theory of affine connections on manifolds by deriving many of the properties of these operators without introducing coordinates.

Let f be a function on M. The *gradient* of f, denoted by grad f, is a vector field on M defined as

$$\langle \text{grad} f, X \rangle = X(f) = df(X) \qquad \text{for } X \in V(M). \tag{29.1}$$

The first-order differential operator $f \to \|\text{grad} f\|^2$ is sometimes called the *first Beltrami differential operator*. In fact, we have already seen in Chapter 13 that the function f such that $\|\text{grad} f\|^2$ is constant on the level surfaces of f is a solution of the *Hamilton–Jacobi partial differential equation* associated with the variational problem; for such an f, the integral curves of grad f are geodesics.

Let θ be the n-form on M defining the *volume element* associated with the metric. The easiest way to define θ is by using an orthonormal moving frame $(\omega_1, \ldots, \omega_n)$ of 1-forms, that is, the metric is given by

$$ds^2 = \pm \omega_1 \cdot \omega_1 \pm \cdots \pm \omega_n \cdot \omega_n$$

where $(\cdot)$ denotes the symmetric product of 1-forms. Then θ is given by

$$\theta = \omega_1 \wedge \cdots \wedge \omega_n. \tag{29.2}$$

Let X be a vector field on M. The *divergence* of X, denoted by div(X), is the function such that

$$X(\theta) = (\operatorname{div} X)\theta. \tag{29.3}$$

Thus div(X) $= 0$ is the condition that the one-parameter group generated by X leave invariant the volume on M defined by θ.

Let $f \in F(M)$. We can define $\Delta(f)$, the *Laplace–Beltrami operator* (sometimes called the second Beltrami operator), as

$$\Delta(f) = \operatorname{div}(\operatorname{grad} f). \tag{29.4}$$

We can give a more explicit form of $\Delta(f)$ in terms of the orthonormal moving frame (ω_i) of the connection. Let (X_i), $1 \le i, j, \ldots \le n = \dim M$ be a basis of vector fields dual to the (ω_i); that is,

$$\omega_i(X_j) = \delta_{ij}; \qquad \langle X_i, X_j \rangle = \begin{cases} 0 & \text{for } i \ne j \\ \pm 1 & \text{for } i = j \end{cases}.$$

$$\begin{aligned} X(\omega_i) &= X(\omega_i)(X_j)\omega_j \\ &= [X(\omega_i(X_j)) - \omega_i(\nabla_X[X, X_j])]\omega_j \\ &= \omega_i(\nabla_{X_j} X - \nabla_X X_j)\omega_j. \end{aligned}$$

Now

$$\begin{aligned} X(\theta) &= X(\omega_1) \wedge \cdots \wedge \omega_n + \cdots + \omega_1 \wedge \cdots \wedge X(\omega_n) \\ &= [\omega_1(\nabla_{X_1} X - \nabla_X X_1)]\omega_1 \wedge \cdots \wedge \omega_n + \cdots \\ &\quad + \omega_1 \wedge \cdots \wedge \omega_{n-1} \wedge [\omega_n(\nabla_{X_n} X - \nabla_X X_n)]\omega_n \\ &= [\omega_i(\nabla_{X_i} X - \nabla_X X_i)]\theta. \end{aligned}$$

By (29.3),

$$\operatorname{div} X = \omega_i(\nabla_{X_i} X - \nabla_X X_i).$$

Now $Y = \omega_i(Y)(X_i)$; hence

$$\langle Y, X_j \rangle = \omega_i(Y)\langle X_i, X_j \rangle.$$

Put $e_i = \langle X_i, X_i \rangle$. (Then $e_i = \pm 1$.) Now

$$\operatorname{div} X = \sum_i e_i(\langle X_i, \nabla_{X_i} X \rangle - \langle X_i, \nabla_X X_i \rangle).$$

But

$$\langle X_i, \nabla_X X_i \rangle = X(\langle X_i, X_i \rangle) - \langle \nabla_X X_i, X_i \rangle = 0.$$

Now we have div and Δ expressed in terms of the frames and the connection:

$$\operatorname{div} X = \sum_i e_i \langle \nabla_{X_i} X, X_i \rangle \tag{29.5}$$

$$\Delta(f) = \operatorname{div}(\operatorname{grad} f) = \sum_i e_i \langle \nabla_{X_i} \operatorname{grad} f, X_i \rangle. \tag{29.6}$$

There is another useful form of $\Delta(f)$. Starting from (29.6), we have

$$\Delta(f) = \sum_i e_i(X_i(\langle \operatorname{grad} f, X_i \rangle) - \langle \operatorname{grad} f, \nabla_{X_i} X_i \rangle).$$

Hence,

$$\Delta(f) = \sum_i e_i(X_i X_i(f) - (\nabla_{X_i} X_i)(f)). \qquad (29.7)$$

Equation (29.7) is the form that most closely resembles the usual Laplace (or d'Alembert) operator for Euclidean space. For if the connection is flat, a coordinate system (x_i) can be chosen so that

$$X_i = \frac{\partial}{\partial x_i}, \qquad \nabla_{X_i} X_i = 0.$$

Then

$$\Delta(f) = \sum_i e_i \frac{\partial^2 f}{\partial x_i^2}.$$

(Laplace or d'Alembert are obtained by specializing the e.)

On the other hand, for an arbitrary metric we can always find an orthonormal moving frame (X_i) such that *at a given point p,*

$$\nabla_{X_i} X_j(p) = 0.$$

Further, a coordinate system (x_i) about that point can be chosen so that

$$X_i X_i(f)(p) = \frac{\partial^2}{\partial x_i^2} f(p).$$

(*Exercise:* Prove these statements.) Then, *at one point,* we can always arrange that Δ has the same form as in the flat Euclidean case.

Finally, to illustrate the usefulness of these formulas, we shall derive a formula for the Laplace-Beltrami operator for the metric induced on a submanifold N of M. Suppose that dim $N = p$, and choose the additional range of indices: $1 \le a, b, \ldots \le p; p + 1 \le u, v, \ldots \le n$. Suppose that (X_a) are tangent to N. (Notice that we are implicitly assuming that the metric induced on N is nondegenerate.)

Suppose that grad $f = Y + Z$, where Y and Z are vector fields that are, respectively, tangent and perpendicular to N. Then Y restricted to N is the gradient vector field of f restricted to N with respect to the induced metric on N. Then

$$\Delta^N(f) = \sum_a e_a \langle X_a, \nabla_{X_a} Y \rangle,$$

where Δ^N is the Laplace-Beltrami operator with respect to the metric induced on N applied to f restricted to N. Now

$$\langle X_a, \nabla_{X_a} Z \rangle = X_a(\langle X_a, Z \rangle) - \langle \nabla_{X_a} X_a, Z \rangle = -S_Z(X_a, X_a),$$

where $S_{(\ )}(\ ,\ )$ is the second fundamental form of N. Now

$$Y = \operatorname{grad} f - \sum_u e_u \langle \operatorname{grad} f, X_u \rangle X, \qquad Z = \sum_u e_u X_u(f) X_u.$$

Then

$$\sum e_u \langle X_u, \nabla_{X_u} \operatorname{grad} f \rangle = \sum e_u [X_u^2(f) - \nabla_{X_u} X_u(f)].$$

Finally, then,

$$\Delta(f) - \Delta^N(f) = \sum_u e_u [X_u^2(f) - (\nabla_{X_u} X_u)(f) - X_u(f) S_{X_u}(X_a, X_a)]. \quad (29.8)$$

Example: Spherical Harmonics

Suppose that M is flat Euclidean space, with Euclidean coordinates (x_i), and that N is the sphere of radius r. Let $g = \frac{1}{2} x_i x_i = \frac{1}{2} |x|^2$. Then $p = n - 1$. Choosing the moving frame so that (X_n) is tangent to Δ, we have

$$X_n = \frac{\operatorname{grad} g}{\|\operatorname{grad} g\|} = \frac{x_i(\partial/\partial x_i)}{|x|}.$$

Suppose that f is a function on R^n that is homogeneous of degree λ. By Euler's homogeneous function relation,

$$x_i \frac{\partial f}{\partial x_i} = \lambda f.$$

That is,

$$\operatorname{grad} g(f) = \lambda f, \quad \text{or} \quad X_n(f) = \frac{\lambda f}{|x|}, \quad X_n^2(f) = \frac{\lambda^2 f}{|x|^2} - \frac{\lambda f}{|x|^2}.$$

Now g is a solution of the Hamilton–Jacobi equation for the Riemannian metric $ds^2 = dx_i\, dx_i$, since $\|\operatorname{grad} g\| = 2g$. We know, then, from general principles that $\nabla_{X_n} X_n = 0$; that is, the integral curves of X_n are geodesics. (This is obvious geometrically, of course: The integral curves of X_n are the orthogonal trajectories of the spheres concentric about the origin, that is, straight lines.) We have also seen that the second fundamental form $S_{X_n}(\ ,\ )$ of the sphere of radius r has all its eigenvalues equal to $-(1/r)$. Then

$$S_{X_n}(X_a, X_a) = -\frac{(n-1)}{r}.$$

By (29.8),

$$\Delta(f) - \Delta^N(f) = X_n{}^2(f) - (\nabla_{X_n} X_n)(f) - X_n(f)S_{X_n}(X_a, X_a)$$

$$= \frac{\lambda^2 f}{r^2} - \frac{\lambda f}{r^2} + \frac{\lambda f(n-1)}{r^2} = \frac{\lambda}{r^2}(\lambda + n - 2)f.$$

In particular, we have the following.

THEOREM 29.1

If f is a function on R^n which is harmonic (that is, satisfies $\Delta(f) = 0$) and which is homogeneous of degree λ, then f restricted to the unit sphere in R^n is an eigenfunction of the Laplace–Beltrami operator on the sphere with eigenvalue $\lambda(\lambda + n - 2)$.

In particular, we may consider the f that are polynomials and that also are harmonic on R^n. Those polynomials of degree λ are permuted by the action of the rotation group, and this gives all finite-dimensional linear representation of the group of rotations of R^n.

The Geometric Background for "Separation of Variables"

Now we return to the first definition of $\Delta(f)$ as $\operatorname{div}(\operatorname{grad} f)$. Suppose f, g are functions on M. Then

$$\operatorname{grad}(fg) = f \operatorname{grad} g + g \operatorname{grad} f.$$

$$\Delta(fg)\theta = \operatorname{grad}(fg)(\theta)$$

$$= (f \operatorname{grad} g)(\theta) + (g \operatorname{grad} f)(\theta)$$

$$= f \operatorname{grad} g(\theta) + df \wedge (\operatorname{grad} g \lrcorner \theta) + g \operatorname{grad} f(\theta) + dg \wedge (\operatorname{grad} f \lrcorner \theta).$$

Now

$$df \wedge (\operatorname{grad} g \lrcorner \theta) = \operatorname{grad} g \lrcorner (df \wedge \theta) - (\operatorname{grad} g \lrcorner df)\theta$$

$$= -\langle \operatorname{grad} f, \operatorname{grad} g \rangle \theta.$$

Hence,

$$\Delta(fg) = f \Delta(g) + g \Delta(f) - \langle \operatorname{grad} f, \operatorname{grad} g \rangle.$$

We have now proved

LEMMA 29.2

$$\Delta(fg) = \Delta(f)g + f \Delta(g) \text{ if and only if } \langle \operatorname{grad} f, \operatorname{grad} g \rangle = 0.$$

LEMMA 29.3

Suppose that f is a function on M such that

$$\|\operatorname{grad} f\|^2 = F_1(f). \tag{29.9}$$

$$\Delta(f) = F_2(f). \tag{29.10}$$

Then there exists a function $g = F(f)$ such that

$$\Delta(g) = \lambda g. \tag{29.11}$$

($F_1(\ )$, $F_2(\ )$, and $F(\ )$ are functions of one real variable, say, x.) In fact, g satisfies (29.11) if and only if

$$F''(x) \cdot F_1(x) + F'(x)F_2(x) = \lambda F(x). \tag{29.12}$$

Proof. Suppose we look for $g = F(f)$ to satisfy (29.11).

$$dg = F'(f)\, df;$$

hence,

$$\operatorname{grad} g = F'(f)\operatorname{grad} f.$$

$$
\begin{aligned}
\Delta(g)\theta &= (\operatorname{grad} g)(\theta) = (F'(f)\operatorname{grad} f)\theta \\
&= F'(f)\,\Delta(f)\theta + d(F'(f)) \wedge (\operatorname{grad} f \ \lrcorner\ \theta) \\
&= F'(f)\,\Delta(f)\theta + F''(f)\,df \wedge (\operatorname{grad} f \ \lrcorner\ \theta) \\
&= F'(f)\,\Delta(f)\theta + F''(f)\,\|\operatorname{grad} f\|^2\,\theta.
\end{aligned}
$$

Formula (29.12) now follows.

Functions f satisfying (29.9) and (29.10) are called *isoparametric* (with respect to the given Riemannian manifold). Once such functions have been found, Lemma 29.2 tells us that eigenfunctions for the Laplace–Beltrami operator can be found by solving an *ordinary* linear differential equation, namely, (29.12).

Conditions (29.9) and (29.10) also have a geometric significance:

THEOREM 29.4

Let f be a function such that $\|\operatorname{grad} f\|$ is a (nonzero) function of f. Then $\Delta(f)$ is a function of f if and only if the mean curvature of the level surfaces of f is constant on each surface.

Proof. We see from the proof of Lemma 29.3 that we may change f by a function of one variable, $f \to F(f)$. In particular, we may suppose

$\|\operatorname{grad} f\|^2 = \pm 1$; hence we may choose an orthonormal moving frame $(X_1, \ldots, X_n)$ such that $\operatorname{grad} f = X_1$.

$$\Delta(f) = \sum_i e_i \langle \nabla_{X_i} \operatorname{grad} f, X_i \rangle$$

$$= \sum_i e_i \langle \nabla_{X_i} X_1, X_i \rangle$$

$$= -\sum_i e_i \langle X_1, \nabla_{X_i} X_i \rangle.$$

Now

$$\langle X_1, \nabla_{X_1} X_1 \rangle = \tfrac{1}{2} X_1 (\langle X_1, X_1 \rangle) = 0.$$

Hence,

$$\Delta(f) = -\sum_{i=2}^{n} e_i \langle X_1, \nabla_{X_i} X_i \rangle.$$

The right-hand side is now precisely the mean curvature of the level surface $f = \text{constant}$, that is, the sum of the eigenvalues of the second fundamental form.

Green's Formula

Suppose now that M is a manifold with a boundary hypersurface $\partial M = N$ and a pseudo-Riemannian metric, denoted by $\langle \ , \ \rangle$. We shall be using the concepts involving integration that were introduced in Chapter 7.

Let f, g be functions on M. We suppose that M is orientable and that θ $(= \omega_1 \wedge \cdots \wedge \omega_n$ in terms of orthonormal moving frames) is the volume-element differential form defined by the metric. Then

$$g \, \Delta(f)\theta = g \operatorname{grad} f(\theta) = g \, d(\operatorname{grad} f \lrcorner \theta)$$
$$= d(g \operatorname{grad} f \lrcorner \theta) - dg \wedge (\operatorname{grad} f \lrcorner \theta).$$

$$dg \wedge (\operatorname{grad} f \lrcorner \theta) = -(\operatorname{grad} f \lrcorner dg) \cdot \theta = -\langle \operatorname{grad} f, \operatorname{grad} g \rangle \theta.$$

This is *symmetric* in g and f; hence

$$f \, \Delta(g) - g \, \Delta(f) = d(f \operatorname{grad} g \lrcorner \theta - g \operatorname{grad} f \lrcorner \theta).$$

Integrating over M and using Stoke's formula on the right-hand side, we have

$$\int_M (f \, \Delta(g) - g \, \Delta(f))\theta = \int_N f(\operatorname{grad} g \lrcorner \theta - g(\operatorname{grad} f \lrcorner \theta). \quad (29.13)$$

Suppose now that X^N is a unit-length vector perpendicular to ∂N, pointing *into M* from N. Then $X^N \lrcorner \theta$ restricted to N is the volume element form on ∂N, which we denote by θ^N. If X is any vector perpendicular to X^N, notice that $X \lrcorner \theta$ is zero restricted to N. Now grad $f - X^N(f)X^N$ is perpendicular to N. Hence

$$\int_N f(\text{grad } g \lrcorner \theta) = \int_N fX^N(g)\theta^N.$$

Equation (29.13) now becomes

$$\int_M [f\Delta(g) - g\,\Delta(f)]\theta = \int_N [fX^N(g) - gX^N(f)]\theta^N. \qquad (29.14)$$

This is *Green's formula*, from which many integral formulas and uniqueness theorems can be proved. We shall refer to a textbook on partial differential equations for detail on these applications (Garabedian [1]). As an illustration, we shall consider integral formulas obtained by inserting for g a *fundamental solution* of the Laplace-Beltrami equation $\Delta = 0$.

Let p be a point of M. A function g that satisfies $\Delta(g) = 0$ on $M - (p)$, but has a singularity at p, with

$$\int_M f\Delta(g) = f(p) \qquad \text{for all } f \in C_0(M), \qquad (29.15)$$

is called a *fundamental solution*. Symbolically, $\Delta(g) = \delta_p$. Suppose that $\Delta(f) = 0$. Then, from (29.14),

$$f(p) = \int_N [fX^N(g) - gX^N(f)]\theta^N. \qquad (29.16)$$

This can be interpreted as a " mean-value " formula expressing the value of f at p in terms of the values of f and its normal derivative over the boundary of M.

Suppose now that $g = $ constant on N. Now, inserting $g = 1$ in (29.14), we have

$$\int_N X^N(f)\theta^N = 0.$$

Hence, the second term in (29.16) drops out, and we have

$$f(p) = \int_N fX^N(g)\theta^N, \qquad (29.17)$$

which is a " mean-value formula " for $f(p)$. For example, in Euclidean space it is readily verified that the fundamental solution can be chosen so as to be constant on concentric spheres about p, giving the ordinary mean-value formula for harmonic functions.

30 Characteristics and Shock Waves

We shall give only a sketchy treatment of the subject matter indicated in the title. A full-scale exposition would involve us in a good deal of the theory of partial differential equations and applied mathematics, and hence would require another book. Our starting point is a brilliant but little-known exposition of the theory of shock waves given by Levi–Civita [2].

The main idea can be described very easily in terms of manifolds. Let M and E be manifolds, and let ϕ be a mapping of $M \to E$. We shall suppose that, in local coordinates for M and E, ϕ satisfies a given system P of partial differential equations of order r.

Definition

A submanifold N of M is a *characteristic submanifold* for the system P of partial differential equations if there is a map $\phi: M \to E$ such that:

(a) ϕ restricted to $M - N$ is differentiable to all orders and is a solution of the system P.

(b) ϕ is differentiable of order C^{r-1} on all of M, but not all the rth derivatives of ϕ are continuous at each point of N.

(c) The limits of the rth-order derivatives of ϕ exist along curves in $M - N$ that approach points of N. (This condition will be made more precise below.)

A map $\phi: M \to E$ satisfying (a) through (c) will be called a *shock solution* of P, with N as its submanifolds of discontinuity.

In addition to giving this general definition (not precisely in this language, of course), Levi-Civita points out how the differential equation for the characteristic submanifolds, and the jump-conditions for the rth derivatives of ϕ on N can be obtained as a consequence of "geometrical-dynamical compatibility conditions," which are obtained by combining the compatibility relations implied by (a) through (c) with the fact that ϕ "solves" P.

Rather than carry out the details of this program in full generality, we propose in this chapter to concentrate on what seem to be the most important cases for geometric and physical applications, namely: where E is a vector bundle over M and in addition ϕ is a cross section. We shall be especially interested in the case where E is the tangent bundle (that is, the ϕ are vector fields, which we like to denote by such letters as X, Y, ...). It will be almost obvious how to extend from this case to the most general vector bundles; hence we shall not pursue the more general directions.

The Geometric Compatibility Conditions for Vector Fields

Let M be a manifold and let N be a submanifold of M. All data will be C^∞ unless mentioned otherwise. Let X be a vector field on M which satisfies the following conditions:

$$X \text{ is continuous (as a cross-section map: } M \to T(M)) \text{ on } M. \qquad (30.1a)$$

$$X \text{ is } C^\infty \text{ on } M - N. \qquad (30.1b)$$

Let $\sigma(t)$ and $\sigma_1(t)$, $0 \le t \le 1$, be curves in M, with $\sigma(t)$ and $\sigma_1(t) \in M - N$ for $0 < t \le 1$, and $\sigma(0) = \sigma_1(0)$ for $p \in N$. Let Y be a (C^∞) vector field on M. Suppose that

$$\lim_{t \to 0} [Y, X](\sigma(t)) \text{ exists.}$$

We shall call it $\delta(Y, X, \sigma)$. It is an element of $M_{\sigma(0)}$. Let $f \in F(M)$. Then

$$\delta(fY, X, \sigma) = f(p)\,\delta(Y, X, \sigma) - X(f)(p)Y(p). \qquad (30.2)$$

From (30.2) we have

LEMMA 30.1

$\delta(Y, X, \sigma) - \delta(Y, X, \sigma_1)$ depends only on the value of Y at p. If, for $v \in M_p$, we put

$$\delta_X(v) = \delta(Y, X, \sigma) - \delta(Y, X, \sigma), \qquad (30.3)$$

where Y is a vector field such that $Y(p) = v$, we conclude that $\delta_X(v)$ depends linearly on v.

Thus, if we are given a smooth pair of family of curves, one pair for each point of N, $v \to \delta_X(v)$ can be considered as a tensor field on N which measures the jump in the first derivatives of X across N.

We aim now to find the compatibility conditions that result from the fact that X itself is continuous across N. Suppose that Z is a vector field on M that is tangent to N. For $p \in M$, let $s \to \exp(sZ)p$ be the integral curve of Z starting at p. Let ω be a differential 1-form on M. Then, for each s,

$$\lim_{t \to 0} \omega(X(\exp(sZ)\sigma(t))) = \lim_{t \to 0} \omega(X(\exp(sZ)\sigma_1(t))).$$

Take the derivative with respect to s of both sides of this relation, assume that *it is permissible to interchange limit and derivative*, and set $s = 0$. The result is

$$\lim_{t \to 0} Z(\omega)(X(\sigma(t))) + \omega([Z, X](\sigma(t))) = \lim_{t \to 0} Z(\omega)(X(\sigma_1(t))) + \omega([Z, X](\sigma_1(t))).$$

$(Z(\omega)$ denotes the Lie derivative of ω by the vector field Z, which is again a 1-form.) The first terms on both sides of this relation cancel each other, since X is continuous across N. Since ω is an arbitrary differential form, we have proved the following.

THEOREM 30.2

With the assumption listed above, $\delta_X(v)$ is zero when v is tangent to N. (This condition may be referred to as the *geometric compatibility condition*.)

The extension to the case where X has discontinuities of the rth derivatives across N, but is C^{r-1} on all of M, can be made similarly. For any choice $(Z_2, \ldots, Z_r)$ of vector fields, $[Z_2, [Z_3, \ldots [Z_r, X]] \cdots]$ is continuous across N, but its derivatives have a jump across N. Thus we can define

$$\delta_X(v_1, \ldots, v_r) \qquad \text{for } v_1, \ldots, v_r \in M_p,$$

by choosing vector fields $(Z_1, \ldots, Z_r)$ whose value at p is $(v_1, \ldots, v_r)$, and letting

$$\delta(v_1, \ldots, v_r) = \lim_{t \to 0} [X_1, \ldots [X_r, Z], \ldots](\sigma(t))$$

$$- \lim_{t \to 0} [X_1, \ldots [X_r, Z], \cdots](\sigma_1(t)).$$

We see immediately that δ depends tensorially and symmetrically on $v_1, \ldots, v_r$, and that $\delta(v_1, \ldots, v_r) = 0$ whenever one of the v is tangent to N.

The Dynamic Compatibility Conditions

In general, the "dynamic compatibility conditions" are those conditions imposed on the tensor field δ constructed in the preceding section by the condition that X satisfy a certain rth-order system of differential equations; hence, in particular, certain *functions* of the rth-order derivatives of X must be continuous across N. A common type of differential equation to require of a vector field X is that the Lie derivative of a tensor field on M be zero. For example, we shall examine the cases where the tensor field is a p-differential form θ.

Suppose, then, that $X(\theta)$ is continuous across N. Suppose that $Y_1, \ldots, Y_p$ are C^∞ vector fields on M. Then $X(\theta)(Y_1, \ldots, Y_p)$ are continuous across N. But

$$X(\theta)(Y_1, \ldots, Y_p) = X(\theta(Y_1, \ldots, Y_p)) - \theta([X, Y_1], Y_2, \ldots, Y_p)$$

$$- \cdots - \theta(Y_1, \ldots, [X, Y_p]).$$

Now $X(\theta(Y_1, \ldots, Y_p))$ is continuous across N, since X is. Thus we have proved

THEOREM 30.3

If θ is a p-form such that $X(\theta)$ is continuous across N, then for $v_1, \ldots,$ $v_p \in N_p$,

$$\theta(\delta_X(v_1), v_2, \ldots, v_p) + \cdots + \theta(v_1, \ldots, v_{p-1}, \delta_X(v_p)) = 0.$$

In particular, if θ is a nonzero m-form ($m = \dim M$), then the linear transformation $v \to \delta(v)$ of $M_p \to M_p$ has trace zero.

Example

M has a pseudo-Riemannian metric, defined by an inner product $\langle \ , \ \rangle$; $X = \text{grad } f$, for $f \in F(M)$, that is, $\langle X, Y \rangle = Y(f)$ for $Y \in V(M)$; θ is the volume element differential form defined by the metric; N is a hypersurface of M.

Now $X(\theta) = (\text{div } X)\theta$, where div X is the divergence of the vector field X. Hence $\Delta(f)$, the Laplacian of f, is div(grad f). Suppose that we require that $\Delta(f)$ be continuous across N.

LEMMA 30.4

With $X = \text{grad } f$, we have that

$$\langle \delta_X(u), v \rangle = \langle u, \delta_X(v) \rangle.$$

Proof. Let Y, Z be vector fields on M. Then,

$$[Y, X] = \nabla_Y X - \nabla_X Y.$$

$$\langle \nabla_Y X, Z \rangle = Y(\langle X, Z \rangle) + \langle X, \nabla_Y Z \rangle = Y(Z(f)) + \langle X, \nabla_Y Z \rangle.$$

We see, then, that the only continuity jumps in $\langle [Y, X], Z \rangle$ occur in the contribution of $Y(Z(f))$, which is equal to $Z(Y(f)) + [Y, Z](f)$. Since $[Y, Z]$ is a first-order operator, we have the lemma.

Now suppose that g is a function on M such that $dg \neq 0$ at every point of N, but $g = 0$ on N. Then, for $p \in N$, grad g is perpendicular to N_p. We shall show that:

> If the first derivatives of X are discontinuous across N
> at every point of N, then grad g must lie in N_p for each
> $p \in N_p$. In particular, $\langle \text{grad } g, \text{grad } g \rangle = 0$ on N.

Suppose otherwise: That is, for some $p \in N$, grad $g(p)$ is linearly independent from N_p so that N_p and grad $g(p)$ together span N_p. By Theorem 30.3, the trace of δ must be zero; the geometric compatibility conditions require that $\delta_X(N_p) = 0$. These two facts require that

$$\delta_X(\text{grad } g(p)) \in N_p.$$

Then $\langle \delta(\text{grad } g(p)), \text{grad } g(p) \rangle = 0$. But also, by Lemma 30.4,

$$\langle \delta(\text{grad } g(p)), N_p \rangle = 0.$$

Since $\langle \ , \ \rangle$ is nondegenerate, $\delta(\text{grad } g(p))$ must be zero, which implies that $\delta(M_p) = 0$, contradicting that the first derivatives of X have a jump across N. In other words, we have proved the following theorem:

THEOREM 30.5

Let Δ be the Laplace-Beltrami operator associated with a pseudo-Riemannian manifold. Consider the partial differential equation $f \to \Delta(f) + \cdots$. (The dots indicate terms of lower order than the second.) Let g be a function on M whose level surfaces are characteristics for the equation in the sense that they are shock solutions for which there are the surfaces of discontinuity for the second derivatives. Then the length of grad g is zero; that is, grad g is a lightlike vector field on M.

Shock Conditions for Tensor Fields Occurring in Classical Continuum Physics

Let M be a manifold with an affine connection ∇. For simplicity, we again suppose that ∇ has a zero torsion tensor. Let T be a tensor field of type $(1, 1)$ on M. This means that T is an $F(M)$-linear map of $V(M) \to V(M)$. Let $Y \in V(M)$. The *covariant derivative* of T by Y, denoted by $\nabla_Y T$, is another tensor field of the same algebraic type as T. Explicitly,

$$\nabla_Y T(X) = \nabla_Y(T(X)) - T(\nabla_Y X) \qquad \text{for } X \in V(M). \qquad (30.4)$$

(The reader will verify that $\nabla_Y T$ so defined is $F(M)$-linear on X; hence it really does define a tensor field on M.)

Hold X and a point $p \in M$ fixed: $v \to \nabla_v T(X)$ defines a linear transformation of vectors at p into vectors at p. The trace of this linear transformation is a number depending linearly on the value of X at p. As p and X vary, we get a differential form on M called the *divergence* of T, denoted by div(T).

To get an explicit formula for div T, choose a basis (X_i) for vector fields on $M(1 \le i, j, \ldots \le n = \dim M)$. Let (ω_i) be a dual basis for 1-forms on M; that is, $\omega_i(X_j) = \delta_{ij}$. Then

$$\text{div } T(X) = \omega_i(\nabla_{X_i}(T)(X)) \qquad \text{for } X \in V(M). \qquad (30.5)$$

Tensor fields of the type T can occur in a very fundamental way in classical continuum physics. This tensor operation of "divergence" is the basic one appearing in the partial differential equations of continuum physics. We shall not attempt here to explain why this is so. It seems to be built into the geometric assumptions underlying our understanding of the "continuum." Brillouin's book [1] offers the reader the most convincing detailed explanation of this fact, at least for elasticity theory. Many books on general relativity offer more general explanations. (The books by Levi-Civita [1] and Einstein [1] are the best from this point of view.) Indeed, that this tensor operation of "divergence" occurs in the same way in all branches of classical continuum mechanics was one of the main mathematical clues in Einstein's mind in constructing The General Theory of Relativity.

Suppose, then, that T is such a tensor field on M, that N is a hypersurface of M such that T is C^∞ on $M - N$, but is merely continuous on all M. For each $X \in V(M)$, $T(X)$ is then a vector field that is C^∞ on $M - N$, but which is only continuous on M. Hence, for $p \in N$, for two curves σ and σ_1 starting at p but pointing out into $M - N$, for $v \in M_p$, we can define

$$\delta_{T(X)}(v) \in M_p$$

as base, measuring the jump in the first derivatives of $T(X)$ across N. To make things more symmetric, we can define $\delta_T : M_p \times N_p \to M_p$ by setting

$$\delta_T(X(p), v) = \delta_{T(X)}(v).$$

Explicitly, then, for $X, Y \in V(M)$,

$$\delta_T(X(p), Y(p)) = \lim_{t \to 0} \{[Y, T(X)](\sigma(t)) - [Y, T(X)](\sigma_1(t))\}. \quad (30.6)$$

Now

$$[Y, T(X)] = \nabla_Y(T(X)) - \nabla_{T(X)} Y = (\nabla_Y T)(X) + T(\nabla_Y X) - \nabla_{T(X)} Y.$$

Since X and Y are C^∞ vector fields, and T itself is continuous across N, the last two terms contribute nothing to (30.6); hence

$$\delta_T(X(p), Y(p)) = \lim_{t \to 0} \{(\nabla_Y T)(X)(\sigma(t)) - (\nabla_Y T)(X)(\sigma_1(t))\}. \quad (30.7)$$

The geometric compatibility conditions are then

$$\delta_T(M_p, N_p) = 0 \qquad \text{for all } p \in N. \quad (30.8)$$

Suppose that div T *is continuous across* N. Then, by (30.7), the trace of the transformation $v \to \delta_T(u, v)$ is zero for fixed $u \in M_p$. This, together with (30.8), implies that

$$\delta_T(M_p, M_p) \subset N_p \qquad \text{for all } p \in N. \quad (30.9)$$

To get some interesting information about N, let us suppose that M has a pseudo-Riemannian metric $\langle \; , \; \rangle$ for which ∇ is the Levi-Civita affine connection, and such that

$$\langle T(X), Y \rangle = \pm \langle X, T(Y) \rangle \qquad \text{for } X, Y \in V(M). \qquad (30.10)$$

(In elasticity it is usual to have a $(+)$ sign, while the $(-)$ occurs in electromagnetism.) Suppose that g is a function on M such that $dg \neq 0$ at points of N, but that $g(N) = 0$. For $X, Y, Z \in V(M)$,

$$\langle \nabla_Y (T)(X), Z \rangle = Y(\langle T(X), Z \rangle) + \cdots$$
$$= \pm Y \langle X, T(Z) \rangle + \cdots$$
$$= \pm \langle X, (\nabla_Y T)(Z) \rangle + \cdots .$$

(The terms indicated by $\cdots$ do not affect the jump relation.) Thus we have that

$$\langle \delta_T(X, Y), Z \rangle = \pm \langle \delta_T(Z, Y), (X) \rangle. \qquad (30.11)$$

In particular,

$$0 = \langle \delta_T(X, Y), \text{grad } g \rangle = \pm \langle \delta_T(\text{grad } g, Y), X \rangle.$$

Summing up, we have proved:

THEOREM 30.6

Suppose that T is a tensor field on M of type $(1, 1)$ satisfying (30.11); that N is a hypersurface on M across which T and div T are continuous. Suppose that g is a function such that $g(N) = 0$. Then

$$\delta_T(\text{grad } g, M_p) = 0 \qquad \text{for all } p \in N. \qquad (30.12)$$

Notice that the condition div T continuous is not yet sufficient to indicate a condition for N which is *independent* of T. Such a condition requires additional differential equations that T must satisfy, which in physical problems involve thermodynamic conditions.

31 The Morse Index Theorem

Consider a differential equation of the form

$$v''(t) + r(t)v(t) = 0. \tag{31.1}$$

Classical Sturm–Liouville theory deals with such equations in which $v(t)$ and $r(t)$ are scalar-valued functions of t. The theory of these equations is well known, and of course they appear in many contexts in applied mathematics. However, the theory of systems of type (31.1) in which $v(t)$ is a vector-valued function of t is considerably less developed and less well known, despite the fact that many physical problems lead to such equations in a very natural way, particularly in stability problems. Morse [1] has developed the foundations for a successful generalization of the classical Sturm–Liouville theory to such systems.

We shall now present enough notations and definitions to be able to state the main result: the Morse index theorem. The proof will be given later. Since it may be difficult for the reader to see the forest for the trees while reading the proof, we may point out here that the proof basically consists in putting together certain well-known analytical techniques concerning systems of second-order linear differential equations with the basic ideas of the calculus of variations. The main difference between our proof and Morse's is that we try to work directly with the infinite-dimensional linear spaces that occur, whereas Morse, by a variety of ingenious analytical and geometric tricks, tries to reduce the infinite-dimensional situation to a finite one.

Let V be a vector space of finite dimension† over the real numbers. Elements of V will be denoted by such letters as $u, v, w, \ldots$. It will be assumed that V has a given fixed, positive-definite, symmetric bilinear form $(u, v) \rightarrow \langle u, v \rangle$. Thus

$$\langle au + bv, a_1 u_1 + b_1 v_1 \rangle = a a_1 \langle u, u_1 \rangle + a b_1 \langle u, v_1 \rangle$$
$$+ a_1 b \langle v, u_1 \rangle + b b_1 \langle v, v_1 \rangle. \tag{31.2a}$$

For $a, a_1, b, b_1 \in R \,(= \text{real numbers})$, $u, v, u_1, v_1 \in V$,

$$\langle u, v \rangle = \langle v, u \rangle \qquad \text{for } u, v \in V \tag{31.2b}$$

$$\langle u, u \rangle \geq 0 \quad \text{for } u \in V, \qquad \langle u, u \rangle = 0 \quad \text{if and only if } u = 0. \tag{31.2c}$$

† It seems to be an open problem to extend the theory to infinite-dimensional space.

For $v \in V$, put $\|v\| = \langle v, v \rangle^{1/2}$. Recall that the following inequalities follow from the positive-definite condition:

(a) $\|u + v\| \leq \|u\| + \|v\|$ (triangle inequality).
(b) $|\langle u, v \rangle| \leq \|u\| \, \|v\|$. Equality holds if and only if $au + bv = 0$ for some $a, b \in R$ (Schwarz inequality).

We must also consider linear transformations of V onto itself, usually denoted by $R, S, T, \ldots$, and bilinear symmetric forms other than $\langle \ , \ \rangle$ that will not necessarily be positive-definite [that is, satisfy (31.2a), (31.2b), but not (31.2c)], and that will be denoted by $Q(\ , \ )$. A linear transformation $R: V \to V$ is said to be *symmetric* if

$$\langle R(u), v \rangle = \langle u, R(v) \rangle \qquad \text{for } u, v \in V.$$

Now t will be a real parameter extending over the interval $[0, \infty)$ or a subinterval. We shall consider vector-valued functions of t, denoted usually by $u(t)$, $v(t)$, etc., defined over an interval and usually continuous, piecewise C^2, and taking values in V. The derivative with respect to t is denoted by $u'(t)$, $u''(t)$, dv/dt, etc.

We shall be considering differential operators of the form $v \to v''(t) + R_t(v(t))$, also denoted by

$$J = \frac{d^2}{dt^2} + R_t, \tag{31.3}$$

where $t \to R_t$ is a one-parameter family of symmetric linear transformations of V. (It is possible to generalize the theory by including some kinds of terms in v' on the right-hand side of (31.3), but we prefer to treat this simpler case, referring to Morse [1] for a complete treatment).

We must also consider *boundary conditions*: Algebraically, a boundary condition is an ordered pair (W, Q) consisting of a subspace $W \subset V$ and a bilinear, symmetric form $(u, v) \to Q(u, v)$ defined on W alone.

One fundamental problem may be described as follows: Find a solution of

$$v''(t) + R_t(v(t)) = 0, \qquad 0 \leq t \leq \infty, \tag{31.4}$$

subject to the following boundary conditions:

$$v(0) \in W, \qquad \langle v'(0), w \rangle = -Q(v(0), w) \qquad \text{for all } w \in W, \tag{31.5}$$

$$v(a) \in W^a, \qquad \langle v'(0), w \rangle = -Q^a(v(a), w) \qquad \text{for all } w \in W^a, \tag{31.6}$$

for a given number $a > 0$, and two sets (W, Q) and (W^a, Q^a) of boundary conditions. We refer to (31.5) and (31.6) as, respectively, left- and right-hand boundary conditions.

There is a problem in the calculus of variations associated with (31.4) through (31.6) that is the foundation for the Morse treatment. Proceed as follows to find it: Suppose $v(t), 0 \leq t \leq a$, satisfies (31.4) through (31.6). Then†

$$- \int_0^a \langle v''(t) + R_t(v(t)), v(t) \rangle = - \langle v'(t), v(t) \rangle \Big|_0^a$$

$$+ \int_0^a [\langle v'(t), v'(t) \rangle - \langle R_t(v(t)), v(t) \rangle] \, dt$$

$$= Q^a(v(a), v(a)) - Q(v(0), v(0))$$

$$+ \int_0^a [\|v'\|^2 - \langle R_t v, v \rangle] \, dt.$$

This suggests the following definition: Suppose $v(t), 0 \leq t \leq a$, is a curve in V. Define

$$I(v) = Q^a(v(a), v(a)) - Q(v(0), v(0)) + \int_0^a \|v'\|^2 - \langle Rv, v \rangle \, dt, \quad (31.7)$$

and call it the *index* of the curve v. If our boundary-value problem, (31.4) through (31.6), admits a solution, there is a curve v with $I(v) = 0$; hence it is suggested that we turn this remark around and try to minimize $I(v)$ by a curve $v(t)$ satisfying (31.4) through (31.6). This is an ordinary variational problem. It is readily verified that its Euler equations are (31.4), but this fact will remain in the background.

In this treatment we shall restrict ourselves to the case in which the right-hand boundary conditions (W^a, Q^a) are identically zero.

Definition

A point $a \in (0, \infty)$ is said to be a focal point for the operator and boundary condition (W, Q) if there is a nontrivial C^2 curve $v(t)$ in $V, 0 \leq t \leq a$ satisfying

$$J(v) = 0, \qquad v(0) \in W,$$

$$\langle v'(0), w \rangle = - Q(v(0), w) \quad \text{for all } w \in W, \qquad v(a) = 0.$$

The *index* of such a focal point is equal to the dimension of the linear space of all curves satisfying these conditions (hence, it is always infinite and no greater than the dimension of V).

---

† Where it is felt that it will lead to no confusion, we shall compress the notation by omitting t.

Definition

Let $[0, a]$ be an interval of real numbers. Let $\Omega(0, a)$ be the space of continuous, piecewise C^2 curves $t \to v(t)$, $0 \leq t \leq a$, in V satisfying the following conditions:

$$v(0) \in W, \qquad \langle v'(0), w \rangle = -Q(v(0), w) \quad \text{for all } w \in W, \qquad v(a) = 0.$$

Since two such curves can be added pointwise and multiplied by real constants, $\Omega(0, a)$ is a vector space over the real numbers. For $v \in \Omega(0, a)$, let

$$I(v) = -Q(v(0), v(0)) + \int_0^a \|v'(t)\|^2 - \langle R_t(v), v \rangle \, dt.$$

Define the *index* of the interval $[0, a]$ as the maximum number of linearly independent elements of $\Omega(0, a)$ on which the function I is negative.

Thus there are the two distinct ideas of index of a focal point and index of a closed interval $[0, a]$. They are related via the following main theorem:

THEOREM 31.1 (MORSE INDEX THEOREM)

The index of an interval $[0, a]$ is finite and equal to the sum of indices of the focal points contained in the open interval $(0, a)$. It is also equal to the maximal number of linearly independent elements of $\Omega(0, a)$ that are C^2 and are eigenfunctions of the differential operator $J = (d^2/dt^2) + R_t$ for positive eigenvalues.

As a general intuitive remark, notice that the index of an interval is an analytical invariant of the operator J and boundary condition (W, Q), while the sum of the indices of the focal points is more like a topological invariant. Thus the index of the interval may be expected to vary reasonably smoothly when J, (W, Q), or $[0, a]$ are varied in a reasonably smooth way. As such a variation is performed, it is not expected that each focal point varies smoothly; the remarkable fact contained in the index theorem is that the sum of indices of the focal points does vary in a more reasonable way. Another intuitive remark is that the index theorem provides the foundation for a perturbation-theory approach to the problem of finding focal points.

Proof of the Morse Index Theorem

Let V, (W, Q), $J = (d^2/dt^2) + R_t$, $\Omega(0, a)$, etc., be as described in the Introduction. They will be considered as fixed throughout the discussion.

The proof of the index theorem will be broken up into small steps.

LEMMA 31.2

Given a pair (v_0, u_0) of vectors in V, there is a unique curve in $V: t \rightarrow v(t)$, $0 < t < \infty$, satisfying $J(v) = 0$, and $v(0) = v_0$, $v'(0) = u_0$. In particular, if $v_0 = u_0 = 0$, then $v(t) \equiv 0$. If v_0, u_0, and the coefficients of J depend continuously on additional parameters, so do the resulting solutions, and the dependence is uniformly continuous for t ranging over a bounded closed interval.

This follows from the basic existence theorem for ordinary differential equations.

LEMMA 31.3

The vector space of solution curves of $J = 0$ that are C^2 and satisfy the (W, Q) boundary condition at $t = 0$ has the same dimension as V.

Proof. For later reference, we shall prove a little more and develop additional notations. Suppose $\dim V = n$, $\dim W = m$, $\dim W^\perp = n - m$. ($W^\perp$ denotes the orthogonal complement of W in V with respect to the form $\langle \, , \, \rangle$. Explicitly, $W^\perp = \{u \in V : \langle u, w \rangle = 0 \text{ for all } w \in W\}$.)

Adopt the following ranges of indices:

$$1 \leq i, j, \ldots \leq n; \qquad 1 \leq a, b, \ldots < m; \qquad m + 1 \leq \alpha, \beta, \ldots \leq n. \qquad (31.8)$$

Adopt a fixed orthonormal basis (u_i) of V such that (u_a) and (u_α) are, respectively, orthonormal bases of W and $W^\perp$. Then we can find n-solution curves of $J = 0$, denoted by $v_i(t)$, $0 \leq t < \infty$, $1 \leq i \leq n$, such that

$$v_a(0) = u_a, \qquad 1 \leq a \leq m. \qquad (31.9a)$$

$$\left. \begin{array}{l} \langle v_a'(0), w \rangle \\ v_a'(0) \in W \end{array} \right\} = -Q(u_a, w) \qquad \text{for all } w \in W, \quad 1 \leq a \leq m. \qquad (31.9b)$$

$$\left. \begin{array}{l} v_\alpha(0) = 0 \\ v_\alpha'(0) = u_\alpha \end{array} \right\} \qquad \text{for } m + 1 \leq \alpha \leq n. \qquad \begin{array}{l} (31.9c) \\ (31.9d) \end{array}$$

(The existence and uniqueness of solution curves satisfying these conditions follow easily from Lemma 31.2.) Note also that these curves satisfy the (W, Q)-boundary condition at $t = 0$.

We show that the curves $v_i(t)$, $1 \leq i \leq n$, are linearly independent. Suppose there is a linear relation of the form

$$\sum_i^n C_i v_i(t) = 0.$$

Setting $t = 0$ and using (31.9a) and (31.9c), we have $\sum_a C_a u_a = 0$, implying $C_a = 0$, implying $\sum_\alpha C_\alpha v(t) = 0$. Differentiating, setting $t = 0$, and using

(31.9d), we have $\sum_\alpha C_\alpha u_\alpha = 0$, forcing $C_\alpha = 0$, whence linear independence of the $v_i(t)$.

To complete the proof of Lemma 31.3, we show that every solution curve $v(t)$ if $J = 0$ satisfying the (W, Q)-boundary condition at $t = 0$ can be written as a sum of the $v_i(t)$ with constant coefficients. Now we have $v(0) \in W$; hence $v(0)$ can be written as

$$v(0) = \sum_a C_a u_a = \sum_a C_a v_a C_a v_a(0).$$

The solution curve $v(t) - \sum_a C_a v_a(t)$ is zero for $t = 0$; hence its derivative at $t = 0$ can be written as a sum

$$\sum_\alpha C_\alpha u_\alpha = \sum_\alpha C_\alpha v_\alpha'(0).$$

Thus $v(t) - \sum_i C_i v_i(t)$ is a solution of $J = 0$, is zero at $t = 0$, and its first derivative is zero at $t = 0$; hence it is identically zero.   Q.E.D.

For future reference, we shall refer to the basis $(v_i(t))$ of solutions of $J = 0$ and the (W, Q)-boundary condition constructed above as a canonical basis.

LEMMA 31.4

If $v(t)$ and $w(t)$ are two solutions of $J = 0$ satisfying the (W, Q)-boundary condition at $t = 0$, then

$$\langle v'(t), w(t)\rangle = \langle v(t), w'(t)\rangle \qquad \text{for } 0 \le t < \infty. \tag{31.10}$$

Proof. Note the identity

$$\frac{d}{dt}(\langle v'(t), w(t)\rangle - \langle v(t), w'(t)\rangle) = \langle v''(t), w(t)\rangle + \langle v'(t), w'(t)\rangle$$
$$- \langle v'(t), w'(t)\rangle - \langle v(t), w''(t)\rangle$$
$$= \langle -R_t(v(t)), w(t)\rangle + \langle v(t), R_t(w(t))\rangle = 0,$$

obtained by use of the symmetry property of R_t. Now

$$\langle v'(0), w(0)\rangle - \langle v(0), w'(0)\rangle = -Q(v(0), w(0)) + Q(v(0), w(0)) = 0.$$

LEMMA 31.5

If ε is sufficiently small, there are no focal points on the interval $[0, \varepsilon]$.

Proof. Let $(v_i(t))$, $1 < i \le n$, be a canonical basis for solutions of $J = 0$ satisfying the (W, Q)-boundary condition at $t = 0$. Define curves $w_i(t)$ as follows:

$$w_a(t) = v_a(t) \quad \text{for } 1 \le a \le m; \qquad w_\alpha(t) = \frac{v_\alpha(t)}{t} \qquad \text{for } m + 1 \le \alpha \le n.$$

By (31.9), w_α is continuous at $t = 0$ and equals there the $v_\alpha'(0) = u_\alpha$. Then the vectors $(w_i(t))$ are linearly independent for $t = 0$; hence by continuity also for t sufficiently small, say, for $0 \leq t \leq \varepsilon$. Then $[0, \varepsilon]$ can contain no focal points. For suppose otherwise: That is, $v(t)$ is a solution of $J = 0$ satisfying the (W, Q)-boundary condition at $t = 0$ and vanishing at, say, $t = \varepsilon$. By Lemma 31.3, $v(t)$ can be written as $\sum_i C_i v_i(t)$, for constants C_i. Hence, also,

$$0 = v(\varepsilon) = \sum_a C_a w_a(\varepsilon) + \sum_a C_\alpha w_\alpha(\varepsilon) \cdot \varepsilon.$$

Thus $C_a = 0 = C_\alpha$; hence $v(t) \equiv 0$, a contradiction.

Lemma 31.6

Suppose $t_0 \in (0, \infty)$ is a focal point. Then, for ε sufficiently small, $[t_0 - \varepsilon, t_0 + \varepsilon]$ contains no other focal point. We then conclude, using also Lemma 31.5, that each bounded interval contains only a finite number of focal points.

Proof. Suppose $v_i(t)$, $1 \leq i \leq n$, is any basis of solutions of $J = 0$ satisfying the (W, Q)-boundary condition at $t = 0$ such that

$$v_i(t_0) = 0 \qquad \text{for } 1 \leq i \leq p,$$

but $v_i(t_0)$ are linearly independent for $p + 1 \leq i \leq n$ (p is then the index of the focal point). By formula (31.10),

$$\langle v_i'(t_0), v_j(t_0) \rangle = 0 \qquad \text{for } 1 \leq i \leq p, \quad p + 1 \leq j \leq n.$$

The $v_i'(t_0)$ must be linearly independent for $1 \leq i \leq p$ [otherwise the $v_1(t), \ldots, v_p(t)$ could not be linearly independent]; hence $v_i'(t_0), \ldots, v_p'(t_0), v_{p+1}(t_0), \ldots, v_n(t_0)$ must form a basis for V. Now

$$\lim_{t \to t_0} \frac{v_i(t)}{t - t_0} = v_i'(t_0) \qquad \text{for } 1 \leq i \leq p;$$

hence, if ε is sufficiently small, the vectors

$$\frac{v_i(t_0 + \varepsilon)}{\varepsilon}, \qquad v_j(t_0 + \varepsilon), \qquad \text{for } 1 \leq i \leq p, \quad p + 1 \leq j \leq n,$$

form a basis for V. The proof that there are no focal points on $[t_0 - \varepsilon, t_0 + \varepsilon]$ is now similar to that in Lemma 31.5.

We need more notation. If $v(t)$ is a curve in $\Omega(0, a)$ and $W(t)$, $0 \leq t \leq a$, is any continuous piecewise C^1 curve in V satisfying the (W, Q)-boundary condition at $t = 0$; put

$$I(v, w) = -Q(v(0), w(0)) + \int_0^a \langle v'(t), w'(t) \rangle - \langle R_t(v(t)), w(t) \rangle \, dt. \quad (31.11)$$

Let $\Omega_J(0, a)$ be the subset of curves $v(t)$ in $\Omega(0, a)$ defined by taking all linear combinations with constant coefficients of curves of the following type: For each $t_0 \in (0, a]$ that is a focal point, consider a C^2 curve $v(t)$ in $[0, t_0]$ that satisfies $J = 0$ and the (W, Q)-boundary condition at $t = 0$, and that vanishes at $t = t_0$. Extend this curve over $[0, a]$ by defining $v(t) = 0$ for $t_0 \le t \le a$. This is shown graphically in Fig. 6. Then:

> The dimension of $\Omega_J(0, a)$ as a real vector space is equal to the sum of indices of the focal points on the interval $(0, a]$.   (31.12)

$$t_0 \qquad a$$

FIGURE 6

LEMMA 31.7

Let $(v_i(t))$, $1 \le i \le n$, $0 \le t \le a$ be any basis for the vector space of curves in V that are C^2 and satisfy $J = 0$. Suppose that $v(t)$, $0 \le t \le a$, is a differentiable curve in V such that $I(v, w) = 0$ for all curves $w(t)$, $0 \le t \le a$, that lie in $\Omega_J(0, 1)$. Then $v(t)$ admits a representation as

$$v(t) = \sum_{i=1}^{n} a_i(t)v_i(t) \qquad \text{for } 0 \le t \le a, \tag{31.13}$$

where the coefficients $a_i(t)$ are continuous, piecewise C^2 functions for $0 \le t \le a$.

Proof. Obviously, $v(t)$ admits such a representation (31.13) valid except possibly for the values of t that are focal points. We must show the functions $a_i(t)$ obtained in this way have a limit as t approaches a focal point. Suppose, then, that $t_0 \in (0, a]$ is such a focal point. We may suppose the basis $(v_i(t))$ is chosen so that $v_i(t_0) = 0$ for $1 \le i \le p$, and $(v_i(t_0))$ are linearly independent for $p + 1 \le i \le n$. By Lemma 31.3,

$$\langle v_i'(t_0), v_j(t_0) \rangle = 0 \qquad \text{for } 1 \le i \le p, p + 1 \le j \le n.$$

As before, this implies that $v_1'(t_0), \ldots, v_p'(t_0), v_{p+1}(t_0), \ldots, v_n(t_0)$ forms a basis for V. Then, for t close to t_0,

$$v(t) = \sum_{i=1}^{p} a_i(t)(t - t_0) \frac{v_i(t)}{t - t_0} + \sum_{i=p+1}^{n} a_i(t)v_i(t).$$

For $1 \le i \le p$,

$$\lim_{t \to t_0} \frac{v_i(t)}{t - t_0} = v_i'(t_0);$$

hence, for t sufficiently close to t_0,

$$\frac{v_1(t)}{t - t_0}, \ldots, \frac{v_p(t)}{t - t_0}, v_{p+1}(t), \ldots, v_n(t)$$

forms a basis of V and depends in a C^1 way on t. Since $v(t)$ is continuous, the functions $a_i(t)(t - t_0)$ for $1 \le i \le p$ and $a_i(t)$ for $p + 1 \le i \le n$ are continuous at t_0.

These remarks are valid for any v that is merely continuous. Now we want to take into account the fact that $I(v, w) = 0$ for all $w \in \Omega_J(0, 1)$. For $1 \le j \le p$, let w_i be the elements of $\Omega_J(0, 1)$ defined as follows:

$$w_i(t) = v_i(t) \quad \text{for } 0 \le t \le t_0, \qquad w_i(t) = 0 \quad \text{for } t_0 \le t \le a. \quad (31.14)$$

$$0 = I(v, w_i) = -Q(v(0), w_i(0)) + \int_0^a \langle v'(t), w_i'(t) \rangle - \langle R_t(v(t)), w_i(t) \rangle \, dt$$

equals, using (31.14),

$$-Q(v(0), v_i(0)) + \int_0^{t_0} \langle v'(t), v_j'(t) \rangle - \langle R_t(v(t)), v_j(t) \rangle \, dt$$

equals, after integrating by parts and taking into account the fact that $J(v_i) = 0$ and that v and v_i satisfy the (W, Q)-boundary condition at $t = 0$, $\langle v(t_0), v_j'(t_0) \rangle$. Thus, $v(t_0)$ must be a linear combination of $v_{p+1}(t_0), \ldots, v_n(t_0)$. We conclude that

$$\lim_{t \to t_0} a_i(t)(t - t_0) = 0 \qquad \text{for } 1 \le i \le p.$$

Now, since $v(t)$ is differentiable, the functions $a_i(t)(t - t_0)$ for $1 \le i \le p$ are differentiable at $t = t_0$. We conclude (using the definition of derivative) that $\lim_{t \to t_0} a_i(t)$ exists and equals

$$\frac{d}{dt}\left(a_i(t)(t - t_0)\right)\Big|_{t=t_0}. \qquad \text{Q.E.D.}$$

LEMMA 31.8

Let $v_i(t)$, $1 \le i \le n$, $0 \le t \le a$, be a basis of curves in V that are C^2 and satisfy $J = 0$ and the (W, Q)-boundary condition at $t = 0$. Suppose $u(t)$ and $v(t)$, $0 \le t \le a$, are two curves in V admitting representations of the following type:

$$u(t) = \sum_{i=1}^n f_i(t)v_i(t) \quad \text{for } 0 \le t \le a, \qquad v(t) = \sum_{i=1}^n f_i(a)v_i(t) \quad \text{for } 0 \le t \le a.$$

Suppose in addition that the functions $f_i(t)$ are continuous and piecewise C^1 for $0 < t \leq a$, and that $u(t)$ satisfies the (W, Q)-boundary condition at $t = 0$. Then $I(u) \geq I(v)$. Equality holds only if $u = v$.

Proof.   For $\varepsilon > 0$, let

$$I_\varepsilon(u) = -Q(u(0), u(0)) + \int_\varepsilon^a \|u'(t)\|^2 - \langle R_t(u(t)), u(t)\rangle \, dt.$$

$$u'(t) = \sum_{i=1}^n (f_i'(t)v_i(t) + f_i(t)v_i'(t)).$$

$$\|u'(t)\|^2 = \sum_{i,j=1}^n (f_i'(t)f_j'(t)\langle v_i(t), v_j(t)\rangle + f_i(t)f_j(t)\langle v_i'(t), v_j'(t)\rangle$$
$$+ f_i'(t)f_j(t)\langle v_i(t), v_j'(t)\rangle + f_i(t)f_j'(t)\langle v_i'(t), v_j(t)\rangle).$$

Now

$$\int_\varepsilon^a f_i(t)f_j(t)\langle v_i'(t), v_j'(t)\rangle \, dt = f_i(t)f_j(t)\langle v_i'(t), v_j(t)\rangle \Big|_{t=\varepsilon}^a$$
$$- \int_\varepsilon^a f_i'(t)f_j(t)\langle v_i'(t), v_j(t)\rangle$$
$$+ f_i(t)f_j'(t)\langle v_i'(t), v_j(t)\rangle$$
$$+ f_i(t)f_j(t)\langle v_i''(t), v_j'(t)\rangle \, dt.$$

Using the last two identities and Lemma 31.4, we have

$$\int_\varepsilon^a \|u'(t)\|^2 \, dt = \int_\varepsilon^a \left[\left\| \sum_{i=1}^n f_i'(t)v_i(t) \right\|^2 + \langle R_t(u(t)), u(t)\rangle \right] dt$$
$$- Q(u(a), u(a)) + Q(u(\varepsilon), u(\varepsilon)).$$

Hence,

$$I_\varepsilon(u) = \int_\varepsilon^a \left\| \sum_{i=1}^n f_i'(t)v_i(t) \right\|^2 dt - Q(u(a), u(a)) + (Q(u(\varepsilon), u(\varepsilon)) - Q(u(0), u(0))).$$

Similarly,

$$I_\varepsilon(v) = -Q(v(a), v(a)) + (Q(v(\varepsilon), v(\varepsilon)) - Q(u(0), u(0))).$$

Hence

$$I_\varepsilon(u) - I_\varepsilon(v) = \int_\varepsilon^a \left\| \sum_{i=1}^n f_i'(t)v_i(t) \right\|^2 dt + (Q(u(\varepsilon), u(\varepsilon)) - Q(u(0), u(0)))$$
$$- (Q(v(\varepsilon), v(\varepsilon)) - Q(v(0), v(0))).$$

Since all the other terms in this identity approach a limit, we have

$$\lim_{\varepsilon \to 0} \int_\varepsilon^a \left\| \sum_{i=1}^n f_i'(t) v_i(t) \right\|^2 dt \quad \text{exists.}$$

Since it must clearly be > 0 unless $f_i'(t) = 0$, that is, unless $u(t) = v(t)$ for $0 \le t \le a$, we have $I(u) > I(v)$ except if $u = v$.   Q.E.D.

This lemma is due to Ambrose [1] and serves as a replacement for the arguments from the general calculus of variations that were used by Morse.

COROLLARY TO LEMMA 31.8

The interval $[0, a]$ contains no focal points if and only if $I(u) > 0$ for all curves $u \in \Omega(0, a)$. (In other words, the Morse index theorem holds if $[0, a]$ contains no focal point.)

We must now apply Lemma 31.8 in the special case in which W and Q are both zero; focal points are, in this case, called *conjugate points*. For the reader's convenience, we restate the definition in slightly different form.

Definition

Let a and b be positive real numbers; a and b are said to be mutually *conjugate* if there is a C^2 curve $v(t)$, not identically zero, satisfying $v'' + R_t(v(t)) = 0$ and $v(a) = v(b) = 0$.

LEMMA 31.9

Suppose that a and b are real numbers, $0 \le a < b$, such that the real-number interval between them contains no pair of mutually conjugate points. Suppose that $u(t)$ and $v(t)$, $0 \le t < \infty$, are continuous curves such that u is piecewise C^2 and v is C^2. v satisfies:

$$\left(\frac{d^2}{dt^2} + R_t \right)(v) = 0. \qquad u(b) = v(b), \qquad u(a) = v(a).$$

Then

$$\int_a^b \|v'(t)\|^2 - \langle R_t(v(t)), v(t) \rangle \, dt \le \int_a^b \|u'(t)\|^2 - \langle R_t(u(t)), u(t) \rangle \, dt.$$

Equality holds only if $u(t) = v(t)$ for $a \le t \le b$.

Proof.   First we deal with the case $u(a) = v(a) = 0$. By a translation of the origin of the t-axis, we can also suppose that $a = 0$. The result then follows from Lemma 31.8, since our hypotheses imply that there are no focal points in the interval $(0, b]$, with respect to the boundary conditions $W = 0$, $Q = 0$, at $t = 0$.

Now we reduce the general case $u(a) = v(a)$ to the case just considered. By Lemma 31.3 (since a and b are not mutually conjugate), there is a C^2 curve $w(t)$ satisfying $w(b) = 0$, $w(a) = u(a) = v(a)$,

$$\left(\frac{d^2}{dt^2} - R_t\right) w = 0.$$

Let $u^*(t) = u(t) - w(t)$, $v^*(t) = v(t) - w(t)$. Since $u^*(a) = 0 = v^*(a)$, case mentioned above applies, to give

$$\int_a^b \|u^{*\prime}(t)\|^2 - \langle R_t(u^*(t)), u^*(t)\rangle \, dt \geq \int_a^b \|v^{*\prime}(t)\|^2 - \langle R_t(v^*(t)), v^*(t)\rangle \, dt.$$

But the left-hand side of this inequality is

$$\int_a^b [\|u'(t)\|^2 + \|w'(t)\|^2 - 2\langle u'(t), w'(t)\rangle - \langle R_t(u(t)), u(t)\rangle$$
$$- \langle R_t(w(t)), w(t)\rangle + 2\langle R_t(u(t)), w(t)\rangle] \, dt$$

and equals, after integrating by parts and taking into account the relations satisfied by w,

$$\int_a^b [\|u'(t)\|^2 - \langle R_t(u(t)), u(t)\rangle] \, dt - \langle w'(a), w(a)\rangle$$
$$+ 2\langle u(a), w'(a)\rangle - 2\langle u(b), w'(b)\rangle$$
$$= \int_a^b [\|u'(t)\|^2 - \langle R_t(u(t)), u(t)\rangle] \, dt + \langle v(a), w'(a)\rangle - 2\langle v(b), w'(b)\rangle,$$

(since $v(a) = u(a) = w(a)$). Now $((d^2/dt^2) - R_t)v^* = 0$; hence the right-hand side of the previous inequality is, after an integration by parts,

$$\langle v^{*\prime}(b), v^*(b)\rangle - \langle v^*(a), v^{*\prime}(0)\rangle = \langle v'(b) - w'(b), v(b)\rangle,$$

since $v^*(a) = 0$ and $w(b) = 0$. Similarly,

$$\int_a^b \|v'(t)\|^2 - \langle R_t(v(t)), v(t)\rangle \, dt = \langle v'(b), v(b)\rangle - \langle v'(a), v(a)\rangle.$$

Thus,

$$\int_a^b \|u'(t)\|^2 - \langle R_t(u(t)), u(t)\rangle \, dt \geq 2\langle v(b), w'(b)\rangle - \langle v(a), w'(a)\rangle$$
$$+ \langle v'(b), v(b)\rangle - \langle w'(b), v(b)\rangle$$
$$= \langle v(b), w'(b)\rangle - \langle v(a), w'(a)\rangle + \int_a^b \|v'(t)\|^2$$
$$- \langle R_t(v(t)), v(t)\rangle \, dt + \langle v'(a), v(a)\rangle.$$

Now

$$\frac{d}{dt}(\langle v(t), w'(t)\rangle - \langle v'(t), w(t)\rangle) = \langle v'(t), w'(t)\rangle + \langle v(t), w''(t)\rangle$$
$$- \langle v''(t), w(t)\rangle - \langle v'(t), w'(t)\rangle$$
$$= \langle v(t), R_t(w'(t))\rangle - \langle R_t(v(t)), w(t)\rangle = 0.$$

Hence,

$$\langle v(b), w'(b)\rangle = \langle v'(b), w(b)\rangle + \langle v'(a), w(a)\rangle - \langle v(a), w'(a)\rangle$$

equals, after using the relations $w(b) = 0$ and $w(a) = v(a)$,

$$\langle v'(a), v(a)\rangle - \langle v(a), w'(a)\rangle.$$

Putting the last relation together with the last inequality proves Lemma 31.9.

Lemmas 31.8 and 31.9 may be regarded as particular analytical tools needed to prove the index theorem. They really contain fundamental facts from the calculus of variations in a disguised form.

Now we proceed to another analytical tool, proving (again in slightly disguised form) a " compactness " principle for solutions of the type of differential equations we have been considering.

THEOREM 31.10

Suppose that $J^k: (d^2/dt^2) - R_t^k$ is a sequence of differential operators of the type we have been considering, $k = 1, 2, \ldots$, that (W^k, Q^k) is a sequence of boundary conditions, and that a_k is a sequence of real numbers. Suppose that

$$\lim_{k \to \infty} R_t^k = R_t, \quad \lim_{k \to \infty} W^k = W, \quad \lim_{k \to \infty} Q^k = Q, \quad \lim_{k \to \infty} a_k = a > 0.$$

Suppose further that $v_k(t)$, $0 < t < a_k$, is a sequence of C^2 curves in V satisfying the (W^k, Q^k)-boundary condition at $t = 0$.

$$v_k(a_k) = 0, \quad J^k(v_k) = 0, \quad \int_0^{a_k} \|v_k(t)\| \, dt \le 1.$$

Then at least one subsequence of the v_k converges, along with its first two derivatives, uniformly to a C^2 curve $v(t)$, $0 \le t \le a$, that is a solution of $J(v) = 0$, the (W, Q)-boundary condition, and $v(a) = 0$.

Proof. Let

$$u_k(t) = \frac{v_k(t)}{\|v_k(0)\| + \|v_k'(0)\|}.$$

Since $\|u_k(0)\|$ and $\|u_k'(0)\|$ are ≤ 1, we can suppose after at most taking subsequences that $\lim_{k \to \infty} u_k'(0) = u_0$, $\lim_{k \to \infty} u_k(0) = u_1$. By the existence theorem for ordinary linear differential equations of the type $J^k = 0$, $u_k(t)$ converges, along with its first two derivatives, uniformly to a C^2 nonidentically zero curve $u(t)$, $0 \le t \le a$, that is a solution of $J(u) = 0$, the (W, Q)-boundary condition, and $u(a) = 0$. Then, also,

$$\lim_{k \to \infty} \int_0^{a_k} \|u_k(t)\|^2 \, dt = \int_0^a \|u(t)\| \, dt.$$

But also

$$\int_0^{a_k} \|u_k(t)\| \, dt \le \frac{1}{\|v_k(0)\| + \|v_k'(0)\|}.$$

Hence $\|v_k(0)\| + \|v_k'(0)\|$ itself is bounded, and we can apply the existence theorem for the systems $J^k = 0$ to infer the existence of a curve $v(t)$ toward which $v_k(t)$ and its first two derivatives converge uniformly.   Q.E.D.

We can now proceed to the proof of the index theorem. It is most convenient to arrange the proof so that the final result will appear as a statement which says that different kinds of indices are in reality the same. Hence we now introduce the different indices, and also the so-called *augmented* indices.

Definition

Let a be a positive real number.

$I_1(0, a) =$ the sum of indices of the focal points contained in the interval $[0, a)$.

$AI_1(0, a) =$ the sum of indices of the focal points contained in the interval $[0, a]$. (Thus AI_1 is the *augmented index* corresponding to the index I_1.)

$I_2(0, a) =$ the maximal dimension of a linear subspace of $\Omega(0, a)$ on which the form $v \to I(v)$ is *negative-definite*.

$AI_2(0, a) =$ the maximal dimension of a linear subspace of $\Omega(0, a)$ on which the form $v \to I(v)$ is *negative-semidefinite*.

$I_3(0, a) =$ the maximal number of linearly independent C^2 eigenfunctions of the differential operator $(d^2/dt^2) + R_t$ corresponding to *positive* eigenvalues that also satisfy the boundary conditions implied by membership in $\Omega(0, a)$.

$AI_3(0, a) =$ the maximal number of linearly independent C^2 eigenfunctions of the differential operator $(d^2/dt^2) + R_t$ corresponding to *nonnegative* eigenvalues that also satisfy the boundary conditions implied by membership in $\Omega(0, a)$.

Note that several facts follow readily:

$$AI_3(0, a) - I_3(0, a) = AI_1(0, a) - I_1(0, a)$$
$$= \text{the index of the focal point } w \text{ (if } a \text{ is a focal point)}$$
$$= 0 \text{ (if } a \text{ is not a focal point).} \qquad (31.15)$$
$$I_3(0, a) \le I_2(0, a), \qquad AI_3(0, a) \le (AI_2(0, a)). \qquad (31.16)$$

Proof. Suppose that $v(t)$, $0 \le t \le a$, lies in $\Omega(0, a)$ and satisfies

$$v''(t) + R_t(v(t)) = \lambda^2 v(t), \qquad \text{with } \lambda \ge 0.$$

Then

$$-\lambda^2 \int_0^a \|(v(t))\|^2 \, dt = -\int_0^a \langle v(t, v''(t)) + R_t(v(t)) \rangle \, dt$$

equals, after integrating by parts and taking into account the boundary conditions satisfied by v,

$$-Q(v(0), v(0)) + \int_0^a \|v'(t)\|^2 - \langle v(t), R_t(v(t)) \rangle \, dt = I(v).$$

Then, $I(v) \le 0$.

To prove (31.16), notice now that $v \to I(v)$ restricted to the linear subspace of $\Omega(0, a)$ spanned by the positive eigenfunctions of $(d^2/dt^2) + R_t$ is negative-definite. Similarly, $v \to I(v)$ is negative-semidefinite on the subspace of $\Omega(0, a)$ spanned by the nonnegative eigenfunctions of $\Omega(0, a)$.

LEMMA 31.11

$AI_3(0, a)$ is finite.

Proof. Suppose otherwise: That is, there are an infinite number of C^2 eigenfunctions $v_k(t)$, $k = 1, 2, \ldots$, $0 \le t \le 1$, of $(d^2/dt^2) + R_t$ corresponding to eigenvalues λ_k^2 and satisfying the boundary condition corresponding to lying in $\Omega(0, a)$. We can suppose without loss of generality that

$$|Q(v_k(0), v_k(0))| + \int_0^a \langle v_k(t), v_k(t) \rangle \, dt = 1, \qquad (31.17a)$$

$$\int_0^a \langle v_k(t), v_j(t) \rangle \, dt = 0 \qquad \text{if } k \ne j. \qquad (31.17b)$$

Then

$$\lambda_k^2 = \int_0^a \langle v_k'' + R_t(v_k(t)), v_k(t) \rangle \, dt$$
$$= -Q(v_k(0), v_k(0)) - \int_0^a \|v_k'(t)\|^2 - \langle R_t(v_k(t)), v_k(t) \rangle \, dt$$
$$\le -Q(v_k(0), v_k(0)) + \int_0^a \langle R_t(v_k(t)), v_k(t) \rangle \, dt.$$

There is a real number δ such that

$$\langle R_t(v), v \rangle \leq \delta \langle v, v \rangle \qquad \text{for all } v \in V, \quad 0 \leq t \leq a.$$

Then

$$\lambda_k{}^2 \leq |Q(v_k(0), v_k(0))| + \delta \int_0^a \langle v_k(t), v_k(t) \rangle \, dt$$

$$\leq 1 + \delta;$$

that is, the sequence $(\lambda_k{}^2)$ is bounded. We can then suppose, after possibly taking subsequences, that $\lim_{k \to \infty} \lambda_k = \lambda$, and that $v_k(t)$ converges as $k \to \infty$, along with its first two derivatives, uniformly to a curve $v(t)$ that is an eigenfunction for eigenvalue λ (using Theorem 31.10). But this contradicts (31.17b).

LEMMA 31.12

$$AI_3(0, a) = AI_2(0, a), \qquad I_3(0, a) = I_2(0, a).$$

Proof. We prove the first equality: The second is similar. Let $d = AI_3(0, a)$. Then there are d linearly independent eigenfunctions $v_1(t), \ldots, v_d(t)$ in $\Omega(0, a)$, with eigenvalues $\lambda_1{}^2, \ldots, \lambda_d{}^2$. We can normalize so that

$$\int_0^a \langle v_j(t), v_k(t) \rangle \, dt = \delta_{jk} \qquad \text{for } 1 \leq j, k \leq d.$$

What we must show is that if $v(t) \in \Omega(0, a)$ satisfies

$$\int_0^a \langle v_k(t), v(t) \rangle = 0 \qquad \text{for } 1 \leq k \leq d, \tag{31.18}$$

then $I(v) > 0$. Suppose otherwise: That is, such a v exists with $I(v) \leq 0$. Now *minimize* $I(v)$ over all $v \in \Omega(0, a)$ satisfying (31.18) and $\int_0^a \|v(t)\|^2 \, dt = 1$. Using the "direct method" of the calculus of variations [1], this minimum is taken on by a C^2 function $v_0(t)$ in $\Omega(0, a)$ that is also an eigenfunction of $(d^2/dt^2) + R_t$ with eigenvalue λ_0. But this eigenfunction would then have to satisfy

$$0 \geq I(v_0) = -\lambda_0 \int_0^a \|v_0(t)\|^2 \, dt,$$

forcing $\lambda_0 \geq 0$, contradicting the definition of d.

LEMMA 31.13

If $0 \leq a \leq b$, then

$$I_2(0, a) \leq I_2(0, b), \qquad AI_2(0, a) \leq AI_2(0, b), \qquad AI_1(0, a) \leq I_2(0, b).$$

Proof. Choose ε sufficiently small and positive so that $a + \varepsilon \leq b$, and so that there are no mutually conjugate points on the interval $[a - \varepsilon, a + \varepsilon]$. We are now going to define a linear mapping $\phi_\varepsilon \colon \Omega(0, a) \to \Omega(0, b)$ such that

$$I(\phi_\varepsilon(v)) \leq I(v) \qquad \text{for each } v \in \Omega(0, a) \tag{31.19}$$

by making use of Lemma 31.9. Explicitly, $\phi_\varepsilon(v)(t)$, $0 \leq t \leq b$, is to be a continuous piecewise C^2 curve in V such that

$$\phi_\varepsilon(v)(t) = v(t) \qquad \text{for } 0 \leq t \leq a - \varepsilon. \tag{31.20a}$$

$$\phi_\varepsilon(v)(t) \text{ is a solution of } \frac{d^2}{dt^2} + R_t = 0, \tag{31.20b}$$

with

$$\phi_\varepsilon(v)(a - \varepsilon) = v(a - \varepsilon), \qquad \phi_\varepsilon(v)(a + \varepsilon) = 0;$$

$$\phi_\varepsilon(v)(t) = 0 \qquad \text{for } a + \varepsilon \leq t \leq b. \tag{31.20c}$$

The reader will readily verify that ϕ_ε is a linear mapping that (using Lemma 31.9) satisfies (31.19). Suppose now that $v_1(t), \ldots, v_d(t)$ are linearly independent elements of $\Omega(0, a)$ on which the form I is < 0. By (31.19), $I(\phi_\varepsilon(v_k)) < 0$ for $1 \leq k \leq d$. We must then show that $\phi_\varepsilon(v_k)(t)$ are linearly independent if ε is sufficiently small. Suppose otherwise: That is, there is, for each ε, a relation of the form: $\sum_{k=1}^d a_k(\varepsilon)v_k(t) = 0$ valid for $0 \leq t \leq a - \varepsilon$.

We can normalize so that $\sum_{k=1}^d a_k(\varepsilon)^2 = 1$. Then there would be a sequence of ε going to zero such that $a_k(\varepsilon) \to a_k$, and a relation of the form $\sum_{k=1}^d a_k v_k(t) = 0$, valid for $0 \leq t \leq 1$, contradicting that the v_k were linearly independent.

This proves the first inequality in Lemma 31.13. The second is similar. The third involves a slight modification of the argument. Let $a_1, \ldots, a_f$ be the focal points in the interval $[0, a]$, arranged so that $0 < a_1 < a_2 < \cdots < a_f \leq a$. Let $d_1, \ldots, d_f$ be the indices of each of the focal points. Let $v_1(t), \ldots, v_{d_1}(t)$, $0 \leq t \leq a_1$, be in $\Omega(0, a_1)$, be linearly independent, and C^2, and satisfy $(d^2/dt^2) + R_t = 0$. Then $\phi_\varepsilon(v_1), \ldots, \phi_\varepsilon(v_{d_1})$ span a subspace of $\Omega(0, b)$ on which I is < 0. To see this, use the criterion for equality in Lemma 31.9 and the fact that $v_k(t)$ cannot be zero for t sufficiently close to a_1, $1 \leq k \leq d_1$. Similarly, apply this construction to each of the focal points. It is easily seen that the subspaces of $\Omega(0, b)$ obtained in this way are all linearly independent of each other, hence span a subspace of $\Omega(0, b)$ of dimension $d_1 + \cdots + d_f = AI_1(0, a)$.

LEMMA 31.14

If ε is sufficiently small,

$$AI_3(0, a + \varepsilon) \leq AI_3(0, a).$$

Proof. Suppose otherwise: Let ε_k, $k = 1, 2, \ldots$, be a sequence of real numbers with $\varepsilon_k \to 0$ as $k \to \infty$, and with

$$AI_3(0, a + \varepsilon_k) \geq AI_3(0, a) + 1.$$

Let $v_{j,k}(t)$, $0 \leq j \leq AI_3(0, a) + 1$, $0 \leq k < \infty$, $0 \leq t \leq a + \varepsilon_k$, be curves in $\Omega(0, a + \varepsilon_k)$ that are C^2, that are eigenfunctions of $(d^2/dt^2) + R_t$ with nonnegative eigenvalues, and that, for fixed k, are linearly independent. Using Theorem 31.10, we can arrange (by taking subsequences and normalizing) that

$$\lim_{k \to \infty} v_{j,k}(t) = v_j(t), \qquad \int_0^{a + \varepsilon_k} \langle v_{j_1,k}(t), v_{j_2,k}(t) \rangle \, dt = \delta_{j_1 j_2},$$

that the first two derivatives converge uniformly for $0 \leq t \leq a$, and that the corresponding eigenvalues of $(d^2/dt^2) + R_t$ converge. Then

$$\int_0^a \langle v_{j_1}(t), v_{j_2}(t) \rangle \, dt = \delta_{j_1 j_2} \qquad \text{for} \quad 1 \leq j_1, j_2 \leq AI_1(0, a) + 1.$$

But the v_j are C^2, belong to $\Omega(0, a)$, and are eigenfunctions of $(d^2/dt^2) + R_t$ with nonnegative eigenvalues, and are linearly independent, a contradiction.

Now we can prove the index theorem itself. Note that it is equivalent to the statement:

$$I_1(0, a) = I_2(0, a) = I_3(0, a). \tag{31.21}$$

Note that we have already proved the second of these equalities (Lemma 31.12). The corollary to Lemma 31.8 implies that the first holds if a is sufficiently small. Assuming that (31.21) is true for a, we shall prove it is true for $a + \varepsilon$, if ε is sufficiently small and positive. Now, $I_1(0, a + \varepsilon) = I_1(0, a) + $ (index of the focal point a). By Lemma 31.13,

$$I_3(0, a) = I_2(0, a) \leq I_2(0, a + \varepsilon) = I_3(0, a + \varepsilon) \qquad \leq AI_3(0, a)$$

if ε is sufficiently small, by Lemma 31.14,

$$= I_3(0, a) + \text{index of } a.$$

$$I_1(0, a + \varepsilon) \leq I_2(0, a + \varepsilon) = I_3(0, a + \varepsilon) \leq I_3(0, a) + \text{index of } a.$$

Thus $I_3(0, a + \varepsilon) - $ index of $a = I_1(0, a)$, which proves (31.21) for $a + \varepsilon$. Then the set of all numbers b such that (31.21) is true for all $a \in [0, b]$ is open. To complete the proof, we must show that it is closed. Suppose, then, that a_k is a monotone-increasing sequence, $\lim_{k \to \infty} a_k = a$, such that (31.21) is true for each a_k. We must prove it is true for a also. Thus, we have

$$I_1(0, a_k) = I_2(0, a_k) \qquad \text{for } k = 1, 2, \ldots.$$

From the definition of I_1 we have $\lim_{k\to\infty} I_1(0, a_k) = I_1(0, a)$. By Lemma 31.13, $I_2(0, a_k) \le I_2(0, a)$. Let us suppose that $\lim_{k\to\infty} I_2(0, a_k) \ne I_2(0, a)$; that is,

$$I_2(0, a) > I_2(0, a_k) \qquad \text{for all } k.$$

To complete the proof, we show that

$$I_3(0, a) \le I_2(0, a - \varepsilon) \qquad \text{for } \varepsilon \text{ sufficiently small.} \qquad (31.22)$$

Suppose, then, that $v_1(t), \ldots, v_d(t)$ are linearly independent C^2 eigenfunctions of $(d^2/dt^2) + R_t$ for positive eigenvalues $\lambda_1{}^2, \ldots, \lambda_d{}^2$ that lie in $\Omega(0, a)$ $(d = I_3(0, a))$. Choose $\varepsilon > 0$ sufficiently small so that there are no mutually

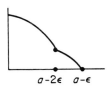

$a-2\epsilon$ $a-\epsilon$

FIGURE 7

conjugate points on the interval $[a, a - 2\varepsilon]$. Let $v_1{}^*(t), \ldots, v_d{}^*(t)$, $0 \le t \le a - \varepsilon$, be continuous piecewise C^2 curves in V defined as

$$v_k{}^*(t) = v_k(t \quad \text{for } 0 \le t \le a - 2\varepsilon, \qquad 1 \le k \le d.$$

$$\frac{d^2}{dt^2} + R_t(v_k{}^*)(t) = 0 \qquad \text{for } a - 2\varepsilon \le t \le a - \varepsilon, \quad 1 \le k \le d.$$

(Use Lemma 31.9 to construct the curves in Fig. 7.) Since $\lim_{\varepsilon\to 0} I(v_k{}^*) = I(v_k) < 0$, for $1 \le k \le d$, we see that $I(v_k{}^*) < 0$ if ε is sufficiently small. By an argument similar to that used in proving Lemma 31.13, we see that $v_1{}^*, \ldots, v_k{}^*$ are linearly independent if ε is sufficiently small. This proves (31.21) and finishes the proof of the index theorem itself.

32 Complex Manifolds and Their Submanifolds

In this chapter we present a short treatment of the local theory of submanifolds of complex manifolds, pointing out the analogy with the theory of submanifolds of affinely connected manifolds presented in Chapter 27, and the relation with the analytical theory of functions of several complex variables.

First we must describe how complex manifolds are to be regarded from a differential-geometric point of view. To eliminate confusion, it is desirable to eliminate complex numbers themselves from the definition, to regard complex manifolds from a "real" point of view. (Just as the complex numbers themselves are interpreted as pairs of real numbers, eliminating any mysticism about the square root of -1.)

Suppose that M is a manifold of dimension $2n$. Consider a coordinate chart from an open subset of M to an open subset of R^{2n}. Now, $2n$-dimensional Euclidean space is just C^n, the space of n complex variables. We say that M has a *complex manifold structure* if an atlas of coordinate charts can be chosen so that the transition maps between two charts are defined by complex-analytic functions. We say that a map between two manifolds with such structures is *complex-analytic* (or *holomorphic*) if, when referred back to C^n by the coordinate charts, it is defined by complex analytic functions. (We shall need to consider as known to the reader the elementary facts about holomorphic functions on domains of C^n.) Two such structures on the same manifold can be regarded as essentially the same if the identity map is holomorphic. It is important to realize, however, that a given manifold may have many different complex manifold structures and that a manifold need not admit any complex manifold structure. (For example, the $2n$-dimensional spheres, for $n \neq 1$ or 3, do not admit any. It is not known whether the six-dimensional sphere can admit one.) Our first aim is to make this remark clearer by actually exhibiting a complex structure as a geometric structure defined by a tensor field on the manifold, just as, say, a Riemannian metric is a structure defined by a tensor field. As a first step in this direction, we describe how the complex analytic structure on C^n itself is determined by a tensor field.

Consider R^{2n} or the space of variables (x_i, y_i), with $1 \leq i, j, \ldots \leq n$. Putting $z_i = x_i + \sqrt{-1}\, y_i$ gives the identification of R^{2n} with C^n that we have in mind; that is, the coordinates of R^{2n} are considered as the real and imaginary parts of the complex variables of C^n. Suppose $F = f + \sqrt{-1}\, g$ is a complex-

420

valued function on R^{2n} that is holomorphic. How do we express the holomorphic condition in coordinate-free terms?

First, the conditions can be described by the Cauchy–Riemann equations:

$$\frac{\partial f}{\partial x_i} = \frac{\partial g}{\partial y_i} ; \qquad \frac{\partial f}{\partial y_i} = -\frac{\partial g}{\partial x_i}.$$

Define a $F(R^{2n})$-linear map, that is, a tensor field, $J: V(R^{2n}) \to V(R^{2n})$ by setting

$$J\left(\frac{\partial}{\partial x_i}\right) = \frac{\partial}{\partial x_i} ; \qquad J\left(\frac{\partial}{\partial y_i}\right) = -\frac{\partial}{\partial x_i} \qquad \text{for } 1 \le i \le n.$$

Then the Cauchy–Riemann equation becomes

$$X(f) = J(X)(g) \qquad \text{for all } X \in V(R^{2n}). \tag{32.1}$$

Notice also that

$$J(JX) = -X \qquad \text{for all } X \in V(R^{2n}). \tag{32.2}$$

We can now characterize complex-analytic maps $\phi: R^{2n} \to R^{2m}$ by means of the J-tensor, namely: For each point $p \in R^{2n}$,

$$\text{each tangent vector } v \text{ to } p = \phi_*(J(v)) = J\phi_*(v). \tag{32.3}$$

To prove this, note that to prove ϕ is holomorphic. It suffices to show that $\phi^*(F)$ is holomorphic for every holomorphic function F on R^{2n}. However, the characterization of the Cauchy–Riemann equations as (32.1) makes it obvious that (32.2) is this condition.

Equation (32.3) tells us that a given complex structure on a manifold M defines a tensor field $J: V(M) \to V(M)$, with $J^2 = -(\text{identity})$. For if the J-tensor on R^{2n} is carried over to M by a coordinate chart, then (32.3) implies that J is actually independent of the coordinate chart associated with the complex structure.

Now, not every tensor field $J: V(M) \to V(M)$ with $J^2 = -(\text{identity})$ arises in this way from a complex structure: Certain integrability conditions must be satisfied (M is said to carry on almost complex structure if it merely has such a tensor. The 6-sphere, for example, has such a tensor, which is not integrable). Such conditions are given by Frohlicher [1], and take the form

$$[X, Y] + J[JX, Y] = J[X, JY] + [JX, JY] = 0 \qquad \text{for } X, Y \in V(M). \tag{32.4}$$

The key point is that the left-hand side, as a function of $X \in Y$, is $F(M)$-bilinear; hence, defines a genuine tensor field. The verification of this is straightforward and is left to the reader. Having done this, notice that to prove it is zero, it suffices to show that it is zero for a basis of vector fields, for example, the basis $((\partial/\partial x_i), (\partial/\partial y_i))$, which is obvious. Then we can carry over (32.4) to a manifold with a complex structure. It turns out that, *conversely*, a J-tensor satisfying (32.2) and (32.4) arises in this way from a complex structure. If the data are real-analytic, this is not hard to prove; it was done in the paper by Fröhlicher [1], for example. If the data are given as only C^{∞}, it is considerably more difficult to prove, but is true. The first proof is by Newlander and Nirenberg [1]; the theorem was first conjectured by D. C. Spencer, and was recently proved following his ideas by Kohn [1], although it turned out that fundamental new ideas in partial differential equations had to be introduced to accomplish this.

At any rate, we shall take our beginning point that a complex structure is defined on a manifold M by a J-tensor satisfying (32.2) and (32.4). Our main concern in this chapter is with the properties of submanifolds of M. First we must consider those submanifolds that themselves are complex manifolds. Let N be a complex-analytic manifold, and let $\phi: N \to M$ be a submanifold map that is also complex-analytic. We shall call this a complex submanifold of M. From the characterization of holomorphic maps in terms of the J-tensor, we see that $J(\phi_*(N_p)) \subset \phi_*(N_p)$ for all $p \in N$. As usual in this book, from now on let us suppress the explicit notation for the submanifold map. Then the condition for a complex submanifold becomes

$$J(N_p) = N_p \qquad \text{for all } p \in N. \tag{32.5}$$

We now have:

THEOREM 32.1

A submanifold N of M is a complex submanifold if and only if (32.5) is satisfied.

Proof. We have already seen that (32.5) is necessary. To prove it is sufficient, notice that (32.5) implies that N itself causes a J-tensor obtained by restricting J to N. That the integrability conditions (32.4) are satisfied, if for the J-tensor restricted to N, is a consequence of the fact that $[X, Y]$ is tangent to N if X and Y are vector fields of M that are tangent to N.   Q.E.D.

Turn now to consideration of a submanifold N of arbitrary dimension. We want to find a method for describing the "maximal" complex submanifold of M that is contained in N. Now if v is a tangent vector of N that is tangent to such a complex submanifold, then $J(v)$ is also tangent to N. Let us call a tangent vector to N with this property a *holomorphic tangent vector*. We can paraphrase Theorem 32.1 by saying that N is a complex submanifold if and only if all tangent vectors are holomorphic. For $p \in N$, let H_p be the subspace of N_p consisting of all holomorphic tangent vectors; that is,

$$H_p = \{v \in N_p; J(v) \in N_p\}. \tag{32.6}$$

Similarly, define H as the following subspace of $V(M)$:

$$H = \{X \in V(M): X(p) \in H_p \text{ for all } p \in N\}. \tag{32.7}$$

Now there is a possibility of "singularities" in the field $p \to H_p$ of tangent subspaces; that is, $p \to \dim H_p$ is not necessarily constant on N. However, we shall not consider this sort of pathology here; then, also, for $p \in N$,

$$H_p = \{X(p): X \in H\}. \tag{32.8}$$

We may ask: Is H_p tangent to a complex submanifold of M that is contained in N? In order that this be so, we must have $[X, Y] \in H$ for $X, Y \in H$. We can construct a tensor field that "measures" the extent to which this is true: For $X, Y \in H$, set

$$L(X, Y) = J[JX, Y] \quad \text{projected into } V(M)/H. \tag{32.9}$$

(We have chosen this particular combination to assure convenient symmetry properties of $L(\ ,\ )$.) Now, we can verify that $L(\ ,\ )$ has a tensorial behavior as a function of X and Y (although the term in the right-hand side of (32.9) does not have a tensorial behavior before it is projected). As usual, to verify this, we must show that $L(\ ,\ )$ is $F(M)$-bilinear: For example,

$$L(fX, Y) = J[J(fX), Y] = J[fJ(X), Y] = J(g[JX, Y] - Y(f)JX)$$
$$= fJ[JX, Y] + Y(f)X,$$

which is equal to $fL(X, Y)$ when the right-hand side is projected mod H. Hence L passes to the quotient with respect to the restriction mapping $H \to H_p$, and we get, for each $p \in N$, a bilinear mapping (which we again denote by $L(\ ,\ )$) of $H_p \times H_p \to M_p/N_p$. This field of bilinear mappings is called the *Levi form* of N. Explicitly, then, for $X, Y \in H$, $p \in N$,

$$L(X(p), Y(p)) = J[JX, Y](p) \quad \text{projected into } M_p/N_p. \tag{32.10}$$

LEMMA 32.2

The Levi form is symmetric.

Proof. This follows from the integrability condition (32.4):

$$J[JX, Y] - J[JY, X] = [Y, X] + [JY, JX].$$

The right-hand side projects into zero when projected mod N_p. The left-hand side, though, is $L(X(p), Y(p)) - L(Y(p), X(p))$.

Let us examine now the consequences of the Levi form vanishing identically.

THEOREM 32.3

If the Levi form vanishes, then the field $p \to H_p$ of tangent subspaces of $T(N)$ is completely integrable. The maximal integral manifolds of this field then define a foliation of N by maximal complex submanifolds. In particular, if N is a hypersurface of M (that is, if dim M = dim $N + 1$), then these complex submanifolds of N are hypersurfaces in N; hence N may be considered locally as a one-parameter family of complex-analytic hypersurfaces† of M. (Such objects are called hyperplanoids in the classical literature.) Conversely, if a real hypersurface of M has this geometric property, then its Levi form vanishes.

Proof. To prove integrability of $p \to H_p$, we must show that $[H, H] \subset H$. If $X, Y \in H$, $L(X, Y) = 0$ if and only if $J[JX, Y]$ is tangent to N, hence if $[JX, Y]$ also belongs to H. This condition is obviously equivalent to $[H, H] \subset H$. That the maximal integral submanifolds of the field $H_p \to H_p$ are complex-analytic submanifolds of M is clear from Theorem 32.1, since $J(H_p) = H_p$, and the tangent space to the maximal integral submanifolds is precisely H_p. The converse is obvious.

For the rest of this chapter, we shall concentrate on the case where N is a real hypersurface. We can give a more convenient characterization of the hyperplanoids.

THEOREM 32.4

The hyperplanoids that are real-analytic are locally, precisely the hypersurfaces that can be written as $f = 0$, where f is the real part of a holomorphic function $f + \sqrt{-1}\, g = F$.

Proof. First notice that a hypersurface determined by $f = 0$ can also be written locally as the locus determined by

$$\sqrt{-1}\, F - t = 0, \qquad \text{where } t \text{ is a real variable};$$

that is, the hypersurface is composed of a one-parameter family of complex-analytic hypersurfaces.

Conversely, suppose that A is a complex manifold of one complex dimension less than M, and that $\phi: A \times R \to M$ is a *real-analytic* submanifold mapping such that, for fixed t, the mapping $p \to \phi(p, y)$ of $A \to M$ is holomorphic. (This is precisely what is meant by a hyperplanoid.)

We can suppose without loss in generality that M is C^n itself, and that A is

---

† There is a constant confusion in the terminology of complex manifold theory between real and complex dimension. A "complex-analytic hypersurface" is a complex submanifold of two less *real* dimensions.

C^{n-1}. Since ϕ is real-analytic, we can extend ϕ to a mapping of $C^{n-1} \times C \to C^n$ by extending t to be a complex variable. The condition that ϕ be a submanifold map requires that this extended map of $C^{n-1} \times C \to C^n$ have nonzero Jacobian. Then, by the implicit function theorem, there is (always, locally, of course) an inverse holomorphic map $C^n \to C^{n-1} \times C$. Following this map by the projection $C^{n-1} \times C \to C$, we obtain a holomorphic function F on C^n, that is, on M. The image of N in M is characterized by the condition that F take real values on N; that is, N is obtained by setting the real part of $\sqrt{-1}\, F$ equal to zero.   Q.E.D.

All through this chapter there has been, in the background, an analogy with the theory of submanifolds of affinely connected spaces that was built up in Chapter 27, with the Levi form analogous to the second fundamental form. We can now make this analogy more explicit.

THEOREM 32.5

Suppose that, in addition to the complex structure, M has an affine connection ∇ with zero torsion tensor such that the covariant derivative of the J-tensor defining the complex structure is zero. Let N be a submanifold of M, let $S(\ ,\ )$ be its second fundamental form with respect to the affine connection, and let $L(\ ,\ )$ be its Levi form with respect to the complex structure. Then

$$L(u, v) = S(u, v) + S(Ju, Jv) \qquad \text{for } u, v \in H_p, \quad p \in N. \qquad (32.11)$$

Proof. The condition that the covariant derivative of the J-tensor be zero is explicitly

$$\nabla_X J(Y) = J\nabla_X Y \qquad \text{for } X, Y \in V(M).$$

The torsion-free condition is $\nabla_X Y - \nabla_Y X = [X, Y]$. Then, for $X, Y \in H$,

$$J[JX, Y] = J(\nabla_{JX} Y - \nabla_Y JX) = \nabla_{JX} JY + \nabla_Y X.$$

Taking the value of both sides at $p \in N$ and projecting mod N_p gives (32.11).   Q.E.D.

The simple formula suggests a relation between "affine conversity" and "pseudoconvexity." We shall discuss this only in case N is a hypersurface, so that dim M_p/N_p is 1. Identifying it with R, recall that N was said to be *convex* if $S: N_p \times N_p \to R$ kept a fixed sign. Notice then that $L: H_p \times H_p \to R$ also keeps a fixed sign: This property of L is called "pseudoconvexity." Notice, for example, that the flat affine connection on R^{2n} satisfies the hypotheses of Theorem 30.5 when R^{2n} is identified with C^n, so that a hypersurface of Euclidean space that is convex in the usual sense is pseudoconvex.

This analogy can be pursued much further, but this would involve us in another book describing the theory of functions of several complex variables.

The last topic we shall touch on is the question of the geometric nature of "domain of holomorphy" idea. To someone who is familiar only with the classical theory of holomorphic functions of one complex variable, the theory for several variables seems very bewildering, since many of the general principles that are familiar in the one-variable case are completely different in the case of several variables. For example, any domain in C^1 is a "domain of holomorphy"; that is, there are holomorphic functions in the domain that cannot be extended to be holomorphic in any larger domain. The situation is completely different in C^n for $n \geq 2$. The simplest example was pointed out by Hartogs, namely: Any function that is holomorphic in the region between two concentric spheres can be extended to a holomorphic function in the interior of the bigger sphere. It turns out the geometric key to this phenomenon is that the sphere is strongly convex; hence it is also pseudoconvex. (Notice that "pseudoconvexity" for real curves in C^1 makes no sense, since H_p must always be zero in this case.) Now the most definitive results along these lines has been proved by Grauert, Kohn, and H. Rossi. We cite Kohn [1] for further details. Again, these involve analytical techniques that transcend the scope of this book; we shall present only a simple remark that gives some intuitive geometric insight into their results.

THEOREM 32.6

Let N be a real hypersurface of a complex manifold M. Suppose that the Levi form of N is nonzero at each point of N. Let f be a function on M that is the real part of a holomorphic function. Then the derivatives of f at points of N in direction normal to N are determined by derivatives of f in directions tangential to N. In particular, f cannot be constant on N unless it is identically constant on M.

Proof. Let $X \in H$. By hypotheses, for each $p \in N$ we can choose X so that $L(X(p), X(p))$ is not tangent to N. Then $J[JX, X]$ is not tangent to N at p; hence, also in a certain neighborhood of p. Then any vector field Z in a neighborhood of p can, after multiplication by a factor, be written as $J[JX, X] + Y$, where Y is tangent to N. Suppose $f + \sqrt{-1}\, g$ is holomorphic on M; that is, f and g satisfy (32.1). Then

$$\begin{aligned} Z(f) &= J[JX, X](f) + Y(f) = -[JX, X](g) + Y(f) \\ &= X(JX)(g) - (JX)(X)(g) + Y(f) \\ &= X(X)(f) + (JX)(JX)(f) + Y(f). \end{aligned}$$

The left-hand side involves a derivative of f in a normal direction to N, while the right-hand side involves derivatives that are in direction tangent to N. The argument can be iterated to show that all normal derivatives can be so expressed.   Q.E.D.

33 Mechanics on Riemannian Manifolds

Recall from our short exposition (in Chapter 11) of classical mechanics of particles and waves that many things are closely related to the geometry of Euclidean spaces. Now that we have acquired more experience with Riemannian geometry, it is interesting to extend these ideas to Riemannian spaces. This is more than an academic exercise. Some ideas become simpler when looked at from such a Riemannian standpoint, and some (for example, constrained motion) must inevitably involve Riemannian geometric ideas, even if the classical treatments manage to disguise this point rather well. Arnold has recently made this point [2], and some of our work will follow his ideas.

Newton's Equations on an Affinely Connected Manifold

Let M be a manifold, with an affine connection, defined by a covariant-derivative operation ∇. If $\sigma: t \to \sigma(t)$ is a curve in M, if $v: t \to v(t)$ is a vector field on σ, then $\nabla v(t)$ denotes the covariant derivative of the vector field.

Recall how this is defined. Suppose X, Y are vector fields on M such that

$$\sigma'(t) = X(\sigma(t)), \qquad v(t) = Y(\sigma(t)).$$

Then

$$\nabla v(t) = \nabla_X Y(\sigma(t)).$$

This immediately enables us to formulate Newton's equations. Let F, a "force field," be a map: $T(M) \times R \to T(M)$. Newton's equations with this force field are

$$\nabla m(\sigma'(t)) = F(\sigma'(t), t) \tag{33.1}$$

(m is a tensor field on M such that its value at a point p is a linear map: $M_p \to M_p$. It will be called the *mass tensor*).

D'Alembert's principle also makes sense on an affinely connected manifold. Let N be a submanifold of M, and let $p \to N_p^{\perp}$, be a field of transversal subspaces of M_p, defined for $p \in N$, such that

$$M_p = N_p \oplus N_p^{\perp} \qquad \text{for } p \in N.$$

Suppose a "particle" with mass tensor m moves under a force law F, with

427

the additional condition that it is constrained to be an N. "D'Alembert's principle" now prescribes that the forces of constraint be in the transversal direction defined by $N^\perp$, that is,

$$\nabla m(\sigma'(t)) - F(\sigma'(t), t) \in N^\perp_{\sigma(t)}. \tag{33.2}$$

In Chapter 11, we described a method for writing these equations in more explicit form. We can now show how this is done from the affine connection point of view. Recall (Chapter 28) that the induced affine connection ∇_N is defined on N as follows:

> If $\sigma: t \to v(t)$ is a curve along σ tangent to N, then $\nabla v(t) = $ projection of $\nabla v(t)$ on $N_{\sigma(t)}$; that is,

$$\nabla v(t) - \nabla v(t) = S(\sigma'(t), v(t)) \in N^\perp_{\sigma(t)}, \tag{33.3}$$

where $S(\sigma')$ is the second fundamental form of the submanifold.

Apply this to (33.2): We obtain the equations

$$\nabla_N m(\sigma'(t)) + S(\sigma'(t)) - F \in N^\perp_{\sigma(t)};$$

that is,

$$\nabla_N m(\sigma'(t)) = F_{\|}(\sigma'(t), t), \tag{33.4}$$

$$S(\sigma'(t), m(\sigma'(t))) = F_{\perp}(\sigma'(t), t), \tag{33.5}$$

where $F_{\|}$ and $F_{\perp}$ are the projection of F tangent to and transversal to N. Notice that Newton's law for the constrained motion, (33.4), is of the same form as Newton's law on M.

Newton's Law of Motion and Killing Vector Fields

Suppose that M is a manifold with a Riemannian metric. In fact, we do not need to assume that the metric is positive-definite. Let $\langle \ , \ \rangle$ be the inner product on vector fields defining the metric, and let ∇ be the Levi-Civita affine connection associated with the metric.

Consider a force-field F and a particle moving along a curve $t \to \sigma(t)$ according to Newton's law:

$$\nabla(\sigma'(t)) = F(\sigma'(t), t). \tag{33.6}$$

(For simplicity, we assume that the mass tensor is the identity. It can always be absorbed in F.)

Suppose X is a vector field on M. Define a function f_X on $T(M)$ as follows:

$$f_X(v) = \langle v, X(p) \rangle \qquad \text{for } p \in M, \quad v \in M_p.$$

We want to investigate whether f_X is a "conserved quantity," that is, whether $(d/dt)f_X(\sigma'(t)) = 0$, where $\sigma(t)$ satisfies (33.6). In fact we have

$$\frac{d}{dt} f_X(\sigma'(t)) = \langle \nabla \sigma'(t), X \rangle + \langle \sigma' \nabla_{\sigma'} X \rangle$$

$$= \langle F(\sigma'(t), t), X \rangle + \langle \sigma', \nabla_{\sigma'} X \rangle.$$

Suppose that X is a Killing vector field, that is, is the infinitesimal generator of a one-parameter group of isometries of M. Then we know (Chapter 28) that the condition for this is that

$$\langle v, \nabla_v X \rangle = 0 \qquad \text{for all } v \in T(M).$$

Hence we see that

$$\frac{d}{dt} f_X(\sigma'(t)) = \langle F(\sigma'(t), t), X(\sigma(t)) \rangle. \tag{33.7}$$

This is a remarkably simple formula that accounts for the comparative simplicity of the equations of motion of those mechanical systems whose configuration space admits a transitive group of motions.

Newton's Equation of Motion on a Lie Group; Euler's Equations of Rigid Body Motion

As we saw in Chapter 14, if a Lie group G acts transitively and simply on the configuration space of a system of particles, Newton's equations of motion take the form

$$\nabla \sigma'(t) = F(\sigma'(t), t), \tag{33.8}$$

where ∇ is the affine connection defined by a right-invariant metric $\langle\ ,\ \rangle$ on G. Consider $\mathbf{G}$, the Lie algebra of G, as the subalgebra of $V(G)$ consisting of the right-invariant vector fields. Then

$$\langle X, Y \rangle = \text{constant} \qquad \text{for } X, Y \in \mathbf{G}. \tag{33.9}$$

Suppose $X: t \to X(t)$ is a curve in $\mathbf{G}$ such that $X(t)(\sigma(t)) = \sigma'(t)$ for all t, where $t \to \sigma(t)$ is the solution of (33.8). Then

$$\nabla_{X(t)}(X(t)) = F(\sigma'(t), t).$$

But the left-hand side equals

$$\frac{dX}{dt}(\sigma(t)) + \nabla_X X.$$

Now, for $Y \in \mathbf{G}$, we have, using (20.2),

$$\langle \nabla_X X, Y \rangle = X(\langle X, Y \rangle) - Y(\langle X, X \rangle) + \langle X, [Y, X] \rangle$$
$$= \langle X, [Y, X] \rangle,$$

by (33.9).

Suppose now that $B(X, Y)$ is a nondegenerate symmetric, bilinear form on $\mathbf{G}$ that is invariant under the adjoint representation; that is,

$$B([Z, X], Y) + B(X, [Z, Y]) = 0 \qquad \text{for } X, Y, Z \in \mathbf{G}.$$

(Such a form, the *Killing form*, exists if $\mathbf{G}$ is semisimple, a condition that is adequate for our purposes. See Helgason [1] or Hermann [8].) Let A be the symmetric linear transformation: $\mathbf{G} \to \mathbf{G}$ such that

$$\langle X, Y \rangle = B(AX, Y) \qquad \text{for } X, Y \in \mathbf{G}.$$

Then we have

$$\left\langle \frac{dX}{dt}, Y \right\rangle + \langle \nabla_X X, Y \rangle = \langle F, Y \rangle \qquad \text{for } Y \in \mathbf{G}$$

or

$$B\left(A \frac{dX}{dt}, Y \right) - B([AX, X], Y) = B(AF, Y).$$

Since this holds for all $Y \in \mathbf{G}$, we have

$$A \frac{dX}{dt} = [AX, X] + AF \qquad \text{or} \qquad \frac{dX}{dt} = A^{-1}[AX, X] + F. \qquad (33.10)$$

In particular, if $A = $ identity, that is, if the metric $\langle \ , \ \rangle$ is left-invariant also, then $dX/dt = F$.

The equations are then (for the case $G = S0(3, R)$) equivalent to Euler's equations (16.14). In the force-free case, $F = 0$, they determine the geodesics of the right-invariant metric on G. (Arnold has particularly pointed out [2] the importance of these equations for problems in point and fluid mechanics.)

Bibliography

ABRAHAM, R.
[1] "Foundations of Mechanics." Benjamin, New York, 1967.

AMBROSE, W.
[1] The Cartan structural equations in classical Riemannian geometry. *J. Indian Math. Soc.* **24**, 23–76 (1960).

ARNOLD, V.
[1] Small denominators and problems of stability of motion in classical and celestial mechanics. *Russian Math. Surveys* **18**, 85–192 (1963).
[2] Sur la géométrie différentielle des groupes de Lie de dimension infinie et ses applications à l'hydrodynamique des fluides parfaits. *Ann. Inst. Grenoble*, **16**, 319–361 (1966).

AUSLANDER, L., and MACKENZIE, R. E.
[1] "Introduction to Differentiable Manifolds." McGraw-Hill, New York, 1963.

BISHOP, R., and CRITTENDEN, R.
[1] "Geometry of Manifolds." Academic Press, New York, 1964.

BLISS, G. A.
[1] The problem of Mayer with variable end points. *Trans. Am. Math. Soc.* **19**, 305–314 (1918).
[2] "Lectures on the Calculus of Variations." Univ. of Chicago Press, Chicago, Illinois, 1946.

BRILLOUIN, L.
[1] "Tensors in Mechanics and Elasticity." Academic Press, New York, 1964.

CARATHÉODORY, C.
[1] Untersuchungen über die Gründlagen der Thermodynamik. *Math. Ann.* **67**, 355–386 (1909).
[2] "Variationsrechnung." Teubner, Leipzig, 1935.

CARTAN, E.
[1] "Leçons sur les Invariants Intégraux." Hermann, Paris, 1922.
[2] "Géométrie des Éspaces de Riemann." Gauthier-Villars, Paris, 1952.
[3] "Leçons sur la Méthode de la Répère Mobile." Gauthier-Villars, Paris, 1936.

CHERN, S. S., and KUIPER, N.
[1] Some theorems on the isometric imbedding of compact Riemannian manifolds in Euclidean space. *Ann. Math.* **56**, 422–430 (1952).

CHEVALLEY, C.
[1] "Lie Groups." Princeton Univ. Press, Princeton, New Jersey, 1946.

CHOW, W. L.
[1] Uber Systeme von linearen partiellen differential Gleichungen. *Math. Ann.* **117**, 89–105 (1940).

COURANT, R., and HILBERT, D.
[1] "Methods of Mathematical Physics," Vol. II. Wiley (Interscience), New York, 1962.

EINSTEIN, A.
[1] "The Meaning of Relativity." Princeton Univ. Press, Princeton, New Jersey, 1950.

FEDERER, H.
[1] Curvature measures. *Trans. Am. Math. Soc.* **93**, 418–491 (1959).

FLANDERS, H.
[1] "Differential Forms, with Application to the Physical Sciences." Academic Press, New York, 1963.

FROHLICHER, A.
[1] Zur Differentialgeometrie der komplexen Structuren. *Math. Ann.* **129**, 50–95 (1955).

GARABEDIAN, P.
[1] "Partial Differential Equations." Wiley, New York, 1964.

GELFAND, I. M., and FOMIN, S.
[1] "Calculus of Variations." Prentice Hall, Englewood Cliffs, New Jersey, 1963.

GELFAND, I. M., and ŠILOV, G. E.
[1] "Generalized Functions." Academic Press, New York, 1964.

GOLDSTEIN, H.
[1] "Classical Mechanics." Addison-Wesley, Reading, Massachusetts, 1951.

GOLUBEV, V. V.
[1] "Lectures on Integration of the Equations of Motion of a Rigid Body about a Fixed Point." Off. of Tech. Serv., U. S. Dept. of Commerce, Washington, D. C., 1960.

HALKIN, H.
[1] The principle of optimal evolution. In *Intern. Symp. on Nonlinear Differential Equations and Nonlinear Mechanics, 1961* (J. P. LaSalle and S. Lefschetz, eds.), pp. 184–302. Academic Press, New York, 1963.

HARTMAN, P., and NIRENBERG, L.
[1] On spherical image maps whose Jacobians do not change sign. *Am. J. Math.* **81**, 901–920 (1959).

HELGASON, S.
[1] "Differential Geometry and Symmetric Spaces." Academic Press, New York, 1962.

HERMANN, R.
[1] On geodesics that are also orbits. *Bull. Am. Math. Soc.* **66**, 91–93 (1960).
[2] On the accessibility problem in control theory. In *Intern. Symp. on Nonlinear Differential Equations and Nonlinear Mechanics, 1961* (J. P. LaSalle and S. Lefschetz, eds.) ,pp. 325–332. Academic Press, New York, 1963.
[3] Convexity and pseudoconvexity for complex manifolds. *J. Math. Mech.* **13**. 243–248 (1964).
[4] Second variation for variational problems in canonical form. *Bull. Am. Math. Soc.* **71**, 145–149 (1965).
[5] Second variation for minimal submanifolds. *J. Math Mech.* **16**, 473–492 (1966).
[6] Remarks on the foundations of integral geometry. *Rend. Circ. Mat. Palermo* **9**, 91–96 (1960).
[7] Some differential-geometric aspects of the Lagrange variational problem. *Illinois J. Math.* **6**, 634–673 (1962).
[8] "Lie Groups for Physicists" Benjamin, New York, 1966.
[9] Equivalence invariants for submanifolds of homogeneous spaces. *Math. Ann.* **158**, 284–289 (1965).

KLINGENBERG, W.
[1] Zur affinen Differentialgeometrie. *Math. Z.* **54**, 65–80 (1951).

KOBAYASHI, S., and NOMIZU, K.
[1] "Foundations of Differential Geometry." Wiley (Interscience), New York, 1963.

KOHN, J. J.
[1] Harmonic integrals on strongly pseudoconvex manifolds. *Ann. Math.* **78**, 112–148 (1963).

LEVI-CIVITA, T.
[1] "The Absolute Differential Calculus." Blackie, London, 1928.

[2] "Caractéristiques des Systèmes Différentielles." F. Alcon, Paris, 1932.
LICHNEROWICZ, A.
[1] "Théories Rélativistes de la Gravitation." Masson, Paris, 1955.
MASSEY, W. S.
[1] Surfaces of Gaussian curvature zero in Euclidean 3-space. *Tôhuku Math. J.* **14**, 73–79 (1962).
MILNOR, J.
[1] "Morse Theory." Princeton Univ. Press, Princeton, New Jersey, 1963.
MORSE, M.
[1] "Calculus of Variations in the Large." Am. Math. Soc., Providence, Rhode Island, (1935).
MUNKRES, J.
[1] "Elementary Differential Topology." Princeton Univ. Press, Princeton, New Jersey, 1963.
NEWLANDER, A., and NIRENBERG, L.
[1] Complex analytic coordinates in almost complex manifolds. *Ann. Math.* **65**, 391–404 (1957).
NOMIZU, K., and OZEKI, H.
[1] The existence of complete Riemannian metrics. *Proc. Am. Math. Soc.* **12**, 889–891 (1961).
OTSUKI, K.
[1] On the existence of solutions of a system of quadratic equations. *Proc. Japan Acad.* **29**, 99–100 (1953).
PONTRJAGIN, L.
[1] "The Mathematical Theory of Optimal Processes." Wiley (Interscience), New York, 1962.
PRAGER, W.
[1] "Introduction to the Mechanics of Continua." Ginn, Boston, 1961.
RADON, J.
[1] Zum problem von Lagrange. *Hamburg Math. Einzelschriften*, Number 2. Teubner, Leipzig (1928).
ROXIN, E.
[1] A geometric interpretation of Pontrjagin's maximal principle. In *Intern. Symp. on Nonlinear Differential Equations and Nonlinear Mechanics, 1961* (J. P. LaSalle and S. Lefschetz, eds.). Academic Press, New York, 1963.
SPIVAK, M.
[1] "Calculus on Manifolds." Benjamin, New York, 1965.
STERNBERG, S.
[1] "Lectures on Differential Geometry." Prentice Hall, Englewood Cliffs, New Jersey, 1964.
TRICOMI, F.
[1] "Differential Equations." Hafner Publ. Co., New York, 1961.
WHITTAKER, E. T., and WATSON, G. N.
[1] "A Course of Modern Analysis." Cambridge Univ. Press, London and New York, 1940.
WHITTAKER, E. T.
[1] "A Treatise on Analytical Dynamics of Particles and Rigid Bodies." Cambridge Univ. Press, London and New York, 1959.
YOSIDA, K.
[1] "Introduction to Functional Analysis." Springer, Berlin, 1965.

Subject Index

Mathematics in Science and Engineering

A Series of Monographs and Textbooks

Edited by RICHARD BELLMAN, *University of Southern California*